THE SCATTERED SCRU

The Scattered Scruffs

HAZEL JACQUES

Panda
Publications

A catalogue record for this book is available from the British Library

ISBN 0-9540905-0-0

Typeset in 10/11pt Giovanni
and printed in Great Britain
by Clipper Print Limited, East Goscote, Leicester

Published by Panda Publications 2001
75 VALLEY ROAD, LOUGHBOROUGH, LEICS. LE11 3PX

ACKNOWLEDGEMENTS

First and foremost I would like to thank my
husband Alan, and our four daughters, for their
support during my labours.

I would also like to thank my brothers and
sisters; together we have become a family again.

I would like to thank Joe, brother of Margaret
and Winnie for permission to publish their story.

Special thanks go to Laura Brown and Beryl
Spriggs for unlocking their past, and our
renewed friendship.

My thanks also to
Dave Springthorpe, and Paul Graham
of Clipper Print Limited East Goscote Leics;
and Rodney Dale of Fern House Haddenham
Cambs; for their help in the production of this book.

IN MEMORY OF

Mum & Dad (Emma and George),
Grandma Holland
and to 'Ma'

PREFACE

Until 1944, tuberculosis was rampant among poorer families. The second World War hampered medical research until 1944 when Streptomycin, the first antituberculosis drug, was invented. But it was too late for the many sufferers who died from the disease.

This is a true story about children who through no fault of their own were taken into care between 1939 and 1949, and about one such family in which both parents developed tuberculosis.

It is about abandoned children – some ill-treated, others on the 'bread line', whose parents had split up, were in prison, or could not cope. Brothers and sisters who were separated, each losing touch with the other. All these children were in the hands of the care system of the day, run by the Public Assistance and The Poor Law.

I would like my book to be read as part of Social Services' training, so that everyone understands the hardship, and the mental cruelty, that all children in care go through. It may take as long as forty years, before such children, now well into adulthood, can even talk about their lost childhood.

With vaccination available today no one should suffer from the dreadful disease of tuberculosis. But when I was young, it was a disease which could spread rapidly through families. My own brother was operated on when he was 15 years old, losing a lung and thereby scarred for life. Fortunately today this does not happen, although the bacillus Myobacterium tuberculosis is still lurking in the background.

Let us not get careless or complacent, and risk losing more precious lives.

Hazel Jacques
June 2001

FOREWORD

Although I was born in Leicester, I first heard of "The Scattered Scruffs" from Hazel Jacques herself, during a late evening conversation in the lounge of a hotel in Ilfracombe, Devon, where we were both on tour with a bowling club from Leicestershire.

I am quite certain that Hazel would have carefully avoided exaggeration in everything of importance and has endeavoured to transpose time, places and all circumstances, in an effort to convey to the reader's mind, a truthful impression of the early years of her life, with all the tears and heartache that came her way.

Maurice Gayton
July 2001

ST STEPHEN'S CHURCH CHOIR PHOTO
(page 139)

From left to right.

BACK ROW
Mr. Goode, unknown, Lewis Winfield, Malcolm Peach,
Mr. Chandler (church Warden), Stanley Buzzard, Mr. Smith, T. Forsell,
unknown, church warden unknown, Peter Harris, John Devereux,
Pip Brown, Lady in choir unknown, Bernard Smith, John Critchlow,
David Goode.

MIDDLE ROW
Lady unknown, Mr. Hall, Mr. Buswell (Green Lane Road Chemist),
unknown, Father Huntley, Bishop Willis, Dr. Braithwaite (Paediatrician
at Royal Infirmary), unknown, Mr. Heathcote (organist), Tenor singer,
Mr. Harrison.

FRONT ROW
Tony Hurt, Stephen Halford, unknown, unknown, unknown,
John Bunting, John Birch.

CHAPTER ONE

December 1942

The warm water splashed over the living room floor as Doris and Edna sat in the zinc bath washing themselves in front of the fire. There were only seven days left to Christmas. The coloured trimmings stretched from all corners of the ceiling, gently moving with the commotion below. The Christmas tree had been taken out of the cupboard for another year, with its six shiny baubles, it sparkled in the firelight. Fourteen-month-old baby, Brian, sat in his pram reaching out to touch its artificial branches. Norman and Hazel were next in the bath, eager to wash away the school grime. Eleven-years-old Norman flicked water from the ends of his fingers onto the bars of the warm glowing fire. The droplets sizzled away, leaving dull white rings on the fireplace. Hazel tried to copy the action, but her handful of water hit the bars with a force that brought steam and ash puthering into the room.

"Hazel, stop that," shouted Mam. "Hurry up, Norman, I want to empty the bath." The excitement grew as they hurriedly dried themselves, longing to wear the new tartan kilts, which hung on the clothes' pulley near the ceiling, mingling with the tinsel and streamers.

"Which is my kilt?" asked Edna.

"The one with the blue in it, get them all down for me, Ted," said Mam.

The four children were going on a surprise car ride, so had to look their very best. Ted, the eldest brother, was staying behind to help Mam with the baby. Drying themselves they kept well out of the way while Mam and Ted dragged the tin bath of water through the kitchen and down the steps at the back door. The empty bath sounded like a gong as it was hung up on the wall in the yard, the water gradually drained away. There was more room now to get ready; the table was put back in the middle of the room. Ted lifted Edna onto the table to see herself in the mirror above the fireplace.

Three red ribbons put the final touch to the three girls; they were ready at last. A black, shiny car arrived at the front door of the terraced house in Lothair Road; they all jumped into the back of the car. Mam stood on the doorstep holding the baby, while Ted stood on the pavement waving as the car pulled away. Smoothing the pleats of their new kilts,

1

Washing away the school grime.

Hazel, Doris and Edna settled back into the red plush seats, wondering where the mystery trip was taking them. The car sped along Saffron Lane, not towards Grandma's as was their only guess, but in the opposite direction. Norman soon recognised London Road, and the shop where he took the flower buttonholes that Mam made. Suddenly, the car turned into a narrow lane and slowly came to a halt outside a big house with two identical front doors. The driver rang the bell - it was the end of the journey, the bewildered four clambered out on to the pavement.

The door was opened by a woman wearing a long black dress, covered by a white apron. She smiled at the driver, then with a heavy hand guided the four into a large hallway. The heavy door closed behind them. In semi-darkness the Matron moved towards them, she was a dumpy person with a stiff, frilly, white cap on her head, a white bow tied under her chin. Her long black dress just revealed her thick ankles and black shoes. None of them understood what she was saying, her rasping voice and southern dialect confused and bewildered them as to why they had been brought to this place. The lady who had opened the door appeared again.

"Go with Miss Kelling. She will look after you."

That last, cutting, sentence produced the only plausible words from the Matron. Miss Kelling pushed the three girls along the passage into a large bathroom. The tap was on, filling the bath with steaming hot water.

"Take off your clothes and get into the bath," said Miss Kelling with an air of no-nonsense.

"But we've just had a bath." All three objected together, realising that Norman was no longer with them.

"Do as you're told, then everything will be all right," was the cold reply.

Obediently they undressed and folded their precious kilts neatly on the only chair in the room. Miss Kelling was back in record time, with a bottle in her hand she poured some solution into the bath. With the three girls in the bath together, she methodically washed each one, including hair. Miss Kelling scooped the piles of clothes up on her way out of the bathroom. She returned just as quickly, her arms full of different clothes. Vests, knickers, liberty bodices, black stockings and a dress each. "Put these on when you're dry," said Miss Kelling. Standing in the bath, they demanded to wear their own clothes, to wear their new scotch kilts that Mam had specially made them for Christmas.

"You'll have them back later," said Miss Kelling, "Now hurry up Matron is waiting.

It was useless talking to the woman who jostled in and out of the room. They slowly dressed themselves; the clothes were hard to put on, the thick stockings clinging to damp legs. Miss Kelling was back again and began brushing the wet hair, replacing the ribbons that Mam had so carefully tied that same afternoon.

Miss Kelling pulled the plug out of the bath, and with a menacing look she glared at them over the rim of her spectacles. Her black eyebrows met in the middle as she frowned; turning away she mumbled to herself and stood up.

Feeling uncomfortable and strange in the itchy dresses, they followed Miss Kelling through a large kitchen, down another passage, passing another bathroom with the same carbolic smell, at the end of the passage was a door; the shiny gold letters read DAY ROOM. In the day room Norman stood alone, he also had undergone the same treatment and a change of clothes. A tight-fitting jumper with a striped collar now replaced his shirt, with a tie round his neck. The door closed, they were alone.

In the centre of the room was a large, polished table covered in books and comics. Ominous dark sliding cupboards were fitted either side of the fireplace, smoke curled up the chimney from the coal on the fire, but very little heat came from the heavily guarded hearth. The reason for the bath and the itchy clothes was still not quite clear as they whispered together. Norman stood on a chair to look out of the barred windows, nothing could be seen through the frosted glass of the bottom windows. Edna started to cry.

The day room door opened, a thin lady hobbled into the room, dressed in long, old-fashioned clothes. The lady appeared not to hear, as they tearfully asked, 'Why are we here?' With a pile of linen from the sliding cupboards, she went out of the room. They stood huddled together, and after what seemed ages, Miss Kelling came back into the room.

"Come," she beckoned to the girls, they followed her through the kitchen and up the stairs. Miss Kelling was a step or two ahead.

"This is where you are going to sleep," she said.

Those few words were a bit too much for them, they had co-operated

"...but we've just had a bath."

so far, but they didn't want to sleep in this place, they wanted to go home. By the time they had reached the top of the stairs, panic had set in, all three screaming and squealing, to go home.

With tears in her eyes Emma Hunt closed the front door, she didn't see the curtains move across the street, neighbours peering out, wondering why the Hunts' children should be taken away in such grand style. They would know soon enough that Emma was in no mood for anything, her hardest job had been keeping up the pretence until the children were safely in the car. Ted made a cup of tea for his Mam while she made the baby comfortable for his afternoon sleep, she put the Christmas tree next to his pram in the front room window, it would be the last thing he would see in that house. It had all gone according to plan, a second car arrived shortly afterwards, and a young woman lifted the sleeping baby and with very few words, they were gone. Emma, too upset to speak, was hoping that her baby wouldn't wake up until he was safely on his way to the Countesthorpe Cottage Homes Nursery.

They had all lived at number 22 since Great Grandma had died a few years ago, and Great Grandad Hunt had gone to live in the Alms Houses up near the cattle market. Emma couldn't help thinking of the other baby she had lost - little Dennis, who had died from pneumonia in the cottage down by the canal; the walls never did dry out, not even on a summer's day. It was a picturesque cottage, just right for a young married couple, with the barges going up and down, calling in at the pub just beyond the lock gates.

Ted was their first child, a strong healthy boy who loved the canal. On Sunday mornings he would run to the lock keepers cottage whenever a barge came along, swinging on the long beams while Arthur wound the ratchet handle to open the lock. Arthur had lived at the lock keepers cottage all his life, when his own father had given up living on the barges, and his wife had died years before. Having no children he looked forward to the happy hours he spent with young Ted, showing him where to find the frog spawn in the summer, and with a jam jar, fished for stickle-backs on the edge of the water. On special days, Ted would accompany Arthur in his rowing boat, to free debris at the edge of the weir.

It all seemed so long ago, when George was a long distance lorry driver, working away from home a week at a time. The doctor had called for the second time that week Dennis's breathing had worsened, he had been a weakling from birth, but it was after the doctor insisted on opening all the windows that the baby died. Now she had let her youngest baby, Brian, go to some unknown destination, the doctors had convinced her that he would be well looked after in the Homes. Emma could hardly bring herself to think about him, waking up in a strange place, he would miss his sisters pushing him up and down the street in his big pram, now standing near the window, still warm and empty.

Ted, who was in his teens had been told everything; his Dad would be pleased with him, especially with the way he had helped things to go smoothly over the past few hours.

He too had been upset when they took the baby away; he put his arms around his Mam, giving her what small comfort he could. Ted was going to live with his Grandma for the next few months as his Dad had explained both he and his Mam were ill and were going into hospital.

Footsteps sounded in the entry and up to the back door, Grandma and Ted's Dad George came into the living room, it would soon be time for the ambulance to arrive to take them to the Groby Rd Hospital. Ted 's bag had been packed long ago, he and Grandma would be the last to leave the house.

The house was noticeably silent; the absence of five children was almost unbearable. Grandma busied herself with the tea, and took a cake out of her basket, she knew there would be no food left in the house, what was left she would come and clear away another day.

George had finished his job that afternoon and collected his wages, he sorted out a ten-shilling note for Ted for being a good lad, and it would help with his bus fares from Grandma's. He had told his work mates on the Corporation Buses to look out for him on his way to school; 'you might get a free ride some days,' he told Ted.

Emma, still in a traumatic condition had packed what possessions they were taking to the hospital, there were no other jobs left to do. The sooner they were away, the better it would be for all. Grandma checked over the final details of the rent book, and she would come down and sort out the washing another day.

There was a loud knock on the front door, the ambulance had arrived.

It was dark outside; Ted opened the front door, Emma was first to be helped into her seat, and George sat next to her. George asked the driver if he could give Grandma and Ted a lift to the bottom of the road. Grandma locked the front door and sat with Ted. Good-byes were made a little easier as there was no time for more than a kiss from them both, and that she would be visiting the hospital tomorrow.

Ted and Grandma waited for the bus in silence watching as the ambulance sped away. Matron suddenly appeared on the landing, she shrieked at the top of her voice, drowning their pitiful sobs. That rasping voice demanding to know who was making all that noise. Her sudden appearance brought relative calm, as she continued to explain the shocking news.

"Your Mother and Father have gone into hospital, they are both very ill," Matron stood holding the banister repeating herself again.

A feeling of total disbelief came over them, Mam didn't look ill, she had just bathed them hours ago, and their Dad was a big, strong driver.

"Ted has gone to live with your Grandma, and the baby is in a nursery," said Matron.

They didn't believe her. They were all sobbing again as Miss Kelling ushered all three through a door into a large dormitory, with beds either side of the room. Edna was given the bed nearest the door. Miss Kelling marched on up the room, Doris's bed was third on the left, and Hazel's bed was fifth on the left. They enquired 'which bed is Norman sleeping in?'

"Your brother will sleep in the boys' dormitory."

Miss Kelling checked the curtains, there were seven beds and three windows on either side of the room, and a large paraffin lamp stood on a fine lace cloth on the table in the centre of the room. Standing by their allotted beds, the tears rolled down their cheeks. Miss Kelling fussed and turned the counterpanes down uncovering the pure white sheets and pillows. Only half believing their plight, they followed Miss Kelling back to the day room. They blurted it all out again to Norman, telling him what Matron had said. Norman confirmed the truth of the situation.

"If we're good, they might let us go home next week," he told them.

The girls had always felt secure with Norman, he had fought their battles in the school yard, protected them from the Boundary Road gang when they had played on 'The Green' on Hughendon Drive. As a special favour he'd walk with them to the pictures on a Saturday afternoon before joining his mates. Some time later, Miss Kelling put her head round the day room door, beckoning to Norman; clinging together, the girls were not letting him out of their sight.

"You can make the cocoa in the scullery, get the tin of cocoa down from the shelf," said Miss Kelling bustling about again.

Norman dragged the bench from under the table and climbed up to reach the tall red tin from the shelf above the fireplace.

"Sit at the table, you girls," Miss Kelling followed Norman into the scullery and supervised the measuring of the cocoa.

The heavy wooden seat was dragged back to the table, they sat waiting. They couldn't remember if they'd had any dinner or tea or what time it was. Edna suddenly said, "Can I have some bread?"

Miss Kelling stood in the doorway, wondering where the little voice had come from. Looking at Edna she managed a funny smile, and promptly went back into the kitchen.

"Can I have some bread, please, and me too, please?" The voices echoed round the green painted walls of the kitchen. "Alright, alright," Miss Kelling shouted from the scullery.

Norman carried in the beakers of hot cocoa; Miss Kelling followed with a plate of bread.

"One slice each," she said.

With supper finished, it was time for bed. The dreaded moment had come too soon. The three girls followed Miss Kelling up the stairs. Each step of the stairs was an ordeal, the sense of abandonment growing stronger, then with a single sob from Edna; they all burst into tears. Miss Kelling quickly took charge of Edna, helping her to undress whilst giving orders to Hazel and Doris to fold their clothes neatly on the chairs. They climbed into bed. The white cotton sheets were cold and uninviting. In the darkened room, their thoughts carefully went over the events of the day, desperately wondering why they had been tricked into that awful situation. Heartbroken they cried themselves to sleep.

Early next morning the light was switched on, Hazel could see the thickset figure of Miss Kelling hovering around Edna's bed. Her eyes hurt. It hadn't been a dream and they really were in that awful place.

"You've wet your bed!" The voice boomed out, at the other end of the room.

"Leave her alone," shouted Doris, who was wide-awake and sitting up.

"She can't help it!" Hazel shouted making sure Miss Kelling could hear.

Miss Kelling made her way up the dormitory, glaring at both girls through her round rimmed spectacles. She pulled the bedcovers back and told them to get dressed. By the time she had opened the curtains

"she can't help it, she's got a weak bladder".

she was back at Edna's bed. Edna was still curled up and half-asleep. Miss Kelling hauled her off the bed saying, "Come on, down to the bathroom."

Doris and Hazel dressed quickly and quietly both wondering what would happen to them today.

They washed at the four washbasins fixed to the bathroom wall, and then holding hands they ventured into the kitchen, where Norman had already laid the table. Sitting on the wooden bench, Miss Kelling put a plate of porridge before them. Norman brought in the beakers of hot cocoa and sat down, the spoons were picked up. Miss Kelling's voice boomed out again.

"For what we are about to receive, may the Lord make us truly thankful. Amen."

With hands together and closed eyes, they had been introduced to God at Sunday school. Amen they all said. With her back to the cooking range and warm fireplace Miss Kelling watched as the lumpy porridge was eaten.

"No-one leaves the table until all the plates are clean."

Almost before breakfast was over, Miss Kelling gave out jobs for them to do each day. Edna, who was six, was to tidy and dust the day room. Seven years old Doris was to scrub the kitchen floor. Eight-year-old Hazel was to help dust the bedrooms, Norman who was eleven was to chop the firewood, and fill all the coal buckets. With the table and pots cleared away, Hazel and Doris went to the day room to help Edna to tidy the mountain of books. The doorbell rang; all three crept along the passage to see who was at the door. Mrs Lambourne the domestic help had arrived.

In the kitchen Mrs Lambourne changed her shoes. Out of her bag she took a brightly coloured apron, which wrapped over at the front and tied at the back, exactly the same style that Mam always wore. She smiled at Hazel revealing a mouthful of grey teeth when Miss Kelling told her that she was to help her.

Up the stairs Edna's bed was first to be made.

"Go and fetch a draw sheet from the day room, it's half a big sheet to cover this waterproof. You'll find a pile of them in the cupboards on the right hand side of the fire," said Mrs Lambourne turning the mattress.

Dashing down the stairs Hazel, was on her first errand, not only was she curious to look in the sliding cupboards, but she wondered how

Doris and Edna were getting on. In the corner of the kitchen Doris had made a start, the bucket of water looked heavy, and the red tiled floor looked very wet. In the day room Edna was refusing to do any more tidying up. Hazel collected the draw sheet and ran back up the stairs. With Mrs Lambourne she smoothed the sheets and tucked in the mitred the corners.

"You'll get used to it," she said.

Starting near the door, the dusting was done in the same methodical way. On hands and knees Hazel slithered about dusting under each bed, first down one side then back down under the next seven beds. The windowsills, bed ends and chairs all had to be done. She closed the dormitory door and went to look for Mrs Lambourne. On the landing was an open door, a row of tweed coats hung on rails, the potent smell of mothballs and warm air filled the room.

"That's the box room, don't let Matron catch you in there," Mrs Lambourne made her jump as she slammed the door. "Don't forget to dust between the banisters my duck, these are Matron's stairs and have to be done properly," Mrs Lambourne handed her a clean duster.

From the stairs, Hazel watched the large tin of RONUK floor polish being slid across the brown lino as Mrs Lambourne meticulously polished the landing. With the first flight of stairs finished she looked down through the banister. Matron was standing in the hall below shouting at Edna for wetting the bed.

"She can't help it, she's got a weak bladder," Hazel shouted, with her face pressed against the banister.

Matron looked up in disgust at the unexpected outburst.

"Who do you think you are shouting at? Stand up when I speak to you."

Hazel stood up; Matron looked as if she was about to burst.

"While you are at The Receiving Home, and under my care you will speak when you are spoken to, now get on with your work."

Matron took Edna through to the kitchen. Mrs Lambourne, looked down at Hazel, she put a finger to her lips and gestured her to be quiet, not saying a word. By the time Hazel had dusted the stairs, Doris had finished scrubbing the floor, it looked rather wet.

Hazel kept close to Mrs Lambourne as they passed Matron's office, there was still the bathroom to clean.

"The bowls have to be vimmed and the taps must shine," said Mrs

Lambourne. Being so close to Matron's office she silently obeyed.

Hazel washed the dusters in the scullery. Coming back through the kitchen it looked bigger than ever. Doris must have scrubbed the equivalent of four of their living rooms at home. On the shelf above the cooking range was the solitary tin of cocoa. A kitchen dresser stood opposite against the green painted wall. Above the door was a bell box with red and white disks, which indicated which room was requiring attention. The bell on a spring hung at the side of the box. For the rest of the day they were confined to the day room, only allowed out at mealtimes. Uncovering her red knees, Doris complained about having to scrub the kitchen floor.

"Miss James walked all over it, I wish she was dead," Doris shouted.

Miss James, the seamstress-dressmaker, called the girls into her workroom. They stood in a line as she measured them for future dresses. The sewing room had material stacked up at one end of the table, with piles of mending near the sewing machine, a pin-cushion with all sizes of needles and a large tin holding all her scissors. The armchair near the door made it a cosy room. At home the girls had often stood round the machine when Mam was making clothes. Miss James was a quiet person, and they stayed talking to her as long as they could.

Back in the day room the hours were long and endless, there was plenty of time to think of home. Each one had their own memories as they sat round the table. Each one making a vow as to what they will do when they get home.

"I'm going to chop the firewood and get the coal in," said Norman. In reality there was no coal, and no firewood to chop.

"I'm definitely not scrubbing any more floors," said Doris "I'll take little Brian a walk in his pram."

Edna declared that she wouldn't wet the bed any more, and started to cry again. Miss James put her head round the door. "Be quiet or you'll have Matron come in to you."

With elbows on the table Hazel stared into the open book, not reading, just thinking about the happy time they'd had when Brian was born.

*   *   *

13

It was November 1940; they all sat huddled around the warm fire glad to be home from school on such a cold day. Mam was busy cutting the bread for tea. Suddenly she collapsed on the floor the knife was laying beside her. Norman ran to fetch the neighbour, the girls gathered round her as she began to sit up. Mam looked very pale, and the neighbour made her a cup of tea, and she felt a little better. The ambulance men arrived to take her to hospital, and still sitting on the chair they carried her out of the house.

They had all been to the infirmary for stitches in toes after paddling in the brook, or after falling down the back door steps, or when Edna had the slab fall on her foot that crushed her toe when the new pavements were laid. Mam had cut herself on the carving knife and she would soon be home. Ted, the eldest brother, took charge, giving out his orders as he sat near the fire. They had just finished their bread and jam when the backdoor opened and Grandma walked in. Grandma with her basketful of goodies, biscuits and cakes from Dunmore's biscuit factory where she worked, and usually a fat bottle of milk. She listened to the explanation why Mam wasn't there, and then she told them quite a different story.

"Your Mam is having a baby, so you can come and stay with me 'til she gets back."

It was dark when they reached Repington Row, just managing to keep up with Grandma, having done the journey several times before, but never in the dark. The warm smell of Grandma's kitchen was welcoming, but in the living room they knew what awaited them. Grandad sat in his chair by the fire his casual glance was an icy stare.

"Come here let me look at you." The ex-Merchant seaman stood up.

"Show me your hands and teeth."

The children stood in a line in front of him as he inspected each one in turn.

"Shipshape and Bristol fashion, hang your coats up in the hall," he said, resuming his seat by the fire.

Grandad couldn't stand any noise; he always spoke very softly and not very clearly. His mutterings were the same as if he still had a cigarette in his mouth. Grandma on the other hand, was always jolly, laughing at Grandad's whims.

After a supper of cocoa and biscuits, a good wash and a further inspection, it was time for bed. They made their way up Grandma's stairs.

"Where are we going to sleep Grandma?" they asked.

Ted and Norman went into the back bedroom, while the three girls jumped into Grandma's big brass bed. Buried in the softness of the feather mattress, and with a goodnight kiss from Grandma they were soon asleep. By Sunday teatime they had given up guessing whether it would be a boy or girl. Grandad sat at the head of the table, while Grandma poured the tea. Grandad spoke.

"Hazel, Doris and Edna are going to Southfields Drive School in the morning, and Norman and Ted will catch the bus to their own schools. "Thank you Annie," he said, taking his cup from Grandma. This was quite a blow for them, they had hoped the stay at Gran's would be a holiday from school, very disappointed it obviously showed in their faces

"No pouting my girl, you've got to go to school."

Grandad wagged his finger at Hazel sitting next to him at the table. On Monday morning the school looked as cold and frosty as the morning. The white concrete building, a very prominent structure, was nothing like the old Victorian school on Lansdowne Road. It stood back near a row of shops and the off licence where Grandad bought his jug of beer. They made their way into the school with the multitude of children, busily rushing about as they tried to find the way in. The girls took an instant dislike to their new surroundings, no friendly faces, and just a sea of strangers. The only nice thing that morning was Grandma's porridge. After tea in the second week, Grandma covered the table with newspapers, and with a fine toothcomb she combed and combed the girls' heads, they had all caught nits at the new school. The creepy crawlies were examined as they dropped on to the newspaper it was good fun as they learned to crack the lice with the back of the thumbnail until they were dead. The strongest treatment until morning was the carbolic soap.

After breakfast, Grandma walked with them to the school clinic in Marriott Road. They were surprised to see so many children there. Some had sores on their faces, some had bald patches on their heads. The whole clinic smelled of ether and antiseptic, making the girls uneasy as to what happened in the nurse's room. Boys came out with Gentian Violet painted on the corners of their mouths, and on the bald patches of their heads.

"They've probably got ringworm," said Gran.

Whatever it was it certainly was in a ring. Feeling very brave, the three followed the nurse, for a quick inspection of heads.

"Nits!" declared the nurse

The stinging nit lotion was rubbed well behind their ears, and to their great relief they didn't have any hair shaved off. On the way back to Grandma's, skipping along the road by the side of the park, they told Grandma, 'we cannot go to school because we've got nits.'

"There's no point in you staying away, the whole school's got nits. You can have the rest of the morning off and help me with the dinner," Gran said.

The great day finally came, after school, Gran told them that they had a baby brother called Brian. Now there were three boys and three girls. Ted, Norman, Hazel, Doris Edna and now Brian. Back at home a few days later Gran lit the fire and the girls helped to tidy the house. The excitement grew as the afternoon went by, dashing back and forth to the front room window to see if the ambulance had arrived. Grandad wasn't there to tell them off, or make them stand in the corner for giggling. A knock on the front door brought the bubbling excitement to shrieks of joy. Mam was there with the baby. The ambulance man carried in the suitcase, and Gran quickly took charge of the tiny bundle wrapped in the big shawl.

"You've got plenty of helpers here missus," said the ambulance man as they kissed and hugged their Mam.

Looking at the girls he said. "Santa's brought you a real doll and pram this year, look after him won't you. I'll let myself out, 'bye then."

Sitting down, Mam held the baby, while Gran mashed a cup of tea, they crowded round to see their new brother as Mam moved the shawl.

"Sit on the settee and you can all have a turn to hold him," said Grandma.

"I'm so glad to be home Annie," said Mam to Grandma. "Have they been good?"

The school, the nits, standing in the corner, ironing Grandad's handkerchiefs, Grandma's lovely porridge every morning, were all in the past, as they sat waiting to hold their new baby.

*   *   *

16

Back in the day room, there were no nice dolls to play with. Hazel looked down at the open book.

'On the first day of Christmas my true love sent to me, a partridge in a pear tree.

'On the second day of Christmas my true love sent to me, two turtle doves and a partridge in a pear tree.

'On the third day of Christmas my true love sent to me, three French hens, two turtle doves and a partridge in a pear tree.'

There were twelve verses in the rhyme, and just six days left to Christmas, if she learned two verses a day she would know it by the time they went home. Hazel settled down to learn 'The twelve days of Christmas.'

Later that afternoon, two new children arrived. They were taken into the bathroom on arrival, receiving the same tortuous treatment. They were crying and finally ended up in the day room. The boy was younger than Norman, and the girl timid and pale and a lot younger than Edna was. Their sense of abandonment had been near Matron's office, when whoever brought them in, had to leave. Norman comforted the boy, taking him to a seat at the table, the little girl clung on to her brother's jumper. Each time the girls caught a glimpse of Matron, always the same questions were asked. "When are we going home?" and "can we go outside to play?"

One day Miss Kelling took the key from her pocket and unlocked the scullery door, they all ran outside. It was disappointing, what they thought might be a garden was a drab high walled back yard. Edna and Lisa sat on the wet sludgy sand, a one-time sandpit. Norman and Lisa's brother, Tony, climbed the gnarled branches of the ivy, which clung, to the wall. Doris and Hazel took turns on the swing trying to see over the high wall. With no coats on in the biting wind, they soon gave up the fresh air for the warmth of the day room. A little later that morning Matron was shouting at Miss Kelling. Miss Kelling hurriedly looked in the day room, the door was shut again and they heard her footsteps as she ran along the passage. Adding to the confusion the door bell rang in the kitchen, opening the day room door the girls crept along the passage as far as the kitchen, they could hear a man's voice. Then silence, they hurried back to the day room as Miss Kelling came into view. Whenever the doorbell rang there was always hope that someone had come to take them home. The day room door opened a little later,

Norman and Tony came in looking flushed, they were chatting like old friends.

"Where have you been?" the girls wanted to know.

"We climbed over the wall and ran off," said Norman, "we got as far as London Road station, we were pretending to look in this shop window, when this policeman came up and asked us why we hadn't got coats on."

"He took us to the police station," said Tony, who seemed elated by all that had happened.

" When they asked where I lived, I said "22 Lothair Road," We didn't know where we had come from," said Norman. "They gave us a mug of Ovaltine" and we had a great time.

Norman and Tony started laughing at their escapade.

"They brought us back in a big police van, Matron took us in her office and she took out this great big cane and whacked us both," Norman held out his hand showing the red weal's across his hands. "She called me the ringleader," he said.

Norman and Tony stood close to the fire, warming themselves, quietly giggling, it was through a lady's hat shop window that they had seen the reflection of the policeman coming towards them. Matron Buttridge had reported them missing, describing their identical institution jumpers.

A whole week passed by, there were no more outings into the big yard, but they had been good, still in the hope of going home. Doris and Hazel finished their morning jobs, and together confronted Matron asking her when would they be going home.

"There are lots of parties next week, you would like to stay for them wouldn't you? Then we shall see what the doctors say about your parents," Never having any time for the girls, she carried on talking to Miss Kelling. "And we shall have it in the far dining room; make sure everyone on the list is sitting down when the Lord Mayor has gone."

Back in the day room Hazel and Doris told Norman that they had to stay another week. Christmas morning came and the expectancy of a new toy to play with. Hazel, Doris and Edna, who had been dragged out of bed, dressed quietly, and crept down the stairs so as not to wake Matron. Miss Kelling was busy in the kitchen she was surprised to see them all.

"Happy Christmas," she said.

"Happy Christmas, Miss Kelling," they all replied.

"Come and sit in the dining room, you're lucky today, you are having all your meals in here. At one end of the long table six presents clearly marked their places.

The children unwrapped their gifts, Hazel had a purse and a panda, Doris also had a purse and her toy was a lamb. Edna unwrapped her present and threw the purse and the teddy bear across the room.

"I don't want that, I want to go home," she shouted.

Picking up the rejected present, Miss Kelling hushed them up. "Ssh, Matron's coming downstairs," she said.

After breakfast they had to stay in the day room until the visitors arrived. About twelve boys from the boys' home arrived first in their warm coats, long socks and shiny boots they had walked from St Saviour's Road where they lived with their foster mother, Miss Pickering. Miss Hammond's girls arrived next from the home on East Park Road, wearing identical coats to those of the boys, the same tweed coats that hung in Matron's box room on the landing.

Still clutching their Christmas presents the Receiving Home children followed like sheep through the front door, for the first time since arriving seven days ago. Standing on the pavement, all the children waited for the 'special guests' to arrive. Suddenly the black, shiny car turned slowly into the lane. Hazel felt she knew this car as the car that had brought them to The Receiving Home. The same red plush seats now occupied by The Lord Mayor and Lady Mayoress, and Councillor Court. The car came to a halt to the cheering of the children. The chauffeur opened the car door, and the Lord Mayor stepped out to more cheers. The eldest girl from the girls' home stepped forward.

"Good morning, my Lord Mayor, and Lady Mayoress, we wish you good cheer a bright merry Christmas and a Happy New Year." The Lord Mayor acknowledged her greeting and took off his large hat, then with Matron they went inside. All the children were then ushered back to the warmth of the main dining room, standing quietly around the table, as did the staff and the entourage of guests. The Lord Mayor and Lady Mayoress and Councillor Court came into the room and stood near the tall Christmas tree, then at a given sign from Matron all the children started to sing.

O come all ye faithful, joyful and triumphant,
O come ye, O come ye to Bethlehem.

Come and behold Him, born the King of Angels.
O come let us adore Him, O come let us adore Him
O come let us adore Him, Christ the Lord.

The carol, so well known to them all, reminded Hazel of carol singing at home, out with friends in the dark, knocking on the neighbours' doors singing away. It also reminded her of last year's Nativity play at school, how she was chosen to be the archangel Gabriel because Grandma had a spare sheet, and she would make a halo. 'Fear not, for I bring you glad tidings of great joy.' She still remembered her lines, all sung in happiness, now, they were singing for the Lord Mayor of Leicester. The Mayor applauded the singing, and more carols were sung. Then as if by another hidden sign, all the children chanted together.

"We wish you a Merry Christmas and a Happy New Year."

Children and adults were then invited outside for the annual photograph.

Whilst the camera was being set up, Councillor Court, a well built man who had been Lord Mayor the previous year, walked along the line of children and gave them all a sixpence, pressing it into the small palms of each child, for which they individually replied.

"Thank you, Mr Court," With everyone in place, the camera clicked.

Silently, the car pulled up in front of the Receiving Home, assisted by the chauffeur, the Lord Mayor and Lady Mayoress sank back into the red plush seats waving goodbye to the children. The boys said their goodbyes to Matron, as did the East Park Road girls. Revelling in her important role, Matron was quite flushed, and looking plumper than ever. This left the latest assignment of Scattered Homes children to return to the dining room to await their Christmas dinner.

There was nothing different about dinner on Christmas day, it was still food that they found hard to swallow, and having to sit at the table until it was all eaten. Matron and her guests were being waited on in another room, Miss Kelling constantly disappearing to serve them. The remainder of the day was spent as usual in the day room.

With all the trimmings still in place, each picture draped with holly, the tree glistening from floor to ceiling, as far as the Hunts were concerned Christmas was over, they still wanted to go home. At bedtime after tucking the little ones up in their beds, Doris and Hazel whispered together. Questions still going through their minds, why couldn't they

Outside the Receiving Home, Christmas Day 1942.

all stay at Grandmas like they had when Brian was born?

"It's not fair," said Doris "I wonder what all our friends are doing," Doris's voice sounded a long way off. "I wonder if we shall ever see them again." Do you remember Betty Muddimer? Last week on the way home from school she had to pick up a bag of broken biscuits from her Grandma's. Betty gave me a biscuit, then we had another, and by the time we got to her house, half the bag was eaten. She got a good telling off from her Mam. I ran off home while her Mam was still shouting at her." From a strained whisper, Doris suddenly burst into a giggling fit. They both lay there laughing at a memory, and the latest disaster of Betty Muddimer, who was always getting into trouble.

"June Hubbard's still got my skipping rope," Hazel suddenly remembered, wishing she'd had a skipping rope for Christmas.

Iris Brindley had just had her new glasses, Doreen Chambers was the school monitor; she and her brother, Keith, live in the posh house next door to the Brindleys. From door to door they thought of their friends.

"Do you remember Lily Loach, and her dog that got stuck to another dog?" said Doris still giggling. "And that horrible woman Mrs Preston next door and her smelly chickens; she was always shouting at us. "Get off that fence!" Hazel shouted.

"The smell of bacon and eggs cooking on a Sunday morning, and whitening our shoes ready for Sunday school, putting them on the shed to dry," said Doris.

"The big spotted rag dolls that we had for Christmas, and we took them for a walk on Christmas day to show them our school," Hazel said.

"I liked those dolls," said Doris.

Marjorie Prince lived near Mason's corner shop, Hazel always remembered her birthday, it was the same day as hers, and they had often shared the same tea party. Ron, her brother was Norman's friend, they went everywhere together, usually ending up fighting on the Green with the Boundary Road gang. To get away from them they would both run and hide on the stairs of the doorway that led to the front door of the dye-works on Lothair Road. Hazel and Doris exchanged reminiscences, but it was too much to speak of their baby brother. Hazel wiped her tears on the sheet trying not to let Doris know that she was crying.

Their thoughts were in the back yard at home, and neither spoke again. Hazel was chewing frantically on the corner of the sheet, grinding her back teeth on the stiffly starched edge, it seemed to provide some comfort between the darkened dormitory, and the black velvet darkness of sleep.

*　　　*　　　*

In Ward twelve, Emma Hunt had spent her first weeks away from her children, George had been allowed to visit her from his ward. They were both still trying to come to terms with the fact that they would be in hospital for some months. Emma had been sedated for most of Christmas, only thinking of her children and how they were coping with their new surroundings. Complete rest and quiet were the prescribed medication until the doctors had reviewed X-rays, and medical reports.

Grandma had visited the hospital every other day. She had also been to visit Brian in the so-called Nursery at Countesthorpe. It had taken an hour to get to The Cottage Homes, and at first she was refused entry as it was not the stated visiting time, but Grandma insisted she see the Superintendent, and eventually she was taken to the Nursery. It was a type of building resembling an Infirmary, or so the notice read on the wooden post outside the main door. There was only a middle-aged woman about and she opened the two swinging doors and pointed to a large cot at the side of the room. The large ward had several cots on either side, the brick walls were painted green, and everywhere was bare except for one chair at the far side of the room. Grandma sat beside the cot, the baby was asleep, but breathing uneasily as if he had a heavy cold. There were two other babies in the ward, wincing every now and then. Grandma wanted to pick him up but she couldn't bear it if he should start to cry, she only had a few moments. There was no way she could tell Emma that her baby was in such a God-forsaken place, it was like the workhouse for babies. The woman in charge beckoned to denote the end of her visit, Grandma would not leave until she had asked how he was, and why had they cut off his curly hair.

Emma looked weak as she rested on the many pillows. Grandma kissed her even though it had been frowned upon because of the risk of infection.

"Have you had time to go and see him yet, Annie?" Emma asked with a painful look in her eyes.

Grandma had always been called by her first name. George, her eldest son, was grown up by the time she married the merchant seaman who was not his father.

"He's doing all right, Emma, there's nothing for you to worry about, he has settled in quite well," she lied.

Perhaps it was a good time to reassure her, while she was still under half sedation, to know the truth would not assist her recovery. The sudden appearance of George was a timely help to change the subject, apart from saying that she would be visiting the baby again Annie was more concerned about their health.

George's white hands sticking out of the end of his dressing gown told Annie a lot. They had soon recovered from the hard work and heavy lifting, tying down the sheets on the lorries the grime had gone from his fingernails. In his ward were several on-going pastimes, watch making, jewellery and leatherwork. George was at present making Annie a new purse; it was easy to concentrate on small items and kept his hands busy. Every afternoon there was the compulsory hours rest, then after the tea trolley had been round George made his way to visit Emma, during the first weeks he had been taken by wheelchair.

"I could do with a pint of beer," he whispered to Annie as he gave her a hug. "How yer doin', Pem?" It was Emma's nickname from long ago.

Emma and George exchanged kisses and he tickled her under her chin. "I'll be glad when I can wake up properly," said Emma.

"You'll soon be knitting again, I've brought that red wool that you've always been meaning to knit up," said Annie. Her basket was full of goodies as usual, small items of washing, a few biscuits and cakes to have with their cups of tea.

They talked of Ted and how he was getting on with exams for college, satisfied that one of their children was in happy surroundings.

"How does he get on with his Grandad?" said George knowing what a stickler he was for discipline.

"They are getting along fine, Ted runs to the off licence for his jug of beer so that keeps him happy," said Annie.

"Norman and the girls are doing fine, I got the doctor to find out about them the other day," said George.

Emma was just listening, still coming to terms with the nightmare that she was in. A bell tinkled in the corridor, their hour was up, it was teatime and George was staying to have his tea with Emma. Annie was glad that they could be together for a while, it made their goodbyes easier.

The journey back to the bus was down hill all the way, Annie chatted to the other departing visitors about their loved ones, and how they were progressing, or not doing so well, as the case may be. It was enough to cope with the wartime rationing, and the air raids besides having to make the journey across Leicester.

Emma's sister, Rose, would be going on the next visit so Annie would not be making the journey again until Sunday. If she hadn't got the job at the biscuit factory she wouldn't be able to afford the bus fares. Every morning she was up early, to catch the special bus to work. Grandad had finished working on his milk round when the war started, motorised vehicles had made his horse and cart redundant. At the end of the milk round Grandad always ended up at the pub, and it was the horse that would take him home.

*   *   *

CHAPTER TWO

January 1943

Another seven days had passed by and there was still no sign of going home. It was New Year's day, the day when Matron gives her annual party for the children of the Scattered Homes.

In their Christmas Day clothes, The Receiving Home children went into the dining room. Three long tables were set with places for about thirty children. Plates of sandwiches, like they had never seen before, large glass bowls full of jelly and trifle, decorated with cream and cherries. A Christmas cracker and a bar of chocolate were neatly placed at each setting.

The noise from the kitchen meant that the boys' home had arrived as Miss Kelling fussed over certain young lads. The same excitement came from the girls' home as they hung their coats in the hall. With everyone standing, they said grace. Matron's grand entrance had gone unnoticed. With paper hats and serviettes, Miss Kelling and Miss James in their best clothes handed out sandwiches. Some requested jelly, but the sandwiches had to be eaten first. The noisiest moment came when Miss Pickering insisted that 'her boys' pull the crackers, getting the party off to a more relaxed affair. At the end of the table in pride of place was a large Christmas cake, decorated with miniature colourful fruits. The camera clicked as Matron cut the cake, and the centre of attraction. The bars of chocolate were carefully saved as the tables were cleared, everyone taking the pots and cutlery into the kitchen. The dining room was now full of noise, not only Miss Kelling and Miss James, but also Miss Pickering, and Miss Hammond, Mrs Lambourne and her daughter were there, and most of the Christmas guests.

Matron organised the games. There was plenty of floor space for all the children to sit in a big circle. An enamel plate from the kitchen provided the implement for the first game. The plate was spun in the centre of the circle and someone's name was shouted out. That person had to catch the plate before it stopped spinning or they would have to sing a nursery rhyme as a forfeit. It was one way of finding out each other's names. By the time the first game was over a mutual feeling had grown between the children, in readiness for a team game. More enamel dishes were brought in, and pieces of newspaper torn up in the shape of a fish for

'Flip the Kipper'. The fish, or 'kipper' as it was called, had to be wafted along by the plate on to another plate at the end of the room. This noisy, popular game was played several times. Musical chairs followed, by accompaniment on the piano, which led on to the singing of carols. Matron clapped her hands for silence, with immediate response, listening, tinkling 'sleigh bells', could be heard. The dining room door suddenly burst open, a flash of red and white filled the doorway. With his long beard and heavy sack, Santa Claus jingled his way into the room, now surrounded by children of all ages.

Happiness descended on the whole room, his cheery 'hello', and happy smile, shone through his whiskers, reaching the hearts of everyone around him. Sitting in there midst Father Christmas delved into his sack and called out the many names.

Everyone had a present, plus an apple and an orange. The last presents were for the staff, who each in turn gave Santa a kiss. The main light was then switched off, in the warm glow from the flickering fire, and the coloured lights of the tree it was the turn of the children to say, 'thank-you.'

"Away in a Manger" was sung to all the adults, and Father Christmas. Then with the light back on, he was gone. Only his 'sleigh bells' could be heard...in the region of Matron's office. The party was at an end.

*   *   *

In the days that followed, the routine was the same, except that one morning Hazel woke early, she took it upon herself to get the other girls up, swiftly and silently she made all the beds. All the girls were washed and dressed before Miss Kelling appeared. With breakfast over and the arrival of Mrs Lambourne, Hazel told her that Edna had not wet her bed, and all the beds were made much to the surprise of everybody. Matron was told, and Edna's bed was found to be perfectly dry. With the dormitory dusted, Hazel closed the door; she was quite pleased with her early start to the day, and was soon back in the day room. With the Christmas party still fresh in her mind, she opened the favourite book on the day room table. The six days to Christmas were over, she had learned all twelve verses of the poem, but the day for going home had come and gone, so too had the uneventful birthday of Norman, who was now twelve.

"If only we could open the front door and take Brian for a walk in the pram, or play whip and top," said Doris, trying to whisper so that Edna didn't get upset again.

It was the one thing that they all missed the freedom of just going out to play in the street whenever they wanted to. The day room door opened, Miss Kelling's eyes were fixed on Hazel.

"You are wanted in Matron's office," she said.

'Ooh good,' Hazel thought, 'Perhaps we're going home.' She rushed through the kitchen almost running into Matron, who was standing at the bottom of the stairs.

"Come with me," Matron's snarls were worse then ever.

Hazel followed as she marched up the stairs, straight into the dormitory, coming to an abrupt halt at Edna's bed.

"So she didn't wet the bed my girl!" shouted Matron in that strange accent again.

A single 'No' was the reply..

Then, standing to one side, Matron pointed up the room. Mrs Lambourne stood a long way off, she had found the wet sheets on Hazel's bed. Turning, Hazel looked at Matron as a hand whipped straight across her face.

"You deceitful liar," she snarled. "Don't make these beds again until Mrs Lambourne gets here, do you understand?"

"Yes, Matron." The tears had welled up in her eyes, now Hazel knew how Edna felt every morning. She bit her lip, half expecting another blow as Matron raised her arm again, pointing up the room.

"Go and help Mrs Lambourne to put that mess right." Still shouting and waving her arms Matron bustled out of the room.

Mrs Lambourne looked across the bed at Hazel she made no comment as they smoothed the clean sheets. Mrs Lambourne was an understanding lady she was still wearing the same shiny hair clip in her hair that she wore to the party. Her face always seemed to have a smile. Hazel put her hand up to her burning face as she crept passed Matron's office on her way back to the day room.

Some days later when Doris had finished scrubbing the kitchen floor and Hazel had washed the dusters in the scullery, Doris whispered

"Have you seen Norman anywhere?" "He hasn't filled any coal buckets this morning, and I haven't seen him."

They looked for Miss Kelling.

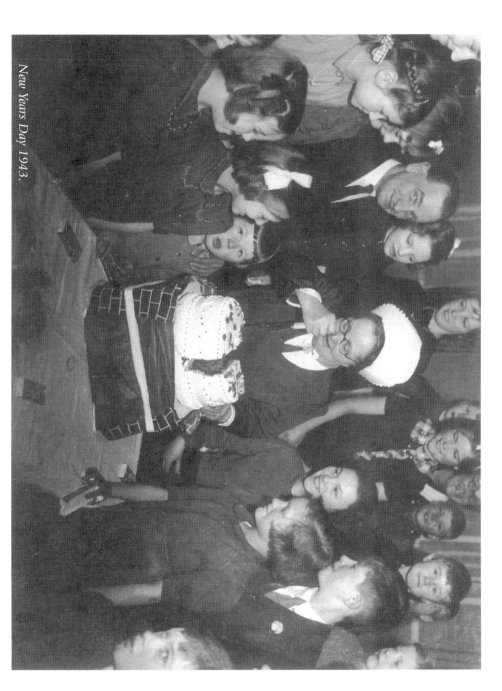

New Years Day 1943.

"Where's Norman, Miss Kelling?" they both asked, "we can't find him."

"I think he's gone to live with your Aunty," answered Miss Kelling.

"When did he go?"

"Who came for him?"

"Why didn't they let us know?"

Their stunned questions received no answers. In the day room they sat and cried no-one seemed to care about them. They had been in the Receiving Home for thirty-five days, it had been a long time, and Norman had gone away without saying goodbye.

"That evening Miss Kelling came into the day room.

"Come along, Hazel, you're the eldest now, come and make the cocoa."

It had already dawned on Hazel that she was now responsible for her younger sisters. Measuring out the cocoa, just as Norman had, she rather liked the scullery job, searching for spoons, poking about in the drawers. Hazel carried the beakers of hot cocoa into the kitchen. It was quite a change from dusting under beds. After drinking their cocoa, Matron made an unusual appearance they had never seen her at night before. All the girls were taken into the best dining room where a fire burned brightly they were told to sit at the large table. Matron gave each one a new pencil and a sheet of paper each.

"I want you to write a letter to your parents," she said.

Hazel was the first to pick up her pencil, knowing exactly what she wanted to say.

'Dear Mam and Dad,
I hope you are feeling better and that the doctors will soon let you go home. Norman has gone to live with Aunty Rose, and we want to go home - we don't like it here.
We have lots of jobs to do, and Doris scrubs the kitchen floor, I dust the bedroom. Edna still wets the bed, but they don't tell her off any more.
Hoping to see you soon.
Love from Hazel. xxxx'

The letter was handed to Matron; there was a look of displeasure as she censored the single page.

"No, you don't want to put all that, we want them to get better, now let's start again," Matron handed out another sheet of paper and this time Hazel was told what to write.

Their parents really were in Groby Road Hospital, they really had got tuberculosis, and the truth was only just beginning to sink in. After the letters were approved they were placed on the dining room shelf. Matron told them that if they were good girls they might be able to go and live with Miss Hammond at the girls' home until their parents were well again. Hazel, Doris and Edna made their way up the stairs, Hazel's true feelings had been written in her letter. Matron now knew how she felt about the Receiving Home.

The door of Matron's sitting room was open, the wireless was on loud, and The Tommy Handley Show was just beginning.

"It's that man again, its that man again, that Tommy Handley is here," Doris and Hazel joined in the jingle, singing at the tops of their voices.

"Get off to sleep," shouted Matron and slammed her sitting room door.

It was nice to hear ITMA again. The audience laughing and clapping reminded them of listening to the wireless at home. Still straining their ears they could still hear the happy banter between Tommy Handley and Mrs Mop.

"Can I do yer now, sir?" They joined in with Mrs Mop, only much more quietly.

"Diss is Phumph shpeaking," said Doris.

That wireless was the only link with the outside world, sometimes strains of music, escaped onto the landing from the formidable Matron's room, or maybe it was the news they could hear, solemn voices reporting the terrible bombings of the different cities throughout Europe. They had forgotten about the war, and had not heard any sirens while they had been there. They felt like prisoners, locked away, through no fault of their own. The letter that Hazel had just written, she had wanted to write more and tell her Mam and Dad about the awful place they were in, and how they missed Norman.

In the darkness every night they renewed memories of all their friends, recalling the happy days at home, their silent tears wetting the pillow.

*   *   *

Two letters arrived for George Hunt, the first letters he had received since he and Emma had been in hospital. He opened the first it was from The Receiving Home. Matron Buttridge was pleased to tell them that the girls were well, and if circumstances stay the same, in the interest of the girls they will be moved to the girls' home on East Park Road. Three letters dropped onto the bed. George read the letters from his little girls he could not believe that they were as happy as the letters made out. In Hazel's letter was the phrase 'we are writing hoping you are well' it sounded a bit dictated, Hazel was more of a 'blab it out' puts what she thinks type of girl. But the letters were happy. George would take them to Emma as soon as the doctors had done their rounds.

The second letter was on the bed, George had almost forgotten it. He looked at the letter - 'baby' and 'hospital' were the words that hit him. He read it more slowly Brian was in the isolation hospital with bronchitis. George needed a cigarette, he had given it up or so the doctors had been led to believe.

What he would give to be driving his lorry right now, singing along with the drone of his engine with a 'ciggy' in his mouth, away from home for two or three nights at a time, earning overtime. He abandoned his thoughts about the nights he slept in his cab, waking up in the morning frozen, having to clear the frosty windscreens before continuing his journey, and looking for a roadside café to have his breakfast. He always saved the allocated money for his lodgings to help out with the family budget and a few drinks at the City Arms at the weekends.

George tapped on the door of the two-bedded ward.

"Hello, Edith, Hello, Pem," George made his way to his wife, she was looking much better, and he kissed her warm rosy cheeks contrasting against her black hair.

"George, you've been smoking" she said.

"And drinking," he teased - "strong tea," He floated the letter onto the bed, as Edith discreetly made her way to the rest room.

Emma read the letter from Matron Buttridge, and then he took her hand and put it in his dressing gown pocket.

"George!" Emma gave a little shrug, knowing that there was to be no personal contact between them. Her hand touched the letters, she took them out and smiled, he was always teasing her.

"We've found a room with a lock on the door, and some of the blokes

Emma Hunt, Groby Road Hospital. ▶

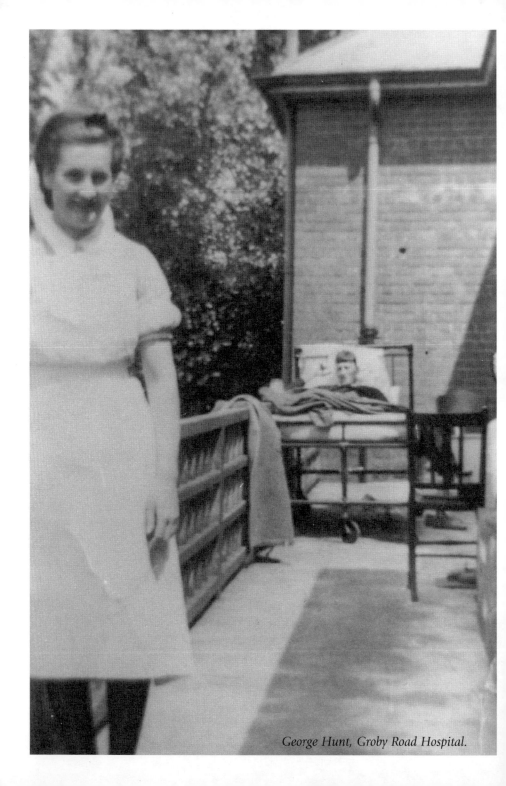

George Hunt, Groby Road Hospital.

on our ward use it to go and have a 'quickie' when the Sister's not about. I will show you where it is when you are a bit better."

Emma wasn't listening she was reading what she had wanted to know for the last few weeks. The neat handwriting, so grown up. Together they read the letters again, laughing at Edna's spelling and all the kisses, her writing was very good though, and after all she was only six. It seemed like the children had settled down at last. Norman was now living out in the country with her sister, Rose, she could only take Norman as she had five children of her own. The fresh air would do him good. Emma wondered would they all be able to walk through the fields again. Go for picnics over the fields at the back of Rose's house, like they had on so many summer days. Calling at the pub on the way back for a cooling beer, and lemonade for the kids. How on earth had they managed to walk so far, and travelling home late at night? Now she could hardly walk as far as the rest room even with two nurses helping her. But she was feeling better, and she read the letters again.

George left Emma with the letters; he would come back later with the tea trolley. The other letter was in the locker at the side of his bed.

"Is there anything I can get you before I get into bed?" Edith asked.

"Look at these," Emma said handing the letters to Edith.

"You must be proud of them, look at the lovely writing," said Edith who had no children of her own.

Jack her husband had been granted compassionate leave when Edith had collapsed, his handsome photo in his army uniform sat on her locker with a small posy of flowers at the side. Jack had been shipped off to France about a year ago, his telegram had just said 'I'm on my way.'

"I've just been talking to Sister, she told me a train load of soldiers arrived in Leicester yesterday. Do you want your knitting out?" said Edith and she started coughing again.

"Get into bed, thanks Edith, you look worn out," said Emma, who could see the red trickle of blood as Edith replaced the lid of the 'sputum mug.'

All was quiet as Edith dozed, Emma looked up from her knitting, Edith was the same age, and if things had been different it could be George who was in the army. Only a few months ago his call up papers arrived, and his medical examination confirmed that he was very ill, which led to Emma having to have her chest X-rayed, there was no other option for them both but to be admitted to hospital.

It was during the quiet moments that Emma could think about her baby, Brian, when there was nothing else to clutter her thoughts. She tried to imagine the nursery he was in, and what other children he would be playing with. How was he eating, had he still got that nasty cough? Would he be taken out for walks, the questions milled around in her head. Would he know his mother the next time she sees him? He was only two years old, and the only one she was really worrying about. The knitting looked out of shape as Emma fought back the tears that had welled up in her eyes. But, she was feeling better, and each day she would improve.

The door to the balcony opened, visitors could get in through this door if they followed the outside path. The sunshine blotted out the figure standing there, Emma could see his army boots...it was Jack. Emma shielded her eyes as the door closed, he was handsome and very tall, and she pointed to the sleeping Edith and the chair at the side of her bed.

"She'll be awake in a minute, she usually has five minutes at this time of the day," Emma watched as Jack gently took hold of Edith's hands.

The dormitory light was switched on - it was just another day. Edna automatically half sat up while the wet sheets were pulled from underneath her. Her eyes were still closed, not able to acknowledge Miss Kelling as she made her way up the room.

They dressed slowly, there was no urgency to please the adults any more. The girls had given their best, now they just had to wait for their unknown future. The early morning strip wash, breakfast, the dusting and scrubbing. With their jobs finished they were glad to get back to the day room, away from the agitated officious supervisors. Today, it was Mrs Lambourne's turn to be shouted at. Miss James was raising her voice in her sewing room Miss Kelling was also joining in. Quite a dispute was going on. Whatever Miss James was cross about seemed to be all over, and beyond the day room door it was all-quiet again. Miss Kelling made her usual morning check up, leaning round the day room door. A full bosomed apron, looking as though she had no legs, and only one hand hanging on to the door.

The hand let go to beckon her.

"Hazel, you're wanted."

With little enthusiasm Hazel left the table and walked to the door.

Miss Kelling walked to the kitchen as if she wanted her to do another job.

"Matron wants you in her office," Miss Kelling almost pushed her through the hall door.

Hazel knocked on Matron's door.

"Come in," Matron's voice was quite calm.

The shiny knob turned in Hazel's hand. Matron sat at her desk moving books and papers about. It was a small office, and hardly big enough for the roll top desk in front of her. With the door closed Hazel was only two feet away from her at the most.

"I want to know how you manage to get holes in your sheets," Matron leaned towards her. There was a pile of sheets on the corner of the desk Matron moved them closer for Hazel to see. The corners of the sheets were folded back uncovering the holes of the freshly laundered sheets.

"WELL!" she snapped.

After a long pause Hazel looked up.

"I chew them Matron," she said in almost a whisper.

"CHEW them! CHEW them! Do you know what you are" Matron was looking straight into Hazel's eyes. "You're a CANNIBAL."

The word 'cannibal' was repeated again and again. Hazel tried not to listen, but Matron's voice filled the tiny room, then a heavy blow struck her face. She bit her lip and tried to focus on something in the room. The slap to her face stung, much more than it had before.

"Look at me when I'm talking to you."

Hazel braced herself, ready for anything. The hand that she raised to deaden the sting was immediately forced to her side. Matron's distorted features and little eyes seemed to penetrate right through to her soul. The strap of the frilly cap was buried in her double chin, which pulled and strained as the lecture went on.

"Never in all my years..,"Matron continued.

Hazel was still trying not to listen, biting hard on the inside of her cheek. Matron eventually stopped as if to draw breath, she seized the moment to utter.

"Sorry, Matron."

At this point the sheets were flung into Hazel's arms.

"Take them to Miss James, she wants a word with you," Matron rearranged the papers on her desk. As the door closed, Hazel put the cool sheets to her face. Miss Kelling didn't look up as she passed through the kitchen. Knocking on the sewing room door, Miss James was waiting for Hazel. Her voice was timid compared to Matron's, the name 'cannibal' had been heard by all, and was repeated by Miss James. There were far more interesting things to look at in the sewing room and the telling off was over. But now she was facing the lady who mended the sheets. Miss James opened the sheets that she had mended from previous weeks; the corner flap was turned over and machined down into a triangle. The oval rubber stamp of 'THE SCATTERED HOMES, LEICESTER' was firmly stamped in the centre.

Hazel could now see that Miss James was a cripple, with one leg shorter that the other. Her rubber heeled shoes squeaked on the lino as she twisted about the room. She was very tall and thin, her eye affliction made it easier to bear, and not knowing which eye was looking at her.

"I promise I won't do it again, Miss James," Hazel said, still holding the pile of sheets.

"See that you don't," said Miss James "I'm not mending any more." The pile of sheets was thrown on to the table.

There was a knock on the door, it was Miss Kelling, and Hazel made a quick exit to the day room.   Greatly relieved, Hazel sat at the table, Matron's words still ringing in her ears. Mrs Lambourne had helped to find the bed with the torn sheets, and Matron would send Hazel to 'the Barnardo's homes away from her sisters.   Miss James threatened that she wouldn't make any new dresses, she would give her the old ones to wear.

Miss James certainly kept her word. A few days later she came into the day room.

"You three 'Hunts' are going to Miss Hammond's this afternoon, get these clothes on," Miss James placed a pile of clothes on the table. "Keep the stockings on."

"Can we wear our scotch kilts please, Miss James?" Hazel said still pleading for their return.

"I've no idea where they are, they'll do you for now," she shouted from the sewing room.

Hazel looked at her pile of clothes, the first thing she noticed was a pair of boys boots, she tried not to cry, they were leaving the Receiving Home, and that was all that mattered. They pulled at the piles of clothes, deciding which garment they should put on first. Edna was the best dressed, she had a bonnet to match her coat, and it was the right length - just below her knees. Doris's outfit was bad, the long coat was well

On their way to Ma's with Miss James.

worn and her large beret was out of shape. Hazel had the navy coat that covered everything, it came down to the tops of the boots. The tam-o-shanter on her head was heavy and loose with a large pom-pom flopping about on top. It balanced the boots on her feet, which felt two sizes too big. They were too excited to care what they looked like, and said a courteous 'Goodbye' to Matron. Suddenly the three girls were outside walking down the lane, feeling fresh air and freedom again. Just glad to be out of the Receiving Home even without their precious kilts.

The three suddenly burst into a giggling fit, when they suddenly realised what they looked like. With every step that Hazel took, the heels came out of the boots, making walking difficult. Miss James started to lecture them.

"No wetting the bed, Edna," said Miss James.

"No, Miss James," said Edna.

"And don't get chewing any more sheets."

"No, Miss James," Hazel replied, knowing the remark was meant for her.

Miss James hadn't found her latest chewing material.

They walked slowly at Miss James's pace; her crippled gait was more noticeable now with no furniture to hold on to. The hysterical, uncontrollable giggling was nothing to do with Miss James they were intoxicated by freedom, fresh air, and the ill-fitting clothes. Travelling by tram, Miss James and the three Hunts arrived at East Park Road. Miss Hammond smiled as she opened the front door. Immediately she told them to call her Ma, 'not mother, I'm not your mother, nor your Aunty - just Ma.'

The house was a large, palisaded type with bay windows upstairs and down. The front room was the dining room, down the hall, passing the stairs on the left they followed Miss James and Ma, into the kitchen. Ma opened the pantry door where the girls stood, she gave them a banana each, and the first one they had ever had.

"Go through the back door," Ma said, "and have a look outside while I give Miss James a cup of tea."

"Thank you, Ma," they said, then with no hesitation they opened the back door, and sat on the steps, enjoying the bananas, making sure that Edna didn't eat the skin.

The gate to the entry was not locked. There was an outside toilet, and a gate through to a big yard at the back of the house. An air-raid shelter

This is the hatch, we call it the 'bobby hole'.

at the far side was dwarfed by a munitions factory, which towered above. When Miss James had caught the tram back to the Receiving Home, Ma called the three in to have a closer look at the clothes they were wearing.

"I think they must be the oldest rags Miss James could find," said Ma inspecting their clothes.

"Miss James kept our new scotch kilts that our Mam made for us, and she wouldn't let us have them back," said Doris, removing her coat.

"Good Lord, have you come on the tram in them boys boots?" Ma looked down at Hazel's feet. " Take them off," she said.

"How do they expect me to provide shoes for this little lot?" Ma said. "Hang your coats up, we'll sort you out."

In stockinged feet, the new girls followed Ma up the stairs, purposely slipping about on the polished linoleum. Straight-ahead on the first landing they passed the bathroom. "This is the brown room," said Ma. The five beds spaced around the room was much cosier than the fourteen beds in the dormitory at the Receiving Home, a large chest of drawers stood against the wall.

"Here, get these on," Ma opened several drawers, and put the clothes on the beds.

Three vests, next the combinations, an item of clothing they had never seen, and didn't know how to put it on. Ma told them to step into it, then pull it up over the vests. On top of that went the liberty bodices, then the knickers. The oval stamps, kept on Miss James's sewing table, appeared on every garment. 'THE SCATTERED HOMES, LEICESTER.' Still only half dressed they followed Ma.

"That's the bathroom, mind the step, upstairs toilet," Ma said, turning and striding up another step to the next landing with the banisters over the stairs. "This is my bedroom," said Ma without stopping, "and this is the blue room."

Following on again through the door was another five beds, and another chest of drawers, both bedrooms had bay windows. The blue room wallpaper was covered with bunches of cherries. Four gold curtains with short white net curtains were covered by a long blackout curtain, which fitted into the bay. The lino on the floor was green.

"Why is it called the blue-room, Ma?" they asked, as there was nothing blue to be seen.

"Don't ask me why, perhaps it was because it used to have blue curtains," said Ma.

Opening the blue-room drawers, the flowered summer dresses lay neatly folded.

"Wrong drawer, you'll be wearing them when the weather gets warmer. Try these."

The warm dresses were pulled over the thick under clothes, by now they were feeling quite over dressed. Edna was to sleep near the door so that Ma could get her out of bed at night for the toilet. Hazel and Doris had a bed either side of the chest of drawers. The old clothes were folded and put in the cupboard under the attic stairs. Ma was getting quite a pile of 'Receiving Home rags.'

"The girls will soon be coming out of school," said Ma.

"Who sleeps up there, Ma?" said Doris pointing up the attic stairs.

"Nobody if I can help it, I've got as many kids as I can cope with," said Ma, holding the knob of the banister as she reached the bottom step.

In the back hall, a large shoe rack stood near Ma's sitting room door.

"Sunday shoes, school shoes, and slippers," said Ma.

All were neatly placed on the shelves, with the shoe polishers at the bottom. Ma was a kind person she wore ordinary clothes, and pretty pinafores. There was nothing stiff and starched about her at all. Her accent was different too, as she explained when they were upstairs, 'if yow can't understand what I'm saying, its because I come from the Black Country, 'Brumm', you'll sown get used to it.' After four o'clock the first girls arrived home from school.

"Good afternoon, Ma," each girl shouted as they came through the back door.

From her sitting room, Ma could tell who had arrived home. The new girls felt uneasy in their new surroundings, they felt jostled as the girls changed their shoes at the shoe rack.

"I'm Nipper."

They were whisked away into the dining room where Nipper who was the youngest, had to lay the table. She opened two small brown doors in the wall.

"This is the hatch, we call it 'the bobby-hole'." Nipper launched herself up on her elbows, her top half in the kitchen, and her legs dangling in the dining room.

"Come on 'Pasty' pass the silvers," said Nipper jumping down again.

Pasty Pauline put her head through the bobby-hole," Don't call me that, I'll tell Big Margaret," and she slammed the cutlery on the serving hatch.

"What's for tea?" Nipper asked.

"Jam," said a voice in the kitchen.

The cloth was spread over the table making sure that equal lengths hung over the edges.

"Put a knife in front of each chair, starting at the top," said Nipper as she moved clockwise round the table.

"Big Margaret sits here, because she's the eldest, then Olive, she's my big sister, I sit here because I'm the youngest," Nipper stood, with her back to the fire. "Next to Big Margaret's."

"Ma will tell you where to sit," said Pasty Pauline, who was hanging through the bobby-hole from the other side.

Various 'heads' peeped through the hatch to see the new girls.

"Good afternoon, Ma," they shouted as more girls came through the back door.

"I'm not deaf," said Ma, bumping into some of the last arrivals.

"Put them coats on the pegs, don't hang 'em up on the floor."

Through the bobby-hole, Hazel, Doris and Edna could see the activity going on in the kitchen. Ma took a large tin from the cupboard, and scooped a spoonful of jam onto each plate. The plates were then passed through to the dining room; each plate set beside a knife. A plate of bread followed, then the plate of cake, one slice each. The small table in the bay window was set for Ma. It had a china cup and saucer, a matching milk jug and sugar basin, a pretty glass jam dish with a silver spoon. Thinly sliced, buttered bread came through the hatch on a larger china plate, with a small plate with her slice of cake. Ma came into the dining room carrying her pot of tea half hidden by a tea cosy. All the girls by this time were standing behind their chairs.

"Do you all know where to sit?" Ma said placing the teapot on its chrome-plated stand.

"Yes, Ma," replied Big Margaret who had organised 'the Hunts.'

"Begin," said Ma. The girls started singing grace:

"Be present at our table, Lord,
Be here and everywhere adored.
Thy creatures bless and grant that we
May feast in paradise with Thee...Amen."

There were eleven girls sitting round the table, in order of age. Big

Margaret, aged thirteen was the eldest, next to her sat Olive who was eleven. Brenda was ten. At eight, Hazel was the fourth eldest, also eight was 'Little Margaret' Winnie's sister. Ruth was next, she was seven, Doris next, also seven. Then Winnie, Pauline, and Edna, all age six. That left Nipper who was five. The plate of bread was passed round; they plunged their knives into the lumps of jam. Half the jam was for the other slice of bread.

"Nipper has lived with Ma since she was two years old, and wore nappies," said Big Margaret.

"Her little bottom used to drag on the floor," said Ma, joining in the conversation," She's still the baby now."

"Can we pass the cake round, Ma?" said Big Margaret.

"Has all that bread gone?" said Ma.

"Yes, Ma," half the girls replied.

"That was quick, go on then," Ma looked on from her gate-legged table in the bay.

The cake plate was passed round the table starting with Big Margaret, and ending with Nipper.

"Can I have another cup of tea please, Ma?" said Brenda.

"Does anybody else want one? Get the teapot, Maggie."

At the bobby-hole the large teapot rested on the tray as second cups were poured.

After tea Ma left her table and stood near the fire.

"I want the potatoes done for morning, you'll all have new jobs tomorrow. Stand."

The girls shuffled their chairs under the table and stood behind them.

"Begin," said Ma.

"We thank Thee Lord for this our food,
But most of all for Jesu's blood.
Thy creatures bless and grant that we,
May feast in paradise with Thee. Amen."

"Our Father which art in heaven, hallowed be Thy name...."

At the end of prayers, everyone left the dining room, except for the ones whose job it was to clear the table. The pots were relayed to the sink in the scullery, washed and dried and put away. Olive filled the coal buckets, and Brenda peeled the potatoes, for morning.

Back in the dining room, the blackout curtains made the room look dark. The ages of the new girls were sorted out, and it was decided which school they should attend.

Ma called to the little ones to go upstairs for a wash. "Do you know which bed you are sleeping in tonight?"

"Yes, Ma, I'm in the brown room," said Nipper.

Up the stairs they found their own peg number, hand towel, bath towel, and flannel. They also had a hairbrush, and comb and a toothbrush. The twelve hairbrushes fitted into twelve slots, above the twelve holes for the toothbrushes. The combs rested on the shelf between. They had all had a busy day, but that didn't stop the chatter in the blue-room. In the other three beds were Little Margaret, Winnie and Edna. All the clothes were neatly folded on the chairs between the beds. With everyone in bed, in the darkened room, it was as if they all had the same signal thinking of home.

"I bet you're glad to be out of that Receiving Home," said Winnie.

"Ooh I hate that Matron Butterwitch," Hazel said sitting upright in her bed.

So do we," said Winnie, chuckling, " I've never heard her being called that though, that's good," said Winnie.

"Butterwitch should be Fatwitch," said Little Margaret.

"Lisa at the Receiving Home, used to call her 'Maytwun Butterwitch.' Doris said.

"How long were you there? said Winnie.

"We went their seven days before Christmas," Hazel said remembering the six verses that she had learnt.

"That was the eighteenth of December.1942," said Margaret, "the same day that we came to Ma's. We've been here SIXTY-EIGHT DAYS."

"SIXTY-EIGHT DAYS," they all said.

"They told us we might go home after a week," Hazel said.

"That's what they told us, didn't they?" said Winnie thoughtfully," How many days were we at the Receiving Home, Margaret?"

"We were in there for fifty-six days, locked up like prisoners," said Little Margaret. We haven't seen our baby brother for one hundred and twenty four days, today."

"Where's your baby brother, Margaret?" said Doris.

"They took Joe to the Countesthorpe Cottage Homes nursery, and we haven't seen him since," Said Winnie.

"That's where they've taken our baby, Brian, he's two years old," Hazel said.

That's how old Joe is," said Margaret.

"Joe was seriously ill in December, and was rushed to hospital," said Margaret. "They didn't look after him at all in that nursery, he'll soon be two."

"Dad took us to the Receiving Home, and when we got there all our lovely clothes were taken away, and we had to have a bath. We'd only just had one at home," said Winnie.

From the landing light they could now see each other, they were all frantically waving their arms about, protesting about their 'new jumpers and skirts,' and 'scotch kilts'.

"Our Mam made them for us for Christmas, we never saw them again. I even asked Miss James for them today, but she said she couldn't find them," Hazel said.

"Ma says she calls herself a Matron, I bet she's not a qualified nurse," said Winnie.

They all started giggling, the Hunts had never heard anything said against Maytwun Butterwitch.

"She called me a CANNIBAL!" Hazel shouted.

"A CANNIBAL, whatever for?" said Winnie.

"Just because I chewed the sheets," Hazel said laughing.

"Chewed the sheets!" both Margaret and Winnie were now giggling uncontrollably.

"Whatever made you chew the sheets?" said Margaret.

"I just liked grinding the corners on my back teeth. There were big holes in them when they came back from the laundry, Hazel said.

"Oh Hazel you'd better not chew the sheets here, 'because we have to do all the mending," said Margaret.

"Let's have a bit less noise up there, this light's going out in a minute," shouted Ma from the bottom of the stairs.

"Yes, Ma" replied the sleepless girls. The excitement died down a little as Margaret and Winnie told them of their ordeal. Winnie was in a serious mood again.

"Our Mam is in hospital," said Margaret, "and we were at home looking after our baby while Dad went to work. We managed alright didn't we, Winnie?"

"Yes, he's a lovely baby, and ever so good," said Winnie.

47

"I bet he was just left to cry in that nursery," Margaret said sadly.

Hazel was now thinking about their baby, would he be crying? Would they be looking after him?

"He's out of hospital now," said Winnie "he's back at Countesthorpe. With your baby brother I expect."

Big Margaret came along the landing, being the eldest; she slept in the small bedroom by herself. She stood in the doorway of the blue-room.

"Ma said you've got to be quiet in here." There was no response to her command. The landing light went out.

"Goodnight, Ma," shouted Big Margaret. "Goodnight", replied Ma.

"Goodnight, Ma" several repeats echoed from various corners of the bedrooms. "Goodnight Winnie, Goodnight Margaret, they all whispered."

"Goodnight," they both replied.

"Don't chew the sheets Hazel," whispered Winnie.

"No, I chew my pillowcase now," Hazel said.

A little giggle came from the two beds beyond.

"Be quiet now ,I'm going to say my prayers," said Winnie.

The blue-room was quiet, all of them thinking of their baby brothers. On Saturday morning, Ma came in and opened the gold curtains. Edna had wet the bed despite Ma taking her to the toilet in the night.

"Never mind, we'll keep trying, said Ma. "Make your beds, then get downstairs when you've had a wash."

Ma served the porridge up and the plates were passed through the bobby-hole. They sang grace, perhaps not quite word perfect, but nobody noticed. Ma gave them all Saturday jobs.

"It's the busiest day of the week, and if it's done properly you can all go to the pictures this afternoon," said Ma.

"Big Margaret does the kitchen, and don't get in her way. Olive gets the coal up and sweep the cellar. Brenda dusts the brown room. Hazel dust the blue-room, Little Margaret the bathroom, Winnie dust the attic stairs,"

"Ooh, I don't like going up the attic," said Winnie interrupting.

"You'll do it - like it or lump it!" said Ma.

"Ruth, you and Doris can polish the stair rods, and Edna and Nipper can dust and mop this dining room."

"What shall I do?" asked Pauline.

"Oh, have I left yow out, I was interrupted wasn't I?" said Ma. "Yow can mop the hall."

"Oh, I hate mopping," sighed Pauline.

"I'll swap with you Pauline," whispered Winnie," You do the attic stairs."

"OK", said Pauline.

"When you've done swapping about, we'll have grace. Stand - begin," said Ma.

All the girls busied themselves for the next hour. Ma cleaned the cooker, and scrubbed the front door step. The flat irons were put on a low light on the gas stove, ready for pressing the school tunics.

Big Margaret had closed the kitchen door, not allowing anyone in until she had finished.

The sausages were laid out in rows in the pan, and carefully pricked with a fork, ready for the oven. The semolina was mixed in the basin, ready for the boiled milk. The cocoa and sugar was mixed in the jug ready for the midmorning drink. The latter jobs were assigned to whoever finished their own job first. Big Margaret had finished the kitchen, the floor had been scrubbed, the flues cleaned, and the fireplace black-leaded. Everywhere was clean and shining. The ironing blanket was put on the kitchen table, and the school tunics were brought in from the hall. Ma brought in the hot iron, held with a special cloth, she touched the iron with a wet finger, if it sizzled it was hot enough. After being shown how to press pleats, they all pressed their own tunics. The cocoa was mixed, and the batter was made for the 'toad in the hole.' The smell of boiling potatoes, sausages cooking, the wet steamy rag from the ironing table, and boiling milk. This was their first smell of Saturday morning.

After dinner, Ma gave out the pocket money, which varied from one to three pennies, she gave the little ones extra out of her own purse so that they could get into the pictures. Eleven pieces of paper were placed on the table, then Ma brought out the sweet tin and placed the weekly ration of seven sweets each on a piece of paper, Big Margaret having the first choice as usual.

With their three pennies and seven sweets they walked in 'twos' to the Evington Cinema. It felt like old times going to the pictures on a Saturday afternoon. The Evington Cinema was much better than Aylestone picture house. Beautiful velvet curtains were closed in front of the screen, there was a balcony where the spotlight came from. The manager was threatening the noisy kids on the front row that he would put them out if they didn't behave. The film started, and the curtains parted in great folds to the side of the screen.

The children's newsreel came on first. The children all cheered as Mr Winston Churchill came on the screen, signing the Atlantic Charter with President Roosevelt, and the Russian representative Mr Litvinov. The Japanese were now fighting our soldiers in the jungle, they had bombed the American warships at Pearl Harbour, now attacking the Philippines. It was the Germans who had dropped bombs on their Sunday school chapel, now the Japs were fighting us as well. The newsreel ended by showing the King and Queen and the two princesses. Next came the cartoons, followed by the feature film. Last of all came the Saturday serial, "The Scarlet Horseman," Always in danger, leaving them on the edge of their seats. What will happen next week?

They had all been taken into the world of movies, forgetting their troubles for a few hours.

"Good afternoon, Ma," they shouted one at a time as they entered the back door.

The smell of cooking came from the kitchen, and there on the table Ma had made a big cake. On the black shiny range the prunes for Sunday tea were cooking in the casserole dish.

On Saturday night, Ma listened to her radio in her sitting room. Big Margaret didn't come to bed until later, so in the blue room there was more time to get to know each other.

"Whereabouts do you live Margaret?" Hazel asked.

"We live on Avenue Road, Clarendon Park," said Margaret. "Mrs Thorpe our neighbour will be wondering where we are."

"She looked after us while Dad was at work," said Winnie. "Well she didn't really, we looked after the baby."

"Our neighbours keep ferrets in their cellar. Mr Kirby goes poaching, he's got two thin dogs as well," said Doris.

"They're greyhounds, he goes racing with them," Hazel said.

"Dad will be going to work now, I bet he's gone on his bike," said Winnie.

"Does he work at night then, Winnie?" asked Doris.

"He works for the Leicester Mercury, and they print the papers for the next day," said Margaret.

"Our Dad's a bus driver, but he's in hospital with Mam," Hazel said.

Weekly ration of seven sweets.

"A bus driver," Edna said picking up the conversation." He used to pick us up on the way to school when he was driving along the Aylestone Road."

"How long has your Mam been in hospital?" Doris said.

"Ever since Joe was born. Dad eventually brought the baby home, but Mam stayed in hospital, he goes to see her every week," said Margaret.

"Visiting times here are the first Monday in every month, for two hours," said Winnie.

"Can we have visitors?" Hazel asked, wondering who in their family would visit.

"I wonder if Grandma will visit us," said Doris.

"Where do you live?" said Winnie.

"We live in Lothair Road," said Edna from the next bed to Winnie.

"Aylestone Park" said Doris. "Our brother, Ted, has gone to live with Grandma, and Norman has gone to live with Aunty Rose."

"Oh, you've got older brothers as well," said Margaret.

"Yes, there's six of us," Hazel said sitting comfortably at the end of her bed.

"A big family then, you still miss your baby though don't you?" said Winnie.

"Yes, we used to take him out in his pram," Doris said.

Big Margaret was stalking the landing - the blue room went noticeably quiet before she reached the bedroom door.

"Yes, you'd better be quiet," Big Margaret then opened the door to the little bedroom, half undressed then went to the bathroom for her wash.

"Its not fair that she should have the little bedroom," said little Margaret. "Its really the sick room, but Ma let the working girls have it before they left, now she thinks she is entitled to it. She's so bossy," said Winnie. The landing light went out.

Winnie began to say her prayers.

"I can still hear you," said Big Margaret.

"I can say my prayers if I like," shouted Winnie.

"Dear God, please take care of Dad, wherever he is tonight. Make Mum well again so that we can all go home. Take care of Aunt Siss, and all our cousins, and Uncle Ben, who is fighting the war. Make Aunt Sarah's leg better so that she can come and visit us. And last of all take care of little Joe, I hope he's fast asleep in his little cot. Amen."

The blue room door opened, Ma came in, her rubber heels squeaking on the polished lino.

"What day is it, Ma?" said a voice from under the bedclothes.

"Sunday," she said as she swished back the curtains.

"Do we have to do our jobs again today Ma?" Hazel asked.

Ma was standing near Hazel's bed, looking out of the window.

"Yes yow do. Just because its Sunday, it don't stop the dust rolling about under the beds," she said. "And don't be all day about it. You all go to church this morning.

Hazel made her bed, excited about the fact that they would be going to church, and out for a walk.

"Don't get too excited," said Winnie "the church is only next door but one."

"Well we didn't get out at all at the Receiving Home," Doris said.

The wet sheets were taken off Edna's bed, and the relay of washing in the bathroom went on quite smoothly, the little ones having their wash first.

"FINISHED!" The one word was shouted as they left the bathroom, bringing the next two in from whatever they were doing. The smell of fried bacon wafted up the stairs.

"Do we have bacon?" Hazel asked Little Margaret, who was her washing partner.

"Only on Sundays," said Little Margaret.

'Sunday, and bacon,' Hazel wanted to be standing on the wall at home in their back garden, watching Preston's chickens being fed. Like they did every Sunday, waiting for Mam to call them in for fried bread.

"Better hurry, Hazel, or they'll sing grace without us. If we're late we'll have to sing it by ourselves," said Little Margaret.

Standing behind the chairs, the breakfast plates were all in place. One piece of fried bread, and one slice of bacon, and an extra slice of bread and margarine, with marmalade.

After breakfast the best coats were brought down from the box room in the attic. The box of berets was placed on the kitchen dresser. The new girls were given a 'Sunday dress' and 'Sunday shoes.'

Olive was still struggling up the cellar steps with the buckets of coal, and Brenda wiping the wooden draining board in the scullery. The solitary bell started ringing, bringing an urgent atmosphere into the kitchen. Ma tied the last ribbons in their hair and only after Ma's approval could they all wait in the scullery near the back door. In the crispy, clean outfits, the girls walked the short distance to church. Up the entry, turn right, pass the neighbour's house, and then turn right again into the churchyard.

Once inside the church it was a different world. The organ was playing as, 'follow my leader' style, all the home girls filed through the door. Dipping their fingers in the holy water at the door, and making the sign of the cross, they reverently bent down on one knee.

With their hymn books they followed Big Margaret up to the front of the church. A life-size crucifix hung from the ceiling, red blood trickled down the face of Jesus hanging from the cross, a crown of thorns around His head. The sorrowful eyes seemed fixed on all of them.

Lowering her eyes Hazel's gaze fixed on the Holy Bible supported on the outstretched wings of a golden eagle. The sharp claws firmly gripping the shining orb of the pedestal. Further to the right, a red oil lamp flickered at the feet of the statue of the patron Saint, St Stephen.

Father Huntley, wearing his long black gown chatted to some of the congregation on his way to the vestry. Young boys smartly dressed followed behind, all disappearing to get ready for the service. The bell stopped ringing, the vestry door opened. Father Huntley announced the first hymn. The new girls watched the procession winding its way towards the back of the church. Leading the procession was a man with a small boy wearing white linen tops over black gowns, the swinging orb filling the church with clouds of wonderful aroma from the burning incense. The crucifix followed the incense bearer, and the entire choir made their way down the centre isle towards the altar. Father Huntley brought up the rear of the procession. Now decked in his long, beautifully embroidered cope, which matched the altar frontal. The hymn came to an end as everyone reached his place at the side of the altar.

Father Huntley said, "Let us pray."

The tranquil setting of the church provided the new girls with the opportunity to be alone with their own thoughts, going over the traumas of the past few weeks.

The last hymn saw the procession back to the vestry door. Father Huntley said a final prayer. In contrast to the serenity of the service, the one-handed organist played happily, as if he had screwed on more than one hand. The congregation was a bubble of conversations.

Miss Adams, the Sunday school teacher came over to meet 'the new girls.

On the way out of church, Father Huntley gave Nipper an extra pat on the head for being a good girl.

Next door but one, a short walk again, and they were at the back door of the home to the smell of Sunday dinner.

"We're back, Ma," shouted Nipper, on behalf of them all. In their tweed coats they filled the scullery, the incense still clinging to their clothes.

"We had this incense, Ma, it was lovely, you can still smell it on my coat," they said.

"I'm not so keen on it," said Ma.

Changed into 'working dresses' the table was laid.

"Anyone want any cabbage water?" Ma shouted from the scullery.

Some followed like sheep down the hall to the scullery door. A queue had formed at the jug on the draining board. The green beverage was poured into the cups.

"You'll never have spots if you drink that," said Ma.

It was too late to retreat to the dining room they had taken a swallow.

"Does it cure styes, Ma?" Hazel asked, showing her the sore eye.

"Let me look, it cures anything," said Ma.

The hot cabbage was now in the colander, draining in the sink.

"There's a little job for you, chop that up," said Ma handing Hazel the knife.

The hot platefuls of dinner were passed through the bobby-hole. There was no hesitation in the singing of grace and the rituals before they sat down.

"What's that?" Doris pointed to the thick triangle on her plate.

"Yorkshire pudding," said Ruth.

"We have that with jam at our Grandma's."

The pudding soon whizzed through the bobby-hole.

"Spotted dog, my favourite," said Brenda.

"What's spotted dog?" The raisins shone like spots in the suet pudding.

"It's not a real dog, thank goodness. Imagine cooking a dog," said Big Margaret.

Everybody examined the 'dog' under the custard.

"Yow want to think yourselves lucky, they're eating cats and dogs in Germany," said Ma.

"Tibby Gamble better watch out then," said Big Margaret. "He sleeps in the air raid shelter when he can get in," Big Margaret looked accusingly at Olive.

"He's a lovely cat, and he's mine now," said Olive.

"Tibby Gamble belongs to the dentist next door," whispered Winnie to the new girls.

"A dentist next door," they said, not liking the thought of a dentist so close.

"You can see the dentist's chair out of the blue room window," said little Margaret.

"Yow can keep your heads out of that blue room window, it's not a butchers shop," said Ma.

"Or you'll get a silly sender," replied the girls all together.

The first week-end was nearly over, Hazel, Doris and Edna had welcomed the outings to church and Sunday school after being shut up for weeks in the Receiving Home.

For Sunday tea, they had two slices of bread and six prunes on a plate.

"Tinker, tailor soldier sailor, RICH MAN, I'm going to marry a RICH MAN" said Brenda who had flipped a stone onto Olive's plate.

Several prune stones swapped plates for the desired amount.

"I don't want your stones on my plate," said Olive who had also received one from Big Margaret.

"Tinker tailor soldier sailor, rich-man poor-man beggar-man THIEF. You're going to marry a thief," said Big Margaret.

Olive tipped the plate up side down hiding all the stones underneath she stuck her thumb in her mouth and rolled her eyes up towards the ceiling. Ma intervened.

"Right, that's enough. Do you know which school you'll be going to tomorrow?" She addressed the Hunts.

Dressing seemed to take a long time on Monday morning, especially when Hazel was told she'd got her comb's on back to front.

"Don't put your blouse and tunic on until you've dusted under the beds," said little Margaret.

Olive and Big Margaret were first to leave for school. Big Margaret with all the 'airs and graces 'of Lady Duckmuck carrying her school case. Olive on the other hand, slung her satchel over her shoulder, and with both hands pulled up her black stockings adjusting the garters at the tops of her legs. She plunged her hands into a large pair of gloves, and shouted "Bye, Ma, as she closed the back door.

Brenda, Little Margaret, Ruth and Hazel were next out of the back

door. It was a cold morning Ma had given them old socks to keep their hands warm. On the way to school they brushed against people waiting for the tram, dodging cyclists as they crossed the road. More and more children joined them the nearer they got to the school. The old Victorian school was on Bridge Road, the senior classrooms were upstairs, and the juniors down below. Most of the classrooms were shored up with big iron poles to protect the pupils if a bomb dropped. Hazel stayed with Brenda, she was the class monitor and gave out all the books ready for the day to begin. The knife-sharp pleats of her tunic, and crisp, white blouse, made her the best-dressed girl in the room. Her thick hair was tossed about as she made her way between the desks.
"Good morning 3C."
"Good morning Miss Barker."
The day started with a hymn.

"Daisies are our silver, Buttercups our gold,
This is all the treasure we can have or hold....
Raindrops are our diamonds, and the morning dew
While, for shining sapphires, we've the speedwell blue."

During this interlude of children singing, Miss Barker was eyeing Hazel up, who in turn was being closely scrutinised by her. Miss Barker was a very plump person like Matron Buttridge. She was dressed in a thick brown tweed suit; the most striking thing about her was her jewellery. Miss Barker wore a necklace of very large amber beads, and thick rings on her fingers. An especially large ring was worn awkwardly on her index finger, which pointed to the place on the page of Hazel's hymn book. She sang the words louder as if Hazel couldn't read.
"Raindrops are our diamonds."
Hazel fixed her eyes on the words in the book, glancing under her eyebrows at Miss Barker, in her shiny laced up shoes as she gently moved to and fro, almost waltzing, keeping time with the tune. After prayers for the soldier's sailors and airmen, and for the King and Country, Brenda again popped up to the rescue and was ordered to take Hazel to see the Headmaster. Mr Baum an elderly man sat in his office, Brenda introduced Hazel as if she was her sister, letters taken from his drawer explained the situation, and he gently smiled. After a short test Hazel was placed in class 1A. She stood at the side of Mrs Newsome's desk,

which was raised up on a platform. All their details were written in the school register in neat handwriting. 'Seaton, Margaret, 170, East Park Road'. She looked up and saw Little Margaret sitting at the back of the class. Mrs Newsome was just the opposite of Miss Barker, she was a very thin lady with a satin blouse and grey cardigan which matched her skirt.

"Right go and sit next to Grace," said Mrs Newsome.

That first morning passed quickly, with a new pencil, and exercise book, the six-time table was written in neatly and they had repeated it, parrot fashion to Mrs Newsome several times. Their wartime school allowance of milk was given out at playtime, third of a pint bottles and a straw, given to them by the milk monitor. They seemed to have monitors for everything.

"Good morning, Ma," they shouted on entering the back door.

"Miss McKenna from Lansdowne Road is at our school," said Doris who was as excited as Edna.

"Miss McKenna our old teacher?" Hazel said.

"Yes, she asked me how we were all getting on, she knows we are all in a home. She knew all about us," said Doris.

"She's headmistress at Moat Road, she took us both to her office, we've had a lovely morning," said Edna.

"Its our favourite" shouted Nipper from the dining room. "Cottage Pie."

"Get round the table," shouted Ma, trying to make herself heard above the noise of eleven girls all talking at the same time. The clatter of shoes on the terrazzo tiles in the hall, to the polished lino of the dining room was enough to indicate that everyone was now standing behind their own chair and ready to sing grace.

It was the first time in three months that Hazel had been separated from Doris and Edna. She had wondered how they would take to their new school, but having Miss McKenna there she knew they would like it.

"Whose class are you in, Hazel?" said Ma.

"I'm in 1A, the same class as Little Margaret," Hazel said,

"Oh, that's good," said Ma.

During their first months with Ma, they learned all the rules. Nobody goes in Ma's sitting room. Get all the jobs done properly. Come straight home from school. Keep away from the windows. Bath nights, Monday, Wednesday and Friday. Head wash and sewing night, Thursday. Tuesday afternoon was Ma's half day

In March, Hazel was nine, and Doris was eight. Edna wouldn't be seven until May. A parcel arrived for them and a birthday card from Mam and Dad. Three pairs of red woollen mittens, each embroidered with their initials. In Ma's sitting room the girls untied the parcel. Ma herself had received a letter from Mrs Hunt. At the end of the letter was a ray of hope, Mam was going to have a review with the doctor on April 8th. Give the children my love, I am now knitting them a bonnet each. Hazel, Doris and Edna took their new mittens into the kitchen to show the other girls, but the other girls were too excited, waiting for the doorbell to ring. It was visiting night.

Mr Seaton, was first to arrive, they could see the outline of his cap through the stained glass window of the front door. Ma came out of her sitting room. Margaret and Winnie crept up the hall to greet their Dad.

"Just be quiet," said Ma as she passed the girls, all craning their necks round the kitchen door. Ma's heavy footsteps plodded on to open the front door.

"Good evening, Miss Hammond, I hope you are well, have they been good girls?"

"Yes, I've no complaints, if they're all like that I'll have no problems.

Mrs Minton was next to ring the bell, as Margaret and Winnie were still hugging and kissing their Dad. Big Margaret, Brenda and Pasty Pauline were already at the dining room door. Dragging their Mam into the dining room with two hands they sat their Mother at Ma's table in the bay window. Mrs Minton was a big woman, and sat heavily on Ma's chair.

In the kitchen Olive sat on the table listening for the rumble of the next tram. Then she counted as many footsteps as it would take to reach the front door she waited for the bell to swing on the bell box. She sprang off the table, ran to the front door and back again before Ma was out of her sitting room.

"It's my Mam," shouted Olive with Ruth and Nipper following her.

Nipper was Ma's little baby, until the front door opened, then she had 'two Mamas.' Mrs Cartwright was a small woman with dark, flashing eyes like Ruth's, the same dark hair half hidden under a well worn felt hat. On her way back to her sitting room Ma put her head round the kitchen door,"Do yow think you'll have any visitors?" Ma said.

"Don't know, Ma, Grandma's probably visiting Mam and Dad at the hospital." Neither Doris nor Hazel expected anyone.

"It would be nice if she could come, I should like to meet her," said Ma. " Don't be too disappointed if she doesn't get to see you this time," Ma added as she left the kitchen. It was a kind way of telling them that they would not be having any visitors this time either.

The kitchen clock struck eight there was a definite movement in the dining room. Time for the visitors to leave. Ma came out of her sitting room to see the visitors, and have a chat with them before they left. Mr Seaton quietly chatted to Ma while Margaret and Winnie still clutched his hands, not letting go until the very last minute.

The Hunts could now join the girls in the dining room. In the hall they passed the 'Dad' in Winnie's prayers. He was tall and rather thin, and a bit older than their Dad was. Nipper was standing on the chair kissing her Mam, and Olive and Ruth were gathering their things together. Mrs Minton was still firmly seated on Ma's chair in the bay window, she said 'hello' to Hazel, Doris and Edna, Big Margaret stood with them near the fire.

The jug of cocoa was on the tray in the kitchen, and a plateful of bread and dripping. The girls talked to Ma about their visitors. Big Margaret was especially voicing how soon she would be going home.

"Whereabouts do you live?" Hazel asked Big Margaret, not expecting an answer.

"My Mam's house is in Millstone Lane," she said.

"I think I know where that is, we catch the Saffron Lane bus near there," Hazel said.

"You mean the bus stop near 'John Biggs' statue," said Big Margaret.

"Yes that's it." The thought of the bus journey to Grandma's made Hazel feel quite homesick. "I want to go home," she whispered.

The tall girl who usually bullied them into doing things for her took Hazel to one side and simply said, "Just run away, catch the tram, and go home." Big Margaret tossed her hair back, a habit she had when giving out orders. "It's as easy as that," she said.

"Clear them 'crocks' away, shouted Ma from her sitting room.

In the scullery Hazel helped Big Margaret with the pots, eager to learn how easy that was. In the blue room they listened to the latest news of Margaret and Winnie's baby Joe.

"Dad told us tonight that Joe is in hospital, he's very ill with pneumonia," said Margaret.

That wasn't good news at all, they all felt sad, and hoped that their baby, Brian was all right.

"Dad said if he didn't come next visiting day, Aunt Sarah might be able to come," said Winnie.

"If her leg's better," said Margaret.

"At least real nurses are looking after him," Hazel said trying to cheer them up.

"That's what Dad said, he's in the best place," said Margaret.

The blue room took on a sombre atmosphere, and Winnie's prayers tonight were special, so she kept them to herself.

"G'night, Margaret, G'night, Winnie, G'night, Doris, G'night, Edna," Hazel whispered.

"Good night, sweet dreams, of Fairy Queens of all the lands," said Doris.

Hazel gave a half-hearted giggle, in an attempt to think of something else, but she had other things on her mind, she was going to run away. With her eyes closed, Hazel could see the statue of 'John Biggs.' It was firmly implanted in their brain as the place they would have to ask for if ever they got lost in Leicester. The days that they had caught the tram with Norman, to take the buttonholes to the hat shop on London Road they stayed close to Norman, helping to carry the box, taking care not to crush the bunches of purple violets that Mam had made. Norman had also taken Hazel and Doris to the De Montfort Hall in the summer for an outdoor concert. It was when Doris got lost at this event, that 'John Biggs' became 'their saviour.'

On Tuesdays Ma made 'mucky stew' so nicknamed because of its colour. The hot stew made with vegetables and meat bubbled away in the saucepan on the kitchen range, the lumps of hot fat floating on the top. The knives and forks clattered on the plates as they tucked into the hot stew and potatoes.

"I'm not eating that," said Winnie, and moved a lump of fat to the side of her plate.

"I want all them plates cleaned up, or there's no pudding," said Ma.

I'll eat it," Hazel whispered to Winnie.

"Ma, Hazel's eating Winnie's fat," said Big Margaret who was in full view of the fat being slid onto Hazel's plate.

"So long as it's eaten up, I don't care who eats it," said Ma.

"Do you want mine?"

Several lumps of fat swished from the plates across the table.

"That's enough," said Ma, "You needn't go daft."

During the dinner break there was ample time to wash the pots and clear away and still have time to play in the big yard before going back to school. It was lovely to wear the new mittens, they didn't have to keep their hands in their pockets to hide the socks that previously kept their hands warm.

One day, on the way home from school, a fire engine, ringing its bell was racing along East Park Road.

"It's the blue room," shouted Margaret to Brenda and Ruth across the street.

"No it's the brown room," shouted Brenda and Ruth, as they ran off towards the clanging noise.

Running in the opposite direction Hazel and Margaret reached East Park Road before Brenda and Ruth. Clouds of choking smoke billowed across the road towards Saint Stephen's church.

"Somebody's chimney's on fire," said Margaret.

The fire engine had stopped in Saint Saviour's Road, not many yards away from the home.

"Look at the flames coming out of the chimney pot," said Margaret.

They stood there amazed as the fire engine stretched out a long ladder to the roof. Bill was shouting to Jack, and Fred was ready, and up the ladder with the long hosepipe. A great surge of water hit the chimney pot. Quite a crowd had gathered, watching the daredevil actions of the fireman. A tram rumbled past, the conductor shouted. "That's a good'un," and a few more people joined the crowd.

"I'm glad that's not my fireplace. Have you seen the mess afterwards? It's unbelievable, soot everywhere," said Mrs Gaten who owned the sweet shop. "I know, because it happened to our Rita in them old houses on Melbourne Road"

A loud crack suddenly came from the roof.

"That's it, the chimney pot's gone," said a lady in the crowd.

Looking up they could see that half the chimney pot was ready to fall away. The crowd on the other side of the fire engine was moved to a safe distance.

"There's Brenda and Ruth, come on, Hazel we can see it from the dining room window," said Little Margaret.

"Good afternoon, Miss James," shouted Little Margaret as she opened the back door.

"Oh, it's Tuesday," Hazel sighed. "Good afternoon, Miss James.

They had just closed the back door when Miss James appeared in the hallway.

"There's a chimney on fire across the road Miss James," said Little Margaret. "It's three doors away from the paper shop," she said, observant as ever. If she had been asked, Little Margaret could tell them what colour the curtains were.

"I'm well aware of that," said Miss James. "Get your coats off, and get washed you smell of soot."

Miss James went over to the bobby-hole.

"Is that table laid?"

The two ran upstairs for a wash, and crept along the landing to look out of the blue room window. The firemen were rolling up their hoses, and the crowd had almost gone. Brenda and Ruth came in the back door.

"Good afternoon, Miss James." They shouted together.

"Did you see the chimney fall off?" said Brenda coming into the bathroom.

"It fell into the back garden," said Ruth.

Standing behind chairs they sang grace as Miss James watched over them from the bobby-hole. Ma's table wasn't laid on Tuesdays, Miss James ate her tea in Ma's sitting room. They sat down to scrambled egg.

"Take your elbows off the table, and don't put your knife in your mouth," Big Margaret was already taking charge and giving out her orders. Miss James's presence always brought 'Receiving Home gloom' to East Park Road and Big Margaret made sure that they didn't make any noise.

The topic of conversation was still the fire engine and the chimney fire. It was all over by the time the 'seniors' were out of school, Big Margaret and Olive had missed it. Brenda gave all the details and Ruth managed to get a word in, when Brenda forgot about the fine.

"She's got to pay one and sixpence fine," said Ruth. "She was a little old lady, and she was crying," said Ruth quietly.

"Well you would be crying if water poured down this chimney," said Big Margaret sarcastically. Ruth said no more.

"After tea we'll have some of 'Miss Cart's Chorus', then you'll know them all by the time you lot get into the seniors."

Carl's chorus's on the dud piano.

They could hardly refuse, when the dining room was the only place they were allowed in, after tea. Big Margaret walked round the table with the plate of cake

Miss James came into the dining room she stood with her back to the fire.

"Have you finished?" she said.

"Yes, Miss James," came the communal answer.

Their angelic voices sang grace, Big Margaret dominantly prolonging each note like a funeral march. The table was cleared, the pots washed and put away, the potatoes peeled for tomorrow, the scullery cleaned and all the coal buckets filled, without a reminder from Miss James. They were all back in the dining room in record time, ready but not willing to be bullied into a sing-song.

"Olive, have you got your chorus book?" said Big Margaret. She opened her school case while Olive rummaged through her satchel. A chair was placed at the flap of the bureau, and the chorus book stood like a music sheet on a piano.

"I will make you fishers of men, fishers of men, fishers of men. I will make you fishers of men if you'll follow Me,
  if you'll follow Me,
  I will make you fishers of men if you follow Me."

Big Margaret now joined by Olive and a few others were singing their heads off. The writing desk had taken a bashing over the years, with only one chain holding the flap the other chain swung loosely on the other side, shaking vigorously with the beat.

"Come on, join in Miss Cart's Chorus," said Big Margaret, continuing to press her fingers on the imaginary keyboard.

Around the table the girls watched the eldest girl, some slumped on their elbows, Doris was drawing, Ruth and Edna sitting nearest to the 'entertainers' were playing 'cats cradle' with Ruth's bit of string. With dominant gestures, Big Margaret carried on.

"Let's sing the one about King Solomon," Pauline requested. The long legs of her rag doll had already been twisted into knots, having 'marched with Moses across the DEAD SEA.'

"Come and stand here then, Pauline, look at the words," Pauline's older sister was now lightly touching the dud keyboard, and humming the slow tune.

Consider the lilies in the field how they grow,
They toil not, neither do they spin,
Yet Solomon in all his glory,
Was not arrayed like one of these."
Everyone clapped Pauline for her crystal clear singing.
"Join in, everybody," Big Margaret tossed her hair and proudly smiled, encouraging Pauline for a repeat performance. With more applause Pasty Pauline and her doll sat down.
"Give!" shouted Winnie," on page ten, but I'm not singing it on my own."
Olive thumbed through the well-worn pages and shared the book with Brenda, Margaret, and Winnie.
"The East Park Road Sisters," announced Olive.
Brenda with a rather croaky voice, and Little Margaret's soprano blended together with the shy voice of Winnie, all singing to the well-known tune by Elgar.

"Give and it shall be given unto you,
Give of thyself in service ever true,
This is the promise God has given to you,
As thy days, so thy strength shall be."

The four simple lines were sung again. If Big Margaret had tried to please Miss James, she had been successful, Miss James had been listening in the kitchen, and she appeared at the bobby-hole smiling.
"What lovely singing," she said looking across the room. The rest of the girls had resumed their seats at the table, and Big Margaret had quietly put away her dud piano.
"Little ones can start going up for a wash," said Miss James nodding her good eye towards Edna and Nipper.
Nipper murmured dissatisfaction. "Ma lets us stay up a bit longer than this," she said. The slight protest fell on deaf ears, as Miss James closed the bobby-hole doors. With no fuss the two youngest started off the relay of bedtime. Edna knocked on the sitting room door. Nipper nearly forgot she was the only one who walked into Ma's sitting room without knocking. Miss James sat by the glowing fire, the room was warm and

cosy, and she stood up to inspect their ears, neck and feet, making sure they'd had a thorough strip-wash.

"Go and drink your cocoa, oh, you don't have cocoa at night do you?" Miss James said as an afterthought, casting her eye on Edna.

"Ma lets me have half a beaker," said Edna. They both left the room and closed the door tightly behind them.

"You can have a beaker full if you want, Edna," said Nipper, not frightened at all by Miss James's stern manner. By half past eight all the girls were in bed, Big Margaret washed the cocoa beakers and made supper for Miss James.

A large, deformed teddy bear appeared round the blue-room door.

"I'm a poor old bear, full of straw and nobody loves me," Squeaked Olive as she hid behind the door, holding the teddy bear at arm's length.

"Ah, let me hold him," said Winnie," Come and have a cuddle with 'Puckinapiepie'. That's what I used to say to our baby, Joe. 'Puckinapiepie,' and then give him a big kiss."

"This is 'Brown Room Ted'," said Little Margaret.

"Whose is it? He's lovely," the Hunts said looking at the teddy bear in a baby 's night-gown.

He belongs to all of us, but he lives in the airing cupboard because he's losing all his stuffing," said Olive.

"This night-gown, was the one Nipper was wearing when she came in the homes, so you can tell how big she was," said Winnie holding the bear up to her face. "No wonder Ma loves her," said Winnie.

"Let me hold him," said Edna.

Brown room Ted, was passed from bed to bed, losing bits of straw on the way round. The noise level started to rise, Big Margaret had sneaked upstairs, and crept along the landing, and stood at the blue-room door," Miss James said you've got to be quiet, she's coming up in a minute.

Olive took the teddy bear and waved its paw behind Big Margaret's back.

"Night-Night," said Olive, and crossed her eyes. Looking over Big Margaret's shoulders, she followed Olive out of the room.

They all felt it was too early to go to bed, and carried on whispering to each other, just to defy the bossy orders of the eldest girl.

"Ma will soon be home, the last tram leaves at nine, and Miss James has to be on it to get back to the Receiving Home," said Little Margaret.

"Four corners, to my bed,
Four Angels round my head,
One to watch, and one to pray,
And two to keep me safe all day."

Winnie had smoothed her sheets and was sitting up in bed hands together eyes shut tight.

"Dad taught us that one years ago, it's his favourite," said Winnie.

The Tuesday gloom was over.

On Wednesday morning, the hot porridge was served up. The cold March winds howled as they trudged their separate ways to school. Little Margaret remembered to take swimming costumes and towels, the last two lessons for 1A were spent at Spence Street swimming baths with Mrs Hackett. Hazel and Margaret were the first to arrive home after school. They stayed in the scullery when they heard Ma talking to Matron Buttridge in the hall. Matron Butteridge was just leaving. They hung the wet towels on the line in the big yard, and met Ma in the hall as they came back into the house.

"What did Matron come for?" Margaret asked confidently.

"She's been to condemn the socks," said Ma, "I've seen it all now, she took the scissors, and cut the socks in half, she thinks I'm going to sell 'em, full of holes and darns. I sent all those boys' vests back the other week, if she thinks I'm letting you lot wear boys' vests she's got another think coming. And I told her so."

Ma was in full flow, the West Bromwich accent, always came to the fore when she was annoyed.

"And I told her I flatly refuse to let the girls wear boys' jerseys for school," Ma took the tin opener and started wrestling with the tin of corned beef.

'"Thank goodness she only comes once a month, and it's always after my half day. I wonder sometimes what Miss James goes tittle-tattling about. Is that table laid?" Ma slid the corn beef on to a plate.

The dried peas that had been soaking for a day were now mushy and plopping away in the saucepan next to the potatoes.

Dinner was eaten almost in silence, it was as quiet as if Miss James was still lurking in the kitchen. Matron's visit had angered Miss Hammond, she was normally an easy-going person, and being brought up in the 'Black Country' she knew what hardship was. Being mother and housekeeper to her father and five brothers had tested her patience many a day. It was when the bread and butter pudding was brought in that the silence was broken.

"Ooh, the pudding's lovely, Ma," they all said.

"My favourite" said Big Margaret, sitting close to Ma.

"Thank goodness I can do something right," said Ma clearly still thinking about the socks that Matron had cut up. The socks that the girls wore to keep their hands warm on the way to school.

"I've got a swollen thumb, Ma," said Ruth, having difficulty holding the spoon.

"Let's look," said Ma.

Ruth stood next to Ma, in the light from the bay window.

"That's a whitlow," said Ma. "We'll have a kaolin poultice on that before you go to bed tonight."

After the baths, a funny smell came from the scullery, the tin of kaolin was cooking in the saucepan of water. Round the kitchen table all the girls watched to see what a Kaolin poultice was. Ma spread the hot, thick, grey, treacly stuff and sandwiched it between two pieces of pink lint. Ruth held out her shiny swollen thumb.

"Oooooh, Owwww... it hurts Ma," sighed Ruth.

"Its not too hot is it?" said Ma, and tested the poultice on the back of her hand.

"Got to have it hot or it won't get better, and the doctor will have to lance it," Ma put the bandage on as Ruth cringed bravely.

Every Thursday the laundry man brought the clean laundry back from 'the workhouse,' Hill Crest Hospital, and on his way collected the hamper of groceries from The Receiving Home. Matron Buttridge, not giving an ounce of butter, or dried egg powder more than was allocated carefully weighed out the weekly rations.

"Come on, many hands make light work. Whose turn is it to unpack the groceries?" shouted Ma through the bobby-hole. "Hazel and Doris come and help as well, it'll be your turn next week."

"The margarine and lard go in the cold box on the thrall in the larder," said Ma.

They had wondered what was kept in the box with the steel mesh side. The dry provisions were kept in the kitchen cupboards. All enamel containers, TEA, COCOA, DRIED EGG, FLOUR, OATS for porridge. The blue bags of sugar were carefully poured into the SUGAR container. The

Thursday, sewing and hair wash night.

currants and sultanas, and other scarce commodities which were only sent every three weeks, were carefully stored in Ma's sitting room, to stop little hands delving into the tin. The laundry hamper was emptied everything was placed on the kitchen table and inspected from socks to torn sheets.

After tea, the pile of mending was put in the middle of the dining room table. Thursday was also 'head wash night'. They all queued up outside the bathroom door, while Ma washed their heads one at a time in the bathroom sink.

With wet heads the girls sat around the dining room table, anyone who could hold a needle had to do their little bit, even if they could only sew buttons on. The moans and groans started.

"I can't sew, Ma," said Winnie.

"Whose are these knickers?" said Olive "they've got no elastic in 'em."

"They're mine, " said Brenda, remembering how she had borrowed a safety pin at school.

"Well you can sew them then," said Olive.

"I don't know how to put elastic in," said Brenda.

"Look, you just thread this bodkin with elastic, ease it through the top of the knickers, then sew the ends together," said Olive.

"Who can darn socks?" Ma held the socks up, inspecting the big holes.

"I'll do them," said Big Margaret.

"Show these two what to do, and they can help," said Ma, throwing a pile of socks in front of Little Margaret, and Hazel.

"Socks! Just our luck," said Little Margaret.

"Make a good job, its you that's got to wear them. Has everybody got something to stitch?" said Ma.

More sighs, and the tossing of wet hair as phrases of sheer frustration flew across the table.

'I can't thread this needle.'

'How do you use this bodkin?'

'How much elastic do I need?

'Where's the rubber buttons?'

"Be quiet and get on with it, or we'll be sitting here all night," said Ma.

"I'll be glad when it's bedtime," said Pasty Pauline.

"And I don't want it done with a red-hot needle and a burning thread, or you'll have to do it again," said Ma.

Ma sat at her table in the bay, turning the handle of her sewing machine, guiding a torn sheet through with the other hand.

"Some of you don't know you're born, when I was a girl I had to mend all the clothes for my Father and four brothers. Up early every morning doing the washing, cooking and cleaning," said Ma.

"Did you have four brothers, Ma?" said Big Margaret.

"I had five," said Ma, "one got killed in the First World War.

"What was his name?" said Nipper.

"Sydney, our Sydney was twenty one when he was killed, it broke my Father's heart. Help me fold this sheet Margaret," said Ma. "I was the youngest of twelve, and had to do all the donkey work, you think I don't know what it's like," Ma placed the sheet on the table.

"You had to help your Mother then didn't you, Ma?" said Brenda, still trying to sew the elastic ends together.

"My Mother died when I was thirteen, and some of my brothers and sisters were married by that time. I was the only girl left to do all the chores," Ma looked across the room. "So think yowselves lucky."

"I've sewn a button on," said Nipper.

"Right you can go and get your wash then," said Ma.

"Can I come down again, please Ma?"

"Go on then, we'll make sure your hairs dry," said Ma inspecting the rubber button on the liberty bodice.

"Not bad for a littl'un," said Ma.

"Is that all right, Ma?" both Little Margaret, Hazel and Doris went to Ma's table to have the darning inspected.

"Well it's not brilliant, but it'll do, you're supposed to darn it not sew it," Ma gave the socks back.

"Do a bit more weaving in and out just there," said Ma.

"I've never done any darning before, but I can knit, my Grandma taught me on two wooden meat skewers from the butchers," Hazel said proudly.

"We'll set you on then," said Ma.

The sewing night ended at long last, all the needles were back on the pin cushion, elastic, and buttons back in the sewing box. Big Margaret had made the jug of cocoa, and the last strip-wash had finished.

"Thank goodness that's over," everybody sighed.

They all loved Friday, at school the first two lessons were taken up in assembly. Prayers were said for the soldiers at war, and a chosen pupil read out of the Bible. It was a morning of hymn singing and religious instruction. It was the first time Hazel had ever seen anyone have a fit. The girl standing next to her slumped to the floor, wriggling in an uncontrollable way. Her face almost scraped across the rough wooden floor, she was quickly taken to the teachers' staff room to recover.

Friday's dinner was fish with potatoes and mushy peas, and pudding was a triangular piece of jam tart. After tea, the girls could play in the big yard, the sounds of the church organ filled all the back gardens, and the choirboys were busy practising the hymns for the Sunday service. Before going to bed they all lined up, in the kitchen again, for a spoonful of white peppermint, and a spoonful of cod liver oil and malt. Edna and Nipper had to have two spoonfuls, because they were the youngest. Big Margaret took longer with Ma's supper, she knew Ma listened to the Friday night play on the wireless. In the blue-room they sat on each other's beds, giggling and laughing at incidents of the day. The sound of plodding footsteps came along the landing, sending everyone scurrying back to their own beds.

"Caught you," said Olive.

"Oh, we thought it was Ma, you scared us to death," said Winnie.

"How about this then," said Olive, as she proceeded to walk with the same gait as Miss James.

They looked down at Olive's feet, she was wearing Ma's shoes.

"That's just like Miss James," said Little Margaret.

"Get off to sleep you low-down common lot," said Olive, chanting one of Miss James' favourite 'howling' up the stairs.

Still in Ma's shoes, Olive stood at the window, and put her head under the blackout curtain.

"Ssh, the choir boys are coming out," she whispered.

The whole of the blue-room joined her under the curtains.

"Which one do you like, Olive?" said Doris, peering into the darkness at the figures standing at the church gate.

"I think his name's Pip. That's what his sister calls him anyway," said Olive.

"Can you see him?" said Winnie.

"No it's too dark, but I know he comes this way," said Olive, still standing in Ma's shoes.

"That's Father Huntley's voice, quick close the curtains," Little Margaret jumped back into bed she had recognised the robust figure of Father Huntley's in his long cloak.

"I think he's coming here," said Olive.

"Who?" said Winnie jumping into bed.

"Father Huntley," said Olive.

The front door bell rang in the kitchen.

Olive dashed out of the blue-room, and the rest dived back into bed, straightening all the bedspreads.

Ma was talking at the front door then her footsteps came nearer, along the landing, to the blue-room. "Anybody been out of bed?" said Ma.

"No, Ma.

"Father Huntley says the blackout curtain's not closed properly." Ma straightened the curtains. "Now get off to sleep," she said.

The weather was beginning to get warmer the winter had left the big yard in a mess, with twigs and dead leaves from the apple tree. They had all watched and waited for the last apple to fall. Like a shooting star they could make a wish on the falling apple, a secret wish made by all the girls. A wish to go home.

Ma inspected the dining room curtains and said 'they looked more brown than gold.

"Time for a spring clean," said Ma, recollecting the day she bought the material from Grice's in the High Street in Leicester. She had taken all the girls with her, leaving them outside the shop. Being wartime passers by wondered what they were all queuing for and joined the queue. On the tram coming back, Ma asked the conductor for 'one and twelve halves', and he said, 'are they all yours missus?' and Ma said, 'yes they are and they've all got different fathers!'

"He didn't know what to say to that," said Ma, laughing and scratching her head.

During the week Ma washed the curtains herself, she never trusted the 'workhouse' laundry with her hard fought for curtains. It had taken months for Matron Buttridge to sanction the money to buy them. Making them herself, Ma was able to have all matching curtains at the front of the house, replacing the old, faded blue curtains. The rooms had a sunshiny gold atmosphere when the setting sun streaked though the windows from across the park. It wasn't until Saturday morning that they really understood what 'spring clean' meant. After an early breakfast everything was sheeted down and covered up. The chimney sweep arrived he strode in and out of the house, bringing the rods and brushes. The girls were strictly told to keep out of his way, the first chimney to be swept was the dining room, a ready made audience watched his every move.

"Do you clean chimneys all the time?" one said.

"I bet you have to get up early so that people can light their fires," another said.

"Up at six every morning my duck," replied the sweep.

"We saw a chimney on fire the other week," said Brenda.

"That won't need cleaning then will it?" he said.

"I bet your wife has a job to wash your clothes," another said.

"Do you have to have a bath every day?" said Winnie worrying about the sooty state of his hands and face.

The sweep screwed the brush head on to the first rod, and partly pushed it up the chimney. And with a second rod on he pulled and pushed on the rods bringing the first of the soot puthering down the chimney.

"We clean our teeth with soot, because we don't have toothpowder," they told him.

"Good stuff," said the sweep showing his particularly white teeth against his black face

"Have you got any children?" asked Brenda, still standing quite close to the man, who had now covered the fireplace with a sack, and only a small hole for the rods to pass through.

"My boy's name's Donald, I bet he goes to your school," said the sweep, adding another rod.

Brenda suddenly jumped backwards as more debris fell down the chimney.

"Go and see if the brush is out of the chimney for me," he said.

A sudden rush of girls fled to the back yard, all eager to see the brush sticking out of the chimney pot. The wondrous brush that had travelled up the height of the house, with the aid of a few rods, giddily swayed about. The kitchen was next and Big Margaret was ready for the sweep, not allowing anyone in as usual. Ma had prepared her sitting room for the last attack on the soot, and their last chance to shout out, the moment the giddy brush leaped out of the chimney. In the short time that the sweep had been in the house, he had created a dust, together with the pattering feet, which followed his every move. He also re-created in them the sense of loss of their fathers, they had bestowed upon him the love of the Dad that was missing from their predominantly female abode.

"What would you do with this little lot then?" said Ma as she gave the, even sootier sweep, a cup of the Saturday morning cocoa.

"I'd get them all washing my socks, and ironing my shirts," he said. The girls all chuckled at the thoughts. In his grimy clothes he looked as if he hadn't got a good shirt to his back, and it would take more than one bar of soap to get him clean.

With a wave to them all he left the house, and cycled away, the brushes firmly tied to his crossbar. Now it was the girls' turn to earn their Saturday morning cocoa.

"Right that's the end of the fun and games, now let's get this place cleaned up or there'll be no pictures this afternoon," said Ma as she threw a handful of soda into the buckets of hot water.

"Brenda, dining room fireplace, Hazel wash the floor, and I don't want any soot left anywhere," Ma placed the buckets on the scullery floor.

"Olive, see to the coal buckets, we'll have the fires lit before dinner," Ma stood waiting to see who was next in line while Olive disappeared down the cellar steps.

"Margaret and Ruth, you can mop the halls, I don't care who does which. Edna, go and fetch that sheet off the line, and put it in the airing cupboard. Winnie and Doris, you can straighten the bathroom, and make sure that it is tidy up there. Nipper and Pauline, I've got a job for you, come with me," Ma went off down the back hall to her sitting room. There couldn't be any other day to get all the jobs done with such ease, each of them wanting to go to the pictures. Once the smell of sizzling sausages wafted the air, they knew they were nearly finished.

There were quite a few shops in the vicinity of the home. The newsagent was on the corner opposite the park gates. Round the corner, the first shop on the main road was the sweet shop with sweets that could only be bought with the necessary coupons. Opposite was the butchers shop, the florist, then the fish shop, next to the grand building of the bank. The shop they dreaded most of all was the hairdressers, even the new girls had been made to walk on the opposite side of the road on the way to school. They hated everything about it, the smell of the chemicals used in the Eugene perm, the perming curlers that were attached by wires to the customer's head, and the smell of scorched hair. Whenever there was an air raid, they prayed for a bomb to drop on it.

The visit to the hairdressers was always after school on a Thursday.

Sitting on the high chair the girls' arms were pinned down under heavy smocks, firstly the hair ribbons were pulled out, then a good tugging with the comb got rid of the cots. The hairdresser then parted the back of the hair and fastened each piece with a pinching waver clip, now armed with scissors she cut the girls' hair as high as she could. They could only pull faces at each other in disgust. Then as if by a spiteful gesture, she took the clippers out of the box and shaved the back of their necks like the boys.

On her first visit Hazel complained bitterly.

"I don't like that, I don't want my neck shaved," Hazel said leaning as far forward as she could.

"Got to get rid of your pigtail," she said. The scissors snipped away, almost to the tops of her ears, and then the long bit was combed and put back in a ribbon.

The hairdresser then took a brush, and turned Hazel's collar back and put more hair down her neck, causing as much discomfort as having six hedgehogs living in her vest. On such days, Ma could be persuaded to let them wash their own hair before tea, so they could get rid of the unwanted hair stuck to the vests. They could also take their time and lather the carbolic soap into froth. The white lumps of foam vainly swept up on top of their heads, as if moulded like the blonde curls of Dorothy Lamour. After beetroot and cheese, two slices of bread, and a piece of cake, without fail, the dining room table was again covered with the usual Thursday night mending.

The days and weeks passed by, and still the Hunts' had no visitors. Again they were seeing Mrs Minton, visiting Big Margaret and her sisters, this time Little Margaret and Winnie had their Aunt Sarah to visit them. Mrs Cartwright came in the same crumpled hat, and again Nipper had 'two Mamas' for an evening. Hazel sat at the kitchen table Doris sat drawing as usual. Edna had smuggled Tibby Gamble in and was chasing it under the table. They all felt homesick.

The following day Hazel decided to run away, and stayed behind in the little yard toilet while the girls went off to school. She changed into her Sunday beige stockings. The shilling she had saved was in her pocket. It was just as simple as Big Margaret had said. Hazel crept down the entry, knowing that Ma had gone into her sitting room when everyone had left for school. The tram rumbled along London Road, Hazel looked in the direction of the Receiving Home to see if Miss James was anywhere about.

At the terminus, she soon found 'John Biggs' statue, standing at the junction where the bus was waiting. She gave the shiny sixpence to the conductor and asked for half fare to Southfields Drive, the conductor gave Hazel a ticket and no change. She immediately confronted him with the mistake, he insisted that he had not been given a sixpence. Hazel sat on the long seat just inside the bus, and each time he gave another passenger a ticket, she appealed to him again. A few stops later, an inspector got on the bus, and Hazel told him what had happened, and mentioned that her Dad was a bus driver. The sixpence was returned without charging the fare. The bus travelled along Saffron Lane, Hazel decided not to go to Grandma's, she could not resist the urge to have another look at their house in Lothair Road. Hastily she got off the bus, excited as if she was coming home from Grandma's.

Forgetting the conductor, she re-assured herself that she was right. The road wasn't as long as she thought, and Hazel was soon peering through the lace curtains of number twenty-two, she could see nothing. Down the entry the gate wasn't locked, everywhere looked so small and grimy. The garden was overgrown, and the house looked as abandoned as she felt. There was nothing that she could recognise, the zinc bath had gone from the hook on the wall, and the outside toilet was draped in cobwebs. Hazel stood on the top of the three steps, holding the knob of the locked door, peering into the gloomy kitchen she could hardly believe that her family had all lived there before Christmas. Walking to the edge of the small yard, Hazel looked at the forgotten air-raid shelter, then turned to gaze back at the house, at the thin closed curtains hoping that someone was hiding in there ready to open the door. She knocked the door once again just in case. Closing the gate behind her, Hazel took another look through the front room window, in case she had missed some small thing. Hazel then decided to retrace her steps and walk back to the bus stop. The last house was where her friend lived, she thought of Marjorie, and was soon knocking on the door. Mrs Prince came to the door.

"Is Marjorie in?" Hazel asked.

"No my duck she's at school," said Mrs Prince looking as bonny as ever.

"Who are you then?" she said, showing all the gaps between her teeth.

"Hazel Hunt," she replied.

Mrs Prince suddenly realised who Hazel Hunt was, and with tears in her eyes she gave her a big hug.

"Come in my duck, you have changed, it is nice to see you. Mrs Prince went on," What are you doing here then?"

Still in the grips of her arms she looked down at Hazel. "Marjorie's at school."

Hazel stood to one side, feeling strange being squeezed by the buxom woman.

"Did they tell you about your Christmas tree?"

"No, what about it?"

"The Christmas tree was left in your front room window, it upset the neighbours so much that we had to get your Grandma to take it away," She wiped the tear that trickled down her cheek.

"It was in the window all that while and its nearly Easter," said Mrs Prince.

"I'm going to my Grandma's this morning, I'd better go and catch the bus," Hazel said, feeling embarrassed.

"All right my duck, come and see us again," said Mrs Prince.

In her confusion Hazel turned right at the bottom of the entry, passing number twenty-two again, she peeped through the window. Mrs Prince was watching from the bottom of her entry, she waved, and went in. Hazel slipped away down another entry, and knocked on Mrs Brindleys door.

"Is Iris coming home for dinner? I'm Hazel Hunt I used to live at number twenty two."

Mrs Brindley looked at Hazel in her stern manner, she was very strict, and would think nothing of coming out into the street to give someone a good hiding if they had been fighting with any of her five children. In the kitchen Hazel sat with another lady.

"Stay here a minute," said Mrs Brindley, "I've just got to nip out."

Hazel began to wish she hadn't called. The kitchen still smelled of paraffin, and gas from the stove. She never did like Iris's Mam. Mrs Brindley came back, and was friendlier.

"You can stay here until Iris comes home," she said," Where do you live now, are your sisters with you?"

Hazel gave her a general picture of the last few months, however long it was, and who was living with whom, she even told her about Ma. Footsteps came down the entry Hazel stood up thinking it was Iris.

"There's a lady here for you my duck," said Mrs Brindley.
The lady said. "I've come to take you back."
Mrs, Brindley and the lady whispered together, she did not look at Hazel or say goodbye. Still in shock, and being held tightly by the hand, they walked across the Aylestone Road. Hazel and the lady turned into Batten Road, she knew this road very well, and she had often been to the Off Licence for a jug of beer for Dad. The Off Licence was still there, so was the owner, Mr Mason, an old soldier from the first World War, his moustache was twisted to fine points across his face. Just across the road from the Off Licence, the lady knocked on the door of a house. Hazel was 'handed over' like a piece of baggage, 'to be collected later.'
In the kitchen, a man sat making fancy feathery things, carefully twisting them on to a bent hook.
"Do you know what these are?" he said.
"No," Hazel replied.
"Have you had any dinner?" he said.
"No," she replied again.
"These are flies for catching fish when I go fishing. Seems like you've been caught and I haven't been fishing.
Do you know what this place is?" he said still twisting the pretty feathers.
"No," Hazel said, looking around the quite ordinary room.
"It's a remand home for boys, and I'm Mr Morton. What's your name?"
"Hazel Hunt," she said not giving anything else away.
"Would you like some dinner? It's not much the boys have peeled the carrots, so expect what you get. OK?"
"Yes, please, Mr Morton," Hazel replied. She liked Ma's mucky stew, and was so hungry she was ready to eat anything. Mr Morton carefully packed the hooks away in a tin, then put knives, forks and spoons on the table. Mrs Morton brought in the platefuls of 'mucky stew' Hazel could see that the carrots had not been peeled. The house was very quiet and there was no sound of boys at all. Questions were asked throughout the dinnertime, Mr and Mrs Morton now knew as much about Hazel as she did.
"Well you haven't done anything wrong, you only wanted to see your Grandma didn't you?" He said, generally summing up the situation.
"Yes I like it at Ma's," Hazel said, helping to dry the pots.
"Do you see them?" Mr Morton held a screwed up piece of paper

under Hazel's nose.

"They are tomato seeds, out of a tin of tomatoes. I will soon be planting them, and with a bit of luck they should grow."

Before Hazel could answer, there was a knock on the door, she was 'handed over' to another lady, and said goodbye to Mr and Mrs Morton, thanking them for her dinner. The tram stopped at Mill Hill Lane, and to Hazel's horror the lady said.

'This is where we get off.'

The doorbell, a white round button, in the centre of a large brass dish, was firmly pressed. The lady was thanked and she departed, leaving Hazel with Miss Kelling who closed the door with a bang. Inside the hallway, the smell of the bathroom, reminded her of the day that they had arrived at the Home a few weeks ago.

"Wait in Matron's office," said Miss Kelling "and leave the door open."

Matron was probably in her sitting room, prolonging the agony. Hazel decided she would just tell her the truth, she wasn't so scared of Matron since their 'discussions in the blue-room,' with Margaret and Winnie.

Eventually Matron waddled in. "So you thought you'd run away did you? Nobody runs away from these homes."

Then slam, her hand slashed across Hazel's face, with the full force of Matron behind it, Hazel took a step to one side to correct her balance, not able to move far in such a small space. Matron's eyes were now fixed.

"You've been a nuisance ever since you came in. I was going to send you to the Barnardo's Homes but I gave you a chance with Miss Hammond. You've let me down. You are the most ungrateful child, just started a new school, they are wondering where you are today. I don't suppose you thought of that," Matron's teeth were brown, and her double chin was parted with the bow of her frilly cap.

"I can see I've got to keep my eye on you, wandering about Leicester. Where were you going?" Matron's eyes were tiny and brown.

"To see my Grandma, Matron," Hazel said.

"Well what were you doing in Lothair Road then, your Grandmother doesn't live there does she?" Matron pushed her lips forward.

"I thought I would see my friend," Hazel suddenly thought of Mrs Brindley.

"It's a pity that Remand Home didn't keep you there," said Matron, now sitting behind her desk.

81

Hazel stood a little easier now, as Matron could not reach her from there.

"One more chance, I'll give you one more chance and any repetition of today and you will not see your sisters again," Matron picked up her pen and made a note in her book.

"Dr. Barnardo's, if this happens again, do you understand?" Matron placed the pen in the holder on the desk.

"Yes, Matron," Hazel took a step nearer the door

"Miss James will take you to the tram, and I'm putting you on trust to go back to Miss Hammond's."

Miss James was annoyed at having to turn out on such a cold day her crippled gait was very noticeable as they walked to the tram. Miss James told the conductor at which stop Hazel was to get off. Once inside the back door of the home, Hazel knocked on Ma's sitting room door.

"Come in," said Ma.

"Sorry, Ma it's me," Hazel said, before Ma could utter a word.

"I suppose yow think yow clever," Ma said not, getting up from her chair.

"No, Ma," Hazel stood in readiness for another good telling off.

"Look, yow might not like it here, but while yow are here, you'll have to do as yow told. Don't yow think I have enough to do without having yow run off as well," Ma put her sewing on the table.

"Yes, Ma," Hazel said.

"I know it's not nice having your Mam and Dad in hospital, I understand more than yow think. I was the youngest of twelve, there's many a time when I could have run away but it doesn't change anything. What did your Grandma say?"

"I didn't get to my Grandma's, I went to have a look at our house."

Hazel thought for a moment about the empty dismal place they had lived in.

"Yow didn't expect anybody to be there did yow? Have yow had any dinner?" said Ma.

"Yes, Ma, I had it at a Remand Home," Hazel said rather meekly.

"Good grief, I should think you'll go again won't yow. What did Matron have to say about it all?" Ma looked at Hazel again.

"She slapped my face and told me off," Hazel said, feeling the cheeks that were still burning.

"She did that?" Ma sounded shocked.

"She'll have you in the Barnardo's Homes if she has her way," said Ma.

"Yes, that's what she said Ma," Hazel said.

"Perhaps you'll settle down now, get yourself some supper, and let's hear no more about it," Ma's voice was gentle.

"Hazel gave Ma a kiss and closed the sitting room door.

Big Margaret was waiting outside Ma's sitting room.

"You didn't say anything about me did you?" said Big Margaret, squeezing Hazel's arm as if she had got her into trouble.

"No," Hazel said, "What would I mention you for?"

"Come in the kitchen, I've got some supper for you. Did you find you're way all right? You should have stayed on the bus and gone to your Grandma's."

Big Margaret had obviously been listening at the door.

"That's yours, I'll take Ma's in," said Big Margaret arranging the knife and fork neatly on the tray cloth.

"What is it?" Hazel asked.

"Cheese and tomatoes on toast? Welsh Rarebit," she said on her way to Ma's sitting room.

The girls had gone quietly to bed, they were still whispering when Hazel reached the blue-room, she had hardly reached the bed before they were all sitting up.

"Hazel, I don't know how you dare run away," said Little Margaret. " I couldn't believe it when Mrs Newsome marked the register. I hadn't got a clue where you were."

Hazel retold the story of the day's events, still a little mystified as to how someone could pick her up at Mrs Brindleys.

"It was Mrs Brindley, she must have phoned the police," said Little Margaret.

The experience in Matron's office was now spoken of lightly, they had all watched Matron's distorted features in the past, giggling again about Matron's double chin, how it wobbled faster and faster when she was telling them off. Brenda and Olive joined in from the brown room.

"You girls are very lucky to live with Miss Hammond. At Christmas you will be having sardines for breakfast," Brenda's squeaky voice imitating Matron, while Olive was doing the Miss James walk, it was quite a homecoming.

Brenda and Olive ran back to the brown room, Big Margaret was closing the kitchen door.

The landing light went out.

"Good night, Ma," they all shouted.

"Good night, and may the night last twenty-four hours," shouted Ma.

Big Margaret looked round the blue-room door, "Ma said I'll be going home soon," she said," So there's no need for me to run away."

Silence fell on the blue-room as Winnie said her special prayers. In the darkness Hazel could still see the sad little house, locked up with all her memories.

*　　　*　　　*

Hazel's earliest memory of Lothair Road was sitting on the front door step. It was May 1937. Everyone in the neighbourhood had gone to Aylestone Park for the celebrations of the Coronation of King George VI. She was three years old. She remembered seeing Norman pushing the pram down the street, covered with red, white and blue streamers. There was a little present for her, a red, white, blue, and silver ball on a piece of elastic because she had measles. Doris sat on the pram waving a flag, whilst Edna, who was only twelve months old, was fast asleep, oblivious to the jubilation's around her.

Hazel remembered her first day at school, drinking a bottle of milk through a straw, and every afternoon sleeping on canvas beds. When the war started all the windows were taped up with brown paper crosses. After school it was out to play in the street, no matter what the weather, there was always someone to play with. Playing hopscotch with a stone from the gutter. The lucky ones had whips and tops, energetically whipping them up and down the street. All the girls in the street skipping with an old clothes line, which stretched across the road, sometimes being tormented by the boys bowling old tyres up and down.

Every summer they had all paddled in the brook on Hughenden Drive. One day, the cows fell in the same brook on the way to the cattle market. The Green was a play area, were all the trees had been felled, and two air raid shelters had been built at either end. The brook was on the edge of the Green, and a boundary for the allotments. Hazel remembered the gypsies, the knife grinder, and the rag and bone man, who always persuaded them to change some rags for a goldfish. Sunday morning going to the Chapel. Holding hands in a circle singing 'Hear the pennies dropping, listen how they fall, every one for Jesus, He shall have them all.' The pennies were dropped into a cradle holding a black doll, for the children of Africa. Anniversary Sunday was the special Sunday every year when they all wore white satin dresses. The Chapel had been re-organised to seat all the children under the organ. Everybody marvelled how all their Mums had managed the 'sea of white' in wartime.

Hazel felt she could touch all these memories spinning in her head. She remembered the day the bomb fell in Cavendish Road, the Chapel was badly damaged, as were some houses. Standing on the front door step, Mam and the girls had seen the German plane fly over the rooftops. The blast that followed knocked Norman off his bike, he had just been to the butchers. It was because of this air raid that the Anderson shelters were built in all the back gardens. Everyone was issued with gas masks, and air raid drill was fun going down the underground shelter. Today, Hazel had actually looked inside the shelter with its corrugated protective covering, now full of water and overgrown with weeds. There had been no sign of Mrs Preston or her chickens that morning.

Her wakeful thinking eventually drained away, tiredness slowing down her thoughts, Hazel hadn't heard Winnie's prayers, and everyone was asleep. After nine o'clock at night all the streets were quiet, the shift change at Imperial Typewriters had finished, there were just a few people on bicycles going home. There were no street lights, and cycle lamps were shielded to shine on the road. The wind in the poplar trees across the road, was normally the only sound to pierce the tranquillity of the blue-room. There was only one other sound, that of the sirens, the inescapable loud wailing noise that penetrated into every house, every building, and every street. The sirens brought everything to a standstill by day, and woke everybody up at night.

*   *   *

The unexpected noise startled everybody, waking them up from a deep sleep. Ma was the first person out of bed. From the landing she shouted her orders.

"Wake up, everybody, get down to my sitting room. Come on be quick about it." Ma ushered the little ones from the brown room down the stairs.

85

In the darkness Winnie shouted, "Who's that? You're going the wrong way."

"I'm going to get my blanket," said Brenda who had experienced long hours in the shelter.

"Bring me one."

"Grab a blanket if you can," Ma shouted with approval.

A few other bodies then changed direction, to retrieve blankets from their beds.

"Mind you don't fall down them stairs," Ma was waiting at the bottom.

With blankets trailing, some carrying pillows, the girls found their way down the back hall. The lucky ones sat on Ma's easy chairs, three to one chair, huddled up with blankets and pillows, the rest sat on the floor. They sat talking, then listening, wondering if any bombs were dropping nearby. Ma slipped the bolt off the French door, ready for a quick exit to the shelter in the big yard.

"Are we going in the shelter, Ma?" asked Nipper.

"No not yet," said Ma, "we'll wait and see."

"It smells in the shelter," said Big Margaret, "can't we stay here. We can all get under your table, Ma."

Ma lit the candles on the shelf, and two on her sideboard. "Shall I put some sticks on the fire, Ma, it's still warm?" said Olive, eager to fill a coal bucket if necessary.

"It wouldn't hurt I suppose," said Ma.

"We slept in the shelter for a week, didn't we Ma?" said Brenda.

"Yes, that was when Coventry got bombed, I don't want to go through all that lot again," said Ma.

The extra blaze made the room much brighter. They could see each other in the shadows.

"Behave yourselves while I go and put the cocoa on," said Ma.

"Ooh good, we're having cocoa," said Brenda.

The girls were all excited, in the half-light Olive made shadow pictures with her long fingers on the wall. Dogs, cats, butterflies, and birds, all changing shape in the dancing firelight. Big Margaret poured the cocoa into the beakers.

"Is everybody here?" said Ma. We each checked our own sisters.

"Edna's missing, Ma," said Doris.

"Where the devil.....?" Ma hurried out of the room.

"Trust Edna, she's always last," said Big Margaret.

Soon afterwards, a sleepy Edna came into the sitting room, wrapped in a blanket.

"Come on Edna, you're missing all the fun," said Nipper.

"Didn't you hear the sirens Edna?" They all asked at once.

"No," said Edna, yawning.

"Here you are, drink this," said Ma, handing half a beaker of cocoa to Edna. "Go on, you won't wet the bed it's nearly morning."

"Would you like us to sing to you Ma?" said Big Margaret.

"Anything, so long as it's not We Three Kings, you wore that one out at Christmas. 'Star of this and star of that,' you sent me crackers with that one," said Ma.

"We'll sing your favourite then Ma," said Big Margaret. "The Lord's My Shepherd."

"Sing it properly then," said Ma," I don't want driving round the bend just yet.

Big Margaret divided the room into two." The second verse we'll sing in rounds."

"The Lord's my Shepherd, I'll not want,
he makes me down to lie."

After the second verse was sung in rounds the older girls sang the last verse in descant like the choirboys did in church. Ma was very pleased.

They were just deciding what to sing next when the doorbell rang in the kitchen.

"Oh, strike, who can that be at this time of the night?" said Ma.

"It's the Germans. They've come for us," said Brenda.

They huddled close together, while Olive and Big Margaret offered to go with Ma.

"Be quiet while I go and see," said Ma taking a candle.

Olive and Big Margaret crept as far as the cellar door listening.

"It's a man," whispered Big Margaret, as they both ran back into the room.

Someone else accompanied Ma's footsteps. The candle was still burning in her hand, as she came into the room. It could only be one person in the long black cloak.

"Hello, girls," he said. "What's this, a midnight feast? I've come just right," said Father Huntley.

Nightgowns or blankets quickly covered all feet and naked legs.

"How's it going out there?" said Ma.

"I think Leicester is having it tonight from what I can hear," His deep voice echoed round the room, as it did in church.

He joined them with a mug of cocoa.

"Are you going to sing to Father Huntley?" said Ma.

Shrieks of shy giggles were stifled into the blankets around them.

"Some other time perhaps Miss Hammond, I must visit some of my other parishioners. Thank you for the cocoa, I hope it doesn't last too long. Goodnight girls don't forget to say your prayers.

"Goodnight, Father Huntley," they all replied.

The ALL CLEAR sounded, drowning the end of their singing. Picking up their various blankets and pillows, a race was now on to see who could get into bed before the ALL CLEAR had finished. With the light now on, they settled into bed, still time for a little sleep before morning.

"Goodnight, Ma."

"Goodnight! Good morning's more like it," said Ma.

*   *   *

Groby Road Hospital was situated on a hill just outside Leicester, the new part, a semi-circular veranda terrace, was upheld by pillars which divided the two-bedded compartments. French doors opened up onto the terrace. On warm sunny days the beds were wheeled out for the patients to have maximum fresh air. The gardens and lawns edged along the half circle of magnificent Roman columns, which shone out under the night sky, as the sirens sounded yet again.

The Air Raid Wardens patrolled the grounds, and from under the eaves of the veranda they looked out across Leicester. The searchlights criss-crossed the sky, searching for the German bombers. The sky was lit up glowing red from the already burning buildings over the Highfields and other areas. Some of the night nurses joined them. They had opened the dark green curtains to let the patients who could not sleep see what was happening over Leicester. The Air Raid Wardens had reassured Emma Hunt that the bombs had not reached East Park Road, and that her children were hopefully safe. Emma had always told them to get under the table.

On nights like these the whole hospital seemed to be awake, George joined Emma, and sat at the side of her bed, he was used to working all hours, and an air raid provided just the excuse for him to get away from his ward and visit Emma. They had both had a very tiring week, with more X-rays, and some new treatment for Emma, he was always there to tell her how much he loved her, giving her sweet kisses when the nurses were away. It was a brief time to talk things over so she didn't worry too much about the children. George was not allowed to stay too long, his condition was far too weak for him to be out of bed but he stayed as long as the air raid lasted.

The long wail of the sirens filled the night air, for George it was back to bed. For the workers in Leicester it was time to face another day, clearing the streets of rubble from the bomb sites, freeing anyone trapped and putting out the fires. All sorts of jobs that needed strong hands, like the hard working hands George used to have, if only he was able to drive the buses again, would he ever work again he wondered, as he slowly wandered back to ward six.

"Come on, George, have you been courting again?" they teased.

"If only I had the strength," said George.

The nurses were waiting to be relieved they had finished their tour of night duty, the breakfast trolleys were swinging into the wards. It was almost daylight, another day had begun.

Emma was taken for her early morning bath, a luxury that she could never have at home. The nurses were kind and fussed over her. Today she was to have the results of her review. She had been trying not to cough during the last few days, because she saw the traces of blood in the sputum mug, which held anything, brought about by coughing. Some days she was too tired even to hold the knitting pins, but it was the only thing she enjoyed doing while she was on complete bed rest.

The doctors duly arrived, commenting on the nighttime raid, and how they found it difficult to get down certain streets, fire engines blocking the roads, and traffic diversions. They took out their notes and after much deliberation concluded that Emma should have another six months hospitalisation, they knew she wanted to get back home, but with six children that was an impossibility. They did say however that one day when she was stronger they would allow her to visit the girls' home on East Park Road, to see where the girls were living. It was something for her to think about, while she was resting. It was the same news for Edith in the next bed, only she hadn't any children, but she was always eager to hear about Emma's little 'flock'. Jack was almost as regular a visitor as George, and when the two got together they would put the world to right. Jack supplied all the Leicester News bringing the Evening Mail and a daily newspaper for them to read. The Picture Post, was a favourite, full of war photographs.

Jack was night watchman with the A.R.P. and had seen the devastation on Tichbourne Street. "I don't know what they're aiming at round there," Jack said "its all houses."

*　　　*　　　*

It wasn't until the next visiting day that the Hunts had their first visitors, they were so pleased to see Grandma after such a long time. Ted looked so grown up in long trousers, Grandma sat on the chair next to Winnie's Dad, they knew that Joe and Brian were at the Countesthorpe Nursery. Ma said the girls could show Grandma the blue-room. Grandma thought it was very nice, but she couldn't understand why it was called the blue-room. They all decided the lino was green. Ted took the opportunity to tell Hazel off for running away, an argument started, he was always bossy when they were at home, but Hazel gave her simple reasons.

"I just wanted to see Grandma," she said.

Grandma was sympathetic, but she didn't want to talk about it. They returned to the dining room. The awful day they had been sent into the homes, was never spoken about, neither was the subject of Norman going to live with Aunty Rose. They didn't say much at all, they were just happy to have Grandma there. Ted told them that he would be coming on his own next time, and he would bring some pencils, and would teach them how to draw.

"Find something round to draw," he said on his way out.

Visiting time was soon over, the hour had gone so quickly. They all crowded into the bay window, trying to peep through the curtains as the tram went by, but the trams had blinds rolled down, making it impossible to see.

"Get out that window, close that blackout curtain," shouted Ma from the bobby-hole.

On Sunday, in identical tweed coats and coloured berets, they all attended the morning service. The smell of the incense gave the church a quietly reverend atmosphere. They felt they knew Father Huntley a little better, and that he cared for them, they were part of his family.

The processional hymn was announced at the vestry door.

"All Glory Laud and Honour, to Thee Redeemer, King.

The whole congregation sang at the top of their voices. The incense bearer and his five-year-old 'server', who carried the aromatic grains in a casket, led the procession down the aisles of the church, the swinging orb giving off the sweet smelling aroma.

Today was Palm Sunday; each choirboy carried a palm branch over his shoulder. The angelic singers like cherubs in their red gowns white lacy tops, and starched ruffs around their throats.

The service continued with lots of prayers, from the red and green books.

Come faithful people come away,
And Homage to your Monarch pay,
It is the feast of palms today,
Hosanna in the Highest.

Slowly the congregation filed out of their seats and up to the Chancel step to receive a small palm cross from Father Huntley. The home girls were proud of their palm crosses, and placed them all on the dining room shelf.

Good Friday was a holiday from school the service in church was for 'the Stations of the Cross' around the church. At twelve measured intervals the following congregation stopped to say a prayer at each picture of the crucifixion. All the statues were covered in purple chiffon, for Holy Week. The last of the pictures was still imprinted on our minds, 'The Death on the Cross' and how the earth trembled and a great darkness fell upon the land.

Outside true darkness had befallen East Park Road. The poplar trees were waving angrily in the wind. Then suddenly a storm of hailstones came down, blocking the gutters.

This truly was Good Friday.

At teatime the girls sang grace and sat down. Ma went into the kitchen to get the second cups of tea, and coming to the bobby-hole she put a large plate of hot cross buns on the hatch.

"Big Margaret, mind it's hot," said Ma.

Everyone 'Oohed and Aahed' at the wonderful sight. As each one received their Good Friday treat, the bun was examined to see who had the most perfect cross, that one would be the 'holiest'. Easter time was of great importance Hazel, Doris and Edna received a card from Mam and Dad. New summer dresses were issued from Miss James at the Receiving Home. The summer blazers were brought down from the box room, instead of the tweed coats. In church, the purple chiffon had been removed from the statues. Everything now gleamed and shone, garden flowers now decorated every corner of the church.

In their 'newest' clothes the girls made their way over to the 'Easter Garden' it had been created by the Sunday school teacher Mr Smith. A whole layout of the Garden of Gethsemane, miniature statues near the tomb where the stone had been rolled away. The tiny rolls of white linen that had wrapped the Body of Jesus still lay in the sepulchre. Real primroses and small flowers blossomed on mossy banks of the garden. Mary talking to the 'Gardener'. The whole story depicted in natural tableaux, colourful and lifelike.

The vestry door opened, Father Huntley announced the hymn, 'Hail Thee festival day'.

The usual procession came down the centre aisle, and Father Huntley brought up the rear with two other clergy, all dressed in heavy embroidered copes which matched the altar frontal. The clouds of incense ascended like prayers into the rays of the sun, which shone through the brilliant colours of the stained glass window. Every Sunday, notices were given out halfway through the service. Prayers for all the soldiers, sailors and airmen. Then Father Huntley gave a list of the sick and the dying, especially for Kritty Kapper the same name was mentioned every week. Hazel replaced the name in her prayers to George and Emma, their own loved ones. The messages and prayers ended.

'And of your charity pray for the souls of the faithful departed, may they rest in peace.' On this lovely Sunday, the happy service continued with more processions, the next one winding its way to the back of the church.

"Jesus Christ is risen today - Alleluia
Our triumphant Holy Day - Alleluia
Who did once upon the cross - Alleluia?

Suffer to redeem our loss - Alleluia...

The procession paused at the Easter Garden and the Garden was blessed.

The jumpers were replaced with crispy cotton blouses, but they still struggled into the combinations and liberty bodices every morning.

"Never cast a clout till May is out," Ma told them.

After the school register had been called and the morning hymn, each new term, exercise books were given out by the monitor.

The first pages were always neatly written, as the whole class copied the tables from one times two, to twelve times twelve from the blackboard. Hazel found the arithmetic on the following pages, had more red crosses, than red ticks, and found that the problems, were problems. The classrooms had been shored up with big round poles from floor to ceiling, she always felt fortunate to sit behind one of the green painted pillars, it was somewhere for her to hide when she didn't know the answers. At playtime, the children drank their daily third of a pint of milk, allocated to each child for calcium in growing bones. Outside in the playground there were nauseating smells from the local dye-works, and brewery a few streets away. Hazel made friends with a girl, quite timid, who always stood by her, her legs were covered in scabs from the tops of her short ankle socks to her thighs under her tunic. She came from a big family, and lived 'up Charney' a part of the district known as Charnwood Street. Hazel shared the bread and dripping with her at playtime.

The only girls in the home to own real handkerchiefs were Little Margaret and Winnie, a special present from Aunt Sarah

During a lesson the girl who sat next to Hazel took a 'hanky ' out of her pocket.

"Ay, that's mine," Hazel said, so shocked that the whole class heard.

"What's the problem?" asked Mrs Newsome.

"Please, Miss, she's got my hanky," Hazel muttered.

"It isn't yours then, it's mine," said Grace.

"What makes you think it's yours, Hazel?" asked Mrs Newsome.

"I know its mine because it's got rosebuds on it," Hazel insisted

It was unmistakably Miss James's summer dress material. Little Margaret sitting at the back of the class could only produce her own pretty handkerchief, and wasn't sure about the East Park Road material.

"We'll sort it out at dinnertime," said Mrs Newsome. "Now get on with your work."

At dinnertime the problem of the hanky was not forgotten.

"Ma cuts our dresses up for hankies, I'll bring you a bit of material like it this afternoon," Hazel said.

Mrs Newsome put the 'hanky' in her drawer.

At the dinner table, whilst eating 'mucky stew', Hazel told Ma about the hanky episode.

"Do we have to talk about nose dusters at the dinner table?" said Ma.

"Snot rags," muttered Brenda.

A fit of giggles ran round the table, and Brenda started choking.

"Go on, choke yourself, that's judgement on yow," said Ma.

The plates were scraped until they were clean. After dinner, Ma searched out another bit of the 'rosebud' rag.

"Tell her she can keep it, I won't have yow being called a liar over a bit of rag," she said.

The 'rosebud hanky' was taken to school, and given to Mrs Newsome who quietly took the girl to one side, and gave her the identical 'hanky'.

"Ma says she can keep it", Hazel said.

"Good afternoon, Ma," Hazel shouted.

"Good afternoon, Miss James," said Little Margaret.

"Oh it's Tuesday, Good afternoon Miss James," Hazel quipped.

"You'll get used to it," said Little Margaret.

With slippers on, Hazel and Margaret stood against the kitchen range, warming their hands. Miss James waltzed into the room with her crippled gait.

"What are you hanging about here for, get that table laid," she said.

They almost threw the tablecloth, and knives, through the bobby-hole with fright.

"Why haven't you laid the table, you know its your job," said Little Margaret, shouting at the younger girls.

They stood around like statues looking at Miss James who was peering through the hatch.

"Never mind who's job it is, get it done," said Miss James.

Brenda, Ruth and Doris were next to arrive, each of them filing into the dining room with 'gloomy Tuesday' faces. By the time Big Margaret and Olive arrived, the scrambled egg was ready for them to serve up. With the plateful of cake in place, they sang grace, as Miss James looked on, she then returned to Ma's sitting room. The lumps of scrambled egg rolled about on the plates like rubber balls. If any dropped on the floor, it was usually retrieved from the other side of the room, and eaten. To prolong teatime, Big Margaret's orders were.

"Chew each mouthful twenty-eight times."

There wasn't time for anyone to speak, as if they dare. It wouldn't take long to scoop up the scrambled egg on to one slice of bread, put the other allocated piece on top, three good bites and teatime would be over. Whenever Miss James was in charge, Big Margaret took the plate of cake round she stood behind each girl digging them in the back with her boney fingers, if they took the wrong piece of cake.

Prayers after tea were long and drawn out, Big Margaret's voice booming out slowly for them to follow. Doris was the lucky one, on a Tuesday evening she always sat drawing, illustrating her Sunday school book. The paints that someone had for Christmas were now being put to good use. The rest of them had to follow like sheep while the eldest girl bullied them into her activities.

With the alteration of the clocks, being put forward two hours for double summertime, the mornings were darker and the evenings lighter. They could now play in the big yard after tea.

"If any balls go over the wall you can all come in," said Ma.

That meant they couldn't play tennis, or rounders. They could play 'double ball' against wall of the shelter. Even then, the ball could be projected over into the neighbour's garden. Olive always had the job of retrieving any lost balls from the dentist's garden. Her long legs straddled the wall under cover of the lilac tree. She took her time knowing that the house was empty, looking at the fish in the pond, standing on the pile of logs against the other garden wall, and peering into their garden. Olive crept about the garden like a cat, silently and carefully, her most important duty was to make sure her adopted cat, 'Tibby Gamble' was safely in his box.

"Is it all clear?" she shouted before venturing back over the wall.

The house on the other side, next to the church, had a dog called 'Rex Adnitt', he guarded their back garden well. Any balls straying over that wall were never seen again, unless they were thrown back another day all chewed up.

The little terrier barked whenever the girls peeped over the wall to say 'hello' to him, and if 'Tibby Gamble ' ever sat on the wall, the old cat just sat there and took no notice of his furry foe, waiting until 'Rex' was called in for making so much noise.

One warm afternoon during the holiday, Big Margaret organised a concert in the big yard.

"How can we have a concert without a stage?" they all shouted and, with no enthusiasm at all. Big Margaret sent Nipper to Ma's sitting room.

"You know how to get round Ma, Nipper. Ask if we can use the kitchen table," said Big Margaret.

Listening at Ma's sitting room door, she heard the favourable answer, and before Nipper had returned, the kitchen table was on its way to the big yard.

"We're going to have a concert," shouted Brenda on her way to the attic stairs cupboard to get the old curtains. As well as helping with the stage, they were the actors as well.

"What are you going to do, Brenda?" said Olive, helping with the bundle of curtains.

"I'm just going to say a poem," Brenda said, not really having thought about it.

"I think I'll sing 'Underneath the Lamplight'," replied Olive, as they crept down the stairs.

The table was dragged into the big yard, and draped with the curtains covering up the legs. Anyone doing a tap dance had to be careful not to fall off the edge. The word soon got round about the concert, and everybody rallied to do their bit.

"I'm not singing, definitely not!'

'Oh, I'm just going to say a nursery rhyme.'

'I'm just going to clap.'

'Who's going first.'

'I'm going to sit under the table, to help them get ready.'

"The audience sit on Ma's steps," ordered Big Margaret.

The table legs dragging across the big yard had brought Ma to the window, watching the proceedings. With everybody sitting down, Ma opened her French doors.

"I didn't say you could bring the table outside, yow cheeky blighters," said Ma.

"The kitchen's too small, Ma," said Nipper, who was really helping out.

"It better be good then," said Ma.

96

"Do we start off with 'God save the King?'" said Brenda.

Big Margaret started the concert off by singing some of her 'Cart's Choruses,' and cheating a little by making them all join in. Without her 'dud keyboard,' she waved her arms about, conducting wildly, especially to those who were not singing.

"Underneath the lamplight by the barrack gate, darling I remember the way you used to wait."

Looking every bit like Marlene Dietrich, with her sultry almond eyes, and her hair over half her face, Olive was a child image of the star.

Ma was quite impressed, and they all clapped her performance.

Brenda's favourite poem was said with a clear voice, as she stood on the kitchen table

'I wandered lonely as a cloud, that floats on high.' Big Margaret helped her out as she had forgotten the last verse.

Hazel's party piece was tap dancing, but her rubber-heeled slippers had no effect on the scrubbed top table, and Ma objected to the black rubber scuffs appearing, so she chose 'Drakes Drum.' by Henry Longfellow.

Little Margaret was next to stand on the stage. Everybody was quiet, wondering what 'Clever clogs' would do. "A Tragic Story by William Makepeace Thackeray":

There lived a sage in days of yore,
And he a handsome pigtail wore.
But wondered much and sorrowed more,
Because it hung behind him.

He mused upon this curious case,
And swore he'd change the pigtails place
And have it dangling at his face
Not dangling there behind him."

Little Margaret enacted this tragic tale twisting herself about:

"I'll turn me round, he turned him round
and still it hung behind him."

They were all intrigued as to how the sage would move the pigtail's

position, as Margaret carried on turning around, up to the last verse.
"And though his efforts never slack.
And though he twist and twirl, and tack.
Alas! Still faithful to his back.
The pigtail hangs behind him."
"Clever clogs," said Ma clapping with them, at the top of the steps.
"Who's next" shouted Big Margaret, still organising everybody.
Nipper peeped through the curtains under the table.
"I'm not ready yet, let somebody else go on," she shouted.
Doris was next to climb upon the 'stage', still not quite sure which poem she liked best.

"Up the airy mountain, down the rushy glen,
We dare not go a-hunting for fear of little men.
Wee folk, good folk, trooping altogether,
Green jacket, red caps white owl's feather..."

The concert was going very well, Ma brought out a box of Canadian apples as a reward. The girls all sat on the steps chewing away, discussing how the delicious apples could possibly come all the way from Canada.
Nipper peeped through the 'curtain' from underneath the table.
"I'm ready. Can you play some music, please, Ma?" said Nipper.
"Some of you lot want a maid," said Ma, winding up the old gramophone in her sitting room. The music started, and Nipper emerged dressed in a coloured grass skirt.
"Ooh, this'll be good," said Ma.
With bare feet, borrowed beads and bracelets, and the hula-hula skirt from the box room in the attic, Nipper danced with all the elegance of a Hawaiian dancer. With Olive's lipstick on, and cocoa powder all over her face and shoulders. Her arms waved across from side to side swaying as if she was under a tropical sun, her dancing fitted in quite well with Vera Lynn singing, 'We'll meet again.' The gramophone needed winding up, the girls were now all singing, 'but I know we'll meet again some sunny day.' They all applauded Nipper, she had jumped down from the table, the cocoa looked a bit blotchy, but the effect was good. Their amateur performance was over.
"Clean them apple cores up, fold them curtains, and take the table back. I'll leave it to you Maggie, or there'll be no more concerts," said Ma

to Big Margaret.

"I think I'll do 'Where the pools are bright and deep' next time," said Doris.

"I didn't think you'd remember 'Up the airy mountain'." Hazel said helping to guide the table through the gate.

"Little ones up for a strip wash, and get all that cocoa off," shouted Big Margaret to Nipper.

"Alright," said Nipper carrying all her clothes and the hula hula skirt box.

A few days later Ma called the three Hunts into her sitting room, with crossed fingers, thinking they were going home.

"I've had a letter from your Mam today, would you like me to read it to you?" Ma picked up the letter from her sideboard.

"20th March 1943.

Dear Foster Mother,

I'm very pleased to hear that the children are quite happy and well. I hope the gloves fit all right, I had to guess the size. I am now making them hoods for the winter. Very sorry to hear Edna still wets the bed, but the doctor says she will grow out of it.
I don't know how much longer we shall be here, but our next review is April 8th, so we'll see what the doctors say. Give my love to the children
    Yours sincerely, Mrs Hunt.

"That's in two weeks time," said Ma. Hazel uncrossed her fingers it was not their lucky day.

The two weeks passed by, and the first visitors arrived on the cold Monday night. Mrs Minton had brought a man with her.

"Big Margaret, your Dad's come," said Olive being the first to get her head round the kitchen door to see who Ma was letting in.

"Where? How do you know, come on Pauline let's go and see who it is," said Big Margaret now halfway up the hall.

"This is your uncle," said Mrs Minton, as the girls reached the dining room door.

"It's not their Dad," said Olive, "it's her friend."

Olive's Mum also had a friend, called 'uncle'.

"Let's hope they are going to take her home, then I'll be the eldest," said Olive.

Mr Seaton and Mrs Cartwright arrived together. The kitchen suddenly seamed empty when the five girls ran to the dining room. Two more trams went by, Ted Hunt was on the third one, and by himself. The girls were disappointed that Grandma wasn't with him. They all sat at the table, Ted produced pencils and papers from his bag.

"Did you get something to draw?" he said, as if it was only yesterday when he had asked them to produce something round.

"I'll get the jar of Malt," Hazel said, as it was the only round thing that they had access to, other than a saucepan.

Ted placed the jar in the centre of the table for them all to see, the art lesson was the star attraction, all the visitors watching the drawings progress. Big Margaret was having a bad time with her Mother, Hazel could hear all that she said.

"You said I could come home with you last visiting day. Why can't I come home?" Big Margaret was leaning across Ma's table pleading with her mother to take her home.

"You'll soon be leaving school, you've only got 'til August, and that's not long to wait. They won't let you out, but I'll ask them again," Mrs Minton sat on Ma's chair in the shadows of the bay window. Pauline was sitting on 'uncle's' knee. Brenda was engrossed in looking at the pictures in the Picture Post magazine.   At the other end of the dining table Little Margaret and Winnie, whispered softly to their Dad.

"It's the best place for him at the moment, he's being looked after by real nurses, and he's getting better," said Mr Seaton.

"Give him a big squeeze for us, next time you see him Dad," said Winnie.

"Does he know who you are when you visit him, I bet he won't remember us when we get out of here," said Margaret.

"Now you mustn't be ungrateful, Miss Hammond's' looking after you alright, she's got her work cut out with twelve of you," said Mr Seaton. His gentile voice covering for the embarrassing fact that their mother was in the Towers Hospital Mental Institution. Mrs Seaton had been taken into hospital with 'milk fever' when she had just given birth to their baby brother, Joe. At the time of the birth Mrs Seaton was rather depressed so it was decided to keep her at the hospital.

"Eleven, Dad, Ida Goodwin left before the Hunts came in," said

Margaret.

Mr Seaton was a worried man, and it showed in his ageing face. He had married late in life and his two little girls were his pride and joy. He had been pleased about the birth of their son in nineteen- forty, but now Mrs Seaton had been separated from her baby for two years, and no longer recognised that she had a baby boy, she only had two daughters, Margaret and Winnie.

Now he had three children and a sick wife, he made a big effort to keep them informed about their baby.

"The nurse lets him sit on my knee, and I read him a story, he usually goes to sleep before I come away," said Mr Seaton.

It was comforting news that their baby wasn't left to cry. Winnie couldn't bear it.

"Aah, I bet he's getting big now, how far can he walk?" said Winnie.

"Well, his legs are not very strong, Mr Seaton choked a little, at the weak condition of his motherless baby. "Does she do a lot of drawing?" he said, changing the subject. Margaret picked up one of Doris's books, "Can I show Dad?"

"This is her Sunday school book, Dad," said Margaret.

Ted was rather disgusted with the feeble drawing.

"That doesn't look curved at all, Hazel," he said, and with his black pencil he outlined a new jar for her to fill in. It was like having the teacher put more red crosses through her work.

"I'm not bothered who wants to draw anyway," Hazel said.

"Look at that pencil, you've chewed it." Ted was still the arrogant elder brother, with everyone watching he couldn't say too much.

Edna was rather fed up as well she had drawn tiny flowers all over the page. The few questions, the girls had managed to ask, 'When are we going home? Who visits our baby? Is Grandma coming to see us?' were all answered the same way. "I don't know!" They were glad when visiting time was over. Ma rang the bell, as the cosy chats between the families, and the drawings had gone on for another half hour, the frantic 'goodbyes' started, and 'When will we see you again? Will you be coming next time? When will I be able to come home?' Olive showed Ma the lipstick from her Mam.

"Yow needn't put that muck on your face," said Ma.

"My Mam says it'll make me look pretty," said Olive, and quickly put it in her pocket.

"Did your Mam bring yow anything, Ruth?" said Ma.

Ruth held out her arm revealing a coloured bracelet.

"Oh, that's nice," said Ma.

"Look what I got, a dolly, said Nipper holding up the rag doll with a knitted dress.

"What are you going to call it?" asked Ma.

"Mam says its name is 'Silver', said Nipper.

"Sylvia," said Olive and Ruth together.

"Mmm. What is that?" said Ma to Winnie.

"Its Eucryl toothpowder, Ma, Dad says we've got to clean our teeth with it," said Little Margaret.

"Right, get this place tidied up, and lay the table for morning. Oh that's good," said Ma looking at Doris's drawing.

They huddled round the fire, the drawings were put on the shelf while the table was being laid.

"Our little Joe is still in hospital," said Winnie.

"Is your Mam still in hospital as well?" asked Big Margaret.

"Yes she is but she's getting better," said Little Margaret.

"Why didn't your Grandma come tonight?" Big Margaret directed her question at Hazel.

"She's visiting our Mam and Dad," Hazel said, hoping that was where she was.

Countesthorpe's a long way, that's where we went when we first came into the homes. We were in number eight cottage," said Big Margaret.

"I didn't like it there," said Brenda. That's where the ones who don't go to school live."

"Is that the nursery?" Hazel said.

"No, the nursery's separate, babies in cots go there. Nurses look after them," said Big Margaret.

"They're not nurses, and my Dad says that they don't look after them at all. Our little Joe has got meningitis, through being there," said Little Margaret.

Hazel took her drawing off the shelf, screwed it up and threw it on to the fire, it slowly uncurled as it burned, she could see the black lines of Ted's pencil, only proving to her that some-one had visited them. Big Margaret placed a photograph on the shelf for them all to see.

"That's me and my baby sister," she said proudly.

"She is a big baby, is that Brenda? You look as if you are nearly dropping her," said Winnie."

"I like the lacy bonnets," said Brenda coming to have a closer look at herself in infancy.

The photograph was carefully replaced in Big Margaret's 'new handbag.'

"Look what I got, new gloves," said Brenda. "Pauline's got a scarf."

Pasty Pauline had the scarf wrapped round her neck, while she laid the table for morning.

Ma appeared at the bobby-hole.

"Who's next for a wash, come on let's have you we'll be here all night at this rate," said Ma.

Visiting day unsettled everybody, at night they cried for the visitors they hadn't had. Wondering if they would ever go home again. Sometimes they pretended they were on the tram going home, and tried to imagine how far they would get before they fell asleep.

One morning after breakfast Ma kept the three Hunts away from school. Again, it was thought that they might be going home, but their disappointment turned to joy when Ma told them that they were going to the hospital for a chest X-ray.

"Shall we be able to see our Mam and Dad?" They asked.

"I don't think so, but we'll ask the doctor when we get there," said Ma. In clean underclothes and best Sunday coats, with Ma, they caught the tram into Leicester. They felt quite important out with Ma she walked much faster than Miss James did, and smiled and talked to them the whole of the journey. Upstairs on the bus, they had a good view of all the shops and fields, as they reached the hospital.

"What's an X-ray Ma?" they all asked as they walked up the long hospital drive.

"It's like a photo of your chest," said Ma.

The path to the left led to a big house, they entered through the swinging doors.

"We've come to see the doctor," said Ma handing the letter to the nurse. The doctor sat behind a huge desk in the large room. He smiled at the girls, and with an expert eye he said.

"They look very healthy children, Miss Hammond."

"Yes they are," said Ma, and they eat well."

"Let me look at your chests," said the doctor.

The girls removed their clothes and stood in a line in front of him. He listened intently through his stethoscope, tapped his fingers with a little hammer, all round their ribs. He asked them if they were good girls.

"Do you think you could be good and very quiet if I let you go up to Ward six?" said the Doctor.

"Yes, yes, please," They answered together just wanting to jump for joy off the velvet cushioned chairs.

Leaning against the cold plates of the X-ray machine, the nurse shouted from behind the screen. "Take a deep breath in, hold your breath. Thank you."

Ma looked at them on the main drive, making sure they had dressed properly.

"I'm going to see a friend, while you see your Mam and Dad. Don't forget you mustn't kiss them. Ward six is at the top of the hill, and round to the left. Be very quiet because all these people are very ill. I'll see you back at the church when your time is up," said Ma.

"And don't run," she added.

Ma watched as they walked up the hill, once she was out of sight the girls ran to the top of the hill. A small arrow pointed to the semi-circular ward, a veranda held up by pillars. They walked quietly along the crescent, peering into each two-bedded compartment passing the rose beds and lawned arena. The occupants of each bed watched as they intently crept by, trying not to stare they searched for the mother that they had not seen for six months. Suddenly, there she was, her black hair shining against the white sheets and her pale complexion. Brightly coloured knitting lay on the bed near the equally pale hands. The black iron beds were just like the ones in the blue-room. Mam was sitting propped up with gleaming white pillows against the high backrest. She wasn't thin like she used to be, and didn't look ill at all, her round face smiled as they ran towards her, all three eager to get the first kiss. In all the excitement they forgot all the rules, the lady in the next bed gave up her chair, then she went for a walk.

"Can you get out of bed as well, Mam?" they asked.

Edna climbed on to the bed and sat close to Mam, the wall at the side of the bed prevented her from falling on the floor. Doris sat on the chair and Hazel sat on the bed. Their red mittens, with embroidered blue initials were placed inside the berets after Mam had inspected them to see how they were wearing. The Ward Sister put her head round the door.

"Everything all right, Mrs Hunt?" she said.

The walls were painted the same pale green as the Receiving Home walls. The glass French doors were wide open.

"Do you have the doors open all the time Mam?" Hazel asked.

"Yes, did you hear the sirens the other night?" said Mam.

"Yes, we stay in Ma's sitting room, and sing songs, and Father Huntley comes to see us," said Doris.

"Edna didn't hear the sirens, she was still in bed, Ma had to fetch her downstairs," Hazel said.

"Are you still wetting the bed?" Mam asked Edna.

"Sometimes she does," Hazel said, protecting her little sister. "You've got bottle green curtains," Hazel said.

"We close them at night for the blackout," said Mam.

"Ours are black," she said.

"We can see the searchlights all over Leicester from here at night, and we have the doors open when it's hot," said Mam.

"Are the headphones for the wireless?" said Edna, and she placed them over her ears.

"There's nothing coming out of this one," Edna shouted.

"Don't shout," said Mam, "You'll have the nurse coming in to see who's making the noise."

Doris and Hazel giggled at Edna shouting to make herself heard over the radio that only she could hear. They all had a turn with the same effect.

"Do you go in the air raid shelter when the sirens go, Mam?" asked Doris.

"No we stay here, we could see the flashing through the curtains when the bombs went off in Leicester. The sky lit up for miles," said Mam. The corridor door opened, Hazel jumped off the bed, expecting the nurse to come in, but there stood Dad in his dressing gown and slippers.

"I could hear all the noise from my bed," he said.

"Dad," they all shouted.

"Ssh, don't make so much noise," Dad sat on the chair with Doris on his knee. After they'd kissed him and kissed him, he gave Mam a kiss. Then Edna sat on his knee while Doris sat near Mam with the headphones on.

"Are you being good girls?" Dad asked them

"Yes, Ma brought us up for a chest X-ray," Hazel said.

"Where is Miss Hammond," Mam said.

"She's gone to visit somebody," said Doris.

"We've got to meet her at the church down the hill," said Edna.

"We didn't know we were coming, Ma told us after breakfast," Hazel said.

The conversation was kept light-hearted questions suppressed and stifled like the heartache they lived every day. The prayers for their baby brother, and adversities of the blue-room were not mentioned. Ma had said, 'mind what you say.'

Their schoolwork was quickly glossed over by Doris's wonderful artwork, and Big Margaret and her 'Cart's Choruses'.

"On Saturdays we go to the pictures, it's ever so good," said Edna.

"Then church every Sunday, we go on our own, it's only next door but one," Hazel said.

"Have we been baptised?" said Doris," Miss Adams our Sunday school teacher wants to know."

"Why?" said Dad?

"When we are older we can get confirmed, but we have to be baptised first.

"You wear a white dress and a veil and gloves," Hazel said, more interested in looking like a bride, than the communion services.

"No you haven't been Christened," said Dad.

There was a distinct clatter of cutlery in the corridor.

"They're bringing the dinner round now," said Dad. "I'm having my dinner with your Mam today."

"We don't have to go yet, do we?" said Doris.

"Ma will be waiting for you," said Mam.

Like three teddy bears in their tweed coats they walked to the brow of the hill, looking back, waving every step of the way. They had already run back for another kiss, but now they were too far away, and only the roof of the veranda was visible. Looking down the hill the three could see Ma standing near the Church.

"Have you behaved yourselves?" asked Ma.

"Yes, Dad came to see us, he's having his dinner with Mam," Hazel said.

"Mam was sitting up knitting," said Doris "They can all walk about if they want to," said Doris.

"I listened to the wireless with the headphones on," said Edna.

"Right, let's get back to East Park Road, or they'll think we've left home," said Ma.

Looking out of the upstairs window on the bus, they were as high as the branches of the trees. Hazel tried to picture Mam's face again, and how different she looked, she could still see her standing on the door step in Lothair Road waving to them as the car took them away seven days before Christmas. Dad didn't look much different, except that he wasn't wearing his lorry driver's cap.

The journey was more thoughtful on the way back, the X-rays being furthest in their minds. Floating on air, on top of the bus, as high as the treetops, Hazel was hanging on to all her memories, keeping them for her melancholy dream world, the bus suddenly jerked, the daydreaming was over, back in the home she went about the routine chores.

Each night in the blue-room, as Winnie said her prayers, Hazel could see the hospital on the hill, with its two bedded compartments and the dark green curtains.

Dusting the blue-room each morning Hazel stood on the forbidden spot in the bay window, and looked beyond the curtains at the ever-changing world outside. Some of the trees in the park were being cut down, there was quite a clearing, earth moving bulldozers clumsily made their way between the poplar trees, dumping huge mounds of clay at the side of the brook. From the window she had a bird's-eye view of its progression and after a few days a deep hole had been dug out, in its depth, the men could no longer be seen as they worked on the bottom. By the end of the week, the concrete sides were in place, forming a complete circle around the concrete base.

"What is it going to be, Ma?" they asked, having given up the idea that swings and roundabouts were to be put there,

"It's a water holder, to be used for fire fighting if any incendiary bombs drop. The firemen have pumped the water into it from the brook today. It's nearly full, so don't let me catch any of you near it. The mounds of clay soon hardened, and attracted the local boys, after school they ran up and down, chasing each other, playing hide and seek. The 'hills' as they were promptly called, were a new playground, already smooth from the rain. Competitions were held on Saturday mornings to see who could ride their bicycle along the hills to the end without falling down the sides.

"Can we go and play on the hills Ma?" The girls asked

"No", said Ma

Nipper had been sent to persuade Ma, but the 'Matron Buttridge rule' prevailed and they were not allowed out after school. But 'the hills' did not evade the soles of their feet entirely, and lumps of clay stuck to their well-groomed shoes on the way home from the pictures on Saturday afternoon. The girls followed the 'cowboys' riding their imaginary steeds, racing away down the road, to the hills in the park.

Big Margaret was keen to get to the shops after the pictures to spend her pocket money, and walked on ahead. Once she was out of sight the girls crossed the road and joined the gangs of kids up and down the hills.

One warm sunny day in the school holidays, Ma told the Hunts that they were going to have a special visitor, some time during the morning Mrs Hunt was being allowed out of hospital for a few hours to visit the girls.

It was an exceptional occasion, and not the normal visiting hours. After all the jobs were done, Hazel, Doris and Edna watched and waited at the dining room window, Ma looked through the bobby-hole now and again, and said. "Are they here yet?

The taxi eventually arrived. Mam was sitting in the back of the car. A nurse helped her up the stone steps of the front door.

"They're here Ma, they're here!" Such a hullabaloo went on that Ma was at the front door before the bell was rung.

The nurse and Mam stood in the hall talking to Ma. Then in the dining room the girls were with their Mam, they greeted her like a long lost friend, and sat her down on one of the hard dining room chairs. The smile on her pale face did not belie to them that they would not be going home for a few months, she had come to see where they lived, to make sure that her girls were happy. Sambo, the very best pot doll was sitting on top of the bookcase, no one was allowed to play with it. The only rag dolls they had belonged to all the girls, and they were littered in the corner in an old dolls cot. Doris's drawings were taken down from the bookshelf. Walking slowly around the house, they showed Mam the blue-room, then the kitchen where she met the rest of the girls. She loved the house, and thought they were very lucky to have someone as nice as Ma to look after them. Big Margaret brought in a cup of tea, she was in one of her nicest moods, and the bullying was forgotten for the time being. The cup of tea was very welcome, and helped to prolong the visit.

"Keep the nurse busy," they said, "Mam doesn't want to go yet."

The girls snuggled up to Mam and gave her a rundown of their daily tasks, telling her that every Tuesday they had 'mucky stew' for dinner, and scrambled egg for tea, when Ma had her day off. Their favourite outing was on Saturday going to the pictures at the Evington Cinema. Looking out of the window she was shown how near the church was.

"This is where I sit," said Edna, and she named each girl's chair round the table.

Mam looked out of the window across the park. The poplar trees were glistening in the August sunshine. The ominous black taxi stood much closer, waiting on the road ready for the return journey to the hospital. Ma came into the dining room followed by the nurse, who clearly stated that their time was up. Doris gave her some drawings to take back with her taking her time again to delay the departure. On the pavement they helped to open the car door, they managed a few more kisses, and some for Dad, as she settled in the back of the taxi.   With Ma, Hazel, Doris and Edna stood on the pavement waving until the car was out of sight.

"Perhaps she'll be able to stay a bit longer next time," Ma said.

However long the visit, it all seemed so unreal and they couldn't believe it had really happened. At dinnertime they stood round the table to sing grace.   In their 'rosebud' summer dresses, hands together they gazed at the gold links of the bracelets that Mam had given to them.

The sirens went off again that night, Ma was quite worried and all the blankets were taken to the shelter. The canvas beds were cold and most uncomfortable, it took them quite a while to settle down, some giggling, some just annoyed at having someone's else's feet under their nose, being two in a bunk.

The three candles cast eerie shadows on the brick walls of the shelter.

"Try and settle down," Ma said. "Stop that giggling, or we will not hear the 'all clear.'"

"She's tickling my feet, Ma."

"Stop it Brenda," Ma knew exactly who was on which bunk.

Ma sat dozing in the easy chair all the gas masks were under the bottom bunks, ready for any emergency.

The time spent in the shelter didn't usually last very long, but lack of sleep, was often blamed for the eruption of petty squabbles. Each girl with their own particular trauma, living in a home where they do not wish to be. Disagreements turned into full scale crises with handfuls of hair being pulled out by squabbling girls, Ma would come rushing into the dining room, and whoever was nearest got a 'silly sender' and a clip round the ear, then she threatened to send them all to bed.

"You can all sit round the table 'til you can behave yourselves," and there they would sit until bedtime. Big Margaret had got control of them once again, bullying them into one of her silly games. If they refused to play, they would have to forfeit one of their Saturday sweet rations.

Towards the end of the summer holidays, Nipper persuaded Ma to take them all on a picnic. There were plenty of suggestions as to where they could go, and what they should take with them. Sandwiches, was the priority on the list. The tin of cake and a knife to cut it, a table cloth, a blanket for them all to sit on. The house was a buzz of excitement, girls flying about in all directions.

"What can we carry the tea in, Ma?"

"Get them Tizer bottles, and we can wrap them up in tea towels."

"Are we wearing blazers?"

"Who's carrying what?" shouted Brenda who usually got lumbered with the heavy bag. "I've got an idea," said Nipper "Let's take the pram."

The rusty old doll's pram had stood near the dustbin for months, waiting for the rag and bone man to take it away.

"I'm not having you wheel that thing in the street," said Ma.

Looking at the pram. Nipper whispered, "I'll push it."

"You'll do no such thing," said Ma.

Nipper and a few volunteers, like Brenda pulled the pram away from the wall. "Oh, there's a big spider," shouted Pasty Pauline.

"Ssh, we can dust it out, rub the wheels, put the blanket in the bottom," said Olive.

It was ideal and everything fitted in neatly. "Which way do we go, Ma?" shouted the two girls at the front.

"We're going to 'Piggy's Hollow,'" shouted Ma from the rear of the procession. "That little blighter's got that pram," she said.

The pram wheels were squeaking, attracting the attention of the passers by, more so than the crocodile of girls. On the way along the tree-lined road, they stopped every few yards to pick up the beautiful blossoms that had fallen from the trees, each one a tiny flower. For those who had never been, 'Piggy's Hollow' conjured up different ideas. On arrival at the gate there were no pigs at all, just green grassy banks for them to sit on. The pram was soon abandoned, leaving Ma to sit beside

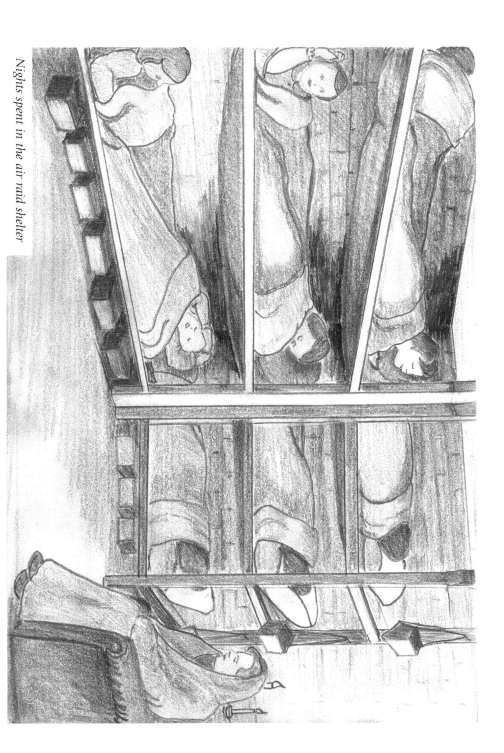

Nights spent in the air raid shelter

it on the grass. The girls chased up and down, climbed the gates, and rolled in the freshly cut grass until Ma decided that the tea would be getting cold.

They gathered round and the picnic was soon organised, everyone munching away at the warm soggy sandwiches. The warm tea from the lemonade bottles quenched their thirst, and every drop was drunk.

"How far have we come, Ma?" Big Margaret asked.

"Oh its only about four miles," said Ma.

"Four miles." They nearly collapsed

One mile sounded a long way, but had they got to walk four miles back again.

"We could have gone on the bus if you hadn't brought that pram," said Ma.

Gathering the empty bags and bottles, they filled the pram again, covering it with the blanket, and pushed the pram homeward bound. The bus was at the terminus and about to leave.

"Are you getting on missus?" shouted the conductor.

"Yes, please," said Ma and they all climbed aboard.

Big Margaret placed the dolls pram under the stairs of the bus, she in particular didn't want to walk back.

"You'll all sleep well tonight," said Ma. "We won't bother with baths tonight, just have a strip wash.

"Strippo, feeto, down to showo," said Nipper.

The dainty, fragile blossoms hadn't survived the two and a half-hours picnic, and the petals were too crumpled to press in their schoolbooks.

Next day they sat eating 'frog spawn' pudding, when the doorbell rang. The 'visitor' was taken to Ma's sitting room, Ma appeared at the bobby-hole.

"Right the first two upstairs and get your teeth cleaned," Ma said.

"Who is it, Ma?" said Big Margaret, leaving the table with Olive.

"The dentist, come on hurry up, the rest of you can follow when they come down. Don't keep Mr Grainger waiting," said Ma.

The rest of the tapioca pudding was hurriedly eaten and the clean plates passed through to the kitchen.

"I think I'll have to have a filling this time," said Little Margaret.

"I had toothache but it went off," said Brenda.

"Does he take your teeth out in Ma's sitting room?" Doris asked.

"No, silly, we have to go to his house on Evington Road," said Brenda hurrying down stairs to be next in the queue.

The brief examination was soon over.

"Does it hurt?" said Mr Grainger.

"No," Hazel replied with a few of his fingers still in her mouth.

Mr Grainger scribbled on his note pad. He plopped the dental mirror into the glass of carbolic water on the table, and took a sharp instrument from the pocket of his white coat.

"Aah, aah," she moaned.

"That's the one," he said helping Hazel back into a sitting position on the chair.

Mr Grainger left, and Ma had the list. We stood round the table and sang grace.

"We thank Thee Lord for this our food,
And also for the dentist's care,
Thy creatures bless and grant our prayer.
May never see the dentist's chair."

Ma appeared at the bobby-hole

"Ay, I heard that, now sing it again. If your name is on this list, you'll be going," said Ma.

"I can still taste the carbolic soap," said Ruth.

"It's horrible," said Brenda.

"Tastes like I've had my mouth washed out with soap again," said Olive.

"What do you mean?" said Doris

"Olive swore at Ma, so she washed her mouth out with soap," said Little Margaret.

"Did you? What did you say?"

"I was sick, I brought all my dinner up, so I got a good hiding for that as well," said Olive.

After the girls had finished the washing up, Ma brought the dentist's list into the dining room.

"Right there's a few going to the dentist on Saturday. Brenda, Hazel, Winnie, Ruth, Edna and Nipper," said Ma.

"I'm not going, Mr Grainger said mine were all good teeth, Ma," said Nipper.

"You've only got to have that loose baby tooth out, it won't hurt you, don't be a baby," said Ma.

"If you tie a piece of cotton round your tooth, Nipper and tie it to the door knob, you won't have to go on Saturday," said Big Margaret.

Nipper pulled a face she didn't want to be tied to the door either.

After several attempts with the doorknob, Nipper was still travelling with them on Saturday. Brenda remembered the way, by tram, and they eventually found the gate with the brass plaque.

Mr Grainger, DENTIST. They walked up the long drive under the trees, the house stood well away from the road. Arriving at the front door, no-one was sure where the door bell was. An old iron bar stuck out of the wall; Blunderbuss gave it a tug.

"Don't pull the house down," said Winnie.

Inside, the nurse took them to the waiting room, rubber heels squeaked on the polished floor.

"Who's going first?" Whispered Brenda.

"I'm not," said Ruth.

The Geographical Magazines were stacked in piles all round the table, together with Picture Post Magazines.

Margaret turned the pages of the Picture Post, staring at the photographs of the bombed buildings, the devastation after the air raids. Firemen digging among the ruins, carrying people on stretchers. Soldiers tanks and guns. Pictures of Montgomery and Mr Churchill. The King and Queen standing among the ruins at Buckingham Palace. These were real photographs like the newsreel they saw on Saturday at the pictures.

"Here's a Cannibal, Hazel," said Winnie with a Geographical Magazine in front of her.

"Let me see," Hazel said.

"Mr Grainger is going to take all your teeth out, by request of Maytwun Butterwitch," said Winnie.

The door opened, Hazel was on her feet, staring at the Cannibal with a bone through his nose. The nurse whisked her away.

With wet palms she gripped the sides of the chair.

"Look out of the window, don't look at me," said the dentist.

Hazel looked up, and a moving picture was displayed in front of her. The doors of the French window were open, a lacy curtain moved in the breeze either side. Beyond the French doors a waterfall cascaded down over rocks to a pond below. In the foreground was a sundial on the edge of the water, surrounded by green shrubs, and cushions of flowers. The picturesque view made the agonising pain much easier to bear.

Hazel returned to the waiting room, Brenda was next, and she also returned with bloodstained cotton wool jutting from her mouth. On the return journey it was left to Nipper to ask for the fares, she had got her baby tooth safely wrapped in cotton wool.

The next visiting day, Mr Seaton told Margaret and Winnie that their baby brother had got better from one hospital, now he was ill again in the Isolation Hospital, they both sat looking very serious with their worried father. 'It's meningitis', he had told them.

Mr Seaton was a very tired man, after working the night shift at The Leicester Mercury. He would snatch a few hours sleep, then every other day he would visit his wife, at the Towers Hospital, a place where she never ought to be. Walking through the corridors of the hospital he could hear the unnerving cries coming from various localities, and like the noise of the machinery at work he could not shut them out of his mind. To go from the lunacy of the hospital, to the tranquillity of the isolation hospital to visit his two-year-old son, he needed a day or two in between to recover from the wearisome tasks.

Once a month on a Monday night, he enjoyed visiting Margaret and Winnie who had fond memories of home and how it used to be before they took their Mother away. They helped to bring some stability and hope into his lonely life, 'when the war is over it might all be different.'

"Never mind, Dad, we'll all be together again one day," said Margaret.

Not knowing the seriousness of meningitis, Winnie agreed, and held her Dad's hand tightly.

Mrs Minton sat in her usual seat at Ma's table, telling Big Margaret, Brenda and Pauline that they would soon be going home. At home Brenda and Pauline would have to share a bedroom, and Margaret will have a small room to herself. Their 'uncle' was working away so they would not see him for a while.

Mrs Cartwright had brought Ruth a set of tin curlers, and Olive now had some powder to go with her lipstick. Bars of chocolate and boiled sweets were secretly taken from her bag. There were many 'uncles' in Mrs Cartwright's life, she was renting a small terraced house near the prison, so she could visit the father of one of her children. She had been a good looker in her time her petite figure could still turn the heads of men who were out for a good time. Now she hid her flashing dark eyes under the old felt hat that she always wore. The Hunt girls had no visitors, Ted had given up coming, and he had lost interest in their lack of drawing for him.

One Sunday morning Ma told the three Hunts they would be going to Grandma's for the day, instead of going to church.

"Who's coming to fetch us, Ma?"

The church bell had stopped ringing, and the house was quiet, as they stood breathless waiting for their day-out to begin.

Inside the taxi with Brother Ted, they waved to Ma, and felt like three princesses.

Ted was still as bossy.

"Get your shoulders back Edna, you'll get round shouldered," he said.

The girls had learned over the past months to ignore criticism and not get dejected by its implications. A barrier was immediately put up between their chaperone, as they travelled along the Saffron Lane.

Hazel remembered the day she had run away, and looked longingly up Lothair Road, wishing that they were going home for good. The taxi took the shortest route to Grandma's, which was much quicker than the bus ride. Hazel checked the number nine on the front door, making sure of the address, she had been born at Grandma's, in the front bedroom, the house with a garden full of flowers. They raced through the back door, and flew into the arms of Grandma, peeling potatoes.

"I'll do the potatoes, Grandma. You sit on the chair," Hazel said carrying out her solemn vows as if she was back at home.

Grandad shuffled into the doorway of the kitchen.

"You all look very smart," he said, " get an apron on," he muttered.

They all kissed Grandad, who looked rather small especially as they were now equally as tall as he was. Above the sink, Hazel looked through the iron-framed window of the council house and out into the garden.

"Where've all the flowers gone," Hazel shouted, looking out of the kitchen window, alarmed at the rows of vegetables stretching to the bottom of the garden.

Forgetting the job in hand, she stood in the back garden, as if an earthquake had struck, Grandma's pansies all gone. Only the rose bower had been spared climbing up the neighbours' fence.

"DIG FOR VICTORY," said Grandad, who stood beside her.

The pink and white Phlox had been replaced by rhubarb. The multicoloured nasturtiums that cascaded down a wall, full of earwigs each year had sage and thyme growing between the cracks of the brickwork amongst the mint and parsley. They all walked down the

116

garden path as if they were in another world.   Grandad's lettuces, radishes, beetroot, carrots, all in neat rows ready for picking.

"Do you like radishes?" said Grandad and he plucked one each for them to try.

"You can't eat flowers, got to beat old Hitler," Grandad said.

The Merchant Seaman from the First World War, was fighting the war from his own little plot, with his penknife he cut four rosebuds for the table.

"Get them in water, mind the thorns," he said.

The girls laid the table, and placed the bowl of roses in the centre. The smell of roast beef wafted between the two rooms, as they sat with Grandad in the living room, listening to the clock ticking on the wall, the pendulum still swinging as if they had never been away. Ted came through the back door with Grandad's jug of beer from the off licence.

"Oh can we have a shandy please Grandma?" they said.

"Go to the toilet, and wash your hands ready for dinner," said Grandad.

The outside toilet was still the same, the little paraffin lamp on the windowsill, hanging on a nail was a wad of torn up newspaper carefully threaded on a piece of string. Grandma was busy with the flat iron on the kitchen table.

"Can I iron them?" Hazel asked.

"Its only a few of your Dad's handkerchiefs," said Grandma.

"These are DAD'S hankies," Hazel blurted out.

"Yes," whispered Gran, put them in that basket when you've done them, we'll take them with us this afternoon."

Edna and Doris washing their hands at the kitchen sink, turned towards Grandma, the secret was out.

"Are we going to the hospital?" they said in wide-eyed amazement.

Grandad poured the jug of cool brown beer into the glasses. At the three glasses of lemonade he paused and tutted, then with a splash of brown liquid from the jug their lemonades were turned into 'wicked' shandies.   The girls beamed smiles at him, not ever daring to giggle any more for fear of having to stand in the corner. The plates of Yorkshire puddings coated with hot jam were brought to the table.   It was a day when they should surely have been thankful, but grace wasn't said. Grandad carved the roast beef, the jugs of gravy and mint sauce were carefully passed around and poured over the roast potatoes. Their

117

startled amazement at having pudding first went unnoticed.

"Fresh from the garden, you can't beat that, got any mustard gel?" Grandad picked up his knife and fork, sending Grandma back into the kitchen for the Colman's mustard.

"Thank you for my good dinner, and please can I leave the table," the passwords for the girls to clear the table, and start the washing up.

Arm-in-arm, and carrying Grandma's basket they walked down Churchgate to catch another bus out of the city. They remembered the curved brickwork of the hospital gates and excitedly jumped off the bus. At the top of the hill, Gran took the path to Dad's ward, while the three girls hurried along the trail of the veranda, trying to guess which of the two-bedded compartments Mam was in, not wasting a moment. Mam was sitting up in bed knitting; she looked well with more colour in her cheeks. Hazel, Doris and Edna gave her their individual special kisses. The conversation was packed with all the forgone events of the home. They reminded her of the small details like changing into their summer dresses, blazers, and Panama hats, their scotch kilts had been taken away almost a year ago now, but not forgotten. It was only the third time they had seen Mam during that time.

Mam's hands were noticeably soft against their rough little hands. Hazel's bitten nails chewed right down to blunt stubs, had broken skin at the sides, like 'grandad's whiskers.' A blister on her thumb was gently smoothed.

"How did you get that blister?" said Mam.

"We're making a peg rug at Ma's, we have to cut up all the material into little bits, then we all have a go with the pegging. That's where I hold the scissors," Hazel said.

The hard worked hands from dusting floors, washing up, sweeping the big yard, putting the coal on the fire, were hidden away in folded arms.

Grandma came into the ward to see Mam, and it was time for the girls to go and visit their Dad. Walking into the men's ward was quite different to Mam's cosy cubicle, amongst the rows of beds they spotted Dad. In the clinical environment he looked quite pale sitting propped up with pillows, they ran towards him.

"Don't run, you've got all afternoon," he said.

"Are these your girls George?" said the man in the next bed.

"Yes, they get bigger every time I see them," said Dad. "This is Hazel, this is Doris, and that's Edna."

He proudly tapped them gently on the head.

At the side of his bed was a table covered in pieces of shaped leather, ready for making purses.

"Is this yours, Dad?" Hazel asked.

"Yes, I'm making a purse for your Grandma," he said.

"What's this?" said Doris picking up a spiked instrument from the table.

"That's a punch to make holes in the leather, you twist them spikes round to make the size of hole that you need," said Dad.

"Can I have a go?" said Doris.

"Be careful. Don't make holes in your fingers, use the bits that I've trimmed off," said Dad.

Each had a turn with the unusual tool, while the others sat on Dad's bed repeating their news, telling him everything, and anything. During their conversation it was noticeable that he too had bouts of coughing like Mam, and whatever they coughed up was spit into a 'sputum' mug with a lid. There was a 'sputum mug' on every locker in the ward. The tea trolley rattling with cups was coming along the corridor, a sure sign that their time was up.

"I think you'd better get back to your Mam, be good and look after each other," said Dad with a kiss for each of them.

The girls waved to Dad's friends, and took the shortest route through the corridors back to the 'veranda' ward where Grandma was still talking to Mam.

The bell rang in the corridor, the clanging of this bell to end their visit was not welcomed at all. They gave Mam a kiss, and left the Ward, knowing that by the time they reached the grass verge they would run back for another hug and kiss, in time to see that the tea lady had left her a cup of tea and some thin bread and butter.

"Can we come again, Grandma" they asked.

Their busy day out ended when Grandma put them on the tram to East Park Road, waving as it slowly rolled away along the track back to the home.

"Come in," said Ma. In answer to the loud knock on her sitting room door.

"Hello Ma, hello Miss Everett."

Ma sat at the table with her visitor, a white haired lady who listened with interest as they churned out every detail of their day out.

"Did your Grandma put you on the tram," said Ma.

"Yes, Ma," we said.

"Right, go and put those best clothes away, and tell Big Margaret to make the cocoa.

*   *   *

After the summer, the black stockings and tunics were brought down once again from the box room in the attic, and with each month they donned another under garment. Doris, Winnie and Ruth started at Bridge Road Juniors. Little Margaret and Hazel were now in Mrs Pikes class, and Brenda who hadn't passed her eleven plus exam had joined Big Margaret and Olive in the seniors.

In 2A, Mrs Pike never wasted a moment of her time, the arithmetic was already written on the blackboard as the pupils filed into the classroom.

"Good afternoon 2A" said Mrs Pike.

"Good afternoon, Mrs Pike," the class replied.

At her desk she sat busily knitting 'socks for soldiers.' Mrs Pike's husband was an RAF pilot, and all her time was devoted to the Women's' Voluntary Service. Food parcels and supplies were sent to the Red Cross, especially the ladies knitted socks scarves and gloves.

"Who can knit?" shouted Mrs Pike.

Hazel's hand shot in the air.

"I wish you were as quick with your arithmetic answers," she said and tossed the half knitted sock onto her desk.

Finding the end of the wool, Hazel continued knitting urgently on the four pins, while Mrs Pike marked the register and organised the adding and subtracting of the FRACTIONS on the board. The warm feel of the wool in her fingers, reminded Hazel of Mam knitting in hospital, the date on the blackboard was November, nineteen-forty-three, their baby Brian was now three years old.

Nineteen forty-three was coming to an end, and Ma's early preparation for Christmas was well underway. With the pots cleared away all the ingredients for the Christmas puddings were laid out on the kitchen table. Ma carefully measured out the fruit, which was taken into the scullery and washed. The first helper to hand got the job of gently drying all the fruit in a big clean tea towel.

"Have you got clean hands, Ruth?" said Ma. "You can make the breadcrumbs, mind your fingers on the grater."

The large saucepan full of water was already heating up on the fireplace ready for the puddings to boil away for hours and hours.

"That smells horrible, what's that?" said Winnie.

"That's suet, you can grate it up if you like when 'Rags' has done with the grater," said Ma.

"I'll do that," said Brenda grabbing the precious solid lump of fat, only to be had on the 'black market' or from 'under the counter' because of the war.

The large cooking bowl sat firmly on the table in front of Ma, all the scarce commodities were carefully measured.

"Olive you can beat the eggs for me," said Ma," and take that thumb out of your mouth."

Olive sat on the chair with the bowl on her knee, the rest of the girls watched as she broke the delicate eggs with the harsh wires of the whisk.

"Just think, they could have hatched out into little chickens," said Pauline.

"Not now they can't," said Olive who soon transformed the yellow sacks into creamy frothy bubbles.

"Where's the gravy browning?" said Ma.

"Gravy Browning... in Christmas puddings?" they responded.

"Are we having silver three-penny bits in the puddings this year, Ma?"

"I might be able to find a few, if somebody wants the job of cleaning them," said Ma.

"I'll do it," shouted Nipper.

The wooden spoon could hardly cope with the bulk of pudding mixture once all the ingredients were finally blended together.

Now came the time that they had all been waiting for, to throw in a silver three-penny bit and make a wish whilst stirring the Yuletide dessert.

"Don't wish out loud, or it won't come true," said Winnie.

When all the wishes were safely made, some were stirring more than three times just to make sure, the six puddings were securely tied over the linen covers. Three puddings in each saucepan simmered on the kitchen range all night long.

*   *   *

It was the last term at school for Big Margaret, and the girls were reminded every day that she would be leaving the home for good. She had been for an interview for a job in one of the factories in Leicester, and with Brenda and Pauline they were going back home to live with their Mother.

"I shall be starting my job after Christmas, with my wages I shall buy all the things I've wanted," said Big Margaret.

The Mintons were the first girls to leave Ma's. Everybody wondered what they would be able to take home with them. On their last morning they stood in the kitchen with Ma as the rest of the girls left for school.

"Goodbye, Pasty, Goodbye, Blunderbuss, Goodbye, Big Margaret."

"Three less for tea," they shouted. "Bye."

Olive was all smiles as she came through the back door.

"Good afternoon, Ma," she shouted and slung her coat and satchel on the pegs and automatically threw her shoes at the back of the shoe rack.

"Where is everybody?" she asked leaning though the bobby-hole.

The table was laid for only eight girls, two each side of the table.

Ma came into the kitchen to cut the cake for tea.

"What time did the Mintons go, Ma?" Did somebody come and collect them," said Olive, eager to know what the procedure was when the eventful day finally arrives.

"Neck-trouble, being neckie again, always got your mind on what don't concern you," said Ma. "If you must know Matron Buttridge came for them and took them to the Receiving Home."

"Oh, I thought they were going home," said Olive.

"Come on, get that tea through the bobby-hole, and let's have less of your cheek. They've gone and that's all there is to it," said Ma.

Olive sat in Big Margaret's place at the table, and stuck her thumb in her mouth.

"You'll clean the kitchen, Olive, and take that thumb out of your mouth, you are the eldest now," said Ma announcing the change of jobs after tea. "Hazel, you'll fill the coal buckets, Margaret's not 'little Margaret' any more, you're in charge of the scullery, and Ruth the dining room. You'll start your new jobs tomorrow morning. The rest follow suit," said Ma.

Can we put the trimmings up this week-end, Ma, please?" said Nipper.

"When all the jobs are done, Sunday afternoon," said Ma, "I think we'll

Bridge Road Girl's School, 1945.

move the table across the bay window this year, then you'll have more room."

It was nice not to have Big Margaret voicing her opinion, or agreeing with Ma.

After tea, there were no 'Cart's Choruses' sung, no bullying from the new eldest girl who sat reading a book sucking her thumb.

Olive, benevolent and tender hearted, was slightly rebellious for several reasons. Firstly she didn't like being called 'Neck-trouble,' she felt victimised, Olive was the one who always got caught peeping round doors, looking out of the window, sneaking up the entry tapping on the dining room window and running back in the house again. She tested their limited freedom, now the Mintons had left there was no one to 'snitch' to Ma. Olive's 'escapades' were an entertainment, just for giggles. Now she was the eldest, Olive fearlessly took Sambo, the best black doll, down from its resting-place on top of the bookcase. Those who'd had a turn holding the baby doll could also help to tidy the dolls-house, which she also carefully removed from its high dwelling place. She asked Ma if she could sleep in the little bedroom now that Big Margaret had gone, but Ma refused, saying that it was going to be the sick room again. Nipper was the centre of attraction from the time they had come to live with Ma, and being second eldest to Big Margaret, was an unfortunate circumstance for Olive.

They all felt liberated from the tyrant that Big Margaret had been, Olive herself had always taken the easy way out and submitted to many of her malicious plans. Big Margaret had locked the cellar door while Olive was getting the coal up, this resulted in a fight and Ma intervened with a soapy mouth wash when she heard Olive swearing. The real culprit who locked the cellar door was never punished. To protect her sisters from her devious plans, Hazel too was her victim and always tried to stay in her 'good books.' Obeying her orders, warming her bed on winter nights while she made Ma's supper. Olive was deserving of having the little bedroom but it closed an intimidating memory when the small room was not used: "Frairer shacker, frairer shacker, darmayblue, darmayblue, semolemotina, semolemotina, ding dang dung, ding dang dung."

Olive's new song was sung in rounds, none of us knew what it meant, neither did she. She wandered into the dining room, and upstairs along the landing, wearing Ma's shoes, making the girls laugh at their own fear and consternation in case she was caught. The nicknames were forgotten, and only used when Ma was in a jovial mood. The adoration of the head choirboy, Pip, was the focus of Olive's attention in church. Little notes saying 'I LOVE YOU' were left under a stone in the front garden for him to pick up after choir practice. A stealthy daredevil trip to the front garden via the back door was made while Olive 'made Ma's supper,' to retrieve his reply.

The trimmings were all strung across the ceiling each twisted streamer lavishly covered with strands of tinsel, carefully straightened out and used again for another year. The Chinese lanterns hung each side of the bay window, and the Christmas tree stood in the red box on the floor in the corner. The decorations on the tree were a few years old, and the angel on the top had a broken wing. Doris had cleverly decorated the mirror above the fireplace. Happy Christmas to you all, written with a piece of soap, and draped over the top with a sprig of holly.

Mr Seaton was the first visitor to arrive on this last visiting day before Christmas. Margaret and Winnie proudly sat their father at Ma's table in the bay. Ted, and Mrs Cartwright, were next to ring the front door bell. The decorations made the dining room more cheery, but Ted's news of baby, Brian, was grim, he was in hospital with Meningitis.

Mr Seaton reassured them that he would get better, he was in the same hospital that little Joe was in.

"I will look out for him when I go to see Joe," said Mr Seaton, "he's bound to be in the same ward."

On the Thursday the laundry basket arrived, with the weekly groceries. Another basket, which was not opened, was whisked away into Ma's sitting room.

Ma kept the Thursday sewing down to a minimum, as they were on holiday. Friday night the Christmas cake was iced, all eight girls helping in some way in the kitchen, trying to master the icing decorations. With the palette knife Ma peaked the snow on the cake, and placed Father Christmas and the Yule log firmly in the 'deep snow.'

Christmas Eve was the busiest night, with all the help and hindrance, once more they stood around the kitchen table. The turkey had to be stuffed. With a large needle and cotton Ma tucked the stuffing inside the large bird as its legs flopped about in unmanageable movements. Safely tied up, and sitting in the roasting tin, the turkey was ready for the oven. The potatoes and all the vegetables were ready for morning. The damask tablecloth was put on first, then out of the box the red and green holly paper was rolled down the centre of the table. The snowy glitter was then sprinkled on the edges where the six wax water lilies were carefully placed, three on each side. All the serviettes were folded into 'water-lilies' showing the patterned edges, ready to be filled with small sweets. A Christmas cracker for each person was placed next to the spoon. Ma came into the dining room to see what had been done to the table.

"You've made a good job of that. You can do something when you try," said Ma. Carrying a large basket of fruit, oranges, apples, and nuts, she placed it in the centre of the table, and draped the holly and ribbons down to the table.

"Looks good, well done," said Ma.

"Just got to get Santa a glass of sherry and a mince pie," said Ma.

"We mustn't forget Santa," said Nipper.

Doris secretly made a sooty footprint on the hearth before going to bed. With the girls in bed, Ma sorted out the contents of the 'mystery basket' that had arrived on Thursday, filling a Christmas stocking for each girl.

"Is anybody awake?" came a whisper from Doris's corner of the room.

"I am," Hazel said.

"So am I," said Margaret.

"Shall I put the light on?" said Doris.

"You'll have to close the door," said Winnie. "Happy Christmas"

"Happy Christmas," They whispered to each other.

"Don't make a noise or Ma will hear us, and don't fall over your pillowcase, its at the side of the bed," said Margaret.

"What do you think the time is Margaret?" asked Winnie.

"I don't know, but we can have a peep in our 'stockings' it'll be getting light soon," said Margaret.

The door clicked shut.

"Big Margaret would definitely have heard that," said Winnie. "I wonder what they've got for Christmas."

"A pillow case full, blimey, last year I got a purse and a panda," Hazel said.

"Ssh, Ma's only next door, she'll hear us," said Margaret.

"Oh I like that," a blonde haired doll in a blue dress was extracted from Winnie's pillowcase.

"Wake Edna up, she's missing all the fun," Doris said, "we'll be able to play Ludo."

"And snakes and ladders," said Doris. "I've got a drawing book, all that lovely drawing paper, pencils, and crayons.

"What have you got Margaret?" Hazel whispered.

"A pencil box, and a compass set," said Margaret "What have you got?"

"A haberdashery set," Hazel said.

"What's that?" said Winnie.

"I don't know, that's what it says on the box."

"Come on Edna open your presents it's Christmas morning."

"Listen," said Margaret, "I think the brown room are awake."

The knob of the blue-room door turned, Olive peeped round the door.

"Oh," said Winnie, "I thought you were Ma."

"I'm going to make Ma a cup of tea," whispered Olive. "Then we'll all go to Ma's room."

"What's the time?" said Margaret.

"Its half past seven, Ma won't mind," whispered Olive.

"What did you have, Olive?" asked Doris.

"A film stars album, a dictionary, pencil case, a night-dress case, I think that's what it is, it's a bag anyway, and a celluloid doll in a pink crinoline dress," Olive put Edna's pillowcase of toys on the bed.

"Look, you've got a nurse's outfit like Nipper, and a colouring book, it's got one of them cut out dolls that you can dress," she said as she crept out of the room.

Winnie opened a pop up book.

"I've got an Enid Blyton book," said Margaret.

Edna fished out a Rupert book.

"I've got a Rupert book as well," said Winnie.

"What's this?" said Edna, holding up a brightly painted piece of wood with a hole right through the middle, and four nails at one end.

"That's for French knitting," said Margaret, "I had one of them last year. Have you got some wool with it?"

"Yes, its fell out of the box," said Edna digging into the pillowcase.

"I'll show you how to do it later. It's ever so easy" Margaret said.

"Come on, Olive's got Ma's tea," whispered Doris. The girls gathered outside Ma's bedroom door Olive tapped three times on the door.

"Good Morning Ma, Happy Christmas."

Once in Royal David's city,

Stood a lowly cattle shed,

Where a Mother laid her Baby
In a manger for His bed....,"

The girls sang their Christmas morning greeting to Ma. Nipper was the first to encroach upon the prohibited area of Ma's room.

"Come in," said Ma, "Happy Christmas."

Olive gave Ma her cup of tea.

"Thank you for my presents Ma," said Nipper.

"They're not from me, they're from Santa," said Ma. "Did you get what you wanted?"

In Ma's bedroom some sat on the bed, the rest sat on the ottoman.

"What's in here Ma?" Margaret asked.

"Never you mind, don't be nosy," said Ma.

"It's got all Ma's things in it," said Nipper. "All her old fashioned photos, and boxes of jewellery."

"Ha, you make it sound like a treasure chest," said Ma.

Its Ma's treasure chest," said Nipper who knew every nook and cranny in Ma's bedroom.

"Let's have another carol then," said Ma. "Soon be time for breakfast."

"Away in a manger."

"No - O little town of Bethlehem?"

"Once in Royal...?"

"We just sang that, Dopey!"

"Silent night...?"

" Struth, there's nothing silent here, make your minds up I can't sit here all day, got to get that dinner cooked," said Ma.

"We three Kings?"

"Do you want to put me in a bad mood for the day yow blighters. We had enough of that in the air raid shelter," said Ma - "Away in a manger."

Sitting in her double bed, with a wardrobe against the blue-room wall, a large cupboard either side of the fireplace the pretty flowered material covering Ma's 'treasure chest.' Three on the ottoman, and five on the bed, they sang to Ma.

"Right, thank you for the tea, Let's have you all downstairs. Breakfast is in the kitchen, put your pillowcases in the dining room. Make your beds properly," said Ma.

The tops of the boiled eggs were removed with great care Nipper still had her slice of bread cut up into 'soldiers' ready to dip into the runny yolk.

"Don't forget you've all got to go to the Receiving Home this morning. Olive you'll have to greet the Lord Mayor, do you know what to say?" said Ma.

"Yes, Ma, I think so," said Olive.

"Well write it out, then I'll have a look at it," said Ma.

In identical tweed coats and berets the girls from the home walked across the park. Olive knocked on the door of a house. They were unable to see through the lacy curtain covering the stained glass petitions of the door.

"Who lives here?" said Doris.

"Matron's sister," whispered Nipper, quite used to the annual visit.

A tall, thin lady opened the door; she wore a black dress with a white lace collar.

"Good Morning, Mrs Bowler. Happy Christmas."

"Come in," said Mrs Bowler, opening the door of her front room.

The eight girls stood among the highly polished furniture, just staring at all the statues and china ornaments among the many photographs on the walls and shelf. There was no fire in the hearth, but a large, embroidered firescreen, enclosed by a shining brass fender and matching companion set, which shone like new. The tin of humbugs was returned to its lacy mat on the sideboard after they had each taken a sticky striped sweet. They then said Goodbye to the genteel lady, whose voice was much more cultured, and different in every way to Matron Buttridge.

Olive walked crookedly along the pavement with one foot in the gutter. Both of her cheeks were bulging.

"Good Morning my Lord Mayor and Lady Mayoress, we wish you both a Happy Christmas," said Olive with her mouth full.

How many sweets have you got in your mouth?" said Margaret.

"Two," said Olive also indicating with her fingers.

"You were only supposed to take one," said Margaret.

"Mrs Bowler didn't say only take one," said Olive. "Besides, they were stuck together."

I hope she didn't count how many there were," Hazel said.

"Good morning, my Lord Mayor, and Lady Mayoress, we wish you good cheer, a happy, happy Christmas, and a bright merry New Year.

"Oh don't say it all wrong," said Winnie giggling at Olive's purposeful mistakes.

"I'm glad I've not got to say it" Hazel said, "Say it again, Olive."

"Good Morning, my good lord," said Olive still walking with one foot in the gutter. Olive had been a quiet bystander for the last few years watching the older boys and girls 'doing their awesome bit' on Christmas Day. She had a knack of making them all feel nervous as to what she might do next.

Arriving at the Receiving Home, they wished Matron 'A Happy Christmas'. Then with Matron, the eldest boy and girl were taken to one side, while the rest were shepherded onto the pavement outside. For Margaret and Winnie, and the three Hunts a whole year had passed by, they felt sorry for the small children of the Receiving Home standing there with no coats. Olive and the eldest boy greeted the new Lord Mayor as he stepped from the gleaming black Rolls Royce. He listened as the carols were sung for him in the dining room. Matron then took her guests for light refreshments before the annual photograph. The girls walked back to Ma's, pleased that their encounter with Matron was over. The dinner smelled good as they opened the back door.

"We're back, Ma."

The final touches were being put to the Christmas dinner. Standing round the colourful table the girls sang grace Ma made them aware of all the poor people, telling them how lucky they were. Once the search for the wishbone was over and the wishbone broken by two little fingers, everyone settled down to Christmas dinner, giving Ma a full account of the morning. The Christmas pudding was a great success, making more wishes on finding the silver three-penny bits. All the dishes and pots were cleared away. Back in the dining room their Christmas stockings were sorted out once again, as they waited for the King's Christmas Message. At four o'clock it was trifle and cake in Ma's sitting room. By eight o'clock they were all in bed, exhausted from the excitement of the day. Winnie, still remembering to say her prayers, thanked God for all their toys, saying a special prayer for Baby Joe, and Brian, both still in hospital.

*   *   *

CHAPTER THREE

January 1944

The first of January, nineteen-forty-four, Matron's annual party at the Receiving Home again, Ma and the girls travelled by tram as the weather was cold and wet.

"No point in getting wet through for the sake of five-pence," said Ma. "One and eight halves," she said to the tram conductor.

Ma rang the Receiving Home bell, this was one bell that none of them liked to press. Matron Buttridge was decked out in her matronly outfit, the lace on her cap looking more starched than ever. She flitted from room to room, organising the staff down to the last detail. At the table this year each girl sat next to a boy from the boys' home. Miss Pickering, their foster mother watched over them like a 'broody hen,' with her paper hat askew on her head.

Miss Pickering looked on as the plates were offered to her boys.'

"Only one," Hazel said to the boy who had taken two.

"He can have two if he wants, he's a growing lad, boys eat more than girls anyway," said Miss Pickering.

Matron made her way around the table touching the backs of the chairs, each child hesitating until she had passed along the row. She paused at the two young ones' chairs.

"This is Linda, and this is Rita, they'll be going home with you girls today," said Matron, "Rita's brother, Colin, will be going back with Miss Pickering."

"You'll have ten girls and I'll have ten boys," said Miss Pickering.

"Yes," said Ma "I'll soon need a bigger house."

"Our back garden is not suitable for the boys to play in. I let them play on the park," said Miss Pickering quietly.

Olive sat next to Linda, she was younger than Nipper, with blonde curly hair, her baby face was full of smiles.

"You'll be sleeping in our room tonight," said Olive. "We call it the brown room."

Rita was sitting next to her brother, and didn't want to be parted.

"I'll send your brother down to see you at Miss Hammond's," Miss Pickering whispered, seeing that Rita was near to tears.

"She'll be alright, once she gets with Nipper," said Ma.

It took a few party games to get to know the new girls, everyone helping to break the ice for the journey back to Ma's. A large present from Santa was helpful, as Linda and Rita, were pre-occupied carrying it back to on the tram. At bedtime Olive was singing to the new girls in the brown room.

"I will make you fishers of men, fishers of men,
fishers of men, if you follow Me"
Miss Cart's choruses were coming in useful again.
The singing got a bit out of hand, and Ma shouted up the stairs.
"Let's have less noise, this lights going out."
"Yes, Ma, Goodnight, Ma."
"Goodnight and may the night last twenty four hours," Ma's famous last words.

The first visiting day in January the dining room was full. Grandma came to see Hazel and her sisters, Mr Seaton was telling Grandma, that Joe was out of hospital, they had both actually met at the hospital where the babies were.

"Brian has been transferred to Groby Road, to be near your Mam," said Grandma.

"Ah, that's nice, can we go and see him one day?"

"We'll have to ask again, it's not up to us," said Grandma.

"I'd love to have them out for a day, but I'm too busy working," said Mr Seaton, visiting the baby, then their Mother, the time's soon gone," he said.

In freshly pleated tunics, white blouses, and tweed coats, all the girls were well wrapped up against the north wind. The first morning back at school was always a drag. They lingered at the corner shop near the school to smell the newly baked bread as the trays full of cobs came out of the baker's oven. Anyone with a halfpenny could buy a steaming hot cob, which was subsequently broken into half-and-half again to treat the many friends waiting outside the shop.

At the weekend, the girls watched enviously from the dining room window as the first fall of snow brought children flocking into the park with their sledges. They yearned to be out with them sliding from the top of the hill.

"I know where I'm going," said Olive, leaving the dining room.

"Where are you going?"

"You'll see," said Olive.

Still spellbound by the fairy tale scene across the park, the girls huddled together, moving the curtains to get a better view.

Snowflakes as big as pennies transformed the road into a white carpet, disturbed only by a solitary tram that rumbled past the house. Olive appeared at the entry gate armed with a shovel over her shoulder, like a soldier coming out of his sentry box she saluted as she reached the pavement. All the girls were now at the window watching anxiously as Olive's Wellingtons sank into the deep snow. The white powder drifted across her face with every shovel full that she dug out from the front door steps.

"You've missed a bit," the girls shouted.

"What's going on out there?" asked Ma.

"Olives clearing the snow away, Ma," said the girls excitedly.

"Ah, she can be useful sometimes," said Ma.

Amazed that Olive wasn't called in immediately, their reaction was to join her in the snow.

"Can we go and watch them sledging in the park, Ma, please, Ma?" pleaded Nipper.

Ma gave in. "Don't come crying to me if you get hot-aches, and no sledging," said Ma.

The girls didn't have to be told twice, the first ones at the shoe rack were the lucky ones to get the only three pairs of Wellingtons. Olive abandoned her shovel and they were soon trudging through the deep snow, enjoying the thrills and exhilaration of the twenty-foot long glassy slides, made by the kids without sledges. Once they were accustomed to the great outdoors, they rambled on like arctic explorers, dodging the onslaught of uncontrollable toboggans careering down the hill, attacked by icy snowballs coming from the bushes, it was all so very different from the safety of the dining room window. The chain of brown, almost orange, tweed coats that had made its way to the top of the hill was now gradually scattering, yet still clearly visible against the white background, all of them trying to hitch a ride on one of the many sledges.

A scruffy boy in a balaclava who looked like the head choirboy, whisked Olive away down the hill on the back of his toboggan. Rita had spotted her brother, Colin, coming from the direction of the boys' home. Colin and Leslie were dragging an old sledge at the head of an untidy procession of boys running and sliding in all directions as they came to the top of the hill. The two older boys tested the sledge they slid off down the icy slope. With some of their friends the girls took turns to experience the stimulating and nerve-racking journey down the hill.

The daylight was fading, but the brilliant snow glistened, giving extra light while toboggans still thundered down. It was time to get back to the home, the youngest boys sat on the sledge for a ride back to the boys' home, and Colin waved to Rita as the girls made their way out of the park.

"If Olive hadn't cleared the snow away on the front steps, we wouldn't be out here. Thank you, Olive," said Margaret.

"And she wouldn't have been kissed by Pip, I saw you," said Nipper.

"Well, he took me on his sledge, don't tell Ma, or she won't let us come out again," said Olive, whose face now had a fresh pink glow.

The coats were almost steaming as they stepped into the scullery.

"Hang them coats up," said Ma. "Did you enjoy it?"

"Yes, Ma," they all replied.

"I went on the sledge with my brother," said Rita.

"Were the boys' home on the park as well," said Ma.

"Yes. We had a lovely time, Ma," and Nipper gave Ma a kiss.

"You're frozen," said Ma, feeling Nipper's rosy cheeks.

"No, I'm lovely and warm," said Nipper peeling off the smallest of the Wellingtons.

"Lay the table, soon be bedtime at this rate," said Ma. "Olive, dish the beetroot up on the plates, two slices each."

"So you've been sledging with the boys, have you?"

"I fell over," said Linda.

"Yes, we both fell over together, she was holding my hand," said Ruth.

"I sat on Donald Bingley's sledge, and he had a piece of sack to sit on, the sack slipped off and I went sliding down the hill," Hazel said, "and he was still at the top with his sledge."

"Ah, it's all beginning to come out now," said Ma. "I thought I said no sledging."

Olive was telling one of her ghostly stories when Miss James came into the dining room.

"Right, you can sing grace," she said.

The girls made a quiet exit to the scullery to wash the pots and clear

134

away. Ghostly noises added special effects in the scullery, 'howling' into the mugs being washed up. By this time Miss James was well out of range, she didn't make another appearance until it was bedtime, the clanging of the coal buckets on the cellar steps, and sloshing of the mop and bucket in the hall told her that they were all doing their jobs. The floors dried as they sat in the dining room, some drawing, and some exchanging all the clothes from the thin dolls to the fatter rag dolls. The clever ones reading Mark Twain, discovering the pressed flowers of the summer amongst its pages. After they had all knocked on the sitting room door to be inspected, Olive downstairs washed the cocoa mugs and made Miss James's supper. In the blue-room they jumped around from bed to bed, shouting and giggling in lighter mood, waiting for Olive to tell them what she had cooked up for Miss James's supper.

The footsteps came along the landing, twisting in a squeaking motion on the polished lino. Everyone dived into bed, all except one who positively knew that it was Olive.

Miss James swung round the blue-room door, hanging on to the knob, she shouted, "What's all this noise? What are you doing out of bed? If you want to stay out of bed my girl, you can stay out of bed."

Hazel had no doubt about which of her eyes were staring straight at her, she was the only one out of bed.

"Go downstairs," she ordered

Hazel brushed against the brown coloured cherries on the wallpaper, in order to squeeze by Miss James she stood firmly in the doorway. Olive waved as she jumped into bed in the dim light of the brown room. Downstairs Hazel waited in the kitchen, standing against the table.

Miss James' footsteps grew closer and closer, she was still shouting as she reached the kitchen door.

"I'll teach you, Hazel Hunt."

From the shoe rack, Miss James had taken a shoe and, lifting her nightgown, brought the shoe down heavily on Hazel's bottom.

"That will teach you to be out of bed, showing off, making all that noise," Her left hand tightly held the nightgown, pinning Hazel to the table as she balanced against the swinging motion of her right hand.

The punishment wasn't over, she went to the shoe rack and threw several pairs of shoes on the floor.

"You can clean them, and when you've finished come and see me," Miss James then returned to the sitting room.

One of Hazel's favourite jobs was cleaning shoes. She donned the coarse apron over her nightie and tied it firmly around her waist. The smell of shoe polish penetrated through her running nose, she wasn't crying, but felt her stinging bottom as she sat on her heels, brushing away, putting an extra shine on the already clean shoes. Hazel knocked on the sitting room door, with the polished shoes in a neat row for inspection. Miss James opened the cellar door and pushed her on to the steps and closed the door. The damp, fusty smell rose up from the cellar, immediately surrounding her, she was used to filling coal buckets, working in candle light when there was no electric light bulb, but the cold draught came up the steps, hit the cellar door and bounced back onto the cotton nightie. Hazel stood with bare feet; she pulled her arms inside the nightie, and stooped down, tucking the hem under her feet. She began to shiver.

Chattering teeth broke the silence. Ma's sitting room was only a few feet away from the cellar door, Desperately she shivered to make more noise with chattering teeth, close up against the keyhole. Later Miss James unlocked the cellar door.

"Are you ready to get into bed now?" she said.

"Yes, Miss James," Hazel said, her teeth chattering uncontrollably, and kneecaps now reduced to quivering jelly.

There was no sound in any of the rooms. Hazel buried her head well down into the bedclothes. The slight smell of shoe polish was a reminder that she had been down the stairs forever.

The next morning Miss James opened the blue-room curtains.

"Time to get up," she said.

Hazel sat up, and couldn't believe that Miss James was still there.

"What day is it?" Hazel asked Margaret.

"Sunday," said Margaret.

"Where's Ma?" Hazel asked.

"It's Ma's week-end off," said Winnie.

Miss James was on her way down the stairs. "Get your jobs done then come down," said Miss James.

"What happened last night Hazel?" whispered Margaret.

"She belted my bare bum with a shoe," Hazel said.

Winnie burst out laughing. "She didn't, she wouldn't do a thing like that," said Winnie.

"Well she did, have I got any marks?" Hazel lifted her nightgown.

"Not really but your nightie's a bit mucky," said Winnie.

"That's shoe polish. I had to clean eight pairs of shoes," Hazel said indignantly.

"Well I didn't hear you come to bed," said Margaret.

"Neither did I," said Doris, "I tried to stay awake."

"After I cleaned the shoes, she locked me down the cellar," Hazel said.

"Oh, Hazel," said Winnie.

"We'll tell Ma, when she comes back," said Doris.

"Yes, she'll be back tonight," said Margaret.

"Hurry up else she'll lock us all down the cellar," said Winnie.

"Come on Edna let's change your bed," said Hazel.

Miss James watched them from the window as they left for church. Once out of sight, the girls gathered round for the full story of the previous night.

"I thought it was you coming along the landing, Olive," Hazel said.

Olive laughed and made her way into church walking like Miss James.

"You low down common lot, get into church and confess your sins," said Olive.

"But we haven't done anything," said Winnie. "I bet she don't say her prayers."

In the quiet world, inside the church, they sat at the front in their usual place. The whole body of the congregation behind them singing and praying together, probably aunts and uncles of some of their school friends. The same faces sat in the same seats as if they belonged to them. At the back sat Mr Chandler, the churchwarden, and the two Misses Watson, who always smiled gently. On the other side of the congregation, Dr. Braithwaite and his wife occupied the two seats near the aisle every Sunday. Mr Bunting, the bank manager, sat with his wife and baby daughter smiling at their son, John, in the choir. The same John Bunting now looking so angelic in his red gown and white lace edged top, had been dared to kiss Winnie at Sunday school. John Bunting, who was always in trouble at school, and always first out of the pictures, thinking he was Roy Rogers on his horse, racing away down to the hills on the park.

Mr Smith, tall, dark and handsome, devoutly carried the crucifix ahead of the procession, flanked either side by the two candle bearers, Gordon Peters, and David Burrows, all three not eligible to be called up into the armed forces. Mr and Mrs Jordan sat near the front keeping an eye on their five-year-old son Anthony. He proudly walked at the side of his Grandad carrying the grains of incense. Mr Jordan, SRN, swung the incense in full circles, preceding the crucifix.

Miss Adams, the Sunday school teacher sat with her blind father on the opposite side of the aisle, he sang heartily to every hymn without the aid of a hymn book. Miss Gilbert, who taught the infants, sat near the aisle behind Miss Adams, she was usually accompanied by visiting Nuns from the Convents. Miss Morris, and Miss Watkins, two silver haired ladies, sat directly behind the girls, both had lovely singing voices. Miss Morris was short and dumpy, Miss Watkins was tall and thin, both ladies lived together down Green Lane Road. They would tap the girls on the head if the girls were caught talking to each other.

"Stop talking, face the front," they'd say.

The family of Goodeson sat behind them, filling a whole row of seats with their various friends staying with them. Their son David and daughter Jean were also in the choir. Jean and Olive were the only teen-age girls in the choir. It was Olive who had the young brother, Pip, who was idolised by the girls of East Park Road. The other Olive never sat far away, her eyes watching him from the congregation.

The eleven o'clock service was very popular, and the church was nearly always full. There were people who only came every two weeks, sometimes soldiers on leave, and couples who were to be married came to hear their banns being read.

The home girls were not allowed to go to Evensong at six o'clock, and they had to be confirmed before they could attend Holy Communion at eight am. Sometimes the hour long service seemed to take all morning, but they were soon back laying the table for dinner, standing behind chairs for grace. Miss James couldn't cook a Sunday dinner like Ma, what little meat they had, had to be chewed well, and the Yorkshire pudding sat on the plate like a piece of dough.

Miss James always made the girls wait until the very last minute before she let them out of the back door. Sunday school was held in one of the classrooms of Moat Road school, as the church hall was used during the week as a canteen for the munition factory.

They had to tolerate Miss James only on Sunday teatime and prunes and custard.. Olive kept them all in a happy mood with more of her antics, walking and talking like Miss James whenever she had a captive audience, she now included the eye movement as well. It was because

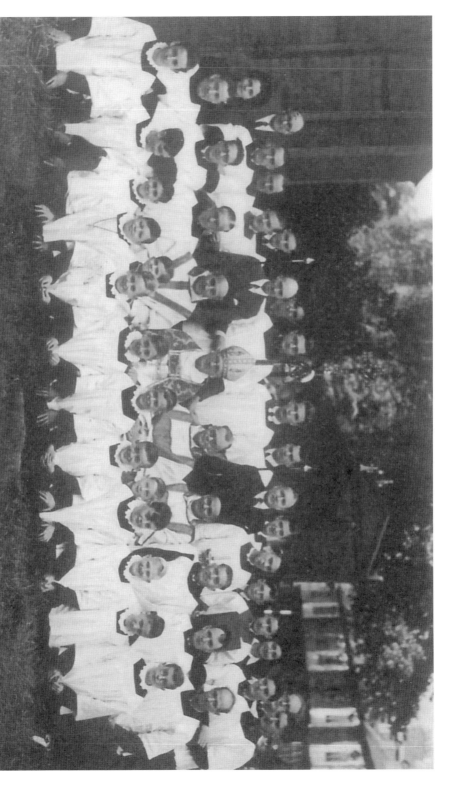

St. Stephen's Church Choir, East Park Road. Confirmation Day with Bishop Willis. 1945.

Miss James crept about that they were fearful of Olive being caught, but she was quick to react at the slightest noise in the hall. Ma would soon be home, and Miss James would be on the last tram to the Receiving Home. The front door clicked shut, Ma's footsteps were returning to her sitting room.

"We're glad you're back Ma," shouted Olive from the brown room. "Aren't you asleep?" said Ma.

"No, Ma, we're glad you're back," came the shouts from the blue-room.

"I have a weekend off every few months, and you're not asleep when I get back, what's up?" said Ma, halfway up the stairs.

"We don't like Miss James, she bent Hazel over the kitchen table and walloped her with a shoe, Ma," said Olive.

Olive and the rest of the brown room gang, followed Ma to the blueroom. Ma's footsteps were positively heavy as she plonked herself down on Margaret's bed.

"What's all this about?" Ma said, rather concerned.

"Miss James caught me out of bed Ma," Hazel said.

"Serves you right then, you shouldn't have let her catch you," said Ma.

"I thought it was Olive coming along the landing in your shoes, Ma, go on Olive show Ma the Miss James walk," Hazel said.

"Yes, go on Olive, show Ma," said Winnie.

Olive disappeared downstairs to the shoe rack, and then she reappeared through the blue-room door.

"You low down common lot," shouted Olive as she twisted into the gait of Miss James.

"You shouldn't mock the afflicted," said Ma. "But I can see the funny side of it. Miss James had polio when her was little, her's more to be pitied I suppose. Are they my shoes? Yow blighter," said Ma.

"Did you tell Ma you had to stand on the cellar steps?" said Olive.

"And clean all the shoes in the shoe rack," said Doris.

"What for, what else had you done?" said Ma.

"That was all for being out of bed, Ma," said Nipper.

"P'rhaps you'll stay in bed in future, H," said Ma. "I'm too soft with you lot. How long were you locked down the cellar?" said Ma.

"I don't know Ma, but they were all asleep when I came to bed," said Hazel.

"She made you stand on the cellar steps in your nightie," said Ma even more concerned.

"Yes Ma, it was cold," Hazel said.

"Right come on, let's have you all in bed, or you'll all be standing on the cellar steps," said Ma.

"Did you have a nice weekend, Ma?" said Nipper.

"I did 'til I walked back in this house," said Ma.

"Come and tuck me up Ma," shouted Nipper, and give me a kiss."

"Kiss me Ma," and me, and me, Ma."

In the Monday morning rush, the events of the weekend were forgotten.

"You didn't iron them pleats very good did you?" said Ma to Ruth whose tunic pleat stuck out at an angle.

"It's the way its been laying on the chair, Ma," said Ruth.

"If I'm not standing behind you the jobs don't get done properly," said Ma. "Come here lets put that ribbon in, have you brushed your hair, looks like you've been through a hedge backwards," said Ma.

Ma's inspection was more thorough than usual, re-checking the jobs that had been left to do.

"Brush your hair, clean your teeth, Ma's on the warpath," the rumour went around the hall and dining room as the girls scattered about, finishing jobs. The final scrutiny was in the kitchen before they left for school.

"Get out of my way," Hazel said to Rita who was trying to reach her coat in the hall. "We're going to be late, you don't have to go yet."

"Stop throwing your weight around," said Ma, as Hazel arrived in the kitchen to have the ribbon put in her hair. " There's plenty of time for you to walk there and back, what's the rush?"

Hazel said no more, for to speak would only result in another tug with the comb, or perhaps a silly sender.

"Go, on you'll do," said Ma.

The morning hymn echoed around the green painted walls of the classroom, the same shade of green and reverberation as Ma's kitchen. Hazel waited for the knitting to come sailing through the air as Mrs Pike marked the register. The few knitted stitches didn't seem to alter the length of the sock in any way but Mrs Pike was always delighted. It was the only time she really smiled at Hazel. Her brain was as dull as ditch water, when the arithmetic books were open, Mrs Pike scowled at her for not knowing the common denominator of the sum, and often threw the chalk at her with the same accuracy as the knitting, especially if she wasn't looking at the blackboard.

'Roll on playtime.'

Sunday dinnertime at the table, Ma served up the ginger sponge pudding.

"My favourite," said Winnie.

"I thought it was spotted dog," said Olive.

"Well I can have two favourite puddings," Winnie said. "All Ma's puddings are nice."

"You three Hunts are going to the Hospital this afternoon instead of going to Sunday school," announced Ma.

"Oh, no Sunday school," Hazel said.

"Who's taking us, Ma?" said Doris.

"Miss Gilbert, from church, she's visiting someone at the hospital so she's taking you three with her, see that you behave yourselves," said Ma.

"Oh, that means we shall see Brian as well," said Edna.

"Miss Gilbert will meet you at the bus stop. As soon as you've done your jobs, you can get ready," Ma looked at them.

They could detect the smell of incense on Miss Gilbert's coat as they stood at the bus stop.

"It's a lovely day," said Miss Gilbert. "There's not a cloud in the sky."

The three girls smiled, suddenly remembering they hadn't been given any tram fare.

"Ma hasn't given us any money for the tram," they said.

"Don't worry about that, I've got the pennies ready in my purse," said Miss Gilbert.

Miss Gilbert walked rather slowly up the hill, and Hazel, Doris and Edna were eager to run to the top.

"If we go this way, I'll show you where to meet me afterwards" said Miss Gilbert.

Halfway up the hill they took another turn, and the first ward had a paved area, like a small playground.

A baby's cot stood in the middle of the slabs as if abandoned. The blonde baby stood in the cot, just waving to passers by.

"That's Brian, our baby," they said together.

"Are you sure?" said Miss Gilbert.

They ran to the baby in the cot, he didn't know them, he sat down and looked at them shyly. For more than a year the memory of Brian, was the baby that Mam was holding in her arms, when he was two years old. That was over a year ago. This baby was now a three-year-old little boy.

"That's him," Hazel said. "Hello Brian."

He smiled, then started to cry, surrounded by strange faces. Dad appeared with a nurse and he picked Brian up.

"These are your sisters?" he said. "They've come to see you."

"Come back and see him in a bit when he's had his sleep," said the nurse.

"I'll meet you here after visiting time," said Miss Gilbert.

Dad thanked her. Then, leaving Brian with the nurse, the girls went to see Mam.

"We've just seen Brian, he's ever so big," They all said.

"He's having a sleep now so we'll see him later."

Mam was propped up with lots of pillows. She still had knitting on her bedside table, she was really happy to see them. Dad sat on the chair beside her, while they explored the gadgets around her bed.

"Is he better now? Grandma told us he was in hospital," Hazel said.

"Yes, he's three now," said Mam. "Not a baby any more," she said.

"Our Sunday school teacher came with us today, I think she looks like our Grandma," Hazel said.

Their Dad just laughed, "That's my Mam you're talking about. She don't look anything like your Grandma," he said.

"Can we go and see Grandma again, one day?" Doris asked.

"Yes, she's a busy woman, your Grandma," said Dad. "All in good time."

"Grandad's dug the garden, and planted rows of vegetables, all the flowers have gone," Hazel described Grandad's garden.

"Well when the war's over, he'll put the flowers back," said Mam.

"How are you getting on at school? Do you do get your sums right?" said Dad.

"I've got to take the eleven plus exam soon," Hazel said.

"If you don't pass, you just go upstairs into the seniors at our school," said Doris.

"Are you being good at Ma's?" Mam said.

"Yes," Edna had the headphones on listening to the radio.

"Do they bring Brian up here to see you, Mam?" Hazel asked.

"Yes they put his cot over there, I see him everyday," said Mam.

"I have my tea here, then I go back to my ward," said Dad.

"Did it snow up here, Ma let us go on the Spinney Hill Park, and we went on a sledge down the hill. It was lovely," Hazel said.

"I won a drawing competition at school," said Doris. "They said I should get a scholarship for the Art and Tech when I'm older."

"That's where Ted was, isn't it George," said Mam.

That was the first time Ted's name had ever been mentioned.

"Where's Norman," Doris said.

"Norman's living with Aunty Flo," said Dad.

"So he's not at Thurmaston any more, we saw him there when Miss Adams took us on a Sunday school trip to the vicarage. The vicar there has got twins," Hazel said.

"Yes, he's living near the 'City Arms' pub. I've spent a few hours in there," said Dad, looking at Mam.

"We know, we know," said Mam.

"I remember going to Thurmaston when we were little, we had new coats with velvet collars and pockets. We went there for a picnic with Aunty Rose," Hazel mentioned all the sunny days they had been for long walks.

"Fancy you remembering that," said Dad.

"You gave us all a piggy-back, singing the donkey serenade," Hazel reminded him. "You told us the sky was going to fall down."

"Must have been going to rain, or you'd had a drop too much to drink," Mam smiled at George.

"I remember the cows falling in the brook," said Doris, who came and sat on Mam's bed.

"Oh that was when the bridge collapsed on Aylestone Road. They had a job with that lot," said Dad. "The fire brigade was called and they couldn't get them out."

"And I remember Edna getting her eye cut when we went to the park," said Doris.

"Oh I've made a few trips to the Infirmary with all of you," said Mam.

"You used to make purple flowers, for buttonholes, I remember going with Norman to take them to the shop," Hazel said.

"On London Road," Mam said.

"Can we go and see if Brian is awake?" Edna said.

"Wait a bit longer," said Dad.

"I help my teacher with her knitting at school, she's knitting socks on four pins for soldiers, and I carry on knitting while she marks the

144

register," Hazel said looking at Mam's knitting.

"Who showed you how to knit on four pins?" said Mam.

"Nobody, I just did it," Hazel said. "It's like French knitting, you just keep going round, Edna had one for Christmas. It's like a skipping rope handle with a hole down the middle, and four nails round the hole, and you just put the wool round and lift the stitch over the nail. It's easy," Hazel said.

"Well, if you can't do your sums, you can knit, can't you?" said Dad.

"Go, and see if Brian's awake," said Dad looking at his watch. "Then come back, when the bell's gone. I'll come and meet you."

They found their baby brother, a sturdy three-year-old, with lots of teeth.

"Can we take him out of the cot," said Doris to the nurse who was watching us from a nearby window.

"Can we take him for a walk?" Doris asked.

The nurse came and let the side of the cot down, and immediately Brian wanted to get out.

"Just for a few minutes then" said the nurse.

One either side holding his hand and one in front so he didn't fall over, the girls fussed over him. He was a bit wobbly on his feet, but Mr Seaton said their baby, Joe, was wobbly because he'd been poorly.

"Is he better now?" Doris asked the nurse.

"Yes, but he's not going home yet," said the nurse.

After walking Brian round and round his cot, the bell rang for visitors to leave. The nurse took over, and held him while he waved to his estranged sisters. Dad met the girls near the veranda, they all kissed Mam and Dad, then made their way through a gap to meet Miss Gilbert.

Their lovely afternoon was over, they thanked Miss Gilbert for taking them.

"We were able to play with Brian for a little while," said Edna.

George re-arranged Emma's pillows. "That was a nice surprise for you wasn't it?" he said, holding her hand.

"It was, and the girls were surprised to see Brian," Emma was definitely weaker, but she felt sure that George had a hand in their sudden visit.

For the last week, he had sat by her side until she was asleep, and he was to be called any time. The doctors had allowed any requests, especially the transfer of her baby.

Seeing the girls and how grown up they were gave her strength for yet another week, George had whispered that they would be visiting again next Sunday. It gave her something to look forward to.

Annie was visiting most afternoons, and her sister Rose had been several times.

*   *   *

Some days later the classroom was taken over, and special machines with earphones were brought in, the whole school was to have a hearing test. Edna's class was tested. All the pupils left the room at the end of the test except Edna and another boy who still sat at the desks. The lady in charge sat with them taking notes, then another class took their place.

The results of Edna's recent X-rays revealed that she had a 'shadow' on her lung and she was immediately admitted to the Groby Road Hospital. She was also deaf in one ear. It must have been only two weeks later when Doris and Hazel were sent home from school.

"Don't run," said Mr Baum as they left the headmaster's office.

Grabbing their coats from the cloakroom they ran all the way to Ma's.

"Good Morning. Ma," both shouted as they opened the back door, suddenly bumping into Matron Buttridge.

"You've got visitors in the dining room," said Matron.

Hazel and Doris walked up the hall, the dining room door was open, and Dad was standing near the fireplace. Both girls made to go towards him but an arm stretched out blocking their path. Grandad sat just inside the door and stopped them where they stood. He coughed and held them close to him. After a long pause, he spoke in almost a whisper.

"I want you to be very brave," he said.

They both smiled at Grandad's mysterious gesture.

"You've got to be brave, I've something to tell you." He pulled them closer to him.

"You're mother's passed away," he said, his voice almost a whisper.

They stood quietly, still in the grip of Grandad's arms.

Passed away? Mother's passed away. They looked at Dad, and went over to him, his head was bowed over the shelf. They stood on either side of him, one under each arm, and he gave both girls a hug without speaking.

A soldier sat at the table, it was Uncle Sonny, he was home on leave. The other person sitting at the table was Norman, who they hadn't seen since the day he had disappeared from the Receiving Home. He looked so grown up, and much older.

Hazel and Doris didn't speak, they just moved slowly towards the door, silently making their way down the back hall to Ma's sitting room.

"They said our Mother's passed away, what does that mean?" they said to Ma.

Ma put her arms around the girls.

"Your Mother has died," said Ma. Then they cried.

"Never mind" said Ma, you've still got me."

Matron Buttridge was talking to Grandad in the hall.

"Come and say goodbye, they're going soon," Matron called, knowing that the girls were with Ma.

Ma wiped their faces and they said goodbye to Dad, Grandad, Uncle Sonny and Norman.

"Is there a pub round here?" said Grandad to Matron Buttridge.

The request was made again to Ma, as Matron didn't know of any.

"The 'Rifle Butts' is just round the corner on Nottingham Road," said Ma.

At such a time Hazel was ashamed of them, how could they ask for a pub, almost in the same breath as telling them 'your Mother's passed away.'

Ma's Victorian standards had rubbed off on the girls. Such places as pubs were immoral, corrupt, evil, bad, wicked and wrong.

That afternoon Matron Buttridge sent the girls back to school, 'to stay at home would not help their situation' Mrs Pike wasn't knitting today, she marked the register and looked at Hazel, amazed that she had come back to school.

Edna had been in hospital for weeks, her bed behind the blue-room door was empty, reminding them every night to include her in their prayers.

"Is she near our Dad?" Hazel and Doris asked Ma on the afternoon that she had visited the hospital.

"No its miles away, I'm worn out, I don't relish that journey very often," Ma changed her shoes in the hall.

"Did she like the things we sent?" asked Ruth who had sent the bit of string for 'cat's cradle' that went everywhere with her.

"Don't worry she's got plenty of things to play with, the nurses spoil her, she's the youngest there. They keep her in bed until dinnertime, then she has to go for a walk in the fresh air, she's quite happy," said Ma.

On Sunday morning, Doris and Hazel wore their black blazers, and new scotch kilts to church, 'as a mark of respect' and Sunday afternoon they went with Ma to see Edna at the hospital.

"We'll have to break the news to your sister," Ma said.

"Haven't they told her, Ma?" Hazel said, still disgusted with Grandad, asking the way to a pub on that sad day, although Hazel and Doris had walked past the 'Rifle Butts' pub on the way to school that afternoon, hoping to see Dad and Norman again.

They had been living with Ma for seventeen months, and had only seen Mam on a few occasions during that time. That last visit was made possible through the kindness of Miss Gilbert, when Mr Hunt had urgently requested to see the girls just two weeks before she died. And the first time they had seen Brian.

At the hospital gates Ma took them a different way, there was only Edna to visit.

They passed all the backs of the wards, and went through a gate as if going through an orchard full of trees. Edna came skipping towards them. Ma helped them to tell her that Mam had died, and like Hazel and Doris she showed no emotion, she just carefully held her dress down in the wind, and skipped away.

Perhaps she didn't hear us, perhaps she didn't want to, Hazel thought.

The girls were told nothing about their Mother's funeral, and were not invited. Nobody came to see them for weeks. The next time they heard anything about Edna, she had been transferred to a convalescent home in Norfolk.

One Saturday morning Ma's wireless was on in the sitting room, the girls were all busy with Saturday morning jobs. Hazel was cleaning shoes at the shoe rack, when an announcement came on the wireless.

"And now we have a request for Edna Hunt who is at The Convalescent Home, Home Place, Holt. All the patients there would like Frankie Howerd singing Three Little Fishes swam over the Dam."

"Ma this record's for Edna," Hazel shouted, the rest of the girls came from all over the house, and at Ma's sitting room door they joined in the singing with Frankie Howerd.

"Swim, said the mother fish, swim if you can
And they swam and they swam right over the dam."

"Fancy you hearing that," said Ma. "Nothing wrong with your ears".

The following week, Matron Buttridge made her Wednesday visit to Ma, and whilst spreading jam on the bread at teatime Ma told them that three new girls were coming, in place of the Minton girls.

"Three," said Olive.

"That's what I said," said Ma.

"Will I still be the eldest Ma? How old are they?" said Olive.

"Where are they going to sleep? That's what I want to know," said Ma.

"Can I sleep in the little room. Please Ma," said Olive.

"No, that's being left as the sick room. I think some of you will have to sleep in the attic," said Ma.

"Oh good, can I sleep in the attic Ma?" said Ruth.

"Can I, please, Ma?"

There was no shortage of volunteers. It seemed everybody wanted to sleep in the attic except Winnie.

"Can we get thirteen around this table?" said Ruth.

"Yes, easy," said Olive.

"One there, one there and one there," said Margaret, pointing at three likely spaces.

"I hope one's in my class, I've never had anybody from here in my class," said Nipper, not even Rita.

"If I go up the attic, one could have my bed in the brown room," said Olive.

"How, many beds are there in the attic," Hazel said.

"Five," said Olive.

"We'll be able to spread out a bit, won't we," said Winnie.

"Can we pass the cake round please, Ma?" said Olive.

"Yes," said Ma.

"So that's Olive, Ruth, Margaret, Hazel, and Winnie, up the attic," said Doris.

"I don't want to go up there," said Winnie. "What if there's a fire. Doris you can go up there."

"Thank you," said Doris.

"One will be in the infants with Nipper, and one will be in the juniors, and the other will probably be in the seniors with me," said Olive.

"You're all wrong and you can stop guessing," said Ma. "They are Catholics, and they're going to Sacred Heart."

"What's Sacred Heart Ma?" they asked.

"Sacred Heart school," said Ma.

"Where's that?" said Nipper.

"Its at the top of Spinney Hill Park," said Ma.

"They'll come with us to St Stephen's on Sunday won't they, Ma?" said Olive.

"No, they'll go to Sacred Heart church, as well," said Ma.

"Oh, that's not fair," Margaret said, why can't they come to our school?"

"Why can't they come to our church, Ma? It's high church," said Olive.

"Because they're Roman Catholics," said Ma. Which now was more confusing than ever.

"Can I still sleep in the attic, Ma?" said Olive.

"We'll have to sort it out," said Ma. "I've told you something, now you keep going on. Hands up who wants to go up the attic."

Everybody's hand shot up except Winnie and Edna.

"I'm not having you up there," Ma pointed to Hazel, who put her hand down.

"Olive, Ruth, Margaret, that'll be enough up there," said Ma.

"Ah, Margaret's going up the attic," said Winnie.

"Its not the end of the world," said Ma. "She'll be just above you, so don't worry."

"Will I still be the eldest?" said Olive.

"Yes, more's the pity," said Ma.

"What are their names Ma," They asked.

"You'll find out soon enough when they come on Friday," said Ma.

The week couldn't go by fast enough, they made the beds in the attic, everybody having a good snoop around, making sure there were no ghosts. A pretty white tiled wash stand stood near the window, to be used as a dressing table and there was also a small chest of drawers and five beds.

Ma didn't tell them that Rita and her brother Colin were going back home with their parents the next day. Thursday teatime, and all sewing night, they sat round the dining table discussing her prompt disappearance.

"Did Rita have to go to the Receiving Home, Ma?" said Nipper.

"Miss Pickering was taking Colin, so she picked Rita up, and they all went off together," said Ma. "She was a sweet little thing."

"Not as sweet as little Linda," said Olive.

Olive threaded her finger into one of the blonde curls on Linda's head.

"Look at that pure gold," said Olive. "You don't keep crying to go home do you?"

Linda put her hands between her knees and shyly smiled at Olive.

"Well Rita didn't, did she?" said Ma.

"Yes she did, every night she cried, I had to make up stories, so that she would shut up," said Olive.

"Ah well they're back home with their grandparents, I think their mother lives there as well," said Ma.

"What's the new girls' names, Ma?" said Winnie "Do you know yet?"

"Marie, Colette and Nancy. I've decided that Marie can sleep in Margaret's bed in the blue-room," said Ma.

"Can I sleep in Margaret's bed, near the window, please Ma?" said Doris.

"Can we change over tonight, Ma," said Olive. "Please Ma."

"Hurry up and get this sewing done then we'll see," said Ma. "Alright then, the new girl can sleep in your bed. Colette and Nancy can sleep in Olive and Ruth's bed in the brown room. I might put one of them up the attic yet," said Ma.

"Which bed are you sleeping in Olive?" Hazel asked.

"That one there, its near the light so I can read my book in bed, but don't tell Ma," said Olive.

"If you're reading in bed I'm sleeping over there," said Margaret. "In that dark corner."

"Is this your bed Ruth?" said Doris.

"Yes, I'm going to ask my Mam if she'll bring me a night-dress case, in case there's any spiders," said Ruth. "Then I can keep my curlers in it as well."

"Good Afternoon Ma," They all shouted, coming through the back door.

The new girls were standing near the fire in the dining room each girl had a premature peep at them through the bobby-hole.

"What are you staring at?" said the eldest girl.

"Ooh, a cat can look at a king," Winnie whispered.

Olive was the one to organise the new girls, asking their ages and sitting them at the right place at the table. Hazel was very disappointed that she was no longer second eldest sitting next to Olive at the head of the table, but third eldest and sitting next to Marie. Margaret sat next to Hazel down the side of the table, then Doris, then Ruth, the new girl Colette sat with Winnie at the opposite end of the table, then up the other side were Edna, new girl Nancy, Nipper and Linda. There were quite a few extra jobs, like cleaning the attic, this job was given to Margaret. Ruth had the attic landing and stairs to dust. Marie was given Hazel's job, filling the coal buckets, and she had to show her what to do. Colette had Winnie's job in the bathroom, and Winnie's new job was the landing and stairs. Hazel was back to dusting the blue-room. Down the cellar Hazel showed the new girl where to pick the lumps of coal, and how to keep all the slack to one side for banking up the fire at night.

"This is where we keep the chopper to chop the firewood, and all the vegetables are kept on the thrall. Ma sometimes puts the cake in the tins up there on that shelf.

"You take a small log and chop it lengthways, then again and again until you have thin sticks to light the fire," Hazel said, chopping the log at the same time.

The candle flickered, and shadows danced across the walls. The new girl had a cold and kept wiping her nose on her sleeve.

Marie wasn't very talkative, and she scowled, her dark eyes looked rather menacing with a chopper in her hand. Hazel left her down the cellar.

"I've got to dust the blue-room," she said.

Colette was already peeling the potatoes, and Nancy was in the kitchen being shown where the cutlery was kept.

The weekend was spent getting to know our new 'sisters', asking where their Mam and Dad were, and how many brothers and sisters were in the family.

"My Mam's at Hillcrest with our baby Simon, our Dad's gone away," said Marie.

"That's where our laundry gets washed," said Olive.

Marie's coughing at the table annoyed Hazel and Margaret. She made a circle with her thumb and index finger and coughed through the hole all over their plates. If she spoke to any of the girls, their surname was always added.

"It's none of your business, Olive Cartwright," said Marie.

The sisterly bond between the girls looked about to be suspended, and it was only their second day.

The three new girls left for Sacred Heart, it was a good half an hour's walk away, and they had to be there early to see the sisters of the Convent. On Sundays, too, they were released from any jobs in order to get ready.

"H, you'll have to get the coal up this morning," said Ma.

"That's not fair, I'm not second eldest," Hazel said and clanged the buckets together in a rebellious mood.

"You'll do as you're told, or get back to bed," said Ma.

Hazel quietly moaned to herself on the way down the cellar. 'If I've got to do this job I should be second eldest.' Her grievance wasn't for today, but that Olive would be leaving school in a few months time and this new girl, Marie, would be the eldest.

Olive came to the top of the cellar steps.

"Hazel, we want some more sticks, Marie hasn't chopped any," Olive shouted. Hazel's dislike for the new girl was increasing.

"It doesn't matter if we're late for church, it's only two doors away," Hazel shouted.

"Colette said they've got four brothers, and another sister named Louise," said Ruth on the way to church.

"That means they'll be here for years, like us," Hazel said.

"Three of the boys have gone to the boys' home, so Miss Pickering's got twelve like Ma," said Margaret.

"If Marie came to our school she'd be in 3C," Hazel said unkindly.

"She's not that bad," said Winnie.

"Well you sit next to her and let her cough all over your dinner," Hazel said.

"I got the full force when she sneezed, right at the other end of the table," said Winnie.

"She forgot to make her bed this morning." Said Ruth

"She hadn't chopped the sticks either," said Olive whispering, they were now inside the church.

All conversation ceased as another Sunday service washed over them.

After church, the catholic girls were not back at the home their three dinner plates were left on the kitchen stove.

"Come on, where've you been?" asked Ma when the new girls eventually came through the back door.

153

"We got lost," said Marie.

"How can you get lost on a straight road," said Ma. "Never mind, get round that table."

At the dinner table the conversation was left to Ma.

"What was the service like Marie," said Ma.

"It was all in Latin, I didn't understand it," said Colette.

"We had to go out halfway through the service, to sit with Sister Agatha," said Marie.

"That was confirmation class, we've got to go every Sunday," said Colette. " We went back into church afterwards."

We've got to be confirmed," said Marie.

"What all three of you?" said Ma.

"We can't get confirmed until we're twelve at our church," said Olive.

"We have to learn the catechism," said Winnie.

"The Nuns gave us a book, we've got to learn all of it," said Marie.

Hazel's jealousy was getting the better of her.

"Do you wear white dresses?" Hazel asked.

"We've got to have white dresses, white veils, white shoes, socks and gloves," said Marie.

Matron Buttridge's going to love that," said Ma,"How come you got lost?"

"We were coming down the hill, and we just followed the houses down and we came on to East Park Road, just down there," said Marie pointing.

"When you come over the hill, you keep on the path near the park, like I showed you yesterday. Did you forget?" said Ma.

"I said we were going the wrong way," said Colette.

"Well there's three of you, you'll get it right tomorrow," said Ma," Did they show you where the school is?"

"Yes Ma," said Nancy. "I've seen my classroom."

"You'll be all right tomorrow," said Ma.

The rest of the night passed off quietly the girls was itching to know more about the new girls.

"Have you been in the homes a long time Marie?" said Winnie that night in the blue-room.

"Yes, I don't know how long, but Mam couldn't look after us when Dad went away, and now she's got another baby, she has to work at Hillcrest to pay for them both," said Marie.

"Where did you used to live, when you all lived together?" Hazel said.

"At Martival," said Marie.

"Where's that?" said Doris.

"Number two Martival," said Marie.

"Two Martival Street?"Hazel said.

"No just Martival," said Marie. "It's at Humberstone."

"We go to Humberstone Park in the summer," said Winnie. Do you remember that concert we went to last year."

"Oh I loved that man dressed up as a sailor doll, tap dancing on that stage. It was like a Punch and Judy box, and this man stuck just his head through the curtain. He'd got this sailor suit round his neck, and the doll's feet were attached to two sticks, and he moved the sticks about to make the doll's feet do a tap dance to the music. Then the next time he was a little Dutch girl," Margaret said,"Oh I'm a little Dutch girl, a Dutch girl, a Dutch girl," sang Winnie. "He was funny with the Dutch girl's cap on his head, he kept tossing his plaits about."

"It was a lovely day out, Vera Lynn records playing over the loud speakers," said Doris. "There'll be bluebirds over the white cliffs of Dover."

"Tomorrow just you wait and see," They all sang together.

"Our brother Joe is at Countesthorpe now," said Winnie.

"My brother Joseph is in the Nursery at Countesthorpe as well," said Marie. "We lived at number eight cottage"

Olive put her head round the blue-room door at night, making them jump, before she crept up to the attic.

"They're all asleep in the brown room, except Colette," said Olive. "Must go, I'm reading my book."

"'Night, Olive" they all whispered.

Olive put the landing light out and crept up the attic stairs.

"Oooh!"

They heard Ruth squeal out as Olive sneaked through the attic door.

"I wish I was up there," Hazel whispered to Winnie. "Miss James will never go up the attic."

On Monday night, the visitors came. Mr Seaton looked happy, he told the girls he had been fire watching.

"Do you still wear your tin hat at work Dad?" said Margaret.

"I do, everybody does," he said. "Your Aunt Sarah will be coming to see you next time, her legs are much better."

Will you be going to see Joe, Dad?" said Winnie.

"I will, he comes running to meet me now. Growing tall, he is," said Mr Seaton.

"When can we see him?" said Winnie.

"Well they ought to make arrangements, but I can't afford to fetch him here, then take him back again, besides it would upset him too much, he's doing all right, leave it a bit longer," said Mr Seaton.

Olive, Ruth and Nipper sat in the bay window with Mrs Cartwright. Ruth had acquired the nightdress case, and her birthday wish, and Olive had a nail file. The rest sat in the kitchen as usual, cutting up the bits of material ready for pegging another rug.

*   *   *

The end of term exams were about to begin. Mrs Pike placed the paper face down on the desks, she gave out a warning about cheating, then told the class to begin. Hazel answered some of the questions as best she could, not really paying any attention to anything, she sat and stared into space, and chewed the end of her pencil. The words kept changing place on the paper. She broke her pencil so that it could be sharpened, always aware of Mrs Pike's eyes staring at her as she clicked away with her knitting. Everything had gone wrong since the new girls arrived. Mam had died, at only thirty-five years of age. Hazel was ten years old the week after she died. Doris was nine, three days after that. Edna was now eight, and still in Norfolk. Brian would be four in November, and they were all half-orphans. All Hazel's thoughts had nothing to do with the examination paper, which sat blankly in front of her. All the wrong things were going around in her head. She'll never be the eldest girl at Ma's, never be able to stop up at night and make supper. Matron Buttridge sends all orphans to Dr Barnardo's Homes. They would all be split up.

The papers were duly collected, and Mrs Pike had a general idea who had passed, she had kept a vigil on the 'Clever clogs' of the class. Margaret sat smiling at the back of the class. She was only one place from the corner and second in the class. The dunces sat near Hazel at the front.

*   *   *

The days were getting much warmer, the summer dresses were all hanging over the banister. Outside Ma's bedroom door, the girls had a fitting session, hoping that the new issue of dresses from Miss James would fit. Hazel must have grown quite a bit from the previous year because the only dress that fit her was made two or three summers ago and it was nearly worn out.

"Miss James hasn't made one to fit me," Hazel said to Ma.

"Perhaps you upset her a bit," said Ma.

The sun shone brightly on Sunday now it was time for summer dresses. Ma told Hazel and Doris that they were going out for the day. The high-spirited feeling had gone although excited at long last they were going to Grandma's again.

"Oh, I like helping my Grandma get the dinner ready," Hazel said.

"Who's fetching us," said Doris.

"I expect it will be a taxi again," said Ma.

They were soon ready, and waited at the front window, peeping round the curtains after the tram had gone by.

"No taxi?" said Doris.

"No," Hazel said.

All the girls were getting ready for church.   Marie, Colette and Nancy had gone and were a long way up the hill.

Suddenly a pony and trap trotted along the cobbles between the tramlines. To their amazement it stopped outside the home. Ted was sitting up the front with the reins, pulling hard to make sure the animal stopped.

All the girls, some half dressed, ran to the window laughing at the unusual sight. They shouted to Ma that Ted was here, in case he couldn't let the reins go.

"I can see that," said Ma. "You'd better go before it runs off."

Hazel and Doris stepped into the chariot which tipped up at the rear, Ted made them sit one on either side to balance it up. The choirboys were on their way to church, and quite a crowd stood and watched as they waved to Ma and the girls.

"See you next week," shouted Doris, wondering if they would ever get back. They clung on tightly to the hand-rail, holding on to berets as the pony and trap trotted away.

Ted took it all very seriously, and was in a sombre mood. They hardly said 'hello' to him when they had climbed aboard.

"Where did you get the donkey from?" they teased.

He was most indignant.

"Have you forgotten we've lost our Mother," he said.

Doris and Hazel exchanged fleeting glances this was the first time they would be seeing relatives since Mam had died. They'd had to cope with no visitors, no news, no funeral, no nothing, nobody cared about them. They sat for a while, subdued by their own thoughts.

The pony started to pick up speed. The clip-clopping of the pony's feet sent them into a hysterical giggling fit, as it trotted along Saffron Lane.

"I'm dropping you off here," said Ted," You can walk across the park, It'll give you time to calm down."

He pulled the pony to a halt, and Hazel and Doris got down and stood on the pavement, still giggling as the pony and trap trotted away.

"We've been dumped here like two sacks of potatoes," Hazel said and started giggling again.

They remembered the way round the park, it was almost deserted, a lone man walking a dog, and in the distance a man and a small boy.

Still recovering from the bumpy ride, they replaced the berets on windswept heads, tidying themselves up ready for Grandad's 'inspection.'

"That looks like Dad, "Hazel said not, quite sure if she trusted her memory any more since she had seen a lady on the tram who looked just like Mam.

"I think that's Brian," said Doris.

They walked faster, then started to run. The little boy was running towards them, encouraged by his Daddy.

The girls picked him up, and kissed him.

"Put him down, let him walk by himself," said Dad.

They kissed Dad as he spoke, whatever he was saying they were not listening. Brian was there in his summer shorts, and little blazer and they couldn't take their eyes off him. He could talk and say names, although still a bit shy. It had been a long time since their last visit to Grandma's. She made a big fuss of her three grandchildren as they walked through the back door. Grandad was his usual self; Hazel and Doris didn't wait for inspection they took their 'baby' brother down the garden to see for themselves what he could do, and what he could say. Dad and Grandad went to the pub, leaving the girls to lay the table and talk to Grandma, and long lost baby. Ted came through the back door.

"Have you taken the 'donkey' back to its owner?" Hazel asked.

He was still as moody, and had no sense of humour. Doris cheered him up by examining all his artwork.

That afternoon Dad took Brian home. He had promised Mam that he wouldn't let Brian ever go back to Countesthorpe. Not ever again. The girls walked with them to the bus stop and waved them off. Gran told Hazel and Doris that afternoon that Dad was living with a woman whose husband had just died in the next bed to Dad, and since Mam had died, he would not go back into hospital.

"Is he supposed to be in hospital then?" Hazel whispered, as Grandad muttered something. He was asleep on the settee.

"Yes," said Grandma, "he is, but if she can look after him, he might get better. I don't know," she whispered.

"Will we be able to leave the homes now, and live with Dad?" Doris asked.

"Its too early to say what's going to happen," said Grandma.

They could see it was too painful for her to talk about.

"Edna had a record played for her on the wireless the other week," Hazel said.

"Yes it was on Ma's wireless we heard it while we were cleaning," said Doris.

"It was Frankie Howerd, singing 'The three little fishes swam over the dam'," Hazel said.

"Edna's at the Convalescent Home in Norfolk isn't she," said Grandma.

"Yes, we wrote to her, and she sent us a postcard."

Annie, their Grandma, couldn't tell the girls about their mother, she was still too upset, and had only agreed to have the girls out of the home for the day because Ted wanted to take out the pony and trap. She was in a state of nervous exhaustion, from travelling between hospitals, and had been thankful when Emma had insisted that Brian be transferred to Groby Road to be near her.

The doctors had consented to Emma's special visit to the girls' home in August, the hot summer day had given her cheeks a warm glow, hiding her weakened condition. Emma anxiously wanted to see where the girls lived. She needed to know that they were happy. George had been told that she had not long to live, six months they had said, and although very ill, she had enjoyed Christmas with her baby, watching his face on Christmas morning for the last time, she knew she was going to die. Emma had watched Edith in the next bed grow ever weaker, until she died on New Year's day - her bed was still empty. Now she was following the same fate, having the same symptoms, fighting for breath, and fighting for life.

It was just a few days after the girls had visited the hospital, that Emma's breathing had worsened and she had another haemorrhage. George pleaded with the doctors to operate if there was a remote chance of her getting well.

The operation to remove half her lung ended tragically, the eight-hour ordeal was too much for her frail body. George was devastated, he had always hoped there was a chance. When he saw Emma's body afterwards, how the surgeons had cut her open, removing half her ribs, he vowed that neither he nor his children would succumb to the surgeon's knife again.

They had been in the hospital for fifteen months, and had given themselves enough time, as they thought to get well. The first thing he did was to book himself out of the hospital, there was no reason for him to get better now, he just wanted to die. There was the funeral to arrange, and he couldn't expect Annie to take care of that. Later his thoughts turned to his children, they would have to be told after the funeral.

With what little money he had, George bought a grave in the cemetery to hold five people, it would be of some use one day for the rest of his family.

For a while now, George and Brian had been living with a woman named Di whose husband had died in his ward. She had grown fond of Brian on her visits to the hospital, and offered to look after him until George was better, it seemed the right thing to do as he had promised Emma that her baby would not be sent back to the Cottage Homes.

Annie herself was now being held back by Grandad, who insisted that she should rest. She had done more than enough for Emma and George and the grandchildren, looking after Ted as well.

He had frowned upon George living with that woman, and now it was up to Annie to build her strength back up. He was in his own little world, not ever moving far from his chair by the fire. Annie had enjoyed her Sunday with the girls, knowing it would be the last one for quite a while.

Arm-in-arm, the girls walked through the dusky streets with Grandma.

The tram to East Park Road was waiting at the terminus. It was arranged for Grandma to put the girls on the tram, then she could catch her own bus home. Grandma put a sweetie into the girls' hands then waved as the tram rolled along the rails, back to the home.

Ma was boiling the remainder of the milk as the girls walked in the back door.

"Be careful, I don't want that knocking over, that's all the milk we've got 'til tomorrow." she poured the milk into the jug on the draining board.

The large enamel milk bowl was washed out and placed on the thrall in the pantry ready for the milkman on Monday. The milk was brought in a churn to the back door, and their quota of milk was ladled into the bowl, then covered by a gauze cloth and kept on the cool pantry shelf.

*   *   *

Miss James was in the sitting room as usual, as they ate the scrambled egg. Olive was up to her antics, chasing the rubber balls of egg round her plate, they quietly giggled as she occasionally left the table to do a quick circuit of the 'Miss James walk', to pass the plate of cake around.

"Eeeer, I'm not eating that," said Winnie who had taken a bite of her cake. "Look its got cobwebs in it.

"Eeeer, so's mine."

The noise level in the dining room had grown considerably. Everyone was now pulling at their piece of cake to see how long the cobwebs were. Down to the smallest crumbs a cobweb could still be found on prising it apart.

"Look at this one then," said Olive who had taken the biggest piece, and held up the cake with several strings joining the cake.

"Look at mine," said Nipper.

"There's no spiders in it," Ruth had looked very closely.

"What's making the cobwebs," said Doris.

"It's been in the tin down the cellar," Hazel added.

"I'm not eating mine," said Marie.

"Have you been opening the tin down the cellar Marie?" Hazel said."

"No I haven't Hazel Hunt," said Marie. "Are you accusing me?" She shook her fist under Hazel's nose.

"Well I'm still hungry, I was looking forward to my cake," said Margaret.

"Don't eat it Margaret," said Winnie. "You'll be ill."

"I don't feel very well any way," said Margaret. "Especially now I've seen that cake."

Miss James was leaning on the bobby-hole, for how long they hadn't noticed.

"Who's making all that commotion? What's all the fuss about?" said Miss James.

"The cake's got cobwebs in it," Miss James said our spokesman who immediately placed her cake on the bobby-hole for Miss James to examine.

"Where, what sort of cobwebs?" said Miss James.

Olive's cake was reduced to crumbs having been split up so many times that she could hardly produce any more of the stringy threads.

"I can't see any," said Miss James.

"If you cut another piece off the cake in the tin, perhaps you'll see them," said Olive.

Miss James took the knife and cut another slice of cake.

"Is that what you mean?" she said, parting the cake herself.

"Yes, just there Miss James," said Olive hanging through the bobby-hole.

"Well those who don't want to eat it, can have another slice of bread. Come and get it Olive," said Miss James.

The cake plate, full of crumbled cake, and was sent back into the kitchen.

The slice of bread was now being scrutinised carefully, just in case cobwebs had infected it, too.

"We thank you, Lord for cobweb cake,
And for Miss James, for goodness sake,
Thy creatures bless and grant that we,
From cobweb cake, evermore be free. Amen.

Miss James was back in the sitting room and hadn't heard Olive's ditty.

Margaret's not feeling very well Ma," said Olive running down the attic stairs the following morning.

Ma's shoes squeaked on the lino, as she climbed the narrow staircase.

"What's up Maggie?" said Ma. "By gum you're a bit hot, the sheets are wet through," she said feeling her forehead. "How do you feel?"

"I've got a sore throat Ma," squeaked Margaret.

"All right stay where you are for a bit, I'll fix the sick room up for you, might as well make use of it. Hazel give it a quick dust."

Ma filled the hot water bottle, and put it in the bed in the little room.

"Come on let's have you in the sick room, I'll go and phone for the doctor," said Ma.

"Its always the same when I've had half a day off, there's always some catastrophe when I get back," Ma talked to herself as she went in and out of the little bedroom.

Hazel peeped in the sickroom when she had dusted the blue-room.

"Lucky devil, no school for you today, I'll tell the teacher," She said. "Do you want any breakfast?"

"No thank you," Margaret whispered.

"Margaret doesn't want any breakfast, Ma," Hazel said.

"Have you been in that room?" Well keep out. I'm in charge here," said Ma.

They sat down to breakfast.

"What if somebody else is poorly Ma, where would they go?" asked Nipper.

"Down the cellar," snapped Ma. "Get on with your breakfast while I go to the telephone."

"I wonder what's wrong with her," said Winnie.

"She was talking in her sleep all night last night," said Ruth. "And grinding her teeth."

"I didn't hear her," said Olive.

"She does grind her teeth when she's asleep," said Winnie.

"She's got tonsillitis," said Olive. "I've had that, your throat's ever so sore, but they didn't get the doctor to me."

"Come on," said Olive, "let's get the pots washed before Ma gets back."

"What about grace?" said Winnie.

"You can say it for us while you clear the table, Winnie," said Olive, rushing into the scullery to wash up for Margaret.

"Oh yes, leave it all to me," said Winnie.

The Catholics put their coats on.

"You can't go 'til Ma gets back," said Olive. "Have you filled all the coal buckets? You missed Ma's yesterday, she had to go down the cellar."

"I've done them all see, Olive Cartwright," said Marie.

Olive stamped on Marie's toe, as Ma walked in the back door.

"Is it that time all ready?" she said looking at the new girls in their coats. "Have you got everything?" said Ma.

"Yes Ma," said Marie.

"I've got to take that letter back to Sister Ma," said Colette.

"So you have, I'll get it," said Ma.

Marie put her tongue out at Olive.

"You'll bite that off one day if you do that again," said Olive.

"Here you are, keep it in your pocket, its very important," said Ma.

"Bye, Ma," said Marie, Colette and Nancy.

"The doctor's coming Olive can you give them stairs a quick dust," said Ma.

"That's Colette's job," Olive retorted. "I've just done Margaret's job."

"Just do it," said Ma, "and be quick about it, the doctor will be here in a minute."

"I'll help you Olive, I'll do the damp cloth, you come down with the polisher," Hazel said.

"Must be serious, if he's coming that soon," said Olive.

"Good morning, Ma," At dinner time the girls all rushed in through the back door.

"Strike, the teachers must have wanted to get rid of you lot, teacher's rest, mother's pest," said Ma.

"Don't be like that Ma, we all love you," said Nipper.

"What did the doctor, say Ma?" said Winnie.

"Oh, she's in hospital," said Ma.

"Ah, poor Margaret," said Winnie.

"Poor Margaret my foot, its me who's been trudging round the hospital with her," said Ma

"Which hospital is she in, Ma?" said Olive.

"Stop standing about like statues, get that table laid, now you're home early we'll have an early dinner.

"My feet are killing me," said Ma.

They sat as quiet as lambs at the table. The corned beef was easy to dish up with the potatoes and mushy peas. Olive made the custard for the pudding.

"Matron Buttridge will have to let your Dad know, Winnie," Ma said, breaking the silence.

"All these people in hospital, Mam, Joe, Edna, now Margaret," said Winnie.

164

"I went with her up the City General Hospital," said Ma. "She's not going to die, she'll be all right."

"Did the ambulance take her then, Ma," said Nipper.

"Yes," said Ma.

"Oh. I've always wanted a ride in an ambulance what was it like Ma?" said Nipper.

"You might have to go in one in the future, then you won't like it," said Ma.

"How can they see in the ambulance, sitting in the dark?" said Nipper.

"The glass is painted dark blue, you can see out, but you can't see in," replied Ma. "Another hospital visit, I'll need to take a week off soon, just for visiting."

After a short pause, and before grace was sung, Ma suddenly said, "Did Margaret eat any of that cake the other day?"

"I ate a bit, but I spat mine out," said Ruth.

"I don't think she did Ma, Miss James gave us all another slice of bread," said Winnie.

"It wouldn't be that anyway or you would all be ill" said Ma. "They'll soon find out what's wrong with her, I expect I'll get a full report when Matron Buttridge comes tomorrow."

"She's not got tonsillitis then, Ma?" Hazel asked.

"No, she hasn't," said Ma.

"Colette, did you give that letter to Sister?" said Ma.

"Oh, I forgot, she sent one back for Matron," said Colette.

"Right - stand," said Ma. "Get this place cleaned up before you go back to school."

*   *   *

The following day, they could tell Matron had been - there was a box of socks which had been cut up, on the kitchen dresser, and Ma was in deep thought. The hot plates were taken from the oven, and a small piece of fish served out from the large pan.

"Is everybody round the table?" shouted Ma.

"Right begin," said Ma. They had almost finished singing grace by the time Ma reached the dining room carrying her own dinner. She sat at her table in the bay window.

"Right, Matron came this morning as you all know. The doctor at the hospital has confirmed that Margaret has got diphtheria," said Ma.

"Diphtheria!" They all stopped eating, and stared at each other.

"I thought only babies got that, Ma," said Winnie. "Poor Margaret, oh Dad will be worried."

Winnie put her knife and fork down.

"I think I'm going to cry," she said.

"Don't worry, One-eye, she'll be all right, its not a bad case, but she'll have to stay until she's really better," said Ma.

"Will we all get it Ma?" said Ruth "I sleep next to her."

"You haven't got a sore throat have you?" said Ma jokingly.

"I've got a sore throat Ma," said Nipper.

"Yes, I know you want a ride in the ambulance," said Ma.

"Get on with your dinner, I want all that fish eaten up," said Ma.

The rhubarb and custard followed and the clean plates were passed through the hatch.

"I wish we didn't have to go back to school on Friday afternoons," said Nancy, I don't like my teacher."

The Saturday morning jobs were well in advance Olive had finished the flues in the kitchen. The cocoa was mixed for the morning drink, and there were enough helpers to stab the sausages.

"I'm going across the road to the telephone," said Ma. "Be good 'til I get back."

"Ma hasn't scrubbed the front door steps yet," said Olive.

Olive filled the bucket and set about scrubbing the stone steps. She was scrubbing away when a man went by and spoke to her. He put his hand in his pocket and gave Olive a shilling. Some of the girls were watching from the dining room window. The long, coarse, sackcloth apron, which came down to her ankles, was rather wet, Olive looked up at the man, her pale complexion and big sorrowful eyes looked more like Little Nell out of Charles Dickens as she held out her hand, accepting the coin.

"Thank you very much," they could see Olive smiling.

The bucket and floor cloth were put away under the sink, just as Ma walked in through the back door.

"Who's scrubbed the front steps?" said Ma.

"I did, Ma," said Olive. "I thought it would be a nice surprise for you. This man went by and gave me a shilling," said Olive smiling.

"WHAT!! What man?" said Ma angrily.

"I don't know he was just passing by," said Olive.

166

"Give it to me," said Ma.

The shilling was given up, and Ma took it into her sitting room.

"You've got to have eyes in your behind to look after this lot," said Ma most annoyed about the charitable gift from the unknown donor.

"Get that cocoa poured out, before I go loopy," said Ma.

They drank the cocoa in almost silence, when Ma was on the 'war-path', they might have to miss the Saturday afternoon three-penny rush. And they did want to know if the 'Scarlet horseman' escapes from the burning hut. After sausage and mash, and semolina pudding, all the jobs finished, they stood round the kitchen table waiting for Ma to give out their ration of sweets and pocket money. The squares of paper were counted several times, making sure that there was one for each of them.

Ma brought in the tin of sweets.

"Right, let's see what sort we've got this week," she said.

"Boiled sweets," said Nipper who was nearest to Ma, getting her nose into the tin as soon as the lid was prized off.

"How many do we get this week, Ma?" said Ruth.

"What about Edna, and Margaret's rations, Ma?" Nipper said.

"Edna, will get hers where she is, and I'll take Margaret a few," said Ma.

"One," they counted as each sweet was placed on the paper. "Two, three, four, five, six, seven."

"There's not enough for any more," said Ma. "Take which you like."

The money box was next to be undone.

"Who's going to the pictures?" said Ma.

"All of us Ma" they said.

"That means I've got to give the young ones another two-pence each," said Ma. "Three-pence for you, and you."

"What about my shilling?" said Olive.

"I've thought about that," said Ma. "You can all have a penny each. You can have two-pence of it, and I'll save a penny for Margaret in hospital."

"Thank you, Ma," said Olive.

"Thank you, Ma, thank you Olive," they all said, and raced off to queue at the cinema.

On Monday teatime, they examined the cake for cobwebs.

"Get on with it," said Ma, "it was only made on Saturday while you were at the pictures, the only time I get a bit of peace and quiet."

"What was wrong with the cobweb cake Ma?" asked Olive.

"I don't know, Miss James took it to Matron. I've not heard any more about it," said Ma.

"Perhaps she'll tell us tomorrow," said Winnie.

"Perhaps she won't," said Ma. "Miss James isn't coming for a while, a new person, Mrs Moore, is coming, I hope."

"Ooh good no more Miss James," Hazel said.

"What's Mrs Moore like Ma?" asked Doris.

"I don't know do I, said Ma "I'm hoping she turns up on time so that I can catch the 'two o'clock' tram.

"Don't have any more, Mrs Moore," said Olive.

"Don't let her hear you say that," said Ma, "she's a bit of a tyrant."

"Is she the one who went to relieve Miss Pickering, Ma, and made all the boys go straight to bed after tea?" asked Colette.

"Who told you about that?" said Ma.

"Our Michael told us at school," said Marie.

"She does sometimes relieve Miss Pickering," said Ma. "She lives near the Receiving Home, so mind what you're saying, it'll get straight back to Matron."

"They were all jumping on the beds," said Colette. "And Mrs Moore went upstairs with a stick."

"Did she hit Michael and the boys?" said Nipper.

"Yes," said Colette.

"Well I'm not going to bed straight after tea," said Winnie, "I've got homework to do."

"I wonder what she walks like," said Olive.

"Hey, you can forget that," said Ma. "I've had enough of Miss James, her's more to be pitied, she had polio when she was little.

"Good afternoon, Mrs Moore." The girls all made the usual bellowing call, as they came in the back door.

Mrs Moore made them jump, appearing from the shadows of the kitchen.

"What are you shouting for, I'm not in London, I'm not deaf either." Her cockney accent was heard by all.

She looked just like Matron Buttridge, without the white frilly cap on. The dining room was a refuge for the girls, they gathered there like a flock of sheep.

"Can I have some help out here," Mrs Moore said putting her head through the bobby-hole.

Olive joined her in the kitchen, and passed the plates of scrambled egg to the table. Each plate was covered in a slice of yellow egg, there were no little balls running around the plate. The egg was as smooth as cold custard.

"Is it egg, or cold custard?" Nobody touched it until grace had been sung. Like Miss James, Mrs Moore didn't sit at Ma's table she went back into the sitting room.

Olive was the first to whisper.

"Tastes nice, it's better than Miss James's scrambled egg. Mrs Moore tipped it out of the saucepan like a jelly on a plate. Mmm I like this," said Olive.

They had more egg than would cover the two slices of bread the rest was eaten with the knife. Mrs Moore had closed the doors of the bobby-hole, leaving just a slight gap, which Olive had noticed.

"Let's play pass the message," said Olive after tea, and with that she whispered to Marie.

"Pass it on," said Olive.

Marie whispered in Hazel's ear.

"I don't know what she said but I think Mrs Moore is spying on us. The egg is nice," whispered Marie.

"You've spit in my ear," said Winnie to Doris. "Come here I'll tell you again."

More giggling went on at the bottom of the table.

"I'm dreading what's coming out of this," said Olive.

A few more giggles from the little ones, and the message was left for little Linda to tell Olive.

"What did Nipper whisper to you, Linda?" said Olive.

"She said, more pie, egg and rice."

"Well done," said Olive.

There was a little movement at the bobby-hole, and the doors flew open

"Have you finished your tea. Did you like the egg?" said Mrs Moore.

"Yes thank you, Mrs Moore," they echoed together.

"Are you the eldest Olive?" said Mrs Moore.

"Yes," said Olive.

"What are you going to do when you leave school?" asked Mrs Moore.

"I'm going to live with my Mam," said Olive.

"What job are you going to do I mean," said Mrs Moore.

"I don't know, we have trips to factories from school before we leave, I shall be going next term," said Olive.

"When I was a girl I lived in London. I left school and went into nursing in one of the big hospitals. It's a lovely job for girls like you. You live in the nurses' home...

That word 'home' put Olive right off nursing there and then, Olive wasn't going to live in another 'home'.!

.... Get up at seven every morning and have your bath; breakfast was at seven-thirty...Who wants breakfast at that time?.... And then you're on the ward at eight o'clock."

Mrs Moore was in her element with the captive audience.

"I'll have to bring you my photos of me in my uniform," said Mrs Moore.

The girls sitting there did not want to be a nurse, nor did they want to go into service. When they eventually get out of the homes they want to find a nice job, not live in somebody's attic, and scrub floors and clean all day. They all sat silent. Mrs Moore could see they were not responding to her life story.

"You can say grace now," she said.

Mrs Moore wafted about from room to room, watching as the tablecloth was shaken in the back yard.

"Get the crumb brush, and sweep the table," she said to the 'dining room' girls.

She followed Marie down the cellar to make sure she put enough coal in the buckets, generally nosing about.

"Haven't you got a proper light down here?" said Mrs Moore.

"The bulb's gone," said Marie. "So we have to use a candle."

In the kitchen she wiped her hand across the shelf as Olive riddled the ash out ready to put more coal on the fire.

"How often do you dust this?" said Mrs Moore.

"It's done every morning," said Olive.

"If this was a hospital, that would have to be spotless, no dust anywhere," said Mrs Moore. "See that it's dusted before you finish in here."

Mrs Moore hadn't finished her tour of the house - she went into the scullery. Hazel stood at the sink with legs wide apart to bring her arms to the level of the low sink, peeling potatoes. Bony fingers prodded her in the back.

"Can't you peel them a bit thinner than that, don't you know there's a war on. Look at those peelings, the pigs get more than us. And don't stand there with your legs wide open, its vulgar," she said, and dug her fingers into her back again. Hazel made a purposeful move, and bent over the sink in a silent protest, just heaving a sigh.

"Where do you put the peelings?" said Mrs Moore.

"We take them to the pig bins, near the factory gates, when the bucket under the sink is full," Hazel said.

"Hurry up and get it emptied, it smells," said Mrs Moore.

"I'll come with you," said Ruth.

"Does it need two of you to carry one bucket?" said Mrs Moore.

"We've got another bucket outside," said Ruth.

They carried the white enamel buckets up the entry like two milkmaids going to milk the cows.

The windows of the house next door were dirty, and the curtains had not been closed for a long time. The rats were the only occupants, and in the evening light Hazel and Ruth hurried by the front garden. Not a week went by without one or another asking Ma if we would be having new neighbours. It reminded Hazel of the empty house in Lothair Road.

The next house was different with floral chintz curtains and another heavy curtain drawn across the bay window. It looked the sort of house to have a maid living in the attic.

The last house before the factory gates was the mysterious one. The lady who lived there always wore black clothes, her black hair was parted in the centre, she had two plaits coiled on each side of her head. They only ever saw her in her garden when they played near the lilac tree. The front of her house was as enigmatic, a large leafy plant stood behind lacy curtains, and dark velvet curtains edged with fringing were draped each side of the window. Large pictures of past generations were just visible hanging on every wall. Her front gate was missing, like the rest of the iron gates along the road they had all been requisitioned for the war.

The large pig bins were unsightly next to the row of neat houses, but they went unnoticed by the workers at the factory who rushed in and out at the change of their shift. The 'pig' lorry changed the bins every night - 'PLEASE REPLACE THE LID', the sign read above the bins.

The clattering of the buckets being washed out brought Mrs Moore into the scullery.

"Scrub them out well, use plenty of water. Then one of you can wipe

171

the floor over, and the other, put some Vim round that sink," Mrs Moore ordered.

"We scrub the floor on Saturdays," Hazel said.

"Well you can wipe all the paddle marks up, it won't hurt you," she said.

When they had at last finished their jobs the two girls walked into the dining room and sat down.

"I wish Miss James was back," said Ruth. "We didn't have to do all these extra jobs."

"What about me then," said Marie. "I had to wash the cellar steps."

Nipper then chimed in.

"We've had to wipe the hearth, and polish the table," she said.

The vase in the centre of the table had a good reflection in the polished wood, but then it always did. Even the rag dolls were sitting to attention in the cot under the equally tidy bookcase. The girls sat motionless, the only movements being made were Doris's ever drawing pencil, and Linda bouncing a rag doll on the corner of the table. They waited for bedtime with as much fear and trepidation as waiting in the dentist's chair.

"Can you cross your eyes?" said Olive.

Sudden bursts of laughter broke the silence, as the comical faces looked at each other across the table.

"Who are you looking at?" said Colette sitting in the direction of one eye.

"Are mine crossed?" said Nipper.

"No," said Olive. "You have to look at your nose."

They were giggling at the same time as catching a crossed glance from somebody else.

Olive added a different version by pulling her eyes down with one hand, and pushing her nose up with the other.

"Oh you look like a pig," shouted Winnie.

"I can do that," said Marie.

The close-up version to Hazel's right was a bit scary.

"I'm not going do it any more," said Winnie. "I might stay like it, besides, it hurts my eyes."

"Haven't you got any books or comics to read?" said Mrs Moore suddenly appearing at the bobby-hole.

"No, Mrs Moore," they said. "The ones we had for Christmas have

172

been thrown away."

"What do you spend your pocket money on then?" asked Mrs Moore.

"We go to the pictures," said Olive.

"Thrupenny Rush," said Ruth sitting nearest to the bobby-hole.

"Do you all get thruppence?" Mrs Moore asked.

"No, the little ones only get a penny so Ma makes up the difference," said Olive.

"And if you're at the end of the queue, you don't get in, there's not enough seats," said Nipper.

"Ma wouldn't let us go until it had stopped raining the other week, and when we got there the doors were closed," said Olive.

"Do you like going to the pictures?" said Mrs Moore.

"Its my favourite day," said Nipper.

"We have the Children's Newsreel, a cartoon, and a main picture," said Winnie.

"And a serial," said Nipper"

Another half hour, then the little ones can go up for a wash," said Mrs Moore.

Tuesday had already reverted back to 'Tuesday Gloom.'

They all sat busily sewing on Thursday night, having the usual moan. Ma sat at her machine mending the pillowcases.

"My sister, Rose, is coming on Saturday, so I want you all to behave yourselves," said Ma.

"Is Aunty Dolly and Billy coming as well?" said Nipper.

"Who's Billy?" asked Colette.

"Billy is Aunty Dolly's little boy, Ma's got a photo of them in her sitting room," said Nipper.

"Are they staying here again, Ma?" said Nipper.

"Yes, they'll be staying here for a short break," said Ma. "They're coming up from the Black Country."

"Where's the Black Country Ma?" said Doris.

They had often heard Ma talking about her relations, in the Black Country, and Nipper was in the home on their last visit.

"Well there's Wednesbury, Oldbury, Smethwick, and West Bromwich, that's where I come from," said Ma .

"The sky is lit up at night from the furnaces of the iron and steel works. It's the muck and dust from these furnaces that give it the name Black Country," Ma carried on, guiding the pillowcase through the machine.

"Oh, I thought all the black people lived there," said Nipper.

"There was this big steel works called Siddons, where they made saucepans and frying pans. When us girls left school, if we didn't go into service we had to work in Siddons' factory. All the women who worked there were known as 'Joe Siddons' Rubbing Rags.' My brother used to work there before he went into the army," said Ma.

"Joe Siddons Rubbing Rags," The girls all had a giggle at the name. "We're 'Miss Hammond's Rubbing Rags," said Olive.

"Life in the Black Country was very hard, you wouldn't survive if you had it all to do, no wonder most of the girls went into service, I wouldn't want those times over again," said Ma.

The sewing was getting done, albeit very slowly.

"Yow lot think you're hard done to, but I was the youngest of twelve children. Four of them died when they were babies," said Ma.

"Ah, there was a big family of you then, Ma, said Winnie sympathetically.

"Yes, and my father was a shoe maker, not a cobbler, it was woe betide anybody who called him a cobbler. He made shoes," said Ma.

"He made all your brothers' boots, didn't he Ma?" said Ruth who had heard some of Ma's story before.

"And mine," said Ma. "I had to wear boots, until I was eighteen, that's when I had my first pair of shoes."

"I'm glad I didn't live in them days," said Winnie. "I don't like boots."

"If it wasn't for my Mother's constant care, I wouldn't be here today. The doctor took one look at me and said 'she might live 'til she's about seven,' and look at me I'm still here today," said Ma.

"Doctors don't know everything, do they Ma?" said Winnie, thinking about her own mother in the wrong hospital.

"Why did he say that, Ma?" said Nipper.

"Because I was such a frail baby, a little weakling like you and Olive when you came to me," said Ma. "Better get that needle box put away, soon be time for bed," said Ma.

"What were your brothers and sisters names, Ma?" asked Nipper. "Tell us, then we'll go and get washed."

"My eldest brother was Harry, then there was Ernest. Rose is my eldest sister, she's coming tomorrow. Next came William, and Herbert. There was Sydney who went missing in the First World War. Then there's Mary my other sister and me. The babies that died were John, Samuel,

Phoebe-Jane and Little Florrie. My father wrote all the names in the family bible. I shouldn't think there was any room left after mine," Ma said.

"It's like a bedtime story isn't it Ma," said Olive.

"Get them washed Olive, and send them downstairs for their cocoa. We'll be here all night," said Ma. The laundry was put away, then as if by clockwork, They filed from bathroom for wash, to sitting room for inspection, to kitchen for cocoa, and then to bed.

"Good afternoon, Ma," one by one the girls piled in through the back door, wondering if Ma's visitors had arrived. There were distinct Birmingham voices coming from the kitchen, with a bit of pushing and shoving they all had a quick peep round the kitchen door, then quickly retreated.

"Cum on, let me look at yow, don't be shy," said Aunty Rose.

Ma's sister sat warming herself near the kitchen range. Aunty Dolly sat on the kitchen chair with Billy on her knee.

"Say 'ello to the girls, Billy," said Aunty Dolly, and immediately Billy hid behind his Mum.

"Cum on, yow not shy, our Billie," said Aunty Rose.

The three visitors sat while Ma poured their cups of tea. Aunty Rose, an elderly lady was rather plump and had her white hair twisted into a bun at the back of her head. She sat with one hand on her knee and the other on the towel rail of the fireplace.

Aunty Dolly was coaxing Billy to speak to them as a few more girls gathered in the kitchen. Her auburn hair was plaited twice around her head like a thick tiara.

"I was froze on the trine," said Aunty Dolly.

"You'll soon get warm, I thought there was heating on the trains," said Ma handing them all a cup of tea. "Come on, Billy, you remember Nipper, don't you."

"He's gone shy," said Nipper. " He'll soon get used to us."

"Are these all your new girls Olive?" Aunty Dolly asked Ma.

"Yes, none of these were here last time you came, only Nipper and her sisters. I've just recently had three new ones, they're Catholics, they'll be home soon, they have a bit further to come," said Ma.

Back in the hall the girls changed their shoes.

"Ma's name's Olive," Hazel said to Olive.

"Yes, Olive Hammond, perhaps that's why she don't like me," said Olive.

"You've got to go back in the kitchen and spread the bread," Hazel said.

When the visitors had retreated to Ma's sitting room and the tea laid out, Billy stood at the bobby-hole with Ma while the girls sang grace, then she took him into the sitting room with a word of warning to them all.

"Olive, I expect you to keep them quiet, I don't see my sister very often."

"Yes, Ma," said Olive.

After tea, the doors of the bobby-hole were suddenly flung open Billy stood on the other side in the kitchen.

"Hello, Billy," The girls chanted all together." "Come in the dining room."

Suddenly he jumped up on the hatch leaning on his elbows, and then with another movement he jumped straight through the bobby-hole landing in the dining room.

"Ooh, Oooh," they shrieked, thinking he had hurt himself, "are you all right?"

Billy stood up, and in another flash, he had gone back through the bobby-hole to the kitchen. Billy had done the forbidden thing, and jumped right through the bobby-hole, they had all leaned halfway through, but had never dared to jump through to the other side. There was a sudden uproar as young Billy leaned on his elbows again between the doors of the hatch.

"Ssshhh," said Olive trying to keep order. "He's not going to do it again, he's a proper clown."

"You can say your prayers," said Billy.

"Did Ma say so?" said Nipper.

Billy nodded, and stood waiting.

"Go on then," he said.

The girls stood behind their chairs at the command of the six-year-old boy and sang grace. By the end of The Lord's Prayer, Billy had gone back to Ma's sitting room. The table was cleared, and the washing up was in full swing. Ma came into the scullery.

"Have you said grace?" said Ma. "Who told you to?"

"Yes, Ma, Billy told us to," said Nipper.

"That little blighter," said Ma with her usual single laugh. "He'll be taking my job over next."

176

"Come on, Bill," said Ma. "Let the girls get on with their work. You're Mother wants you."

The elusive Billy had gone again.

Ma called down the cellar where Billy was last seen.

"Is he down there Marie," shouted Ma.

"I don't know, Ma, the candle's gone out," shouted Marie.

"Just a minute I'll get another one," said Ma going into the kitchen.

Billy appeared at the top of the cellar steps, then scurried into the sitting room.

"Is he down there Marie," said Ma, returning to the cellar steps.

"No, Ma, there's only me down here," said Marie.

In the dining room they sat listening and waiting for Billy's next appearance. His clumsy feet crept into the kitchen, suddenly his head popped up at the hatch like a jack-in-the-box.

"Boo!" he shouted.

"Why hasn't your sister Heather come with you?" said Nipper.

"She's got to go to school so she's staying at home with my Dad," said Billy.

"Has she still got long plaits?" said Olive.

"Yes she has, I pull them when she bosses me about," said Billy.

"I wish we could have plaits," said Nipper

"I bet you can't catch me," said Billy and he jumped through the hatch again.

"Come on, catch me," he teased at the dining room door.

Doris took up the chase and ran down the hall after Billy. Billy was through the bobby-hole again like a shot out of a gun.

Doris came hurtling through, followed by Nipper, and lastly Winnie whose foot got stuck.

Billy was at the back of her, pushing her through with both hands on her backside.

"Ow, I'm stuck, stop it," giggled Winnie, eventually falling through.

A scuffle of chairs and a few more joined in. It was no longer a venture to 'catch Billy' but a queue to manoeuvre the jump through the hole in the wall, a chance to try the banned activity while Ma was out of the way. A chair had been strategically placed to get a foothold to achieve more speed.

"Good game," shouts Billy amongst the shrieks of laughter.

Ma's heavy footsteps came up the back hall. They could tell from the speed of the footsteps that Ma 'meant business', she was on the 'warpath.'

"What's been going on? It's like bedlam. I can't hear myself speak," said Ma.

Innocently sitting at the table, breathless from the chase, they looked at Ma as she reached the bobby-hole. It was easy for Ma to see who had been chasing about.

"Sorry, Ma," said Olive and they all echoed the same.

"Look, I have a few visitors and yow lot go crackers. If I hear any more noise you'll all be 'up the stairs' like it or lump it. Where's Billy?" said Ma.

The girls looked at each other.

Ma closed the hatch.

"Where is he?

"Where's he gone?"

Young Billy who had started it all was nowhere about. They all started giggling about their own negotiations of the bobby-hole. Billy came from under the table.

"Here he is," said Colette as Billy crawled from his hiding place.

"You'll get us into trouble Billy, no more running about," said Olive.

"Ma wasn't mad," said Winnie.

"My sides are aching with laughing."

"My face is aching as well, I've never laughed so much. I know, let's do that jigsaw that I had for Christmas," said Olive.

"I bet you can't do jigsaws Billy," said Colette.

"Yes I can, my Dad showed me, you do all the straight bits first," said Billy.

The lady on the box sat under a tree with a little dog at her feet. Her husband stood by her side with a gun resting on his arm.

"I think I've done this one before," said Billy, "Do the dog first."

All the straight edges were sorted and the frame ready to be filled in.

"If we keep quiet, Ma'll forget about us and she might let us stop up a bit." said Olive.

"She will," said Nipper. "Especially if we keep Billy in here."

All evening they worked on the thousand pieces. The table cloth carefully covered the jig-saw and the table was laid for morning, the Friday night bath was forgone wisely with a strip-wash, Ma could see Billy wanting to join in the bath night as well.

Billy raced up and down the stairs, first into the blue room, then up the attic then into the brown room, screams went up as the impish figure entered the seclusion of their nocturnal abode. The mad half hour ended when Aunty Dolly called Billy down to Ma's sitting room.

"Goodnight, Billy," they all shouted.

"And peace reigneth throughout the land." said Ma at the bottom of the stairs.

"Goodnight, Ma." They shouted.

"Goodnight, and may the night last twenty four hours," replied Ma.

Playing with Billy that night had re-awakened in them the memories of their own brothers, how lucky Billy was to live with his own Mam and dad. They all had brothers in some far off home, or hospital, and the evening with Billy had been ecstatic, he was like the ideal brother, like the 'Just William' stories that Margaret used to read.

"Margaret's missed all the fun." said Winnie, I bet she's thinking about us."

Winnie's prayers began.

"Dear God, please take care of Margaret and Edna, and baby Joe and Brian,....."

Hazel's thoughts were with her baby brother, she lay there comparing him to Billy, who was a year older than Brian. Billy, whose father had his own business, and his sister went to private school, who wore a smart shirt with a real tie, and a jumper knitted by Aunty Rose for his birthday two days before Christmas day. The last time they had seen Brian he was almost as big as Billy, and looking nowhere near as healthy. Brian was now living with Dad in someone's house Billy was probably fast asleep cuddling up to his Mum.

Hazel got to thinking of the front room in Lothair road, so sparsely furnished, with just a sofa, a sideboard. Mam's treadle sewing machine, where she had sat for hours making clothes. She breathed deeply, it was no use thinking about their home any more, it was just a memory, as was the smell of burning wood, and Great Grandad's bonfires on his allotment, watching the smoke curl up as he sat puffing on his pipe, at the side of his shed.

Winnie's prayers continued for her own Mother, and her Dad...

"God bless them both, and let no more bombs drop on Dad's factory."

Tears stung Hazel's eyes, she still couldn't believe that their Mam had died.

Another forgotten memory came back to Hazel; it was that of her Aunty Alice, who was stone deaf. She was married to Grandma's brother Walter, who had died suddenly leaving Alice a whimpering wreck. A year ago, Grandma, had asked Mam if she could spare one of the children to stay with Alice for a few days after the funeral. Mam couldn't spare Norman as he did all the errands, and Hazel, listening to Grandma volunteered her 'seven-years-old's services.' So it was decided that Alice should come and pick Hazel up. Alice arrived a few days later, a pitifully thin lady dressed in black from head to toe. Her sharp, pointed nose protruded from under the brim of her hat, she looked every bit like a witch.

Mam gave Hazel special instructions, to shout at Alice because of her deafness. They set off on the long journey, travelling by bus through the countryside, walking through streets, picking their way through the rubble from the bombed buildings.

Houses were being demolished, halfway up the outside wall a fireplace was still in position surrounded by pretty wallpaper, the remnants of somebody's bedroom. There was debris everywhere strewn into the middle of the road, and far worse than the Cavendish road bombings.

They finally reached their destination and Alice burst into tears, her relatives were very sympathetic and took them both indoors. There was a lot of shouting, and Alice wailed in her sing-song voice, not understanding a word they were saying. Although a visit to the local pub seemed to work wonders for Alice, then after a hot meal Hazel and Alice were taken to the bus stop for the return trip to Leicester.

Alice fumbled in her bag for the door key, the kids from next door peeped round the side of their house. They sniggered and pointed as Alice unlocked the door, they probably thought she was a witch, the same as Hazel did.

Inside Alice gathered the sticks for the fire, and the kettle was placed on the slow burning coals. The table in the kitchen stood in the middle of the room on the red tiled floor. A small cooker stood behind the door near a low sink, and there was a bare shelf above the disused fireplace. Hazel decided there and then that if there was an air-raid she would do what Mam said, and get under the kitchen table. Apart from a passage to the back door, there didn't seem to be any other rooms, Alice's bed was in the corner of the living room. Hazel asked her where she was going to sleep she wasn't shouting loud enough, so Alice didn't reply.

In the living room there was a chair and small table at the bottom of the bed. An aspidistra with its huge leaves covered the pedestal table in the bay window, and a fireside chair each side of the fireplace. The double bed took up the rest of the space in the room. It was suddenly very quiet, no brothers and sisters, only Alice talking to herself in her own ramblings, and both tired from the journey. The hot teapot was placed on the table with two cups, this was the first indication to Hazel that Alice knew she was there, for she hadn't spoken to her directly until she said 'sit at the table.' Her squeaky voice went through all the last moments of her husband's death, repeating the last phrase over and over again - 'then they carried him out of the house'.

Alice didn't look so bad in her pinafore, but sitting with her back to the light the sharp features of her face were more pronounced, looking even more like a witch. The kettle was filled from the only tap in the kitchen and put back on the fire to boil.

'That will be ready for a hot drink before bedtime, and a hot water bottle.' Hazel had never had a hot water bottle, and was looking forward to a nice warm bed. For a while they sat near the fire, Alice first poked it, then she continually wrung her hands together deep in thought. She sighed deeply her incoherent voice trailing off as if she was short of breath. In her nightie Hazel settled into Alice's big bed, the hot water bottle was cosy.

The following day Alice took Hazel to the shops, she thought she was going home until Alice mentioned tomorrow's dinner and what they would have. The house was so bare there was nothing to clean, just the ashes from the fireplace. Hazel tapped Alice's arm if she needed to speak to her, and using signs she could communicate with her more as time went by. It was the next night that the sirens woke Hazel up, she tapped Alice's arm, then shook her from a deep sleep. She had the same whining voice only this time she had no teeth in, her thin voice was like a baby crying. Hazel sat up in bed shaking her until she woke up. The sticks were put on the fire, and the long spooky shadows danced eerily on the walls. The kitchen door was slightly ajar ready for Hazel to dive under the table. Alice suddenly got up and brought a tin of Ovaltine tablets from a drawer, sparingly she placed one in Hazel's hand, she chewed it, and drank her cocoa.

Alice sat down again and poked the fire, continually asking if the "All Clear" had gone yet, then her voice trailed off and she muttered to herself again. Hazel spoke to her frequently, but she was talking to herself again. Alice looked up occasionally with an accusing glance.

"Has the ALL CLEAR gone off and you haven't heard it?" she'd say.

Hazel could only shake her head, knowing it was impossible not to hear the siren. It was all that she could do to keep her from getting back into bed, so she devised a signal for the 'ALL CLEAR,' she renewed the hot water bottle for something to do.   After such air raids Hazel sympathized with Alice in her silent world, and forgave her for shaking the bed, she was restless and wept most nights, grieving for the loss of her husband. The week was spent looking after the Aunt that Hazel had never seen before, she looked forward to the nightly air raids, and the midnight feasts especially when the Ovaltine tablets were fetched out of a hidden place. The longer Hazel stayed, the more Alice relied upon her. One day a puppy was delivered to the door, it was a new replacement for Hazel. Now Hazel's time was spent mopping up puddles in the kitchen, made by the pup that yapped at every sound.

Alice's time was now devoted to her new canine friend, with pointing gestures she still made the same whimpering sounds while Hazel gave the puppy orders to be quiet. Alice held the lively pup and waved from the window the day Grandma arrived to take Hazel home. Before they reached the end of the road, Grandma had to tell Hazel several times to stop shouting. Running down the entry, Hazel rushed in the back door, eager to tell them all about her week away from home. Norman sat there with a big plaster on his head. He had been to the Infirmary to have stitches in his eyebrow after some boy had thrown a brick at him.

Norman's friend also was in hospital, he had jumped off the air raid shelter on 'the green' in Hughendon Drive, and landed on the spiked fence. Another of his friends had been killed by a bull on the way to the Aylestone Road market. Doris, too, had had her share of disaster, she had pulled Edna clear from the brook after she had fallen in whilst trying to rescue her friend. A man in the neighbourhood had rescued the other little girl, who was then taken to hospital. Hazel's week with the eccentric aunt, visiting her relatives, air raids, and midnight feasts, all seemed uninteresting, and already half forgotten, in comparison to the death of their friend.

Winnie's prayers were coming to an end.

"God bless Aunt Ciss, and all our cousins, and help Aunt Sarah to come and see us next visiting day. Oh I forgot bless Ma, and her sister, and Aunty Dolly and Billy. In the name of the Father and of the Son, and of the Holy Ghost. Amen. Goodnight, everybody." said Winnie.

After breakfast on Saturday morning, Aunty Rose and Aunty Dolly took Billy into Leicester on the tram, all the jobs were done without any interruptions.

"Can Billy come with us to the pictures Ma?" said Olive. "We'll look after him."

"We'll have to see." said Ma.

Billy stood round the table with them while Ma gave out the pocket money and sweets.

"Give Billy some sweets, Ma, 'cos he's coming with us," said Nipper.

In twos the girls walked up the hill, but Billy ran off, he didn't want to walk with a load of girls. In the pictures he tried to sit away from them but Olive kept dragging him back to sit with them He was as lively as the rest of the boys who sat on the front row.

"If you sit down there the manager will throw you out." said Olive.

He told his Mam and Aunty Rose that he had had a lovely time, but they couldn't persuade Aunty Dolly to let Billy go to Church with them on Sunday.

"He's such a fidget, he wouldn't sit still five minutes, Father Huntley would send him out," said Aunty Dolly.

"Heather won't take him to Sunday school at all." said Aunty Rose, and his Dad has to take him to school."

"He'll soon grow out of that, won't you Billy?" said Ma.

Billy waved to the girls from the dining room window, on their way to church.

"Look at that little devil, I bet Ma don't tell him off for looking out of the window," said Olive.

Sunday teatime, after prunes and custard, the visitors were getting ready to go home. They were to catch the train in Leicester, and Billy's Dad was to meet them in Birmingham, and take them back to West Bromwich.

Billy ran amok for the last time, he jumped through the bobby-hole, and when the girls chased him he ran up the stairs. He found the bell at the side of the bath, and rang it several times, proving to the girls that it did really work, he flushed the toilet, and hid under the beds in the blue room. Then he jumped from bed to bed, until Ma appeared and took him downstairs threatening to lock him in the dining room with the girls.

After a few carefree days, full of fun, Billy had been like a whirlwind, breaking all the rules, hiding on top of the air raid shelter, disappearing over the garden wall. It was all Ma could do to get them back to normality, a price she had to pay for seeing her relatives, and only one week's holiday a year.

Calm was soon restored when Margaret came out of hospital they had to stay quiet while she got used to the girls again. Ma put on a special party for her homecoming. She looked as pale as the custard in the trifle, Winnie, whose rosy cheeks were like the red apples from Canada didn't move from Margaret's side. The girls sat round the dining table listening intently as Margaret answered their questions, all of them now wanted to be nurses after she had told them how nice the nurses were. In her spare time Margaret had written poems to the boy from her class who was in the same ward, he also had diphtheria.

"Did he write poems back to you, Margaret?" they asked.

"Well they didn't rhyme very well, and the nurse kept asking us if there were any more love letters to be delivered," said Margaret.

"Don't think that means you can start writing to boys," said Ma, who had an ear cocked to their conversations.

*   *   *

Back at school after the summer holidays Miss Harle was in good voice singing the morning hymn.

"Morning has broken, like the first morning.
Blackbird has spoken, like the first word..."

In her plain brown dress, short dark hair and glasses, she sang with the gusto of an opera singer. The results of last term's exams were always given out on the first day of the new term. All the class stood around the edge of the classroom eagerly waiting for the results. Miss Harle called out their names, and the marks. The ones with the highest marks sat at the back of the class, Margaret was the second one to sit down, with ninety nine per cent. It was a draw for top marks for Margaret and the boy she sat next to. The lower marks sat on the next row, and so on until the front row was eventually filled with the dunces Hazel was last to sit down. That first afternoon Miss Harle took out her violin, and stood on Hazel's desk. Very melodiously she played, 'I vow to thee, my country.' The vibrations and sad, dulcet tones ripped down Hazel's spine. A lump stuck in her throat as it had on the day that Grandad told her that their mother had died. Concentrating on Miss Harle's lisle stockings Hazel fought back the tears as the words and music ran through her brain, the bow of her violin hitting every note to perfection. Miss Harle's left foot arched on the tip of its toes, balancing as she swayed with the melody on the desk, her polished shoe just missing the inkwell.

After tea, Ma called Doris and Hazel into her sitting room, she had two parcels wrapped in tissue paper. Ma gently unwrapped them, uncovering two hand knitted dolls, one with blonde hair and the other dark brown, all waves and curls.

"Your Dad has sent them, your mother was in the middle of knitting them when she died," Ma said.

Hazel and Doris burst into tears.

"Come on, yow big girls now, your Dad has made a good job of them dresses, he finished them off. It's not every man as can knit," said Ma, leaving them holding the doll of their choice.

The dresses were knitted in heavy white silk, unwound from the cord of the wartime parachutes. Each doll about twelve inches long had painted plaster masks, secured to the head by four big stitches under the hair, pink arms and legs, and white knitted vest and pants. Doris chose the blonde one, they dried their eyes. In the dining room they showed the girls the lovely dolls. Any new dolls, whatever their condition were gently handled and treated with care. Carefully the dolls were re-wrapped and put in Ma's sideboard cupboard they were too precious to play with.

By the end of September, Edna was out of hospital, and Ma had twelve girls again. The catholic family had brought a letter for Matron requesting that the girls should have extra tuition for confirmation classes.

"Does that mean you'll have to go back after school?" said Ma.

"Yes, Ma," said Marie.

"Oh that's not fair," said Olive, "they'll get out of doing all their jobs."

"Neck-trouble, keep your nose out, It won't affect you, anyway, you'll be leaving soon," said Ma.

"Well I'm not getting the coal up and cleaning the kitchen," Hazel said.

"Yow will if I say so," said Ma, hearing every word from Hazel.

Hazel was bitter and angry, an undercurrent of emotion was welling up between her and Marie. Olive didn't mind so much because she would be leaving soon. Hazel nowadays was quite moody, not only had she lost her right to become the eldest, but also she was doing most of the eldest girls' jobs. At school the last lesson on Friday was craft work, it had taken a whole term for Hazel to knit a teddy bear.

The teacher decided that the class would have a knitting contest. The pins were given out and everyone had a ball of wool, the required twenty stitches was cast on, beginning at the stroke of two o' clock. Some of the girls had difficulty with the wool, some dropped stitches and big holes appeared. The rules were repeated at each catastrophe. A posh girl sitting in the middle row, had a good view of Hazel's knitting, both girls had knitted several rows. Hazel adjusted her speed, trying not to take her hand off the knitting when she wrapped the wool around the pin. The knitting eventually reached the desk like a small scarf. So too did that of her only rival. At the end of the lesson they were ordered to put down their knitting. Only two girls had reached the perfect standard, with no holes and twenty stitches. They both stood in front of the class, and it was left for the class to decide the winner - a unanimous decision - it was Hazel. The prize was a small needle holder in the shape of a lady's hat with a thimble in the middle and it opened up like a book to reveal the needles and pins. Hazel decided that she would give it to her Mam, but suddenly remembered that she had died.

"Ma, I've won a prize," Hazel shouted as soon as she opened the back door.

"How can anyone at the bottom of a class win a prize?" Ma said.

"I won the knitting competition," Hazel said very proudly.

'If only she could do as well with her brain as she does with her hands," Ma made the same remark as the one on her school report.

"You can have it, Ma to put on your sideboard," Hazel said.

"Yow want me to have it," said Ma.

The little blue hat embroidered with red flowers around the brim-looked small in Ma's hands.

"I'll look after it for you," said Ma. "Yow might do a bit more to that peg rug now, we'll have it in the dining room for Christmas then," said Ma.

The kitchen table, with its well scrubbed surface almost shining white, was the centre of domesticity and a silent witness to all the dilemmas, and thrashings. It was used for everything, from making scones, to painting jobs. It had been sat upon while waiting for visitors, or bandaging knees, and little feet had tap-danced on it. It was used to serve up all meals, and stained with everything from beetroot juice to salty tears. It had been the cause of many a lump on the head, when the floor below was being scrubbed. On Saturdays it was covered in a heavy blanket to prevent scorch marks from the flat irons, and every six months it was turned round to save its bulbous, painted legs from being blistered from the kitchen fire. Now it was covered in dust from the clippings for the rug. Again witnessing the moans and groans like its highly polished counterpart in the dining room on a Thursday night, as sore fingers dropped the scissors on its grainy surface.

"Can I go now, Olive, I've had enough," said Ruth.

"I'll come with you," said Nancy, who had also got a blister from the scissors.

"Yes, we're packing up now," said Olive.

"Hazel get the cloth to wipe the table," Olive said putting the last strip into the rug.

"I'll do a bit more before its put away," Hazel said.

Ma came into the kitchen enquiring how the rug was progressing. The rug was spread over the table, creating even more dust.

"Looks good," said Ma. "Could do with a few more bits put in that row."

"Isn't it time some of you went for a strip wash?" Ma said leaning on the bobby-hole.

"We've all been," said Nipper.

"Come here let me look at yow, said Ma.

After examining ears and neck, Ma turned round.

"Right, get this table washed, unless yow want all that muck in your porridge in the morning," she said, leaving the kitchen.

Because of the shortage of farm workers, during the war, busloads of

Rug making in the kitchen.

school children were taken to the countryside to help pick the potato crops. They looked upon this as a day's outing from school, and for a few shillings it was a source of help for the farmers and pocket money for the children. Prisoners of war also shared in the work across the fields.

Also on Monday morning bags of rose hips were brought to school, these were used to make rose hip syrup. The rose hips were gathered from the hedgerows each week end, and for their efforts the children were given a few pence for every pound they collected. The girls from the home were never allowed out on this activity, and so missed out on the extra pocket money. Big Margaret had been potato picking with the school last year as it was in school time, now it was Olive's turn.

"I've put that hessian bag on the shoe rack ready for morning, Olive. Perhaps you'll be able to bring a few 'spuds' home for roasting," said Ma, when Olive took the supper into Ma's sitting room.

Olive put the tray at the side of Ma's chair.

"Oh that looks nice, thank you very much," said Ma. "I've been meaning to talk to you about what you are going to do when you leave school. Have you any ideas?"

"No, Ma, I don't want to work in a factory," said Olive.

"Do you really want to go and live with your Mam? You could go into service. There are plenty of big houses up Stoneygate, and you'd have a roof over your head and a wage at the end of the week. Once a week you'd have a day off," Ma continued to pour out the tea.

"I think I'd rather live with my Mam," said Olive.

"Well this is your last Christmas, think about it," said Ma.

Like the war, nineteen forty-four was coming to an end. It was Olive's last time to help stir the Christmas puddings, and her turn to ice the cake, and fetch the box of tangerines from Mrs Jones whose husband owned a market stall. A belated harvest gift, Ma used to call it.

Dad had visited Hazel and Doris once with Di, the woman he now lived with. The girls were disappointed when they hadn't brought Brian to see them, and their blank faces showed disapproval when he mentioned getting married again. The Hunts had only had two visits to Grandma's since their Mam had died.

The Christmas party at the Receiving Home still had its traumatic memories of the first days in the homes. But they were now older and could slip away to the toilet, avoiding being kissed by Miss Pickering's boys. Someone plonked away on the piano just like Big Margaret had beaten the dud keyboard of the writing desk, to everyone's amazement it sounded like 'a hunting we will go' and the right tune for musical chairs.

*   *   *

Getting the coal from the flooded cellar.

CHAPTER FOUR

January 1945

Before the end of January, the heavy rainfall and melting snow brought the usual chaos to the houses on East Park Road.

"Ma, the cellar's flooded," shouted Olive standing with the coal buckets at the top of the cellar steps.

"Let me look, " said Ma. "Give me the candle?"

All the girls had heard Olive, and rushed to the cellar door peering down into the shadows as a draught of cold air blew the candle out.

"Get out of my light, how can you expect anyone to see," said Ma at the top of the steps, with only a glimmer of light from the hall.

The water from the melting snow had overflowed from the drains and washed back into the cellar, carrots and firewood floated on the water, which was up to the third step.

"Light the candle, and let's have another look, we'll just have to do without coal for tonight," said Ma, about to give up at the eerie sight.

"I'll go down," said Olive "I know where everything is."

Her black stockings were off and her bare feet were on the cold steps, with candle in one hand and coal bucket in the other she disappeared into the gloom.

Ma was insisting that there was no need to act daft, "Come back here," she shouted to Olive.

"Eeerk," shrieked Olive.

"What's up?" the girls shouted as Olive waded round the corner.

"Something touched my leg, oh it's only an onion," Olive reassured them.

"I don't know how she dare, all that mucky water," said Winnie.

They stood there stage struck, listening to the lapping water on the steps. The faint light had gone altogether as Olive had turned into the bay where the coal was dropped down the chute from the entry trap door.

"Come on Olive get back up here," shouted Ma as she shone the torch on to the cellar steps.

They listened as a rumble-like landslide sounded in the distance.

"I'm OK," shouted Olive. "Just a few more lumps."

At last Olive appeared at the bottom of the steps, half submerged in water.

"Where's the candle?" Ma asked as Olive heaved the bucket of coal onto the higher steps.

"I dropped it," said Olive.

"Get a bowl of hot water, H," said Ma. "My God yow look like yow've been down a coal mine."

Olive stood in the bowl, covered in black, wet coal dust.

"Ooh that's lovely and warm," said Olive. "I've thrown the sticks onto the steps, and there's plenty of carrots about."

Her audience gave her a clap for all her endeavours, then with more than the three allocated inches of water Olive sat in the bath singing. Ma locked the cellar door.

"That's enough entertainment for one night, now let's have some peace and quiet," Ma said returning to her sitting room. Unexpectedly, Nipper had the ride in an ambulance that she had always wanted, she was taken to hospital with appendicitis. After visiting her one afternoon, Ma told the girls that she was worried about Miss James who was in the same hospital.

"Miss James, in hospital?" they all chorused together.

"Yes, she's on the danger list, she had polio when she was little," said Ma.

"Is that why she was always limping?" asked Winnie.

"Miss James never did like me," Hazel said, still hating her for taking their scotch kilts.

When all the girls were asleep, Hazel opened her eyes she could hear a lot of disturbance coming from downstairs. The Japs had come and Ma was arrested. In the darkness Hazel could see a Japanese soldier standing at the foot of every bed, she could not move and hardly dared to breathe, she knew that the slightest movement would make them turn around. Hazel closed her eyes hardly daring to breathe, remaining rigid and scared.

Waking up some time later, Hazel looked carefully around the room, it was just beginning to get light. The soldiers had gone, and the girls were still asleep, she dozed again.

BUMP, BUMP, BUMP; the curtains were thrown open.

"Come on it's time to get up," said Ma.

It was Ma. It was Ma herself.

"Oh I've had an awful dream, Ma," Hazel shouted. "I dreamt the Japs had captured you and taken you away."

Ma really hadn't got time to listen to individual dreams, and just said. "I bet you wish I had."

Hazel sat on the bed, momentarily looking at the floor.

"The Japs, they were standing there," she said.

Edna was now attending a special open-air school at Western Park she was put on the tram every morning, in order to catch the school bus in Leicester. Most of Edna's lessons were outside, gardening, and sleeping every afternoon she had just reached her ninth birthday.

Nipper was out of hospital, sitting in the luxury of the big chair showing the girls her operation scar, it was now called the 'sick' chair. They were sure to be having jelly for tea because Nipper was still on 'light foods' and it half served the purpose as Olive's leaving party as she only had a few days left at school.

"We shall miss you doing the 'Miss James' walk," they all said to Olive

"Shut up," said Ma rather sharply. "You shouldn't speak ill of the dead."

"DEAD! Is Miss James DEAD?" they all voiced together.

"Yes, didn't you know?" Ma's voice sounded surprised. "She died while Nipper was in hospital, I thought you all knew," Ma had obviously avoided telling them.

"I must be going crackers. I'll be getting a green ticket next," Ma added as they all sat there in stunned silence. "She was ill for a long time."

Olive's battered school satchel was on the kitchen table, the spare knickers and vests neatly packed with her school reports. She was leaving her favourite jigsaw in the bookcase for the girls to play with. They stood in a line and kissed her as she went out of the front door with Ma who was taking her to the Receiving Home.

"Cheerio, Olive," they shouted from the dining room window when the tram went hurtling past. The girls could almost tell what Ma was saying as they both waved back to them 'It's like a load of sheep's heads in a butchers shop window.'

"I'm the eldest now," said a voice behind Hazel.

Over the months the girls had been learning the catechism at Sunday school ready for their Baptism, and on Whit Sunday there was a special service. Margaret, Winnie, Edna, Doris, Hazel, Ruth and Nipper were all baptised along with the rest of the Sunday school children who had not been christened when they were babies.

Father Huntley leaned over the font, and one at a time he sprinkled water over their foreheads. "In the name of the Father and of the Son and of the Holy Ghost." Their Godparents were Sunday school teachers, Miss Adams, and Mr Smith, who built the Easter garden every year. Standing around the font they each held a candle.

"I'm glad I didn't have to lift you all up, you're a bit too heavy for me," said Father Huntley as he gave each one of them a Baptism cards.

None of their parents attended, it was just another Sunday afternoon.

*   *   *

In May Mr Churchill announced the end of the war. All the children in the school were assembled in the hall.

"THE WAR IS OVER," said the headmaster, Mr Baum.

The whole school erupted. Mr Baum let them all have a few minutes to go wild. It was his last year and he had waited and prayed for the moment to see all their faces when peace was declared. Then singing, "There'll always be an England," and "God Save Our Gracious King," the children all ran out into the street shouting and cheering.

An invitation arrived for the three Hunts to attend the Victory party in Lothair Road.

There were no trams or buses running, the excitement grew as Hazel, Doris and Edna walked to Lothair Road. A couple of sailors walked in front of them on the pavement. They dared each other to touch the sailors' collars to bring them good luck. Several streets were also preparing for parties, along the way. They finally reached Lothair Road. A piano was being wheeled along the pavement. The red, white and blue streamers trailing across the street from all the upstairs windows, men women and children were putting the final touches to the long table down the centre of the road. Rosettes and bunting twisted along the sides of the many tablecloths that joined them all into one. Union Jacks fluttered in the rows of glasses like bunches of flowers down the centre of the table. Chairs of all description were strategically placed at each setting. The three Hunts soon merged with the residents of the street. They bumped into Mrs Prince, who made quite a fuss.

"Oh, they let you come then," she said. "Marjorie," she shouted.

"Oh, I remember you, you used to live just there," said Marjorie and pointed to their old house.

T
8th June, 1946

O-DAY, AS WE CELEBRATE VICTORY, I send this personal message to you and all other boys and girls at school. For you have shared in the hardships and dangers of a total war and you have shared no less in the triumph of the Allied Nations.

I know you will always feel proud to belong to a country which was capable of such supreme effort; proud, too, of parents and elder brothers and sisters who by their courage, endurance and enterprise brought victory. May these qualities be yours as you grow up and join in the common effort to establish among the nations of the world unity and peace.

George R.I.

Message from the King.

"You have grown," said Mrs Prince, taking them to one side. Marjorie, June Hubbard, and Iris Brindley, whose Mother had rung the police when Hazel had run away, ran up to join the party of onlookers. They took the girls and decided who should sit where. Doreen Chambers was there with her brother Keith, and Mrs Chambers hadn't changed one bit. Mrs Lawrence, Mrs Preston and Mr Kirby all seemed to be old people. Mr Kirby's daughter, Joan, was standing on their doorstep at number twenty-four, organising her own children who had come for the party. The middle houses across the road had older children, they remembered their faces but names were forgotten. Mrs Butler was there she remembered all of the girls, especially Hazel for running errands for her. She was the young girl whom she had given a broken pot doll to, it was just about to go in the dustbin. Ron Prince, Norman's pal, sat at the far end of the table with Tony Hubbard and their younger brothers and sisters. The girls were ushered along from one adult to another like ghosts from the past.

"How are Norman and Ted?" Do you see them at all? How often do you see your Dad? Where do they live now?"

A lot of questions went unanswered as the sandwiches passed across the table. No one was allowed an empty plate.

Number twenty-two seemed to be unoccupied it was the only front door not open. They were conveniently placed at the table with their backs to it. Every adult had their own reason for celebrating on VE Day. Hazel detected sorrow in the faces of those who had lost loved ones in the war; they sat together in charge of the gramophone at the far end of the street, going through the piles of records.

"There'll Always Be An England!"

Adults were singing in various groups around the table. "Red, White and Blue....". Now everyone was singing, down to the last child waving flags. The gramophone continuously churned out all the wartime songs, the party was never ending. Squash and fizzy lemonade was poured into every glass, and no sooner had one trifle dish been emptied than another one appeared. Colourful jellies wobbled on the table and fairy cakes were in abundance. Everyone stood for the National Anthem.

"God Save Our Gracious King...
Long Live Our Noble King...
God Save the King..."

Cheering continued for "Winnie Churchill...Hip, Hip Hooray...."
"Are you stopping for the bonfire on the Green?" the girls were asked.
Hazel, Doris and Edna would have loved to be there until nightfall,
but they were out on a limited time.

Some of the tables were being returned to their rightful owners, still
leaving a rather more shrunken table in the middle of the road, all ready
for the adults' party, and dancing.

The time was getting on, they thanked the neighbours for a lovely
party and unwillingly made their way to the end of the street. The
gramophone still played loudly.

"There'll be Bluebirds over the White Cliffs of Dover.
Tomorrow just you wait and see."

Vera Lynn's voice echoed down the street above all the individual
singers who were joining in, tending their children, tidying some of the
debris on the ground, still eating from the table. Children disappeared
down the entries Then re-appeared to carry on with the celebrations.

Waving to their renewed friends, like ghosts, the three girls left the
happy scene. The bonfire on 'The Green' was higher than the air raid
shelter, stacked like a wigwam with household rubbish ejecting from all
sides.

The girls walked slowly along the quieter roads, past the allotments
where Great Grandad had once given them bags of fallen apples. Passing
the gasworks still in camouflage, and the high prison walls, marvelling
how any prisoner could escape over the huge parapets. The Royal
Infirmary was on the opposite side of the road, they remembered
screaming while the nurses held them down to have wounds stitched.

Walking round the back streets some of the bonfires had already been
lit, so they took a slight detour, inhaling the smoke, and soaking up the
atmosphere. Tired and dusty, the three eventually arrived back at Ma's.
All their friends had looked a lot different at the party, but they still had
memories that they could keep forever.

There was a great sense of celebration, everybody was rejoicing one way or another, the war was over and a great relief for many things. In church on Sunday Father Huntley had a festival service, the procession went round the church twice before it reached the altar. The church was full to capacity, the girls' home usual seats were taken, and so for the first time they had to sit on the other side of the aisle.

Posters went up announcing that there would be dancing on the Spinney Hill Park, celebrations run by the council. Dancing was seven until nine for the young ones, and nine 'til eleven for the adults.

There were five sleeping in the attic now, Ma had finally allowed Hazel to sleep in Olive's empty bed. The box room smelled of mothballs, bags full of the white marble like balls hung along the rail with the Sunday coats. The smell was always an unpleasant reminder of the Receiving Home.

The attic itself was quite a big room, the five beds spaced around the walls. The half-circular window fell back on to a metal bar when the window was open. by removing the metal hook the girls could drop the window down, and with a bed pushed up against the window they had a birds eye view of the dancing on the park. They danced to the loud music in their nightgowns and enjoyed the long daylight hours of double summertime. The American soldiers jitterbugged the night away with young girls until eleven o'clock and the finale waltz. On their beds they stood to attention and sang,

"God Save Our Gracious King,"

Ruth with her tin curlers in as usual ready for her 'page-boy' hair style the next day. Winnie with her precious beads on, Margaret staring at the floor singing the National anthem, Doris and Hazel waving their arms, conducting the night attired choir.

Wearing their best clothes, Ma took the girls to see the Victory Parade. Thousands of people lined the route through Leicester to see the three-mile long Parade. Soldiers Sailors, the R A F, representatives of the Commonwealth Countries, The British Legion, The Police Force, The Fire Brigade, The Home Guard, The Red Cross and St John Ambulance, all the Home Front workers, and Civil Servants, all marching to Victoria Park War Memorial.

As each set of troops marched past a deafening cheer went up from the crowds. The only orders from Ma were that if anybody got lost they were to go to the Receiving Home just round the corner. But who wanted to get lost today?

Standing on Evington Road corner among the cheering crowds, was like the crossroads for each one of them. All the girls knew which road they would take them home. Margaret and Winnie only had to walk down London Road, just beyond Victoria Park, to Queens Road. Ruth and Nipper could take the road to The De Montfort Hall, just by the prison that was where their Mother lived. Hazel, Doris and Edna could take the same route, and a little further to the Aylestone Road, and beyond to Grandma's. The fact that the war was over didn't mean that they would be going home, to returning soldiers from the war. None of their fathers were soldiers.

Ma's flat feet seemed rooted to the spot as she watched battalion after battalion of Soldiers in the parade. It was as if she was remembering her own fiancé who was killed during the First World War. A young girl then, she had promised to marry her young soldier. The cheering went on throughout the Parade, their voices croaking each time they tried to speak.

"Can you see?" They lifted each of the little ones up to show them the Parade over the crowds, the many bands, their drums keeping a steady beat for the thousands of feet.

The girls mingled with the crowds on the way back to East Park Road, long after the parade had finished. The pavements were not wide enough to accommodate the throngs of people, cascading away from Evington Road. Different groups linking their arms singing away on their way home, all the time taking care not to get high heels stuck in the tramlines.

*   *   *

Before the end of the term Miss Harle gave out the results of the eleven plus examinations. Margaret had passed, as was expected, and Hazel had failed, as was expected.

"Well done," said Ma to Margaret and gave her a pat on the head. "Never mind, H, we can't all be clever, look at me I hardly went to school." The Grammar School that Margaret was to attend had already been decided.

The uniform for the Alderman Newton Girls' school was bottle green. Early in the summer holidays Margaret and Hazel took a letter to the shop.

"When you get off the tram, anyone will tell you where Graham Gardener's is," said Ma. "Just give that letter over the counter.

Margaret walked up and down the shop in several states of undress, from just a blouse and knickers, to a heavy bottle green winter coat and hat. There was two of this, and three of that, they hadn't seen so many new clothes, the pile on the counter grew, then a real leather satchel was added. After tea Margaret emerged from Ma's sitting room where all the purchases had been carefully placed on Ma's settee. The girls stood and admired the well-groomed look of the bottle green tunic, the white blouse and tie, Margaret gave us a twirl as Ma came into the dining room.

"That's your reward for passing the exam," Ma said to Margaret. "See what you've missed, H. You ought to have tried a bit harder," said Ma.

'What do you expect when my Mam died a week before the exam', Hazel wanted to say.

In July, three postcards arrived through the letterbox, Dad and Di were in Yarmouth for week's holiday.

"The air will do him good," Ma said as she read each one. "Have they gone on honeymoon?" The Hunts just smiled not knowing anything about Dads life out of hospital.

The other highlight of the school holidays was a trip to Bradgate Park, a picnic to celebrate Matron Buttridge's retirement. They were all quietly rejoicing.

The special bus left the Receiving Home with the picnic hamper carefully stowed away, Ma with her girls, Miss Pickering with her boys and the small contingent of Receiving Home children. Matron sat at the front in all her regalia, her long cape neatly folded on the seat beside her. Anyone looking in from the outside would think it was a convalescent home outing. They had all tried in their own way, to keep it a secret that they ever belonged to a 'home,' or orphanage as it was also known as. 'This would 'probably be the last time they will see her' Ma had said.

A 'base' was soon established among the fallen trees, Matron fussed over Miss Pickering's eldest boy Lance, he had been in the homes longer than anyone else had. He had lost all his hair with a nervous disorder and had various illnesses since he was four years old. His mother died in nineteen thirty-six, and he hadn't got a father. Matron seemed to be trying to make amends, worrying about the thirteen-year-old boy.

The children sat on the trunks of the fallen trees like little birds waiting for a few crumbs, and permission to fly away among the trees.

Ma and Miss Pickering were both celebrating, Miss Pickering throwing all care to the wind at the sight of the wineglasses that Matron produced, her boys' were out of sight and it was her 'day off'.

The children from a distance watched the toast for Matron's retirement.

Miss Pickering still wearing her rose pink felt hat and a little worse for the sherry, did call out to her boys periodically.

"Don't go too far, you boys," she shouted.

"Just keeping them in check Matron," said Miss Pickering still clinging to her glass and waiting for 'another toast'.

The boys, who were used to chasing around on Spinney Hill Park, jumped on the girls from low branches, and they rolled down the grassy banks like wild Indians. After a tiring afternoon, they sang a few songs as the miles rolled away on the return journey, then it was a quick goodbye to Matron at the Receiving Home

"I expect she's going to live with her sister near the park," said Miss Pickering to Ma as the bus continued the journey home.

"I expect so," said Ma, "She was sitting behind the girls at church on Sunday. She didn't call in thank goodness."

"I don't know about her retiring, I could do with a rest myself," said Ma.

"It's no joke only one weeks holiday a year, it doesn't give you any time to unwind," said Miss Pickering.

"The boys have done their best, I could do with someone to help me with the mending, they rip their trousers every week."

Miss Pickering's hat was definitely tilted as she got off the bus.

"Come on boys, don't leave anything on the bus," she shouted.

The boys still in a jubilant mood pulled at the girls' ribbons as they left the bus.

"Hey, stop that," said Winnie laughing as her hair fell over her face.

The boys waved as the bus pulled away, they could see Miss Pickering, one hand clutching her handbag, and the other hanging on to her hat.

"She never goes anywhere without that hat," said Ma waving back. "Yow little blighters," Ma had caught sight of the boys blowing kisses to her girls.

The first sign that Matron had actually left the Receiving Home was when Superintendent Madden came to East Park Road. The slightly

201

balding gentleman in a raincoat over his suit came into the dining room.

"Good afternoon, girls, I've come to meet you all," he said.

They all stood up.

"I am Superintendent Madden from Countesthorpe. My wife and I are now in charge of you all. We live at The Residence, there are five boys' cottages, and five girls' cottages on The Drive. We have a Nursery where some of your little brothers live, a hospital, laundry and school, at the back of number six cottage."

"I know some of you already don't I?" he said looking at Marie, Colette and Nancy.

"Yes sir," said Marie.

"You've got brothers at the boys' home as well, haven't you, and you're Mother's got a baby with her at Hill Crest," the Superintendent was looking at them all in turn.

"Yes, sir," said Marie. " Michael's at the boys home.

"Do you like it at Sacred Heart? You've settled down well," said the Super.

"Margaret and Winnie's brother is at Countesthorpe as well Super," said Ma.

"Ah yes, he's the one we nearly lost," said Superintendent Madden. "I've got a little boy about as old as you. Well be good, I'll come and see you from time to time, and you'll no doubt be coming over to Countesthorpe."

"I like it at Ma's," said Nancy.

"Good, you don't want to go back to number eight then?" said the Super as he left the dining room with Ma.

"Sit down," said Ma as she left the room.

The front door with its sunray coloured glass clicked shut, and Ma came into the dining room.

"Well it was nice to see yow had a few manners when he came into the room, but yow could have sat down again," said Ma.

"He didn't tell us to," said Margaret.

"It was awful in number eight," said Nancy.

"The older ones had jobs to do 'til it was bedtime," said Colette.

"Polishing all the taps on the washbasins, that was my job after tea," said Marie.

"All the windows are high up on the walls, with brown paper crosses on them, you couldn't see out of them," said Nancy.

"We never sat in the dining room like this Ma," said Colette, "We had to keep it clean and stay in the kitchen 'til bedtime, and at the week end we had to play in the field they wouldn't let us stay indoors. I hated it."

"Sounds like a big place," said Ma. "Think yourselves lucky you're here."

"I knew Joe was very ill," said Winnie. "I knew it. I didn't say all my prayers for nothing did I?"

Under the new administration Ma received circulars about the schemes which Superintendent Madden was putting into force. The first circular was about a seaside holiday during the school holidays. Ma read it out loud:

"Winthorpe Camp site - August 1945.

1. Pick up bus at Receiving Home.
2. Arrive Winthorpe.
3. Collect palliasses and make up beds."

"What are palliasses Ma?" the girls asked.

"I think they're mattresses full of straw," said Ma.

"Are we going to sleep in a barn then?" said Nipper whose only experience of a barn was in the song they sang in the shelter, 'Old McDonald had a farm, eeh I eeh I ooh.'

"No you'll be sleeping in a tent, its camping we're going not living on a farm," said Ma. "Let me finish:-

4. East Park Road girls' tent near No. 10 & No.11 on left side of the field.
5. Officers quarters to the left of Dining Hall and Kitchen.

Advance party No.1 cottage to erect tent and unpack stores."

Ma rustled the pages. "Crikey it'll take ages to read this lot. Cookhouse duties. Peel potatoes for dinner, wash up, spread bread for tea, wash up, spread bread for breakfast. Sounds like its going to be run like the army. What time you get up, what you've got to wear, I thought it was supposed to be a holiday." Ma was shuffling through the pages to get the gist of it all. "It says that each cottage will in turn be on kitchen duties for one day."

"Have we got to peel hundreds of potatoes, Ma?" Margaret interrupted, she was already calculating on two potatoes each, twelve in each of the twelve homes plus the officers. "Hundreds," she said.

"It says so here," said Ma.

"We'll have to take our own potato peeler," said Doris.

"That's a good idea," said Ma.

"Can we take our dolls?" said Nipper.

"You can take them on the bus I suppose," said Ma.

The girls used the 'Gumption Cleaner' to clean the cooker and the bath, everything had a second spring clean in readiness for the holidays.

Miss Pickering and her boys stood in the sunshine as they turned the corner of Mill Hill Lane.

"Miss Pickering's got that old hat on again," said Ma thinking out loud.

"Good morning Miss Hammond, if the weather stays like this we shall be lucky," said Miss Pickering, pleased that she had locked up the house on St. Saviour's Road, and ready for her first holiday in eight years.

They both looked at the empty Receiving Home, wondering who was going to run the place now that Matron Buttridge had gone. There was no sign of life either in the big house opposite which was a remand home for boys.

" None of my boys are going in there," said Miss Pickering, touching the brim of her hat.

They recognised Cleaver's Bus as it came round the corner. The same driver had taken them to Bradgate park. Miss Pickering and Ma sat at the front while the boys raced to the back of the bus.

"The seats are a bit hard," said Winnie.

"This one's OK," said Doris, who was sitting near the window.

The first few miles were rather quiet, winding in and out of small villages, with a few attempts at singing songs then after the long stretches of open road the bus parked in the centre of a small town, alongside the buses carrying the Countesthorpe children.

This was their first encounter with the masses of children from the Cottage Homes.

After the 'watering stop' the bus travelled on through fields of waving gold corn.

"Look out for 'Boston Stump'" shouted the bus driver.

"What's that?" we asked.

"It's a cathedral."

They were none the wiser as no-one had seen a cathedral either. Miss Pickering was the first to spot it, at the front of the bus she had an open view. All heads were craning to get a view of the 'Stump' that stuck up from the flat contours of the landscape.

The bus finally dropped the passengers off at the edge of a field, they piled out like wartime refugees with their few belongings.

"Is this it?" asked Ma. who was as surprised as everybody else was.

Over the hedge they could see the pointed tips of the bell tents divided by a path from the gate.

"This must be it," said Miss Pickering, who was also stunned into silence.

They were not the first to arrive, a few of the tents were already occupied, and black shorts and plimsolls seemed to be the order of the day some of the children dashed about carrying buckets, and blankets.

"Better go and find our tent I suppose," said Miss Pickering, making her way across to the right hand side of the field, like a mother duck in her 'pink hat' being followed by a long line of ducklings.

The smell of the new-mown hay hit them as they examined each tent.

"This is number six," shouted a voice from within.

"Sorry," they replied.

"What number are you?" a girl appeared at the flap of the tent, which looked more like a wigwam.

"We're from East Park Road."

"That's your tent down there, last but one," said the girl, ready to disappear again.

"Where's the toilets?" said Ma.

"The officers toilets are there and that's the girls toilets next to them," she pointed towards a line of wooden buildings.

The 'East Park Road' tent had the bottom skirting neatly rolled up and secured all the way round allowing air to circulate through. It was easy once they had learned what a guy rope was and to be careful not to fall over them.

The black numbers one seven zero, on the laundry basket indicated that they were in the right tent. After a lot of to-ing and fro-ing with pillows and blankets, life under canvas was gradually beginning to get sorted out.

"Feet to the middle," shouted Doris who had been in another tent to see how the beds were laid out.

"We sleep in rows," said Marie who was standing near the open door. A neat circle of palliasses fanning out from the centre pole covered the ground sheet.

"I'll go and tell Ma we've finished," said Nipper.

Nipper walked down the corridor of the wooden hut shouting for Ma. Immediately she was confronted by several officers, a tall thin lady like Miss James, followed by a fat dumpy woman like Matron Buttridge.

"Get out of here, this is for officers only," shouted Miss Mather the tall thin one.

"Can't you read?" shouted Miss Milner, the short fat one.

Ma's door opened at the same time. "I'll see you outside in a bit Nipper," said Ma. Then turning to the officious two, she said "Her's not to know, we've only just got here," and she firmly shut the door.

"Ooh you're not allowed in there," said Nipper arriving back at the tent. "They don't half shout."

Ma came into the tent shortly afterwards. "Aren't you getting changed?"

"Have we got to wear shorts and blouses like them, Ma?" the girls asked, objecting to removing their cool dresses.

"They're not wearing socks," Hazel said. "Plimsolls without socks."

"Well you needn't if you don't want to, there's no reason why you shouldn't keep your dresses on," said Ma.

"I'm not wearing shorts," said Winnie. "They're made out of blackout curtaining and look daft with no socks on."

Margaret came into the tent. "I've found the toilets, they don't half pong."

"Wait till we've been here a fortnight," said Ma. "Then you'll have something to moan about.

A bell rang outside the main dining hall.

"Let's go and see what's happening," said Ma. "Mind what you say."

A multitude of children and the Officers appeared from all over the two fields, assembling at the dining hall where a man stood on a box. The splash of colour from the floral print dresses was quite noticeable among the black and white clad children, all shapes and sizes. Miss Pickering's boys had conformed to the same uniformity, and no socks.

The Officers stood in a line in front of the mass of juveniles. Ma and Miss Pickering joined them.

"You'll get to know us soon enough," said Mr Walters after giving out a list of duties and a few rules and regulations.

"Breakfast - 8am, Dinner - 1pm, and tea at five o'clock. Take your own towels to the wash tent, keep the place tidy, anyone not behaving will be put on 'fatigues' for a day." Mr Walters got down from his 'soap box' and they all dispersed, leaving the Officers to collect their leaflets complete with rules.

The East Park Road girls stayed together in their own tent getting used to the new surroundings, avoiding the cow droppings on the way to the toilets and wash tent.

"I hope there's no cows in the field, I've got a red ribbon in my hair," said Doris.

"No there's no cows," said Ruth who was sitting on the course stubble grass, not at all comfortable to sit on.

In the dining hall Ma sat with the Officers at the end of the room.

"Stand for grace," said Mr Walters, who seemed to be in charge of everything.

Everybody stood behind the long bench seats, and chanted away: "For what we are about to receive, may the Lord make us truly grateful."

The girls from Ma's on the other hand at the far end of the room, started to sing... "Be present at our table.... they suddenly stopped, being drowned by the many voices from the Cottage Homes. They all sat down, giggling, hoping that nobody had heard. Everybody's eyes seemed to be staring at them, which made them giggle all the more.

"You've got to send a monitor to the hatch to serve your table," said a girl from number eleven table.

"Go on Marie, you're the eldest," Hazel said, thankful that she hadn't got to walk out in front of the whole camp.

Marie brought the plates, and they were passed down the table. It looked like 'mucky stew.' There were about one hundred and fifty children in the hall spread over eleven tables, apart from Miss Pickering's boys, the girls home seemed to be the noisiest. After cold jam tart, they filed out one table at a time and back to the tents. Ma was told about singing grace, and she just told them 'when in Rome do as the Romans do.'

"You'd all better watch your p's and q's, they're a bit strict here," said Ma.

"We won't be put on 'fatigues' for giggling at the table, will we?" said Ruth.

"No they can't tell us off for giggling," said Nancy.

At the end of their first day, the skirting on the tent was rolled down and secured to the tent pegs. They all experienced their first open-air strip wash, flopping about in their nighties jumping across the bedding on the floor, before settling down on the straw palliasses. Ma closed the flap of the tent and bade them goodnight.

They had walked through the fields, which led down to the beach, had a first glimpse of the sea, and manoeuvred their way through the sand dunes. "Is it dark outside yet?" said Doris.

"Marie you're nearest the door, have a look," Hazel said.

"Have a look yourself 'azel 'unt," replied Marie who was muffled down the bed.

"I will," Hazel said and jumped up from the floor, the oilskin ground sheet was cold and sticky underfoot as she edged her way around the tent pole and bumped into the laundry basket.

"Ooh!" Hazel hollered out.

"Who's out of bed?" shouted the Yorkshire woman who was patrolling outside, "Get off to sleep."

Hazel was back on her palliasse much quicker than she had got off it. A torch shone on the tent from outside, and the footsteps went off into the distance.

The straw bedding squeaked and twitched with every movement throughout the night.

"Who's that? Somebody just trod on me," said a voice in the night.

"It's me," said Ruth "I want to go to the toilet."

"Ma said we've got to use the white bucket," said Margaret.

"Where is it?" Ruth whispered.

"It's near the door," whispered Doris who also had woken up.

"I can't find it," said Ruth.

"Perhaps somebody's moved it. It was near Marie's bed," said Margaret.

The lid of the enamel bucket clattered as Ruth found it. A hollow sound of water trickled into the empty bucket.

"I think I'll go," said Margaret.

"And me," said another voice.

In the darkness, Ruth fumbled her way back to her bed. The lid was eventually secured on the bucket and there was more rustling from the palliasses as they tried to get comfortable again.

"It's better than going across the field," said Nipper who had also been out of bed.

They soon adapted to camp life, visiting the wash tent each morning running through the heavy dew on the grass. Rolling up the skirting of the bell tent, tying back the door flap, slackening off the guy ropes. Folding the blankets to each palliasse, just in time for breakfast.

The days were mainly spent on the beach and trudging through fields to reach the sand dunes.

The first sight of the 'potato peelers' was after they had cleaned the tent up after breakfast, the groundsheet was swept and the brushes returned to the kitchen. A mountain of potatoes covered the floor and four boys sat around each with a bucket of water.

"Are you on 'fatigues?' the girls asked the boy who was smiling at them

"No it's our turn to do kitchen duty today."

"What's your name?" Nancy asked the one with the most potatoes in his bucket.

"Roy, what's yours?" he said.

"I'm Nancy, this is Margaret, that's Winnie that's Hazel and her names Ruth."

They were just beginning their conversation when their Officer came from the kitchen.

"What are you doing round here?" said Mr Clist from number two.

They immediately felt guilty. "We've just brought the rubbish to the bin," Margaret said.

Mr Clist, on first impression, reminded the girls of a cowboy film star, and they expected him to be as sweet and smiling just as if he was talking to his horse, 'Trigger'. They now had second thoughts about him, and the 'Roy Rogers' image had gone.

The list was up for the sporting events to be held during the two weeks. Doris and Hazel put their names down for the high jump, an event that was most popular with the girls.   Every evening after tea they practised jumping over a pole in the corner of the field, the pole was raised higher and higher, hearts were really pumping away as they tried even harder.

"I've got jelly legs," Hazel said breathlessly and with that both she and Doris crumpled up, struck by a fit of the giggles. Neither of them could jump any more, and sat watching Ruth and Nancy running up and down the field training for the one hundred yards. Like Siamese twins there were children tied together at the ankles practising for the three-legged race, and with no socks on it looked very painful. Miss Pickering's boys seemed to have vanished, they were no longer identifiable on the other side of the field.

At the end of the first week, the neighbours in number ten, and number eleven tents were becoming more friendly, even the harshness of their foster mother had mellowed a little. They could see how Ma and Miss Pickering disliked force of any kind, their kindness stood out against the threatening gestures of the Cottage homes foster parents. Most of the children were cowed and crept away as if they were about to be beaten. They had all heard about several girls getting a caning in their tents. Roy, the boy who peeled the potatoes had been belted with a leather strap and he had showed the girls the marks under his vest. Every time the girls saw him he darted away like a frightened rabbit. His subservient nature made him wiser, and the misery of himself and other boys was gradually changing him into a quick-witted comic, diverting tragedy into laughter.

"They're just like a load of 'fish wives' shouting in a fish market," said Ma of the other foster parents.

One night, when Ma had closed the tent and said goodnight, there was still noise coming from number eleven tent. The noise was gradually getting louder and the East Park Road tent could feel the vibrations of them all jumping about.

Suddenly there was a loud crack followed by a lot of screaming, the girls peeped from under the skirting of the tent. In the darkness they could just see a moving heap where the screaming was coming from. The Officers ran out from their wooden hut, shining the torches in the direction of the screams.

"Everybody all right in here?" said Ma opening the tent flap.

"Yes, Ma, its Miss Mather's girls they've been making a lot of noise." They all agreed.

"Thank God its not you lot, their tent's on the floor," said Ma shining the torch in the tent.

The screams continued as the girls were extricated from the heavy-duty tent. Officers were helping them out, as more of the foster parents came to help.

The girls stood with Ma, and watched and listened with the same bated breath as when the bombs dropped in Tichbourne Street in Leicester. Glad that it wasn't them under the rubble.

"Miss Mather was shouting, 'I'm sure it's Miss Hammond's, I'm sure its Miss Hammond's," said Ma. "That just serves her right."

The tent was left as it was and the number eleven girls were ushered into the dining hall to spend the rest of the night.

"Settle down now," said Ma securing the tent flap, "Goodnight," her footsteps faded into the distance.

In the morning, the crumpled tent, was just a wet heap of heavy canvas leaning in all directions.

"No wonder they were screaming, it must have been frightening for the little ones under that lot," said Winnie. "DON'T ANYBODY SWING ON OUR TENT POLE."

At breakfast Mr Walters gave them a lecture making sure that it didn't happen again.

It was the second Wednesday for East Park girls' kitchen duty. They were up early creeping about trying not to wake the little ones. The first task was to boil the water for the tea urns then count the slices of bread on to plates, so many were allocated for each table. The porridge was reheated for the girls and it was Ma's job to cook the bacon and eggs for the officers' table. The one hundred and fifty plates were on the table, then they were off again and washed up in the two giant sinks. The tables were wiped down and the floors mopped. Ma split the girls into groups, and set about peeling the mound of potatoes.

"That's the first one," Hazel said throwing the potato into the empty pan. "Only another three hundred to go."

A few boys joined them.

"Are you on fatigues again?" said Winnie.

"No, we volunteered," said Roy "We just wanted to come and help you," he said wryly.

"You can have my peeler," said Ruth.

Ma called Winnie and Ruth in for extra help in the kitchen.

"What are you doing on Sports Day?" the girls asked.

"I'm going in the egg and spoon race," said Roy.

"That's for the little ones" said Margaret.

"Yes, I know, I'll be the winner won't I?" said Roy.

"I'm going in the sack race," said Bobby, "My legs are not long enough for running."

The potato mountain was going down, or rather the bowls of peeled potatoes were filling up.

"What cottage are you in, Roy?"

"Number two. Clist," said Roy. "He's a bully. He stands near our dining room door, and we have to march out after meals. When it comes to my turn to pass him he pulls the door to and smashes me on the head. Get yer head up, he shouts."

"Ooh, does he do it to everybody?" Hazel said.

"No he just tells the Super I walked into a door," said Roy.

What had you done?" said Margaret

"Nothing," said Roy. "You don't have to do anything to get a good hiding."

"I'm glad we're not at Countesthorpe," said Doris.

"Countesthorpe Prison Camp," said Bobby.

"Does he hit you at camp as well?" Hazel said.

"He can't catch me here," said Roy. "I run out of the tent, and he can't shout because everybody can hear."

"We get a good hiding for talking to girls," said Bobby.

"What, while you're peeling potatoes?" said Doris.

"He kicks the bucket of water all over the kitchen floor when you've just scrubbed it," said Bobby.

"I don't fill mine so full now," said Roy.

"How long have you been at Countesthorpe?" Hazel asked Roy.

"Since I was eight, and I'm eleven now," said Roy.

"That's how old we are," Hazel and Margaret said together

"Did you pass the eleven plus?" said Margaret.

"No, they put crosses all over mine so that I didn't pass," said Roy.

"I'm eleven next year," said Bobby.

"You seem to be enjoying yourselves," said Ma coming out to see if the saucepans were full.

"I think you've done enough," said Ma.

"This is the second one Miss Hammond," said Roy.

"Well that's tons," said Ma. "Call me Ma, don't call me Miss Hammond. What's your surname?"

"Astle, Ma," said Roy.

"Well, Roy Astle, you've done very well. What's your name? she asked Bobby.

"Bobby Spriggs, Ma," he said.

"Have all your cottage gone down the beach?" said Ma.

"Yes Ma," Bobby and Roy said together.

"Well get in that kitchen, we're all going to have a drink. I'm in charge of you today," said Ma.

There were plenty of helpers to stab the sausages, and the mushy peas were just right for boiling, ready for dinner. The girls felt they had been there all day, and it wasn't yet dinnertime.

The afternoon passed more quickly, with more hands to help wash the stacks of mushy pea plates. They laid the tables for tea, then for the rest of the afternoon they played in the field.

Later in the day the cooks were in the kitchen, preparing the next day's meal, and there were more pots to clear away. The long sliced loaves were soon spread for tea, and the rest for breakfast the following morning. Their Kitchen Duty was finished.

"It wasn't so bad," said Ma.

On the Thursday cars arrived in camp. The Lord Mayor of Leicester had come to visit them for sports day.

Volunteers not taking part in the sports day did the Kitchen Duty. An automatic potato peeler had emerged, and quite an audience watched as the boys filled the drum with potatoes and water. The abrasive interior cleaned and scraped the potatoes as the drum was wound up with a handle. It worked perfectly. Today everyone was wearing the regulation black shorts and white blouses. Ma's girls had insisted on wearing white socks. The Lord Mayor Mr Cooper was welcomed to camp and the first of the competitions began. The main events were in the morning and the finals in the afternoon.

Ruth was in the finals of the 100yards, and Doris and Hazel were in the finals of the high jump. The bar was raised an inch at a time.

"It's like shelling peas," said the Lord Mayor. "As each one of them popped over the bar.

He might just as well have said 'Jelly Legs'. Both Doris and Hazel could not jump any more for giggling. The opposition won.

They had gained a few new friends, and had photos taken outside the tents.

Number eleven tent pole was replaced, and they had only been woken up once when the cows got into the field. The visits to Skegness had been enlightening, seeing all the shops. Having rides on the fair. Losing their money and sweets on the Big Dipper. The girls had been rowing on the lake, and swam in the sea, paddled perilously through the quick sands in squelchy mud up to their knees, built sandcastles, and worn silly hats.

Miss Pickering and her boys were quite strangers, in the dining hall they were seated well away from the girls, and their tent was on the far side of the field. Miss Pickering's kitchen duty was coupled up with another of the cottage homes, as her 'boys' were quite small. Miss Pickering herself had stayed in the kitchen all day in a long pinafore, shouting her orders from the serving hatch at mealtimes. She was glad to be going home, she told Ma as they waited for the bus to arrive. The camp beds had been far too hard for her to sleep on "I had one or two restless nights," she said to Ma.

"My bed wasn't too bad, " said Ma.

"Oh it wasn't the bed so much as that Mr Walters. He was always telling my boys off, I had a few words with him, and I wasn't going to stand for that. I told him they were on holiday and that was the end to it," Miss Pickering was as outspoken as she was motherly, and would not hear anything said against her brood. The convoy of buses pulled up to the gates and parked inside the field. They were soon filled with the returning campers, to sit on a bus, the comfort of the padded seats was sheer luxury, they couldn't wait to get back to the luxury of their own beds.

*   *   *

It was new schools for most of the girls and the start of a new term. Linda was at Moat Road infants. Nipper and Edna were going to Bridge Road Juniors. Everyone was moving up into a new class. Hazel was upstairs at Bridge Road, and in the seniors without Margaret who was going to the Grammar School. Marie Colette and Nancy were in new classes with the nuns at Sacred Heart.

Margaret was the first to leave that morning, looking like a new pin they waved to her as the tram passed by the house.

"I'm happy for her," said Ma "she deserves that."

Hazel stood there wondering what might have been.

The catholic girls were next to leave.

"I expect you'll have to write a composition on what you did in your holidays," said Ma as she tied the bows of ribbon.

In well-pressed tunics over crisp white blouses, and blazers although handed down over the years were still quite good, the rest of the girls looked equally as smart.

Up in the seniors, girls arrived from other schools and the first morning was quite chaotic. Everyone assembled in the hall, Hazel had learned the entire 'Cart's Choruses' but she had never seen Miss Cart.

A frail looking lady stepped up on to the platform, she was dressed in a long black dress looking like she had just stepped out of a picture with Queen Victoria. There was hushed silence as she welcomed them to the school.

"This is Bridge Road Girls School...B.R.G.S.

It's the same initials as our school motto. Be Ready for Gracious Service. I want you all to remember that," she looked at the girls over her silver rimmed spectacles.

Miss Cart had been teaching for thirty years, and she only had a short time left before her retirement. Her long black clothes matched her sombre mood she was a pious and devout Christian. She had compiled a booklet of choruses, each chorus a text from the bible, in verse and sung to well known tunes by the hundreds of girls who had gone through her school.

Names were called out and they followed their respective teachers into the classrooms. Hazel was in 1A.

The home girls had all been to the Girl Guides Christmas parties, and they had badgered Ma into letting them join St Christopher's Girl Guide troupe, but the answer always came back as 'NO'.

Marie and Colette were now old enough to join the guides at Sacred Heart, and another letter from the Sisters asked if they would be allowed to attend guides every Wednesday night.

All the extra activities that Marie had requested, were sanctioned. Girl Guide uniforms were produced and they could attend on Wednesday nights. This meant even more time out of the home in the evenings for Marie, being second eldest, Hazel was beside herself with jealousy, and stormed out of the kitchen.

"It's not fair, why do they get all the privileges," she said, and went bawling into the dining room.

Because of her outburst, some of the girls also protested they too wanted to join the Guides.

It was in November when the subject came up again.

Miss Cart announced that all the girls who were Guides or Rangers or Salvation Army Guards were to come to school in their uniforms, for the Remembrance Day service. The whole school assembled and everyone wore a red poppy.

The far door in the corner of the hall opened and the assembled girls stood up. The frail looking, yet formidable headmistress held a circle of poppies in her hands. A flash of bright red against the black clothes of this lone figure. Bridge Road School had been opened in 1884, and many of the pupils had died in the First World War. Today they were being remembered together with those who had died in the Second World War.

The first part of the school service was devoted to the Book of Choruses:

'Give and it shall be given unto you,
Give of thyself in service ever true,
This is the Promise God had given to you,
As thy days so thy strength shall be.'

This was sung to the tune of Elgar. Another favourite followed.

'Consider the lilies of the field how they grow,
They toil not neither do they spin,
Yet Solomon in all his glory,
Was no arrayed like one of these.

Then, with bowed heads, the prayers began for the Royal Family, for Dukes and Archbishops, and all in Authority. For Countries of the Commonwealth and all Suffering Nations, for the people, the wounded the sick and the dying and bereaved.

Miss Cart's prayers were for everyone. They sang the morning hymn.

'All people that on earth do dwell,
Sing to the Lord with cheerful voice.'

The colour party made up of two fourth year Rangers, was signalled to form the procession, they walked up to Miss Cart and she handed them the wreath of poppies. The rest of the colour party then followed the two

Rangers, four Guides with the Union Jack in the centre of The Girl Guides trefoil and the Rangers flag.

They made their way out of the hall down the stairs to the Memorial in the school grounds, the second verse of the hymn accompanying their task. The colour party took up their position in front of the Memorial. A small crowd of people stood on the pavement, men removed their caps watching as the flags were lowered. The last verse of the hymn was echoing from inside the school.

At the eleventh hour, of the eleventh day of the eleventh month.

The Rangers read the inscription from the monument that listed all the names of those who fell in the First World War.

'AT THE GOING DOWN OF THE SUN AND IN THE MORNING, WE WILL REMEMBER THEM'

Miss Cart, and the girls' in school repeated the same words, then the public outside, and the whole school stood for two minutes silence. The Rangers placed the wreath of poppies at the foot of the white marble Monument, and stepped back with a firm salute.

The colour party made their way back to the assembled school, the bystanders in the street now replaced their caps, and the Baker returned to delivering his bread.

Miss Cart, after a last prayer sat at the piano and played a march as the school filed out of the hall back to the classrooms.

Betty Matthews came into the classroom in her grey and red uniform, she belonged to the Salvation Army, and was a 'Guard', not a 'Guide' After school Hazel asked her if she knew whether she could join.

The name and address on the bit of paper wasn't far from the home, and Hazel called at the house for all the details on her way home from school. The Salvation Army Guards, met in Baggrave Street, just round the corner from Ma's. Guard Leader Seeby said she would visit Ma, and ask her if they could join. Hazel then broke the news to Ma.

"Who's told you about all this," asked Ma.

"My friend asked me if I'd like to join," Hazel lied.

Marie, Colette and Nancy, were now fully-fledged Girl Guides, and every Wednesday in their blue uniforms the 'Kingfisher patrol' slipped out of the back door.

After many arguments, and much discussion, it was agreed that Edna,

Doris and Hazel could go to the first meeting. Miss Seeby took to Edna straight away, and invited her to her house every Saturday morning to do leatherwork. Doris was to learn the trumpet, and Hazel was given a drum. They arrived back at Ma's with both instruments Ma was horrified at the 'two noisiest bits of the band.'

"Yow don't think yow going to bang that thing in here," said Ma.

"Yes, Ma, I've got to learn the 'mammy daddy roll,' Hazel said proudly.

"Not in this house," said Ma cutting her off, and both the drum and the trumpet were put on top of the kitchen dresser.

The Hunts had their first chance to play with the band one Saturday morning, only when they had finished their jobs. The double bass drum was strapped to Hazel's friend, Betty, who beat in time as they marched up and down the road. Betty twirled the specially padded drumsticks expertly over the top of the drum, which looked as if it was part of her body. Deserted factories lined both sides of the road and no one heard their musical debut. There were no congratulatory remarks afterwards and Hazel and Doris assumed they had failed the preliminary test as both the drum and trumpet were left at the Salvation Army Hall, never to be seen again.

They all missed Olive, and since Marie had been the eldest all the fun had gone from the hours in the dining room

The 'Cart's Choruses' were now replaced by the chanting of 'The Angelus,' and 'The Rosary.'

Olive's replacement was a five year old girl called Peggy, a very quiet girl, with ginger hair. She had been abused and beaten at home so had come to Ma's to be looked after. Linda was still the baby at four years old, sitting next to Peggy at the table her blonde curls a bright contrast to Peggy's deep auburn wavy hair. Neither of them had any brothers or sisters, and after tea they played together in the corner with the rag dolls.

*   *   *

Christmas hadn't been the same. It was the first year that Ma hadn't had a cup of tea in bed on Christmas morning. It started quite early as usual and all the blue-room were awake except Marie. Hazel changed Edna's bed, as there was a strong smell in the room, they decided that it was coming from Marie's bed in the corner.

"Marie wake up what have you done?" they shouted.

Marie did not answer.

The girls from the brown room had gathered outside Ma's bedroom door while the attic girls' were coming down the stairs.

"Come in," said Ma. "It's a bit early isn't it?"

"There's an awful smell out there Ma," said Nipper.

Ma was out of bed like a shot, her nostrils catching the bad odour.

They all gestured Ma towards Marie's bed.

"What's up here, what happened Marie?" said Ma.

"I've had an accident, Ma," said Marie.

Ma stormed along the landing, and put the bath tap on.

"You lot wait in the brown room, nobody's going downstairs until this little lot is sorted out,"

They were all dying to open their presents. This year the dining room was locked, the presents were in pillowcases on their individual chairs in the dining room.

Eventually the girls followed Ma down the stairs, and started singing.

'Once in Royal David's City.' The first line was sung by the time they reached the dining room door.

"It's a bit late for that," said Ma unlocking the door.

"Happy Christmas, Ma" the girls said.

"Happy Christmas", said Ma. Get the kettle on, H."

"Yes, Ma," Hazel said and hurried into the scullery.

Getting Ma a cup of tea was more important to her than sorting out the pillowcase full of odds and ends. Hazel even made time to light Ma's sitting room fire while the kettle boiled.

Marie was in the doldrums, Winnie was comforting her, saying 'it could happen to anybody, I've often dreamt I was on the toilet, but I've always woken up in time, thank goodness," said Winnie.

The first Sunday after Christmas, was St Stephen's Day, and it was announced that Father Huntley would be leaving. The girls were all upset by the news he had been part of their lives every Sunday for years. The routine of the last three years was rapidly changing. This year there was no visit to The Receiving Home, no singing to the Lord Mayor on Christmas morning, they were only too glad that the Matron Buttridge era was over.

CHAPTER FIVE

January 1946

The latest circular from the Superintendent was to say that they would all be going to the Pantomime.

"Ooh, What's it called, Ma?" the girls were eager to know.

"Jack and the Beanstalk," said Ma.

None of them had ever been to a pantomime before, but had read all the fairy stories. It was another lever for Ma to make them behave themselves 'or yow won't go', warned Ma.

The evenings round the dining table were now more serious, with homework, and schoolbooks. Margaret labelled all her exercise books.

"French, three times a week, Algebra, History, Biology," said Margaret.

"What's Algebra?" they asked.

"Mathematics, look," said Margaret.

"Looks like double Dutch to me," Hazel said.

"I prefer Pansy Potter," said Ruth turning the pages of her comic. "So be quiet, I'm doing my homework."

Doris sat drawing a picture for Ma's wall, while Hazel was engrossed in drawing a frog in her biology book.

Its eyes are not right," said Doris. "They should be on top of its head."

Doris's critical eye soon made the drawing of the frog look very professional. Marie had gone upstairs for her strip wash, so Hazel quickly laid Ma's tray, not forgetting the pepper and salt, and whisked the supper into her sitting room.

"Strike, VIP treatment," said Ma.

The play of the week was about to begin on Ma's wireless.

They all said goodnight to Ma, and went to bed.

Margaret and Winnie came down the attic stairs.

"Is Ma in her sitting room?" they whispered.

"Yes, I've done her supper so she won't be coming out again," Hazel said.

They all floated along the landing in their nightgowns, and sat grouped together on the stairs. The loudspeaker was on in the dining room.

"Friday Night Theatre...," the voice of the announcer came from the little box on the wall.

The girls sat quietly, listening to their weekly treat on the cold

'Paul Temple' Episode 2.

linoleum of the stairs, enchanted as the eerie music introduced the thriller of the week, always at the ready to run up the stairs if Ma's sitting room door opened.

At school Hazel was determined to do better, now that she was in the seniors. She liked her teacher, and she was pleased with the 'Brownie Doll' that Hazel was making.

The biology homework books had been marked, and were handed back to the class. Hazel had an awful feeling she hadn't given her work in, and tried to think what she had done with her frog.

"I want you to open your books, and take a good look at your homework," said Miss Heightman.

"For an 'A' class its not good enough. Very untidy work, I want better things from you in future." She took a book from her desk.

"This is what I expect in future," she said holding up a book for all to see.

Hazel felt a surge of heat rise up her face, it was her green frog, and she looked at the marks as the book was placed on her desk. Ten out of ten, she could not believe it.

"Very nice and neatly done, Hazel," said Miss Heightman. "Well done."

Hazel had never had a top mark before, perhaps the dunce from downstairs was improving.

*   *   *

There wasn't so much mess from the chimney sweep this year as the sweep now had a modern vacuum cleaner, but it had still taken all morning to do the spring cleaning.   On that Saturday afternoon, the queue for the pictures had stretched right round the corner. The girls were late and nearly didn't get in. Hazel had noticed a line of girls, similarly identically dressed to themselves, standing in the foyer. Mr Bowerman, the manager, ushered the line of girls upstairs to the balcony. Hazel approached Mr Bowerman, while the East Park Road girls stood in the queue.

"Please, sir, could you save us some seats, as we have to do all our Saturday jobs before we come," Hazel pleaded.

"Where do you come from then?" said Mr Bowerman.

"We come from the home on East Park Road, near St Stephen's Church," Hazel said smiling.

"How many are there from the home?" Mr Bowerman looked towards the queue.

Hazel beckoned the girls to step forward

"Oh, we'll have to do something about that," said Mr Bowerman going over to the cashier.

The girls stood in a line, a neat and tidy row of figures in identical clothes.

"Right up you go," said Mr Bowerman, from now on you can all come in free, just stand in a line and let the lady know."

They showed him their pocket money, and he said,

"Put it away."

"Thank you Mr Bowerman. Thank-you."

They thanked him very much, twelve times over.

"That's all right, up you go," he said

The East Park Road girls went up the stairs in twos, and had the balcony to themselves.

"Good old H. Wait till Ma hears about this. Good old H," the girls repeated.

With their seven sweets, they sat way above the noise coming from below.

"On no account are we to leave any litter behind, or Mr Bowerman might change his mind," Hazel whispered to them.

After the free entertainment, they were no longer hauled along by the tidal wave of children leaving the cinema. They came down the stairs, holding the ornate hand rail like royal princesses, waiting while the cinema emptied. Thanking Mr Bowerman once again on their way out.

"Ma, Hazel got us in the pictures for free," was the cry from the back door to Ma's sitting room.

"What! She's done what? said Ma, just recovering from having 'five minutes' in the chair.

"She asked Mr Bowerman if we could get in for free," said Nipper.

"No I didn't," Hazel said coming up close behind. "I asked Mr Bowerman if he would save us some seats, in case we were late."

"And he's let you go in free?" said Ma.

"Yes, Ma. We all sat in the balcony," shouted all the girls still excited. "And we've still got our pocket money."

"Good old H," said Ma. "Yow good at some things."

"Can we go and spend our pocket money now, Ma?" said Nipper.

"Yow blighters, don't go further than the shops in St. Saviour's Road," said Ma.

On Saturday teatime, they each examined their individual purchases, there was locust beans, liquorice root, a halfpenny's worth of imps, strong liquorice squares in a small tin. Doris had found a shop run by an old lady and bought a matchbox full of tiny beads. Winnie had bought a halfpenny's worth of floral gums, and Edna had bought The Picture Post, which had frightening pictures of a little girl who lived in an iron lung. Some of them had bought 'penny specs' at the green grocers, which could either be half an apple, or orange, with the mouldy bit cut out.

Today, Hazel felt that she was the eldest, she had slightly changed the everyday routine to everyone's delight.

On Thursday night as usual, the dining room table was piled high with mending. All the liberty bodices had been boiled, and the rubber buttons that had perished, then flattened in the mangling, had to be replaced. The new metal buttons covered with cotton material were much easier to sew on. With wet hair they sat looking bedraggled.

"Have you combed your hair, Ruth?" said Ma.

"Yes, Ma," said Ruth.

"Yow look like you've come through a hedge backwards," said Ma.

Margaret, was mending socks, Doris had a pile of the liberty bodices in front of her, Ruth was mending the elastic in her school blouse, she always liked the elasticated ones because she didn't have to tuck them in her knickers for the P T lesson. Winnie elasticated the navy knickers.

"The elastic's gone in these legs, somebody could lose their hanky, and they certainly wouldn't hold any apples if they went scrumping," said Winnie.

Edna had a bad eye, and was managing to hold a needle if someone threaded it for her.

"Oh, Oh.," Edna sighed.

"Leave it if you can't do it," said Ma.

"Can I leave this, Ma?" said Colette.

"Is it beyond repair?" said Ma. "Let's look, whose is that?"

"It's Marie's," Hazel chided.

"It's not mine then see, 'Azelunt," said Marie in her own defence.

"Don't you two start I've had enough of yow two bickering at one another," said Ma.

"She started it," said Marie.

"And I'll finish it," said Ma. "Make that fire up, Hazel."

Ma parted the two girls, before the kicking started under the table.

"I always have to do the mucky jobs," Hazel said, emptying the remains of the bucket onto the fire.

"I need a medal for looking after yow lot," said Ma.

"A rusty'un," Hazel said, passing Ma's chair, upon which she received a 'silly sender.' Unbalanced by the coal bucket, she slipped on the polished lino and both she and the bucket landed on the floor, in a pile of dusty slack.

"STRUTH!" Hazel hollered.

"Winnie shrieked into a fit of giggles and everybody joined in.

"Now get that cleaned up as well," said Ma her broad grin bursting into laughter. "That's a good'un, a Rusty Medal. That's about all I will get from this little lot."

Marie went to bed with the rest of the girls, forgetting Ma's supper. Hazel put her slippers back on and slipped down the stairs. She put the bread under the grill, and sliced the cheese, and when the kettle had boiled quickly made Ma's tea. The tray was neatly laid, she knocked on Ma's sitting room door.

"Thank-you, H," said Ma "That's a nice surprise. Has Marie gone to bed?"

"Just thought you'd like to get your feet up for a bit," Hazel said.

"Pity you can't be like this all the time," said Ma. "I saw Olive when I was on the bus yesterday."

"Oh, is she alright, Ma, does she like it at home?" Hazel said,

"She was standing on the street corner. I didn't like the look of that," said Ma.

"Did she look nice? Was she wearing lipstick?" Hazel asked.

"She was wearing plenty of that," said Ma looking at Hazel long and hard.

"She hasn't been to see us since she left," Hazel said.

"Makes me wonder what sort of job she's got," said Ma worriedly. "She never ought to have gone home. Switch the wireless on, H."

"Which knob? I've never switched a wireless on before," Hazel said suddenly pleased with herself as music came from the Bakelite casing.

"Let's have you in bed now, school tomorrow," said Ma.

"G'night Ma," Hazel said and kissed her cheek.

In the blue room Marie was muttering under her breath, annoyed with herself for forgetting to make Ma's supper.

"Can you say your prayers in Latin yet, Marie?" Hazel said turning out the landing light.

On visiting day, Mr Seaton told Margaret and Winnie that their Mother could come home if she wanted to. Like their Dad, they found it too painful to talk about. Winnie's mother had post-natal depression, after milk fever, and still didn't acknowledge the fact that she had a five- year-old little boy. 'Dad says she thinks she's only got two little girls, she never asks about Joe.'

"Now the war's over, Winnie we'll go and see your Dad, instead of spending our pocket money," Hazel said knowing that Winnie would love to see their house in Avenue Road.

"Ma would never let us, besides we don't know the way," said Winnie.

"I found my way home, and I know the way to my Grandma's," Hazel said.

"Wouldn't it be a nice surprise for him," said Winnie. I'll see what he says next visiting day. and I'll ask him which bus to catch."

"I'll come with you," said Doris, who was also listening.

"Ma will think we've run away," said Winnie.

"Well we can run back again," Hazel said.

"There's a big photo on my Dad's sideboard of my Mam, I would love to see that," said Winnie.

They went to bed imagining and speculating on all the things they could do. Lay the table for his tea, get the fire ready for lighting,and perhaps do a bit of dusting.

The day for the Pantomime finally came.

They travelled along London Road down Silver Street to the Opera House, and were ushered into a magnificent building all gold and royal blue. The gilt filigree on the ceiling enhanced with chandeliers. Blue plush seats matching the edge of the balcony, which was faced with gold tracery, and curtained boxes, either side for 'royalty.'

The seats sloped down to the front of the stage where the orchestra stalls were in advanced stages of preparation. The heavy fire curtain moved slightly, teasing them that it was going to start.

Suddenly from the back of the theatre, came hundreds of footsteps, thumping away down the blue carpeted stairs.

The Cottage Homes children had arrived.

"Strike!" said Ma. "I thought the army was coming in."

They looked out for the few friends made at camp, and spotted Roy Astle and Bobby Spriggs. Laura Brown, with her blonde hair, the abandoned baby who had been at Countesthorpe longer than anyone else. The friends they had made with number eleven after the tent had collapsed.

The orchestra struck up, tuning their cellos and violins.

"Turn round," said Ma, when the girls started waving. "There's other people in the theatre besides you."

The fire curtain was raised, revealing dark blue velvet curtains with gold tasselling and fringing, and when the curtains were finally pulled back, the fantastically colourful show began. They had never seen such brilliance, diamante dresses, and shoes and sequinned outfits. Jack was a girl, and Jack's Mother was a man. The only time they had ever seen a man dressed as a woman was when Stan the neighbour came round for the Victory celebrations. Ma said a lady had come to see the girls in the dining room, at first they thought it was Olive, but they didn't know her (him) until he scratched his head and his hair moved. Jack's Mother 'the Dowager', and 'the Baron' pulled down a printed sheet with a song for the audience to sing,

"Do you know how many beans make five?"

A song they all sang for weeks afterwards.

In the interval they kept glancing backwards to the boys at the back, trying to wave when Ma wasn't looking. They could only leave their seats if it was an emergency, so there was no meeting at the back of the theatre. The curtains rolled back for the second half, the colourful dresses and ginger wig of the dowager, in her kitchen doing the ironing, and making herself look pretty for the Baron coming to see her. The cardboard doors that just slapped her in the face when she was going out, just like 'Old Mother Riley,' at the pictures, making the home girls forget that there had been a war, and some of their memories that they always kept locked away. The finale, was most spectacular, the part of the show where everyone wore their dazzling gowns, in gold and silver. The long legs of Jack in his high heeled shoes, slapping his thighs. The girls were near enough to see that the seams in his stockings were straight.

The whole cast with eyes glistening from the floodlights singing 'God

Save Our Gracious King," The pantomime was over.

The hundred or so boys and girls from the Cottage Homes had gone by the time Ma and her girls were out of the Opera House.

Since the Cottage Homes, had merged with The Scattered Homes Ma had more week-ends off. Her new relief was Miss Glegg who was also a permanent relief for Miss Milner at number ten cottage. Miss Glegg was Irish, her rugged face was framed by naturally wavy hair, and her teeth had enormous gaps and were brown from chain smoking. Her glasses were of a strong magnification, making her eyes look small in the centre of circles. She walked very quickly, and twice as fast as Ma.

Ma left on Friday afternoon, and when the girls came home from school, Miss Glegg, stood with her back to the kitchen fire staring at them. She stood the girls round the kitchen table asking their names, and what jobs they do, how old were they and how long had they been at Ma's. She had seen Marie at Countesthorpe and remembered her. Marie's Dad was Irish, and she wanted to know what part of Ireland they came from and where he was now. If Marie knew she didn't say. The groceries nowadays came from Countesthorpe on a Friday afternoon, Ma usually put them away before the girls came out of school. Miss Glegg chose four of the girls to sort the bags of groceries, and put them in the right containers. The enamel bowls were taken down from the cupboard, FLOUR, SUGAR, TEA , BREAD, CEREAL. The blue bags full of sugar were tipped into the heavy container and put back in the cupboard. Winnie poured the porridge oats into the CEREAL container, while Ruth packed the tea away. The lid of one of the bowls fell on the floor, and Ruth picked it up. the packet of tea that Ruth was holding suddenly burst and the contents fell into the porridge oats.

"Wow..oh crikey, Winnie help me," whispered Ruth.

The tea was scooped up from the bowl of oats, at the same time it was getting covered in the floury particles from the porridge. Once it was in its own container, the tea soon lost the powdery look when it was shaken up. The bits of tea leaves that were still in the porridge oats however were not so easily seen. The more they searched the more the tea mingled with the porridge.

"It'll be alright", Hazel said. "Nobody will be able to tell."

Miss Glegg came into the kitchen.

"Haven't you finished that job yet? Hurry up, it's time it was all away."

The girls explained what had happened.

228

"What do you expect me to do about it," said Miss Glegg. "You'll just have to put it away as it is."

Miss Glegg went back down the hall.

"With those glasses on I didn't expect her to do anything," said Winnie.

"She wouldn't see a football if it fell in," said Ruth.

They could hardly lift the tins for laughing.

When the porridge started to cook that night, lots of black bits were mixed in with the porridge.

"Well I'm not fishing all them out, we'll just have to leave them, they'll probably sink to the bottom by morning," said Miss Glegg.

The porridge didn't smell any different when they went to bed.

On Saturday morning the porridge was passed through the bobby-hole, Miss Glegg was smiling. The porridge was dark brown., with black spots in it.

"Eeer, tea-leaf porridge," everybody said, pulling faces.

"You can eat it up," said Miss Glegg, "If you don't eat it you don't go to the pictures," she stood and watched as the girls swallowed every spoonful.

"It's not so bad if you close your eyes," said Ruth.

"You can eat mine then," said Doris.

Miss Glegg stood there smiling. Later she made them do their jobs all over again, she said the house was filthy.

They all felt rather sick.

It was bacon and fried bread for breakfast on Sunday, so they were spared a second dose of 'tea-leaf-porridge.

On Monday morning the porridge came sailing through the hatch, with no tea leaves. Ma had seen the brown porridge cooking on Sunday night, and when Miss Glegg had gone back to Countesthorpe she threw it in the pig-bin.

Coming into the dining room Ma looked at their stunned faces.

"Yow don't think I could let you eat that," said Ma. "I couldn't eat it myself and I wouldn't expect you to eat it either."

"It was an accident, Ma," said Ruth.

"Well the pigs'll love it," said Ma.

"Good old Ma," said Nipper.

"Less of the old," said Ma.

"What with 'cobweb cake,' 'standing on the cellar steps half the night,' and 'tea-leaf-porridge', I leave the house for five minutes and there's always something gone wrong when I get back," said Ma, eating her porridge.

*   *   *

At church, the induction service for the new vicar took place, with all the visiting Bishops and pomp and ceremony that Father Huntley was used to. It was a sad day for the church, the congregation was full, not only to meet the new vicar but to say goodbye to Father Huntley. His last sermon was to everyone, he wouldn't forget any of them. He'd had a very happy time at St. Stephen's all through the war, he had made so many friends. The parish that he was going to was a small town in a coal mining area, he said he would come and see them from time to time. None of them liked the look of the new vicar, Charles Benjamin

It was the turn of Doris, Winnie and Ruth to take the eleven plus examination. The two-day exam was being revised with Margaret the night before. Hazel was crocheting with some wool that Ma had. Ma's sister had made a set of crocheted mats for her sideboard and Hazel was now having a go at the lacy mats. The crocheting went round and round and was getting bigger and bigger, but instead of lying flat, it looked more like a large egg cosy. Over a few days she just kept going because the wool was too knotty to undo. When the ball of wool was finally used up, the crocheted mat looked like a sock when pulled over her foot. Hazel made another one to match, resulting in a good pair of slippers 'cum bed socks' or polishers for the landing and stairs.

The school term went by very quickly, the 'Brownie Doll' was finished, all that Hazel needed was a piece of yellow material to make the tie. It was one of the chosen articles put on show at the end of the term.

*   *   *

On the first day of the Easter Holidays, Margaret, Winnie, Doris and Hazel caught the tram to Avenue Road. Winnie's Dad was out as was expected and the key was under the doormat. With coats off, they started giving the place a good spring clean, the ashes were raked out and the fire laid with sticks all ready for lighting. Winnie dusted the sideboard, caressing her Mother's photograph in the wooden frame

230

exactly how she had described it to them.

"She looks nice," said Doris.

"She never ought to be in a mental hospital," said Margaret.

"Ooh that's me, when I was little," said Winnie finding an envelope full of photos in the drawer.

"There's Aunt Sarah," Hazel said sharing the excitement with them. "Is there one of little Joe?"

"No" said Margaret, " Mam was too ill after Joe was born."

The time was getting on, with everything put away, and the table laid for one, the four walked back to East Park Road.

"If Ma says anything, we'll just tell her the truth," said Winnie who didn't care now that she had seen her Mother's photograph. They all agreed.

"She can't clout us all together," said Margaret who had never had a 'silly sender' from Ma at any time.

"Where've you been?" said Ma as they shouted 'good afternoon' at the back door.

"We went for a walk to Mr Seaton's house, and cleaned up for him, he'll be ever so pleased, Ma," Hazel said and smiled at Ma.

"Look," said Ma tapping her thimble on the table, "Yow know you're not supposed to go visiting."

"We enjoyed the walk, Ma, and we only laid the table for his tea," said Margaret.

"Yow blighters, get away with murder. Don't make a habit of it. Go on, scram," said Ma.

Three white dresses arrived in a special delivery. white shoes, socks gloves and white veils. They were for the Catholics, and the celebration of confirmation and of Corpus Christie.

Marie, Colette and Nancy had been practising for months for the big day. This year, for the first time since the war there was going to be a big procession round the streets beyond Spinney Hill Park.

The dresses were tried on in the secrecy of Ma's sitting room, as Ma didn't want a repeat performance when their Guide uniforms arrived.

The rest of the girls had kicked up a hullabaloo, complaining that they should be allowed to go to guides as well.

They were all excited when the day finally came for Marie, Colette and Nancy to get dressed for Corpus Christie.

They stood in the kitchen like three angels in pure white from head to toe, all of the girls looking on.

"They make a nice little procession on their own," said Ma, looking at them proudly.

"We don't need coats, do we Ma?" asked Colette.

"No, but you'll have to carry your veils until you get to the church," said Ma. " I think you can go now, you look lovely."

Ma let the three angels out of the front door so they didn't rub their dresses on the walls of the entry.

"I'll bring your coats up when we come, said Ma. I don't think its going to rain, we'll see you in the procession."

The girls waved to them until the white dresses disappeared behind the green leaves of the trees in the park..

"I wish I was a Catholic," said Nipper.

"I wouldn't want to dress twelve of you up like that," said Ma. "It's took me all morning to get them three ready. It's going to be a long day."

There was to be a service for all the first communicants, then the procession would leave Sacred Heart at three pm. followed by High Mass. The streets were lined with people of every age and denomination, box cameras at the ready. The newspaper photographers had a vantage point in the centre of the road.

There were no crowds when Father Huntley took all St Stephen's choirboys through the streets at the first declaration that the war had ended. Everyone was so overjoyed they had all gathered in Leicester at the Town Hall to see the water fountains switched on again.

The two heavy arched doors of Sacred Heart eventually opened, much to the excitement of the waiting crowds. All that could be seen was a sea of white and gold. The crucifix in between two acolytes carrying candles led the procession, with two incense orbs swinging each side. There was quite a disturbance in the crowds as everyone tried to get a better view. A white ribbon of small children followed behind with the white robed Nuns at intervals at their side. Behind them came more Sisters singing and chanting in Latin. The procession had not reached the girls, they could just see the church door, and a flurry of lacy veils blowing in the breeze, each one firmly fixed to a crown of yellow flowers, a beautiful sight and such a lovely day.

"That could be them coming out now," said Ma.

They strained their eyes searching for their Catholic sisters.

"Aah, don't they look a picture," said Ma as the tiny children straggled along out of step, just trying to keep in line with their teachers. Each one looking like a bridesmaid.

The singing got louder as the Nuns passed by, they could see Nancy.

"Where?"

"There she is."

Nancy had obviously been told not to wave, her gloved hands were firmly pressed together bound by a Rosary.

"She looks lovely," said Ma.

The singing changed to a more cherubic sound as they kept up with the Sisters in front.

Both boys and girls followed next and they could see Colette. With one boy either side in long white cassocks, the flowers on her head added just a little colour. She smiled when she saw the girls.

A group of priests were next, their loud voices hushing the crowds, some of which must have known what they were chanting as they made the sign of the cross upon themselves.

"This is Marie's group," said Ma.

All the older children singing The Angelus in heavenly celestial music, followed behind the priests. Marie with her crown of flowers, could see them through the veil covering her face, she was smiling as she was singing, she didn't need a book of any sort, she knew all the words off by heart. Suddenly there was a hive of activity at the door of the church, a shrine or statue was being manipulated through the archway. It was carefully lifted shoulder high, under a canopy of heavy curtains draped at the corners. The four orbs of incense one at each corner, were swinging gently enveloping the Holy Eucharist in perfumed sweetness. It was a proud moment for the bearers who walked carefully up the hill. The priests and Cardinals brought up the rear of the procession in copes of gold over their white raiment's. Most of the crowd genuflected as they passed by. The tail of the white and gold spectacle disappeared up the hill, and the spotless babies following the first crucifix were coming down the other side. The cameras and photographers were busy again, manoeuvring for the best position of their own little cherubs.

"If only their Mother could see them," said Ma.

It took the best part of an hour for the procession to return to church. Ma and the girls could see Marie, Colette and Nancy much better on the return as the procession had spread out quite a lot. Ma left the coats in the school room for Marie, Colette and Nancy as they would be returning home after the party. Then with the rest of her brood Ma made their way back down the hill to East Park Road. They all went to bed, very tired.

Miss Cart announced at school that there was going to be to a day's holiday.

"The King and Queen are coming to Leicester. A special place will be reserved for all school children to line the route through Spinney Hill Park," said Miss Cart.

At Guards that week, Guard Leader Seeby asked for volunteers for Standard bearers to stand at the entrance of the park for the Royal Visit. Betty and Hazel were chosen as they were the same height. They practised with the standards, getting the right arm into position, placing it properly in the holster.

"It may be windy, so you'll have to cling on to the corner of the flag until the Royal car arrives," said Miss Seeby. "Try it again."

They walked up and down, getting the feel of the Union Jack, and the Salvation Army Standard.

"You will be on your own, as I'm taking my mother to The Imperial Typewriters, where the King and Queen will be getting out of their car. The Standards must be treated with great respect, and brought back to my house straight afterwards."

The great day arrived. They called at Miss Seeby's house, looking very smart with holsters in place and wearing white gloves. She gave them the rolled up Standards with sufficient warning that 'they were very precious.' At the park gates Hazel and Betty had plenty of time to practice, they stood opposite each other like sentries at Buckingham Palace.

The King and Queen arrived, the Royal Car slowed down to walking pace as it drove through the park gates, it passed the Standards with a Salute from the King. The children were all cheering, and suddenly Hazel and Betty were left abandoned, rolling up the precious Standards.

In the excitement of the moment, they too ran across the park with the rest of the children trying to get another glimpse of the Royal Visitors. Their important task over.

The following Sunday, it was Edna's birthday Ma made a trifle instead of prunes and custard. The cream was scooped from the top of the milk, and the cake had ten candles on it.

Ma brought a parcel into the dining room.

"I think this is from your Dad," she said giving the parcel to Edna.

"Ooh..! " They were all waiting to see inside the box tied up with string.

"That's nice," said Ma as Edna produced a little leather handbag. Then she produced another one, and another one. Edna opened the flap of the handbag, Doris Hunt, it said inside. Each one had the names printed under the clip. The three Hunts had a handbag each made by their father.

Ma saw the card and read it to them

'Happy Birthday, your Loving Dad.
I am now back in Ward Six.   xxx'

As Ma suggested, they wrote a thank you letter to their Dad.

*   *   *

George Hunt sat on his bed in Ward Six, it was two years since Emma had died, and he had been living with Di ever since. She had been good for Brian, building him up with good food, now he was a healthy six-year-old.

Di, like Grandma, was a hard-working woman, up early every morning, working the early shift at a hosiery factory. She had offered to pay for George to go to Switzerland for some convalescence, but George had refused to take her money. Di could see him getting worse, he was constantly drinking in the pub whenever he got the chance, drowning his sorrows while she was at work. His constant coughing every day worried her and the regular X-ray proved only one thing, he had to be re-admitted, and have complete rest again.

Di was re-living her own past, her husband had been in Groby Road Hospital for two years. The good food during the war had helped his recovery at first, he had put on weight like George had done, giving them a false sense of well being, and he, too, had taken himself home, away from the hospital and treatment. The tuberculosis had not gone away, like Emma and Edith in the next bed to her, George had watched Di's husband slowly die. He had done exactly the same thing, only this time Di thought she could help George to recover. They had taken seaside holidays, but it had all been to no avail, she was back at the hospital visiting George.

George had never had much to do with Archibald, his stepfather. He sensed he didn't want Annie, his Mother, to spend any more time and energy with hospital visits, she was no longer the strong, healthy woman of a few years ago. It was because of the hasty decision to get Brian away from the homes, and the only solution at the time was for George and Brian to live with Di.

Annie was forbidden to visit the girls in the home until she was better, and she only saw Norman because he was now living with her own sister Flo. Annie had been in hospital for an abdominal operation, the rest had done her good. George and Di visited her in the Royal Infirmary, he would do anything for his Mother. Later, during the summer, they sometimes met at the City Arms where the whole family used to meet up before the war, but George was now going through another rough patch.

He had received three letters, he hadn't forgotten his little girls, but they were being cared for and were well looked after, other things came to the fore before visiting them.

He wrote regularly to Ted, and sent him money for his college needs, and tried to keep tabs on Norman, making sure he was happy. He had been miserable living with Emma's sister, Rose. The boys had bullied him, and his health was causing concern.

The girls' letters were full of happiness, and there seemed no need for him to worry about them. They thanked him for the handbags, which he had made in almost a week, working at them every minute he could spare, to take his mind away from the hospital, and Emma. The girls wrote nice letters, the handwriting was very good, they never said 'goodbye', just 'cheerio' for now. They would soon be going to camp again - two weeks at the seaside. Yes, they were in the best place, he thought. He knew they would soon be due for another chest X-ray, so he would be seeing them again.

The nurses were wonderful, and knew that George would be back, now he was to start his medication all over again. Since the war new medicines were out and there was hope for him if he did as he was told. Di had been strong for him, getting him over the worst months since Emma's and her own husband's funeral. If anything happened to George, Di had promised to look after Brian.

*   *   *

The whole of June was spent cleaning the house up ready for going away to camp again. All the tunics were pressed and put in the box room ready for winter. The summer dresses this year came from Countesthorpe and had the Miss Boswell look about them, not a bit as nice as Miss James's summer dresses.

Miss Heightman's class had monitors to put the kettle on in the staff room ready for their break. There were monitors for all kinds of jobs, unlocking the cupboard on the stairs for the hockey sticks. The latest monitor's job was washing the dirty children who came to school without a wash. The monitors took them into the cloakroom, some girls were rather stubborn, and wouldn't take their clothes, it was only when Hazel as monitor, took off her clothes that they strip-washed themselves. With a flannel from the staff room cupboard they personally washed each girl beyond their wrists. All faces shone when inspected by Miss Heightman.

The end of term was coming up and they were all sorry to be leaving Miss Heightman's class. School reports were taken home in sealed envelopes.

"Blimey, wonders'll never cease, you've come fifteenth out of thirty, H," said Ma "You see, yow can do it if yow try," said Ma, looking at the rest of the report. "Spelling...Excellent," Hazel sat looking at the best report she had ever had.

Winnie came home, she had passed the eleven plus exam, and would be going to Alderman Newton's with Margaret. Doris and Ruth hadn't passed but they still had good reports. Margaret was still the best, coming third out of twenty, and Hazel wasn't the dunce any more. During the holidays, Winnie collected her school uniform from Graham Gardener's just as Margaret had done the year before. Her nickname was no longer 'one-eye' but now she was called 'chubby chops', as she looked quite cuddly in her new summer dress.

The girls helped to pack the wicker baskets for camp, with many suggestions as to what they could take this year, the ball and two old tennis rackets from the girl next door were definitely packed.

Miss Pickering and her 'boys' were already on the bus when it stopped outside the house. The bus journey was not so quiet, they were all a year older, and not so shy, when Miss Pickering started singing they all joined in. All the wartime songs that they had sung during the air raids carried them along the open roads.

"It's a Hap..Hap..Happy Day.
Toodle oodle oodle oodle oodle Ay
And you can't go wrong when you're singing this song
It's a Hap, Hap Happy Day....

It's a long way to Tipperary
It's a long way to go.....

There's a long, long worm a-crawling across the roof of my tent,
I can hear the whistle blowing and it's time I went,..."

"I hope the cows don't come in the field this year," said Nipper.
"We don't want any more broken tent poles either," said Ma.
The fields were still green, the harvest still yet to ripen. They all cheered as they overtook the bus in front.
"They're from Countesthorpe, Ma," said Margaret who had a good view from her window.
"It's number eleven," said Nipper.
"Keep out of their road," said Ruth.
At the halfway watering stop, they met up with some of the Countesthorpe girls. Numbers ten and eleven were on the same bus.
"You're Sheila Raynes," Hazel said. "You won the high jump last year."
"Yes I did. Are you going in for it this year?"
"Yes I am." They both walked together back to the bus.
"Come on, ain't got all day," shouted the Yorkshire Foster Mother waiting for the last of her girls, she was definitely scowling.
"I don't think she likes you lot," said Ma.
"We don't like her," said the girls together. "She told us off for putting too much margarine on the bread last year, we had to put it on, then scrape it off."
"They're very strict with them boys," said Miss Pickering after everyone had resumed their seats. "Talk about concentration camps."
"We saw a bit of that on our side of the field," said Ma.
"Can I have a drink of lemonade please, Ma?" asked Colette.
"Didn't you just have one," said Ma.
"No I was at the toilets," said Colette.
"Come here and drink it, or they'll all want another one," said Ma.
The singing started up again as they looked out for 'Boston Stump.'

"There's a seagull, we must be getting near," shouted a voice from the back of the bus.

"Don't mean a thing," said Miss Pickering who this year had actually got a different hat on.

The bus finally ambled down the narrow lane to the open gate.

"It's just the same as it was last year," said Nipper up front with Ma.

This year the bags were a little heavier, the girls now had more ideas of what they needed for the fortnight, and thanks to Mr Bowerman at the Evington Cinema they had been able to save some of their pocket money to spend at camp.

They didn't need Ma to tell them all the rules again, they could hear the regimental barrage of orders coming from the other tents.

"Just behave yourselves, that's all I've got to say," said Ma.

The palliasses looked even smaller as the beds were made.

"Don't forget the bucket," said Ma. "Ruth, you can take charge of that."

"Why me?" said Ruth.

"I'm not sleeping near the door this year," said Marie.

They were soon heading for the beach, taking in deep breaths of fresh air as they slid down the sand dunes, to the ebbing tide. Laura Brown from number eleven walked across the field. She was their favourite girl from the Cottage Homes. A tall blonde girl, Laura had been in the homes since 1935, it was her ever-smiling face and daring antics that kept everyone amused.

"I'm the oldest inhabitant at the Cottage Homes," Laura reminded them. The East Park Road girls sat on the grass, exchanging stories.

"I work at the Residence," said Laura. "But I am with number eleven while we are here."

"Do you like Miss Mather?" said Nipper.

"Old Mother Mather, she's always shouting at me," said Laura.

" Yes we've heard her, Ma doesn't shout at us like that," said Winnie.

"No she just gives us a 'silly sender'," Hazel said.

"When Matron comes round we have to scrub everything, even the toilet seat, she even scrubs her money," said Laura.

"How often does Matron come round?" said Margaret.

"Too often, but she's always ill," said Laura. "But we still have to scrub everything."

"We don't do that," said Ruth, "We just have a job to do every day."

"At night, when she's had a day off, we listen for her bus, we count the steps up the back drive, and right up to the front door, then when Miss Glegg has gone back to number ten. All the lights go on and she gets everybody out of bed..," said Laura. "It's true."

"Whatever for?" Winnie interrupted.

"In bare feet, we have to dust all the ledges and all window sills, if there's a speck of dust anywhere," said Laura.

"Oh poor kids," said Margaret.

"I think she comes home drunk," said Laura.

They all burst out laughing at the thought of Miss Mather being drunk.

"I don't know where she goes on her day off, but I can't imagine her having any friends at all." Laura was laughing with them, threading long bits of grass between her toes.

"It's not like that at Ma's. Tell her about Miss Glegg's tea-leaf porridge Ruth," they said.

"'Glaring Gleggy', do you have her as well?" said Laura and they were all giggling again.

The tea leaf episode was explained in detail and Laura was wiping the tears away, after laughing so much.

"I haven't laughed so much in my life," said Laura. Did you eat it all up?"

"Yes we had to, she wouldn't let us go to the pictures until it was all gone," said Winnie.

"I'd have been sick," said Laura.

"Two of the little ones were sick on the way to the pictures, but we didn't tell Gleggy," said Margaret.

"Miss Mather calls me 'Lorta Brarn.'

"Lorta Brarn... " They were all giggling again.

"What happened last year when the tent pole broke?" the girls asked.

"Oh, we were having a competition to see who could swing round the pole the highest," said Laura.

"I thought that's what had happened," said Winnie. "We never did find out."

"Do you remember that big girl in number eleven? said Laura. "Well it was her, she's left now and gone into service in Northampton," said Laura.

"Will you have to go into service Laura?" asked Ruth.

"No I will not. I would sooner scrub the streets than go into service. I've waited on everybody for years. You don't have any friends, because you don't have any time off to go anywhere. I know," said Laura.

"LORTA BRARN!!" A voice echoed over the bell tents.

"There goes the siren," said Laura, pushing her feet back into her plimsolls.

All of them stood up together, and walked down the field with 'Lorta Brarn," the voice echoed again over the bell tents

In the safety of their tent they listened as Laura was ordered to get all the little ones into bed.

The routine of the camp was simple, get up, and go to the wash tent, make bed, roll up the skirting of the bell tent. Outside it was raining.

"Oh look. I'm not going to the wash tent," said Nipper. "We might as well just stand out in the rain and have a wash."

"Has anybody used the bucket?" Hazel asked "I'll fetch some water over here."

The pail of water was carried back to the tent, while the rest of the camp rushed about in the rain.

"What a good idea, H," said Margaret.

"Don't slop it on the floor," Hazel said. "Or I expect I'll have to clean it up."

"We won't get down to the beach today," said Ruth.

"We can ask Ma if we can all go to Skegness and do some shopping," said Doris who wanted to buy some pencils.

"We'll have to send Dad a postcard," said Winnie.

"Oh yes, we've got to send some this year," said Nipper.

They were all hungry and ready for breakfast.

"Come on, let's see if they will let us in the dining hall," said Marie.

After breakfast they dodged the spots of rain and ran to the bus shelter. Everybody else had the same idea - that they were all going to Skegness. They soon sorted the shops, looking out for the bargains.

"That's a better shop, go and get your cards in there," said Winnie. "They're much cheaper."

"They haven't been used before have they?" said Margaret.

"Look what I've bought, a gold necklace," said Ruth. "It was only sixpence."

"They've got a tray full of rings as well," said Colette. "I think I'm going to buy one."

"Have they got any bracelets?" said Winnie. "I want one to match the necklace that Aunt Sarah bought me.

241

"Ooh, look at those lacy gloves, they're just like the ones you wore for Corpus Christie. Three and sixpence, wow we can't afford them," said Ruth.

"Shall we buy Ma something," said Margaret.

"Ah, that would be nice," said Winnie.

"We'll have to see how much we've got first," said Marie. "I've only got thruppence ha'penny."

"Well if we all give a penny each we'll have a shilling," said Margaret. "We should be able to buy something for a shilling."

By dinner time the rain had stopped. They arrived back at camp to the smell of wet grass and steaming tents.

"I bet it's sausage and beans today," Ruth said. "Number five cottage is on kitchen duty, and I heard them moaning about washing plates with beans on.

"I like sausages," said Marie.

"Have you all washed your hands?" said Ma coming into the tent.

"Yes, Ma," they all replied.

"Let me look." Ma went over to Linda.

Little Linda held out her hands for Ma to see. Her blonde curls looked even curlier because of the rain.

"Did you buy anything today?"

"She bought a lovely windmill, Ma, look," said Nancy hoping that Linda wouldn't let the cat out of the bag about 'the present.'

Right, let's be having you."

The sausages and beans were brought to the table, they didn't care who was monitor any more, if they didn't get to the serving hatch in good time, the last plates hardly had any beans on at all.

"They're running out again," said Doris.

In the afternoon Ma took them on their favourite walk, to a quiet part of the beach that Ma had found. It was a bit further away, but they had the beach to themselves. As the tide went out Doris drew pictures in the sand, and the battered tennis racket and ball were taken out of the bag for another game of cricket.

"Here's Miss Pickering Ma," shouted Ruth who had spotted the red hat coming over the dunes.

The boys were soon down on the beach, splashing in the sea with very white feet. Miss Pickering had managed to slide down the sandy slope.

"Good afternoon, Miss Hammond," said Miss Pickering unrolling a blanket that one of the boys had carried.

"Can't see any ships today. Too misty," said Ma.

Miss Pickering opened her bag, out came the flask, and out came the cups. "Let's have a cup of tea," she said.

Further down the beach the girls organised a game of cricket, the boys were winning all hands up.

"Out!" shouted Bernard the eldest boy.

"I'm not out just because I didn't hit it," shouted the batsman.

"Well it would have hit the stumps," he shouted

"We haven't got any stumps," she shouted back.

"How many runs did we get?" shouted the boy fielding near the sea.

"Twenty," came the reply.

"No you didn't then, you only got seventeen," Margaret joined in.

"That last one was a four," Bernard shouted again.

"Right, bowl," shouted the next one in and hit the ball into the sky.

"Out!" Peter had caught it way up the beach.

"Boys don't play fair," the girls protested, and ran off with the tennis racket. The boys ran after them, splashing everybody in their path as they ran through the shallow water. Miss Pickering shouted to the boys.

"Come on, come and get dry," Miss Pickering replaced her own shoes. "The salt is good for your feet."

The girls ran through the sand dunes, still playing hide and seek on the way back.

"Where's Johnny?" said Miss Pickering looking for her youngest boy. "Go back and look for him Bernard."

"He'd got a stone in his shoe," said Bernard catching up with them at the main road.

The first week was over. On Sunday morning, they lined up in best dresses and blazers, ready to walk the two miles to Winthorpe Church.

In church, every available seat was taken, the service was simple with no incense and just a few choirboys. They sang all the hymns, which they knew off by heart.

The vicar was old, his voice very feeble, compared to Father Huntley's deep rich voice. His sermon lasted for what seemed forever, the girls were more interested in the choirboys. At the church door the vicar said he would see us again on sports day.

On the wet grass the practising went on for sports day, jumping over the stick in the corner of the field, the three-legged competitors were tied together running like Siamese twins. There were more children than ever running amok across the grass. Roy Astle, Bobby Spriggs and Tony Bullous had been joined this year by another boy, Jack Broughton; they crept among the girls' tents shouting,

"He loves you!" The boy in the black shorts disappeared and ran off as soon as the girls got to the tent door. They encouraged them to come back again, when there were no Officers about.

"It's Bobby Spriggs, Ruth, he says he loves you," said Winnie.

"Oh no, shrieked Ruth. "Well he is nice."

"Does Winnie love Tony?" came a voice from the close proximity of the outside of the tent.

"Who's that?" shouted Margaret. "How does he know that?"

All three boys ran off like frightened rabbits.

"We'll get you," shouted Colette.

After tea it started raining again, and the sky looked black. It was a night for staying in the tent, playing ludo and snakes and ladders. It was too dark for a jigsaw.

"Does anyone know how to play dominoes?"

"Don't touch the tent or the water will start leaking in," said Ruth to one of the little ones, swinging her feet.

"Who's going to volunteer to fetch the bucket of water tonight?" said Margaret.

"I fetched it last time," Hazel said. "Marie, it's your turn."

Marie was losing at ludo, so she picked up the bucket and left the tent.

There was a loud bang, they ran to the door of the tent. Marie lay there whilst the bucket blew away up the field.

"Oh, I've hurt myself," sighed Marie, holding her arm.

"What did you do, Marie?" they ran to pick her up.

"I fell over the guy ropes," cried Marie.

"Is it bleeding?" shouted Nipper.

"No but it hurts," puffed Marie.

She stumbled into the tent, her blouse and shorts wet through.

"I'll fetch Ma," said Nipper. "I know which window is Ma's."

Marie's wrist looked swollen.

"You pick a good time to have an accident," said Ma coming from under her coat. "Let's look."

"Oh," said Marie.

"I haven't touched it yet," said Ma. "I'll get the nurse to have a look at it."

244

Marie sat on the wicker basket, going rather pale. Suddenly she fell on the floor.

"Struth!" H, go and fetch the nurse, and mind the guy ropes!" shouted Ma.

Hazel ran to the Officers' block, and knocked on the first door.

"Is this the nurses room?" she said out of breath.

"What's wrong?" said the lady who looked as if she lived on chocolates.

"One of our girls has hurt herself, I think she's fainted," Hazel said repeating Ma's guess.

Marie was sitting on the basket again.

"She's hurt her wrist, and just had a little faint," said Ma.

All the girls sat on their palliasses, Hazel joined them. They could see the tiny bottle of smelling salts that the nurse held in her hand.

"Take some deep breaths," said the nurse. "Can you wiggle your fingers?"

"What were you doing outside?" said Ma.

"Hazel told me to fetch the bucket of water," she said.

"Oh...blame me!" Hazel said.

"Giving your orders again," said Ma.

The bucket was still outside blowing around in the wind. Hazel decided to go and get it, before she got a clout for nothing.

Marie's sprained wrist was bandaged up. Colette washed Marie's face when they had all had a wash.

"Settle down now," said Ma. "I think the rain's stopped for a bit."

In the middle of the night there was a loud clap of thunder, the girls woke up, they could see each other as the lightning flashed.

"Oh.. Blimey...!"

A few screams were heard in the distance from the other tents. Then the rain lashed down again, the noise even louder and frightening the little ones.

"Come over here, bring your blankets," Hazel called to Linda and Peggy.

The girls put all the palliasses in a row, and tensely waited for the next bang.

"Brace yourselves," said Winnie

"Welcome to 'Bracing Skegness'," said Margaret.

BANG!! Another thunder bolt ran through the sky.

"If we count, we shall know how many miles away it is, before the flash of lightening. Wait for the next one."

Another even louder noise hit the field.

"Start counting....one, two, three, four, five, six.....it's six miles away," said Margaret as the next flash disappeared.

"Oh that's alright," said Winnie. "It's not overhead.

That didn't soothe the little ones. They were still clinging on tight.

"There's water coming in here," said Nancy "Quick get the bucket."

They stumbled about in the dark, dashing back to their own beds, keeping Linda and Peggy happy, hoping that the tent wouldn't get struck by lightening.

Ma's voice outside was a great relief, and the door flap flew open.

"Are you alright?" said Ma.

"There's nearly a bucket full of water here, Ma," shouted Colette.

"Everybody is going into the dining hall," said Ma.

"Ooh good," said Nancy, "I don't like it in here."

"Can you help the little ones over, Nancy?" said Ma. "You big ones can carry the palliasses. Mind you don't slip, we don't want any more casualties."

"How is it Marie?" said Ma, shining the torch on Marie's hand.

"I've not been to sleep yet, Ma," said Marie.

"I don't think anybody has," said Ma.

In the dining hall the trestle tables were stacked at the side, and a sea of moving bodies lay everywhere, all trying to get comfortable on the straw beds. The storm raged outside, the lightening lit up every window. One of the officers sat on a chair halfway down the hall, they settled down as best they could, some of them holding hands under the blankets.

The next day the tents were awash, the ground sheets were dragged out to dry in the sun.

"I'm glad I'm not on duty," said Ma, "I feel like a wet rag."

In the afternoon Linda and Peggy slept on Ma's bed until teatime, and the nurse assured Marie that her arm wasn't broken and the swelling had gone down. They all wanted to go home and get back to they're own beds.

Mr Walters stood up at teatime.

"You will all be sleeping in the dining hall again tonight, and sports day tomorrow has been cancelled."

If anyone was pleased or displeased they did not show it, but all of the East Park Road girls were very pleased. It didn't take them long to pack the wicker basket once the decision was made, they were glad to be going home. The girls ran round the field - saying goodbye to the friends they had made, Roy had cut his eye, or so he said, in the thunderstorm last night.

"We're not going home today," said Roy "We've got the job of taking all the tents down." He gave all the girls a peck on the cheek. "Now you don't know which one I love," he said. Then the girls kissed little Bobby Spriggs.

All the buses arrived together each cottage making their own queue for the return journey.

"Cheerio," they shouted. "See you next year." The girls felt sorry for Roy and Bobby, left behind as they mischievously ran to the gate waving.

"We love you," they shouted to Roy, he put his hand on his heart. "I love you," he shouted.

The beds looked big as they jumped into the white cotton sheets in the blue room, no more rustling straw beneath them. Winnie said her prayers, Hazel wasn't listening, and she had given up saying prayers since her Mam had died.

By Sunday morning they were back to their normal routine.

"Margaret have you got it?" they asked when the breakfast was on the table.

"Yes," said Margaret and put a small parcel on Ma's table.

Singing grace sounded much nicer than the grace they had said at camp. With her little teapot, Ma came walking in the dining room.

"Strike! What's this?" said Ma, her eye catching the well kept secret wrapped up in brown paper.

"Be careful when you open it," said Nipper.

"Well fancy that, a milk jug and sugar basin, china as well, very pretty, thank you very much, what a lovely surprise," said Ma.

"We thought the roses would match your cup and saucer Ma," said Margaret, whose idea it was in the first place as she had saved more spending money than the rest of the girls. The china pieces were held up to compare designs, which were almost a perfect match. They were all glad that the camping holiday was over, and after the girls had all said their bit, Ma concluded that 'we need good weather for that sort of a holiday'.

The girls walked into church on Sunday and, forgetting that they had a new vicar, Father Watson, who stood at the back of the church.

"I want you all to sit on the other side of the congregation," he said, and without giving any reason he made his way into the vestry.

"Why have we got to sit over there?" the girls queried.

"Oh, it'll make a change," said Margaret. "I expect he wants to keep his eye on us from the pulpit.

The reason was quite obvious when the service started, the girls couldn't see the choirboys from where they were sitting. Especially Stephen, the new head choirboy.

A few more trips were made to Avenue Road while the holiday lasted, tidying up for Mr Seaton, taking the washing in from the line outside. Winnie always felt sad looking at the table laid for one when they were ready to leave, "If only we could have tea with him once in a while," she said.

"Where've you lot been?" said Ma, knowing that they hadn't taken all that time to spend pocket money.

"We've had a lovely walk Ma," They all replied.

"It's supposed to be pocket money time, not going for a five mile walk.

Winnie and Margaret looked smart in their bottle green blazers and green check dresses. Everybody was a bit apprehensive about starting new schools. Doris was now in Miss Heightman's class and Ruth went into Miss Pilkington's class.

At Bridge Road, after the main assembly was over, they all filed into their designated classrooms. Miss Gilbert was already sitting at her desk.

"You," her ancient finger pointed at Hazel . "Close the door."

As Hazel was the last one through the door, she sat down at the nearest desk. The register was called, and, as on previous new terms, there was no re-shuffle of places, Hazel felt this was a bad omen, She was sitting in the dunce's desk again, and took an instant dislike to Miss Gilbert in her coffee coloured silk dress. A long string of brown beads resting on her large bosom, her elegant stature was a mixture of Miss James and Matron Buttridge. She quite expected her to do the 'Miss James walk' when she went over to the blackboard.

The timetables were copied from the blackboard, all neatly split into five days. Monday - English and Spelling, Tuesday - Science and Biology with Miss Gilbert, and a whole afternoon on Friday was allocated to Miss Cart, R.E. (Religious Education). The Science laboratory smelled of gas, Bunsen burners poked through the middle of the special high benches, each with a red tube leading to the gas tap. The first lesson was Minerals, and the properties of iron, they made fancy patterns with magnetised iron filings. The class watched Miss Gilbert drop the liquid mercury from a great height, shattering into minute balls, which suddenly regrouped into a liquid again, which wasn't wet at all. It was much more interesting than 'the frog' in Miss Heightman's class, and different from anything she had known, Hazel changed her mind, and felt that she was going to do well in Biology.

The P.T. Teacher, Miss Hobday, was very pretty, she was full of energy, running up and down the hall, followed by girls chasing after the ball. The unexpected happened and the elastic in Hazel's knickers gave way, she was rescued by a large safety pin. Another job for the Thursday night sewing.

The dreaded Miss Cart walked into the classroom on Friday afternoon, giving the class the chance to see her at close quarters. The fine woollen black dress with a circlet of black beads under the collar gave her an austere presence. Her eyes fixed on each of them over her steel rimmed spectacles, as if searching for some hidden truth from their 'guilty' hearts. She reminded them of the school motto, "Be Ready For Gracious Service, B.R.G.S. Bridge Road Girls School," Did it mean that they were all to go 'into service' when they leave school that was all it meant to Hazel at the start of the lesson. Miss Cart taught them about the seven deadly sins and 'What are they?' Hazel's hand shot up with 'Jealousy.' she knew that one. 'Wickedness', came another answer. No, they all came under the same heading.

"Envy," said a bright button at the back of the class.

'Pride' goes before a fall, they all had heard that one, especially from Ma, and nobody guessed 'Sloth' or 'Avarice' or 'Lust', they were not in the category of their young lives. And so they were all written in their books.

'Smoking' was the next subject and how it was bad for their lungs. Miss Cart named a few of the pulmonary diseases, including 'galloping consumption' a fearful disease which Hazel dreaded herself, another name for tuberculosis.

'Drinking alcohol' - Miss Cart held up a bottle of neat alcohol which was passed around the class to impress on them that there was enough liquid in the bottle to kill sixty people, they each held the deadly 'poison' in their hands.

At the end of the lesson the whole class was given a card, specially printed it was headed, The Pledge and read as follows:-

'THE PLEDGE'

I....................promise to abstain from the use of alcohol, tobacco, gambling and all injurious habits. To be courteous, helpful, courageous at all times, and in all things.

SIGNED................................

The cards were left for them to keep, most of them signed straightaway not having much knowledge about any of the things.

Hazel's first real friend at school was a girl named Valerie. They walked home from school together laughing and joking at silly things, mainly mimicking the teacher. Valerie had only just moved to the area, and on Sunday morning she waited for the tram outside the girls home on her way to church. Hazel asked Ma if she could go to Chapel with her friend to Dashwood Road.

"You're not swapping and changing about, you've joined the Sally Army already, what more do you want?" said Ma.

Hazel had to be content with just calling for Valerie on the way to school, just to see her baby sister, a real house with a real family.

The Guide activities were still the highlight of the week, and a few activities on Saturdays were beginning to take place. Equally, Guard Leader Seeby took all the Guards on an evening cook-out, to a farm in the country. Sausages and beans sizzled on the fire that the girls had made themselves. It was such a success, that the following Saturday all the children from the Working Men's Club were taken to the farm on a day's outing and given a packed lunch with organised games. There were children and chickens everywhere, all enjoying the freedom of roaming through fields, paddling in streams, climbing trees, and rolling down the hillside. It was organised chaos, no-one got lost or bitten by the donkey, the chickens returned to safety behind the chicken wire, and everyone had a wonderful day.

Back on the bus, the tired helpers counted all the passengers, and returned them back to their waiting parents.

The Western Park open-air school had an open day at the end of term, and Ma took all the girls to see the school. It was no more than a few huts put together, surrounded by gardens of flowers all grown by the children. Edna showed Ma her classroom, and the room where they all slept after dinner. They finished off the day having a picnic on Western Park, and cups of tea in the pavilion.

It was nearly a year since the Hunts had seen their Grandma, or any of the family. Dad was still in hospital, the girls were now X-rayed in a clinic in Leicester, so were not able to make a trip to see him in the ward.

*   *   *

The Superintendent came on his regular visit, and Ma reported the continuing conflict between Marie and Hazel. Suddenly without any warning a few days later a social worker arrived and took Hazel to Countesthorpe, she was sent there for punishment. They arrived at the Main Gate at number one cottage, and after a bit of banter between the social worker, Mr Walters let them in.

At the Residence, the Superintendent informed Hazel that she was to report to number ten cottages, Miss Milner. Hazel's heart went down to her boots, Miss Milner, was the Yorkshire woman at camp, the most hated of all the foster people. Ma's girls had called her a little Hitler. She had a habit of grabbing the girls by the hair, and she was never seen without a cigarette in her mouth. Miss Glegg lived in number ten as well. Two people far worse than Matron Buttridge. Hazel walked along the drive, counting the detached buildings on her way round, and knocked on the front door of number ten. Sheila Raynes opened the front door - her 'high jump' friend from Camp.

"Come on in," said Sheila, and she turned round and jumped from mat to mat. "Don't put your feet on the floor." she said.

The red Cardinal polished floor shone like glass. Miss Milner stood in the kitchen with all the girls.

"What's wrong with the back door?" Miss Milner snapped. "Couldn't you find it?"

"Good afternoon, Miss Milner," Hazel said, ignoring the stares of ten girls, and Miss Milner.

"What's your name?"

"Hazel Hunt," she replied just as abruptly as the question.

"I'm called 'Mother' here," Miss Milner added quickly.

"Yes, Miss Milner," Hazel said, telling herself that on no account was she going to call her mother.

"Are they all the clothes you've brought with you?" said Miss Milner.

Yes Miss Milner," Hazel said looking down at the only clothes she had on.

"What have you come here for?" said Miss Milner.

"I've been sent here," said Hazel.

"What for?" she snapped, making Hazel admit everything in front of all the girls.

"For fighting with Marie," Hazel wasn't going to tell her that Marie had fallen down the cellar steps when they were arguing.

"Well don't get fighting here, I'm the only one who does any fighting in this house," said Miss Milner smiling at all the girls. "And you won't win."

The girls stood like statues in a half circle. Hazel felt like a lamb about to be slaughtered, but a wink from Sheila when Miss Milner wasn't looking made it a little less hostile.

"Better find something for you to wear tonight. Too short, too little," she held each garment in the air as if measuring Hazel from at least six feet away, throwing each nightgown from the cupboard onto the table.

A pair of pale green, satin pyjamas was the next thing to be pulled out of the cupboard.

"They'd fit you," Miss Milner held them up.

"Ooh can I wear them?" said the eldest girl.

Seeing Hazel's eyes light up, Miss Milner threw the green satin into the girl's arms. Hazel knew that from then on she was being victimised and just took the old nightie that was thrown her way.

"What jobs did you do at East Park Road?"

"I cleaned the flues and the kitchen," Hazel said,

"Well, in the morning, you'll clean out fire and scrub floor, before you go to school every day.

Hazel had failed to tell her that she only did the kitchen on a Saturday.

"Keep buckets filled. At dinnertime, scrub porch," said Miss Milner.

The main sitting room was for Miss Milner, and the main dining room was Miss Glegg's bed sitting room. The girls' dining room was small in comparison to the one at East Park Road, and the dining table would never have fitted in. The corridor at the back of the house had six wash basins on the wall and a red brick floor with a combined drain under the wash basins. This passage led to the bathroom and toilets. At teatime, the bread and butter plate was put on the table as soon as grace had been said, instead of taking one slice, their hands grabbed the bread, and it was all gone in one swoop. With one slice in her hand, Hazel didn't make a fuss. Hazel stayed in the dining room trying to get near the fire, she put her hand on the fireguard for a little warmth. Miss Milner shouted from her sitting room. Sheila was to show her the bedroom. Together Hazel and Sheila jumped over the hall floor again from mat to mat, then up the stairs. The bedroom was cold and had five beds.

"It'll be nice to have someone else sleeping in here with me," Sheila said. "I've always slept in here on my own. Don't sit on the counterpane. Mother knows if you've sat on it. Come on, let's go down and get the scrubbing done."

The nightie was left on the chair beside the bed in the corner, there were no eye level windows, they were high up like those in the kitchen downstairs. Three upturned buckets and three scrubbing brushes and lumps of soap were in the cupboard at the end of the passage. After filling the bucket, Hazel started to scrub the kitchen floor. One square yard at a time across the floor and back again. The red brick floor was hard to dry, a few girls were still roaming about, paddling across the floor, and Hazel could see Doris scrubbing the floor of the Receiving Home in just the same way, all those years ago.

Thinking about Matron Buttridge and the Receiving Home, Hazel suddenly realised that she would never be going home again, tears rolled down her cheeks. Miss Glegg silently came into the kitchen.

"Oh, it's you," she said.

Hazel made no attempt to speak to her and kept her head down to the floor. She spoke to Sheila who had nearly finished the bath, the wash handbasins, then the scrubbing of the passage floor. Hazel couldn't understand the Irish brogue, and didn't like the person speaking it. In her soft slippers she moved swiftly through the kitchen, hardly making a sound. Ma's girls were probably sitting on the stairs, listening to 'Paul Temple,' that's if Marie had made Ma's supper in time.

"Have you nearly finished?" asked Sheila. "You have to empty your bucket outside."

"Do we have any supper?" Hazel asked.

"No, are you hungry?" said Sheila.

"I hardly had any tea," she said.

"Yes, I should have told you. They grab it as soon as we've said grace," said Sheila.

"Well if there's two slices each, why can't they eat it properly," Hazel said.

"That's what they're like," said Sheila.

"I liked the cake," Hazel said.

"Oh, that's Parkin, Mother makes that, it's lovely.

"I'll try and get you a bit, give me your floor cloth," whispered Sheila.

"What for?" Hazel whispered.

Sheila disappeared into the pantry. "Put that up your knicker leg," she said, and the sticky brown lump of cake disappeared up the leg of Hazel's knickers. The buckets were put upside down in the cupboard.

"What did you want the floor cloth for?" Hazel whispered.

"If Mother or Miss Glegg come into the kitchen, well I was wiping the smears up."

They crossed the hall jumping from mat to mat again, and up the stairs.

"Goodnight, Mother," shouted Sheila halfway up the stairs.

They could hardly hear the reply, as they both raced up the stairs.

"Whatever you do, don't get any crumbs on the sheets, or she'll know what we've done," Sheila carefully fumbled into the fold of her knicker leg. "If you put it at the side like this, it falls down and doesn't get squashed," Sheila got into bed after extricating the lump of cake.

"I'll have to walk a bit careful then in case it drops on the floor," Hazel said.

"You've had it if ever she catches you," said Sheila. "Turn the light out you're last in bed."

"Where is it?

Hazel woke up several times during the night, the high ceiling and white walls shone bright. At the crack of dawn, she could hear the birds singing. Today was Saturday, no Evington Cinema, no tunics to press for school on Monday, no morning cocoa. If Marie was out at church who would be cleaning the kitchen flues? It sickened Hazel to think about East Park Road, chopping the wood down the cellar at Ma's was a bit different to having to go out in the cold to find bits of dry stick in 'hedge-bottom', especially when the fire went out the other morning. The little ones were sent out to play on the field, it was so cold. Sunday morning was the same, but by ten o'clock they had to be ready for church. Number ten girls stood in twos waiting for the final command for someone to open the door. Hazel was looking forward to a long walk to church, away from the Homes.

"How far is the church?" Hazel asked Sheila.

"Oh it's only just here," she said.

The crocodile of girls turned off the main drive in between two cottages near a couple of evergreen bushes, the door to the hall was open. The Cottage Homes children sat in rows, and number ten filled the seats behind them. The boys sat on the right, the girls on the left. Mr Walters looked even sterner than he did at camp, his eyes settling on anyone venturing to talk. Hazel glanced quickly to the back of the room, there were no smiling faces. The rigidity and harshness had returned to the young flexible bodies that had unwound at camp.

"Hymn four-three-three," said Mr Walters.

A piano started playing at the front of the hall.

"What a friend we have in Jesus."

Hazel didn't sing, she couldn't sing, how could she have such a 'friend' who never answered her prayers?

A short service followed and then all the boys left first. Hazel's heart suddenly missed a beat when she saw Roy Astle, walking out of the door. She coughed out loud, trying to make him look round. Outside Hazel asked Sheila which was his cottage.

"He's in number two, Mr Clist's," she said.

That's them over there," Sheila pointed to a line of boys walking towards the second cottage.

"I like him," Hazel said. "He makes me laugh."

"Well don't let anybody else know, or they won't let you out on the field," said Sheila.

After Sunday tea, they all stood in the kitchen, talking quietly. Suddenly Jane, one of the younger girls, collapsed on the floor, she was writhing and wriggling in uncontrollable movements. Hazel bent down to help her.

"Don't touch her she's having a fit," shouted the girls, and Miss Glegg ran in as Hazel moved away.

She muttered something about 'swallowing her tongue'. Hazel curled her tongue in her own mouth to prove to herself that it was impossible to swallow her tongue. After the muscle spasms had ceased, the young

Laura Brown on Matron's bike.

girl sat on a chair, and looked almost grey. She was put to bed.

The little kindness shown to Jane, was all methodical, and matter of fact.

Hazel's first bath was on Sunday night, after she had been given clothes to wear for school. A queue formed at the bathroom door, there was hardly time to sit in the bath before another person got in at the back of her. There was still the floor to scrub.

"You've got to light the fire in the morning, Hazel," said Sheila from her bed on the other side of the room.

"Our kitchen fire stays in all night at Ma's, we only let it out on Friday to clean the flues," Hazel said.

"The 'coal pile' is going down, so we have to let it out," said Sheila.

In the morning the fire was out, Hazel raked out all the ashes, the first attempt to light it failed, and there were no sticks left.

"You'll have to go out and find some wood," said Miss Milner.

Hazel looked in the coal house, there was none. "Search in hedge bottom," said the Yorkshire woman keeping a watchful eye on all her movements.

On the back drive, Hazel pulled at the young new shoots. Suddenly a bike loomed up out of the mist. It was being ridden by 'Lorta Brarn.'

"Hello, Laura," Hazel said.

"Hello, what are you doing here?" said Laura.

"Oh, I've been sent here for fighting with Marie," Hazel said.

"What are you doing in the hedge?" said Laura.

"Trying to find some sticks to light the fire."

"They won't burn, what you want is dead bits and this sort of stuff," Laura pointed out all the bits of dry leaves, and twigs. "I'd stop and help you but I've got to cook breakfast at the 'Resi.'" she said.

"Whose bike's that?" Hazel shouted.

"Matron's, I don't want her to catch me on it," shouted Laura disappearing into the fog.

Hazel returned to Miss Milner's kitchen. She was shovelling hot coals into the grate from her sitting room fire. She threw her few twigs onto the hot coals.

"Don't put fire out," shouted Miss Milner and Hazel received a swipe from her hand.

She stood there, not knowing what to do.

"Get coal in," said Miss Milner, still busying herself with the fire.

Hazel was glad to be sitting down on the bus and on the way to school, not knowing which one she was to attend, or, whose class she would be in. Her hands were sore, she sat removing the bramble thorns from 'hedge bottom.'

Hazel wandered about the school as everyone disappeared into their own classrooms. She peeped into an open door, it was full of children - 'SPECIALS' it said on the door. She went inside and sat at one of the desks.

"Are you new? said the teacher, spotting Hazel before she sat down.

She sent her brightest pupil to show her where the headmistress's office was. Hazel didn't care and wasn't smiling she just walked and followed, until she was thrown into a classroom. The first question she was asked was.

"Where is your dinner money?" said the teacher.

Hazel had none.

"What's your address?" asked the teacher.

"Number ten Cottage Homes."

All the girls sniggered, thinking she had got the address wrong.

"Sit there," the teacher pointed to a desk.

'Bottom of the class,' Hazel thought.

Hazel sat down, the buttons of her tight dress were gaping open, and she pulled her stomach in, not that it made any difference.

At playtime Margaret Clark, the girl she sat next to, told Hazel she belonged to the Salvation Army and was also in the 'Guards'. She lived in a shop, on King Richard's Road. The more they talked the more friendly they became.

"Where did you live before you went in the homes at Countesthorpe?" asked Margaret.

"Well I lived in another home on East Park Road," Hazel said.

"My Dad's got a butchers shop on East Park Road," said Margaret. "We live in a greengrocer's shop," Another coincidence, they couldn't believe it.

At dinnertime Hazel didn't know what to do, she couldn't see any of the Countesthorpe kids until she looked across the playground. Hazel spotted the institutional coats all getting on a bus. Back at Countesthorpe. After the nine-mile journey, they walked along the front drive to number ten. The smell of the dinner made them feel hungrier than ever. They all sat down at the kitchen table, it was much warmer, and the helpings of stew were served from the pot on the fireplace.

The plates were cleared away, a coarse apron was thrust into her arms.

"Get porch scrubbed," said Miss Milner.

There wasn't much time, the bus would be at number one gate at one thirty, for the bus ride back to school.

Hazel didn't mind the half-hour journey it gave her knees time to recover from scrubbing.

In the afternoon Margaret sat down, her smart tunic and blouse were like the ones worn at Ma's, Hazel's dress felt tighter than ever and the buttons gaped open. There was no afternoon break, they went home earlier instead. The bus was waiting there like an old ambulance waiting to take them all back to the asylum.

The first day was over, Hazel remembered how Winnie's Dad had taught them to make 'paper sticks' to light his fire. 'Roll up newspaper diagonally, then flatten the tube, fold in half and cross the ends over to make a concertina 'stick.' She sat at night making 'paper sticks' while the little ones had their wash.

"Have you been a Girl Guide?" Miss Milner mocked.

"Yes Miss Milner it's come in useful," Hazel said.

Hazel was making life easier for herself, so Miss Milner changed her job at the weekend.

"See if you can do my sitting room out," Miss Milner said.

Hazel opened the door to Miss Milner's private domain armed with a bucket of water, hardly daring to walk on the carpet. The ash flew everywhere as she raked the hot embers. She made the fire and washed the hearth.

"Come here Heerzel 'unt, come and look at this," Miss Milner took her back into her sitting room.

"What sort of mess do you call this?"

Hazel looked down at the hearth. White swirls left by the floor cloth covered the polished tiles.

"If you clean up Ma Hammond's sitting room like that it must be in a bit of a mess," she scoffed.

"Ma cleans her own sitting room," Hazel sneered back at her.

"Well we do things different here, get back in kitchen," and another swipe of her hand landed on her head.

"Maggie, see to fire and clean up hearth," Miss Milner called.

"Yes, mother," said Maggie.

"The coal house is empty Miss Milner," Hazel said that evening.

"Well, you'll have to go and find some. Sheila, take her to 'coal pile'," said Miss Milner, "and take bucket with you."

The two girls walked out into the dark night.

"Where's the 'coal pile'?" Hazel said.

"Back of the hall, you know where we went to church," whispered Sheila. "

You'll have to be quiet, if we get caught we're in trouble. Mr Burley's in charge of the coal."

They crept by number nine, and number eight, all seemed pretty quiet.

"That's the Nursery," said Sheila shining the torch.

"My brother used to be in there," Hazel said. The building was in darkness, and looked far worse than she had ever imagined. A few cots lined up against the bare walls of the disused Nursery, a door at each end.

"They just leave them to cry," said Sheila. "Some babies have died in there."

"Margaret and Winnie's baby brother almost died, the Super said so," Hazel whispered.

Wherever their baby, Brian, lived now, she was glad he wasn't in this place. The torch shone on the pile of coal.

"Listen," said Sheila in a low voice "Nobody about, don't drop the lumps in, place them in the bucket one at a time."

Trying to creep back with a bucket full of coal, the girls were giggling, the handles of the buckets were squeaking with every step they took. At the back of number nine they stopped to have a rest.

"I used to live there," said Sheila. "Miss Garner's ever so nice, I didn't want to leave."

The two buckets of contraband coal were safely locked in the coal house for the night.

On Tuesday it was cookery at the new school, Hazel had no ingredients to cook with, she burnt the toffee with what ingredients she had been given. The teacher insisted that she stay behind until the pan was clean.

In the school playground she waited and watched until the Countesthorpe bus pulled away. Hazel started walking anywhere, she didn't care where. The Royal Infirmary was suddenly on her left and the Leicester Prison loomed up in the lights across the road. Hazel knew her way to Ma's from there so she decided to walk under the shadows of the great parapet prison walls, hoping she would never be put in on the other side. Hazel arrived at Ma's some time after tea, and decided to knock on the back door to surprise the girls. The sudden welcome, from the girls, made her feel like the prodigal son returning, that was, until Miss Glegg slithered into the kitchen in her 'creepers.'

"What are you doing here?" she shouted holding Hazel's arms.

"I thought I'd come back to Ma's," Hazel said.

"You've run away, you've run away!" she shouted.

"Don't you girls talk to her, she's all bad. I'm going to phone the Super," said Glaring Gleggy. She locked the back door and took the key with her. Miss Glegg wasn't talking to number ten girls now, Ma's girls were not browbeaten into such bad mannered discipline.

"What's it like there Hazel?" said Margaret.

"It's awful," Hazel said. "Scrub floors, go to bed, get coal in, go to school, scrub floors," She held out cracked hands.

"You get a clout every time you answer back. That Mother Milner, she's wicked," Hazel said trying to tell them as much as she could before Glaring Gleggy got back.

"Did you forget it was Ma's half day?" said Winnie. "Fancy running away on a Tuesday to find Gleggy here."

"It's like living in the 'nut house'," Hazel said.

"Tell Ma I've got my green ticket."

"Have you seen Laura Brown?" asked Margaret.

"Yes, on Matron's bike at half past seven in the morning, she's a scream, I was on the back drive looking for dry sticks to light the fire, and she loomed up in the fog," Hazel said.

"Looking for sticks?"

"When I've lit the fire we all strip to the waist in the back corridor, its so cold, we have a strip-wash before breakfast. You have to take your knickers off and wash between your legs while the others stand watching in the queue. It's freezing standing on the brick floor." Hazel sat on the kitchen chair exhausted from the walk. "I've come straight from King Richard's Road school."

"We've got a new girl in your place, Hazel," said Winnie.

"Look, hasn't she got beautiful hair, this is Louise." A little dark-eyed girl was pushed to the front. "It's Marie's sister," they said. The long black ringlets touched the shoulders of the pretty five-year-old.

Miss Glegg was back. All the girls were then sent into the dining room, Hazel had to stay in the kitchen. She looked at the homely fireplace, and knew every inch of it and how it worked. It didn't shine so much, but the bare kitchen was more homely than number ten. The routine was still the Tuesday ritual, still going upstairs for a strip wash in twos. The girls whispered 'goodnight' through the bobby-hole before they went to bed. Ma was home before nine o'clock, Gleggy didn't tell Ma that Hazel was in the kitchen until Ma was in her sitting room.

"She can stay here the night until we know what's going to be done with her," said Ma.

"No, it's alright, Miss Hammond, she's coming back with me, I've telephoned the Super," said Miss Glegg.

"What's up, H, don't you like it there?" Ma made a sudden appearance in the kitchen.

"No, Ma," Hazel said. Miss Glegg was standing beside her.

"Get your coat on," the Irish accent lingered as if she had been told before.

A few more words from the adamant Miss Glegg and Ma said casually.

"Perhaps you'll come back if you promise to behave yourself."

Ma looked at Hazel with the look that said 'every time I have a day off something always happens'.

After a silent journey, Hazel and Miss Glegg got off the bus at number eleven gate, she could imagine Laura counting the footsteps to the back gate.

The kitchen floor had been scrubbed, Miss Milner didn't make an appearance at this late hour, and she had obviously had her night-cap and didn't want to be disturbed.

The following day Hazel was sent to the Superintendent's office, where she pleaded with him to send her back to Ma's.

There was no punishment as such, but the girls were forbidden to speak to her. To make sure, Hazel even had the five-bedded room to herself. Sheila had been put in another bedroom.

A few days later it was Miss Milner's day off, Hazel was halfway across the kitchen floor when Miss Glegg who was in charge, came and stood on the part that she had scrubbed; the rest of the girls gathered either side of her.

"Did you like your tea leaf porridge?" Miss Glegg tormented, "has it all gone yet?" Her foot kicked out at the scrubbing brush, which spun across the floor.

"Don't do that!" Hazel retaliated.

"Stand up when you speak to me," her tiny eyes glared at Hazel through the strong lenses of her glasses.

Hazel obeyed and stood up.

"I hate you," Hazel shouted.

Miss Glegg's hand struck her face with full force.

Hazel instantly whipped her own hand across Miss Glegg's face, sending her glasses across the red brick floor.

"Oh, MOTHER!" the shocked girls shrieked in horror. Nobody ever hit an officer.

Hazel stood rooted to the spot, as the now almost blind Gleggy groped for her glasses.

"Are they broken? Are they broken?"

"No, Mother," said Maggie cleaning them on her apron.

Hazel wasn't sorry, she was just ready to run out of the cottage altogether.

"You'll apologise for this, you'll be sorry," said Gleggy who was as much shaken as Hazel was.

The silence continued, and the number ten girls retreated to Miss Glegg's sitting room.

"Good old Hazel." Sheila's head peeped momentarily around the kitchen door, then she was gone.

Hazel felt much better, and went to bed quite happy. The following day she was accused of eating a rhubarb pie, and was sent to The Residence. Striking Miss Glegg across the face wasn't mentioned. Hazel sat in the hall of the 'Resi' all evening, with just a few quick words to Laura as to why she had been sent.

"You won't get the 'flopper'," said Laura, "because Matron's ill, she's been eating too many chocolates."

Hazel burst out laughing, how could anybody be ill from eating chocolate. But Laura put her hand to her lips, confessing it was a joke, but confirming that Matron was ill. "Bronchial," Laura said.

After two hours, Laura told Hazel that she had got to go back to number ten.

"Come back tomorrow," she said.

At number ten most of the girls were in bed. Miss Milner, who had been informed of her return, came into the kitchen.

"WELL!" she shouted.

"I've got to go back tomorrow," Hazel said.

"Well, don't think the floor's been scrubbed, it's still waiting for you to do it. Did you get the flopper?"

"No," Hazel said quietly. At that she marched out of the kitchen as mad as a March hare.

Hazel sat in the hall of the Residence after tea every day for nearly a week, smelling the wonderful roast beef, for the Superintendent's evening meal, that Laura was helping to cook. Laura put her head round the door just to warn her of what was to happen.

"You won't get it tonight," and she was gone again.

"Have you had the flopper?" was the question Hazel was asked every time she reached number ten.

The kitchen floor now only got a licking over, Hazel was getting used to the idea and the floor wasn't dirty, she just had to do it for punishment. After dinner in the usual rush, Hazel scrubbed the porch, the Superintendent stood behind her as she was scrubbing.

"Shouldn't you be with the others waiting for the bus?" he said.

"I have to scrub the porch every dinnertime, sir," Hazel said. "Please sir, can I go back to Ma's, I won't quarrel with Marie any more, I promise. Please, sir," Hazel pleaded.

Miss Milner was at the back door, wondering to whom she was speaking. "You should have been finished that a long time ago," she said. "Go and catch bus."

Hazel wiped her knees with the floor cloth and rolled up her 'boggins,' a shortened name for black stockings, then ran for the bus.

*   *   *

The Christmas Pantomime was a few days away, Hazel hadn't seen Miss Milner make any Christmas puddings, and there had been no wishing, no stirring the mixture. There were no trimmings up, and Hazel wondered if they had anything for Christmas.

The shepherds and angels were being chosen for the Christmas play at school, and carols were being practised in the singing lesson,"Would you like to come to our house for tea one day Hazel," said Margaret. "My Mum has asked me to ask you."

"Oh, I would love to, Margaret, are you really sure?" Hazel said. "I'll

264

have to ask the Superintendent."

"Some time over Christmas," said Margaret then you can come to our service on Sunday. This is where I live, and that's our 'phone number."

"Have you got a telephone?" Hazel said.

"Yes, we have to have one for the shops," said Margaret.

The Superintendent called Hazel into the Residence as she walked along the drive from school. It was a funny time to get the flopper after all this time, Hazel waited.

"Do you know why you are here" the Super said closing the door.

"They accused me of eating a rhubarb pie, sir," Hazel said, hesitating. "And I didn't."

"No that's not the reason," he said gently "I've asked Miss Hammond if she will have you back at East Park Road. When we get to the pantomime you can go back with Miss Hammond," he said smiling. "On one condition, that there's no more fighting."

"I promise I won't quarrel any more, sir, or fight, I promise. Thank you very much, sir," Hazel was almost giggling with excitement, and could have kissed him, but didn't.

Miss Milner was her usual self as Hazel walked into the kitchen of number ten, she had been baking Parkin, the sticky brown oatmeal cake. As Hazel was leaving she thought she would tell Miss Milner how really nice her cakes were. Miss Milner's face dropped in disbelief, and she even smiled, from then on Hazel got a double helping of anything she wanted. Perhaps Miss Milner wanted her to admit that she was a better cook than Ma was but she never actually said so.

"Bye, Sheila," Hazel said, "Thanks for talking to me, and being my friend," she whispered at the door of the Opera House. "Ask the Super if you can come and live at Ma's. I'm sure he'll let you," Hazel said.

When Hazel saw Ma and the East Park Road girls she slipped away from number ten girls, and joined Ma at the front of the auditorium.

Back at Ma's, Hazel was more subdued. Almost browbeaten, she had fought back against the strict discipline of the Cottage Homes. She had made it back to Ma's for Christmas by the skin of her teeth. Hazel made sure that Ma had the best cup of tea in bed, while they sang her favourite carols on Christmas morning.

For Christmas Hazel had a box of 'Housey Housey', a game for them all to play. It was the ideal present for her to mend her emotionally unstable, agitated state. Hazel no longer cared what jobs she was given, her knees were swollen and painful, her feet had chilblains, and she had deep cuts on her hands that wouldn't heal.

After Christmas, Ma inspected the knees, and Hazel was sent to the doctors, there had also been a change in the rules, the girls could now go to the doctors on their own.

"Housemaids Knees," said the doctor, and he gave Hazel a prescription to take to the dispensary. "No school. Keep your feet up." he said.

This was the recovery rest that Hazel needed. With her knees wrapped up in wet bandages, sitting with her feet up, she enjoyed the two weeks off school, especially in the morning listening to the Morning Service on Ma's Radio. She had plenty of time to think about the ill-treated children at Countesthorpe who worked like little slaves.

The laundry was now delivered by a van from Hillcrest, and on Friday mornings Ma always made the young man a cup of tea. He sat opposite Hazel in the kitchen, his black hair smoothed down with Brilliantine, he was very handsome with dark brown eyes. Asking about her knees, Hazel carefully undid the wet bandages to reveal the swollen legs. He helped her to replace the bandages. He gently stroked the puffy knee caps stretching his hands out to the tops of her legs, touching the elastic of her knicker legs, his slim fingers groping for the bandage underneath her thighs. Hazel gave a slight giggle, and Ma came into the room, she had just finished checking the laundry.

The young man thanked Ma for the tea, and, making the excuse that the bandage had fallen on the floor, he said cheerio.

CHAPTER SIX

January 1947

In January, Ma went away for a few days. She was replaced by a young married couple. They had a daughter, five year old Sarah. They were a loving couple, always kissing and cuddling, the like of which the home girls had never seen before. Mr Bee would suddenly grab Mrs Bee just to give her a peck on the cheek, or a long lingering kiss. To have a man around the home in the evenings was much more lively.

The snow started to fall, and the weather grew colder, it was the start of one of the worst winters. Everywhere was frozen solid in a matter of days, then there was more snow, until it was too bad for the trams to run. A snow plough regularly cleared the road, making four feet high walls of snow either side of the road. Openings were cut through the wall of snow to enable people to cross the road. Everybody went about on foot, wrapped up well against the worst winter for years. The schools were temporarily closed and nobody went out, only in an emergency. The girls were all pleased that Ma was snowbound wherever she was, hoping she was having a good rest.

Mrs Bee, although young, had family ideals, and a motherly approach towards the girls. They were allowed out on errands to fetch her daughter, Sarah, from her Grandmother's, trudging over the thick snow through the quiet streets. Their boundaries were widening and they started to take Sarah to ballroom dancing in the middle of Leicester. Sarah, on the other hand, an only child, hadn't known anything only a carefree life with her parents, even if she was a little spoilt.

She was a sweet little girl with long, plaited hair and fitted into the home life quite well, always wondering where the girls 'Mummies and Daddies' were. Mr Bee was an athletic-looking man. In the daytime, he worked at the office, and came home at night. The bad weather continued for weeks, the girls were constantly out on the footpath clearing away the freshly fallen snow. They helped people to cross the road, and noticed the manhole cover at the corner of the park had slid away under the pressure of the flood. The girls kept watch until the police came and cordoned off the area.

When they finally went back to school the girls wore old socks over their shoes to stop them slipping over.

The visits to the cinema on Saturday afternoons continued, as did the Guides at Sacred Heart, and the Guards at the Salvation Army, one evening a week. Mr Bee was back in the hockey team every Saturday afternoon.

Mr & Mrs Bee had been looking after them for about three weeks, and Ma was still away.

"When is Ma coming back?" the girls asked every day.

Mrs Bee at last gave them the truth, Ma was not on holiday, or snowbound at her friends, she was not coming back until the doctor permitted.

"What's the matter with Ma, then?" Nipper chimed in.

"Miss Hammond has had a nervous breakdown. She is exhausted looking after you lot, and now I can see why."

The snow was beginning to thaw at last, the coal pile near the backdoor was covered in a blanket of snow, and several falls of snow from the roof.

The winter nights had gone by rather quickly, They had been entertained by Mr Bee who taught them to play cards. They had played 'Housey Housey', better known as Bingo. It was a Christmas present that had given them lots of pleasure. The girls hurried with their jobs so that they could play when Mr Bee came home from work.

At bedtime the girls insisted, 'only one more game of bingo' - they were addicted. To get them off to bed, Mr Bee would take over, shouting, 'I'm going to undress the last one in the room,' and with that they all disappeared up the stairs, laughing and screaming, the last one was always chased round the table and up the stairs.

He had threatened to wash their backs on bath nights. He chased them up the stairs any time arguments broke out, or if they were cheeky to him. It was a race to see who could get to the bathroom first, as it was the only door with a bolt on it.

The girls had finished the sewing after tea. Mr Bee came into the dining room, he was teaching the girls how to play 'Newmarket,' Later in the evening, he said, "Who's going to the off licence to get me a jug of beer? They all offered - anything for a little outing.

"We haven't got a jug, only the milk jug," they said.

"Have you got a bottle?"

"Yes, there's one under the sink," said the washer-uppers.

The bottle was washed out and with the money they ventured round the corner to the off licence.

"Haven't you got any glasses?" said Mr Bee thanking them for their efforts.

"You'll have to have a mug, that's all we have."

The bottle of beer sat on the tray with the best mug the girls could find. Mr Bee poured the frothy liquid into the mug and they continued playing cards.

"I've signed the pledge," Hazel said, just thinking about Miss Cart.

"What for?" said Mr Bee.

"To abstain from the use of alcohol, tobacco, gambling and all injurious habits," she said, trying to concentrate on the game as well.

"Well you're not drinking it are you?" said Mr Bee, and with that Mr Bee took a long swig of beer from the mug.

"Poo..ff..wow...." Mr Bee spewed the mouthful of beer all over the tray and ran out of the room.

"Barry," shouted Mrs Bee running after him.

The girls sat giggling at the quick exit of "Bazzer Bee" who buzzed out of the room.

"What's that bottle had in it?" he cried from the kitchen.

"That's the disinfectant bottle," said Margaret who was nearest to the tray. Yes they could all smell it.

Mr Bee returned to the dining room looking rather flushed.

"You smell that, Babs."

"I can smell it from here," said Mrs Bee. "You are teaching these girls bad habits."

The game was over, all the cards were now in a muddled heap, and Mr Bee was laughing, recovering from the disinfectant.

Mr Bee started to sing as if he was drunk, the Countesthorpe hymn - 'What a friend we have in Jesus', only the words were a little different.

"Only one more disinfectant,
Then I'll put you all to bed,
Only one more disinfectant,
By that time I will be dead."

They were all laughing, even on the way up the stairs as they fell over each other trying to get away from him.

In her prayers Winnie remembered everyone. They lay talking, knowing that Mr Bee had gone into the sitting room to do his paperwork for the office, but now and again the landing creaked, and they were never sure if Mr Bee was outside on the landing.

Joe was older now, and was transferred to live with Miss Pickering at the boys' home.

"I know he's being looked after there," said Winnie.

Hazel didn't tell them about the dreadful nursery that she had seen at Countesthorpe, the one that their baby brothers had been in. Hazel just made them laugh about the night that she and Sheila had crept out at night to pinch coal from the 'coal pile.'

Painful sores appeared on Hazel's back, she showed them to Margaret and Winnie.

"You ought to show them to Mrs Bee," said Margaret.

"No, I'm not showing her, Mr Bee will be there and I'm not getting undressed to show him," Hazel said. "Don't say nothing, they will get better."

At dinnertime, Mrs Bee cooked the mucky stew, Hazel thought about the Cottage Homes children, running for the bus, travelling to Countesthorpe, having their dinner rushing about in the same time that they had got to get from school, eat their dinner, and wash up. The girls had time to play in the dining room, for half an hour before a leisurely walk back to school.

One particular dinnertime, Hazel went upstairs to the toilet.

"Mrs Bee!" she shouted.

"What's up," shouted Mrs Bee coming halfway up the stairs.

"I've got blood in my knickers," Hazel whispered

"Haven't you had that before? Mrs Bee said.

"No, I think it's coming from my boils." Hazel said.

"What boils."

Hazel uncovered the patch of festering boils,

"Come into Ma's bedroom." Mrs Bee said.

"Put that on," she said and handed her a wadded pad, and a piece of elastic with hooks on it.

"What do I do with it?" Hazel said still thinking it was for the boils.

"You've started your periods, you'll get this happening every month now," said Mrs Bee. "As for the boils, we'll bathe them tonight."

In biology, Miss Gilbert the teacher had said that they would lose the reproduction eggs once a month, she didn't say that there would be blood as well.

On inspection in Ma's sitting room, Mrs Bee discovered an abscess under Hazel's arm as well as five boils, she was sent to hospital straight away, and Hazel came home with her arm in a sling after the abscess had been lanced.

Mr & Mrs Bee were moving to a new house. For a bit of fun, they had a competition to see who could name their house. There were various names, the first and most popular was 'The Bee Hive,' it wasn't chosen, neither was the 'Rabbit Warren', or 'Crows Nest', it ended up with a very select name, 'Sunningdale.'

Ma came back in the middle of February, and took charge as if she had never been away. Mrs Bee had given the girls privileges that she would give her own daughter, and they had visited places that had never been allowed before. The girls were soon back to normal, the cellar flooded the worst ever, after the snow had melted. The water was higher up the cellar steps than ever before. Ma's forward planning had paid off and there was enough coal in the back yard to keep them going for a few weeks.

Easter that year was very cold and the girls couldn't wear their blazers. The Easter Garden in church still had its primroses and mossy banks among the statues in the Garden of Gethsemane. St Stephen's didn't have the same homely feel now that Father Huntley had gone. The whirlpool that they were in was now getting bigger, and they were gradually being spun outwards in the ripples of the ever-changing circles. It was a year full of different opportunities, and tragedies, all happening so fast.

A new school had been built for young art and craft students in preparation for the Art and Technical College. Hazel, being in the second year, had a chance to take the exam. The school was near to Hazel's Grandma's. After the first morning's exams Hazel called at Grandma's to see how she was. She opened the back door, and called to Grandma. Three ladies sat on Grandma's settee.

"Hello, what are you doing here," said Aunty Flo, who was stone deaf, and Hazel hadn't seen her for years.

"I've come to see Grandma," Hazel said.

"She's upstairs, she's not very well," said the other Aunt, also dressed in black.

"They haven't told her," whispered the other lady in black, who Hazel recognized as Di, the lady who Dad wanted to marry.

"Haven't they told you?" said the other Aunt.

"Told me what?" Hazel said.

"Your Dad's died," said Di, her white handkerchief in her hand.

Hazel stood in silence, not knowing what to say.

"I didn't know," she finally proffered.

"We've just come back from the funeral," said the middle Aunt.

Like three witches they sat there, not one of them offering to put their arms around Hazel, or give her an understanding kiss. "Just forty years old, he was."

Hazel felt like an intruder and left by the back door.

She walked back to school, there was a whole afternoon of exams ahead of her. She was an orphan, and she wanted to scream. Grandma hadn't come down to say 'hello', she knew she would be too upset. Their Dad had died a week ago, and no-one had told Hazel and Doris.

Valerie joined Hazel at the school entrance. Hazel was quiet, pretending to have nerves for the exam. She tried to join the contours of the geography maps in front of her, it was no good she couldn't concentrate. The exam papers were never completed.

Miss Glegg was in charge that day. After tea she called Doris and Hazel into the sitting room, and told them of their father's death. Gleggy never told them that he had been buried that day. There was a 'matter of fact' air about her, her eyes danced in the circles of her glasses. Hazel didn't know whether she was laughing or not. The two left the sitting room, not divulging any of their feelings. It was just three days before Hazel's thirteenth birthday, and Doris's twelfth birthday. Hazel secretly told Doris what she had discovered when she called in at Grandma's.

Miss Morris and Miss Watkins, the Sunday school teachers, heard the news of their father's death; they gave Hazel and Doris a tiny book of day to day prayers.

The next visiting day, they had a surprise visit from Ted who, was going away, he had been in hospital suffering from tuberculosis. Now he was going to Norfolk to the Convalescent Home. Ted told them that Norman was now very ill in Groby Road Hospital, and they were operating on him to take away one of his lungs. He was in hospital when Dad had died.

That was the last time the girls had any visitors.

Hazel hadn't forgotten her friend, Margaret Clark, who she had met at

King Richard's Road School, and decided to visit her Dad's butchers shop, on East Park Road. She told him what had happened and that she would write a letter to Margaret. Hazel received an invitation to spend all day Sunday with them at their home on King Richard's Road.

Margaret had three sisters, and it was quite a busy house at the back of a shop that had a wonderful smell of oranges.

Margaret took Hazel out into the street.

"Which way shall we go?" said Margaret.

Being able to choose which way to go made Hazel feel liberated and she was lost for words, she couldn't remember any of the streets.

They walked into town, to the Salvation Army in Jarram Street, and sat in the congregation among ladies with tambourines, and bonnets. The band sat on the stage, all young people with drums and cornets and double bass bassoons.

"That's Philip there," said Margaret. "He's the one I like."

Philip was the most handsome boy on the stage, and Hazel fell for him as well.

"We've got a Philip at our church, and he's our best looking choirboy." Hazel said. "We call him Pip"

Hazel had never heard the hymns that were sung. They were rousing, joyous hymns, the ladies banging on their tambourines, shaking them like leaves on a tree.

"Come forward and be saved." said the Brother on the stage. "Come and give your heart to the Lord Jesus."

One or two people went forward to the stage, and he blessed them. Hazel sat tight in her seat, remembering that she had been baptised.

Margaret's Mum had been busy cooking all morning, and Sunday dinner reminded her of Grandma's. In the afternoon they all went for a long walk, as far as the Museum in Leicester.

That summer evening they joined the Salvation Army band, marching from one street corner to the next, playing as they went. Hazel enjoyed her day out so much she felt that she was now one of Margaret's sisters.

The days in the Guards were numbered for Hazel as she had been caught on the park with Terry Bradley instead of coming straight home. At eight o'clock at night, Mrs Bee, who was on duty, didn't want to hear any excuses about the birds' nest she was going to see, Hazel was just sent to bed without any supper.

The exam results for the Junior Art School came through the post.

Hazel's best friend Valerie had passed, she was very artistic, and her parents were proud of her. It was a short friendship, and within a few weeks she had gone to her new school. The only times Hazel saw her again were out of the blue room window waiting for the tram in her new maroon uniform early in the mornings.

On Saturday afternoons, the pocket money spending time had gradually increased, and Hazel was a regular visitor at Ma's hairdressers in Moat Road. Mr and Mrs Cooper were expecting their first baby, so Hazel offered to help clean up the salon floor, and make them a cup of tea. In return they taught her how to do the pin curls in the customers' hair, and she practised doing an Amami wave set, which was always very successful.

Her school friend, Janet Dalby, was passing the hairdressers shop, just as Hazel was going back to Ma's. She had been on an errand for her Mam to get the decoration for the wedding cake.

"Then I've got to carry it all the way to my Grandma's." said Janet.

Hazel was always full of good ideas and offered to help. Getting Ma's permission, Hazel went home with Janet. The cake sat on the table, it had been made from the contribution of several friends rations, dried fruit was still a scarce commodity, and Janet's Mum had just finished it. The two girls took turns to carry the heavy cake, specially packaged in a large box, which made it difficult to carry. It was the only opportunity Hazel had of being able to ride a bike, and so Janet's bike went along as well. Holding the cake down one street, then riding the bike down the next, and so the cake was delivered safely.

Margaret Adnitt, the girl next door, had been courting for quite some time, her boyfriend had been de-mobbed and was home from the war. They had heard that Hazel had helped in the hairdresser's shop, and at thirteen, she was cajoled into the responsible task of curling the bride's hair. None of the girls had been in on such a big event as a wedding. All the Adnitts belonged to St Saviour's church up the hill beside the park.

The end of the war had brought many couples together, it was quite an occurrence for the girls to see who could spot the bride going into church. The bride's hair took the home perm very well, and Hazel was thrilled when the curly hair was unwound from the curlers. All the girls went to the church to see Margaret arrive at the church with her Dad. It was a special treat on a Saturday morning, throwing confetti.

They hadn't been back from Camp long when the girls were told that Miss Morris, their Sunday school teacher, was very ill. Miss Watkins who she lived with couldn't leave her to do any shopping. "Can we go and do the errands for them, Ma?" four of them asked.

"Well, Miss Morris is too ill, they won't want you bothering them," said Ma.

"We can ask, if they don't want any help we can come home," the girls said.

Winnie, Margaret, Doris and Hazel ran some of the way to save time. They knocked on the front door.

Miss Watkins opened the door, she was rather deaf, and hardly knew what to say.

"There is an errand you can do for me, come in," said Miss Watkins.

She took her purse from the kitchen cupboard, and there the girls saw the sink full of pots waiting to be washed. Two of them went to the shop while the other two set about the kitchen. Miss Watkins resumed the bedside vigil. With all the helpful jobs finished, the girls were given the opportunity to go upstairs to see Miss Morris.

The white-haired lady lay in the single bed under the window, there was no movement as they crept into the room. Miss Watkins told them all to kneel down while she said a prayer. They knelt at the side of the bed. Miss Morris, the short plump one of the two teachers was near to death, Father Watson had been and given her the last rites. They had never seen a dead person before, her face was shining and she looked like a pot doll. Miss Morris's favourite hymn was their Sunday school hymn.

"Would you like to sing her favourite hymn?" said Miss Watkins.

"Dear Lord and Father of Mankind, forgive our foolish ways..."

All four of them sang every line, knowing every verse.

"I'm sure she would have loved that," said Miss Watkins.

On the way back the girls discussed how very religious Miss Morris and Miss Watkins were. They had noticed the famous painting by Holman Hunt. 'I stand at the door and knock.' The big, colourful, awe-inspiring painting of Jesus knocking on the door. A smaller picture hung over the piano, it read 'Suffer little children to come unto me'.

"They are like saints, said Winnie, did you see that picture of Jesus on the stairs, the artist could be related to you, Doris." said Winnie.

They decided to call them Saint Morris, and Saint Watkins.

Every opportunity they had with Ma's permission, they visited Miss Watkins, just to do the washing up.

"Miss Morris is still very ill," Miss Watkins said, as she organised all the jobs that she needed doing.

Each time before the girls left, they popped up stairs to sing her favourite hymn, and one day she opened her eyes.

A few weeks later Miss Morris was sitting by the fireside when the girls arrived.   It was her first day out of bed for weeks.

Her father's photograph was on the table at the side of her chair. They were all amazed to see her, as they had often thought she was already dead while they were singing to her.

"Here are the girls who brought me back to life," she said.

Each girl bent down to kiss her, Miss Morris had made a miraculous recovery. There was no washing up to be done and Miss Watkins brought in a tray of tea.

"Miss Morris is definitely a Saint, she has devoted her life to the church, and God didn't let her die," said Winnie on the way home.

The confirmation classes had been taken over by Miss Adams, who as their Godmother, was making sure that the girls were well prepared for the day which was getting ever closer.

The daily routines were carried out to the letter, Marie sometimes got the coal up, and sometimes she cleaned the kitchen, it all depended on who was going out. Hazel had settled down to the fact that she wasn't the eldest, but Ma treated them both as the eldest, and shared the jobs. Ma's relief was now usually done by Mrs Bee, who had taken the part time job over. They had only seen Glaring Gleggy in November at Countesthorpe when they had been invited to their bonfire night.

The girls had all moved up another class at school, and another year was almost over. Ma made all the Christmas puddings, and as they stirred they made renewed wishes into the mixture. The Christmas cake this year was made without the gravy browning, the black treacle in the cupboard was an added luxury in the pantry. The girls still lined up every Friday night for a spoonful of cod-liver oil, and a spoonful of peppermint or syrup of figs.

A bunch of flowers was taken to Mrs Cooper who had given birth to a baby boy, the pots were washed in the hairdresser's kitchen, before they left. Mr Cooper was managing very well.

Father Huntley paid them a surprise visit at church on the day of their confirmation. Only two of the girls wore white, Hazel wasn't one of them. Both Miss Morris and Miss Watkins were at the service looking proudly on as the Bishop of Leicester placed his hands on their heads. Their first communion was to be on Christmas Day. The girls would now be allowed to go to the eight o'clock communion service providing they got themselves up.

After the service Miss Morris and Miss Watkins congratulated the girls, and Father Huntley wanted to know whose angelic voices had brought Miss Morris back from deaths door. The girls had forgotten about singing for Miss Morris, and Father Huntley said Miss Morris obviously had angels protecting her.

CHAPTER SEVEN

January 1948

The twins arrived in January, after Peggy and Little Linda had suddenly left. It was unusual for little ones to leave Ma's.

"Why have they left Ma?" said Nipper.

"I think they're going to be adopted," said Ma.

Sadie and Jackie, were not identical, but both had blonde curls, and were younger than Nipper, The twins had been in hospital, and were quite used to being 'knocked from pillar to post' as Ma called it. They'd had a rough time, and had come to Ma's to put some love and stability into their young lives. They had also been in different hospitals, so were quite strangers to each other as well. The girls loved the twins, especially when they began to join in with the home life, combing their golden curls, as they had done when Louise had arrived with her jet black ringlets. Louise had joined her sisters at Sacred Heart, and Marie, Colette and Nancy had all improved according to their school reports.

Hazel and Marie no longer quarrelled, the wind had long gone out of Hazel's sails. Doris was now in hospital needing complete rest. Hazel wondered if she would be next, all her brothers and sisters had now contracted tuberculosis.

The schoolwork was improving again with the new teacher Miss Welsh, Hazel was now in the hockey team, and had a new friend, Brenda, who was form captain.

"Have you got a Mother?" said Brenda.

"No, she died with TB, four years ago," Hazel said.

"So did my mine," said Brenda, "when I was little."

"Do you live with your Dad, then?" asked Brenda.

"No, he died as well, I live in an orphanage on East Park Road."

"Oh, I know what it's like, I live with my Grandma," said Brenda. "My brothers live with my Dad, I don't see them very often."

The two girls bonded very well.

That year, they made cushion covers in the sewing class, and overalls for the nursery children. They learned how to darn properly, and made their own cookery overalls ready for Domestic Science the next term.

In March, Edna ran away from Ma's, she wasn't well, she had very bad eyes, and was generally in poor health. She was found at Market

Harborough. Edna was then taken to the Receiving Home, which had now become a refuge for older children. Mrs Simpson slapped her face, and when Edna retaliated by slapping Mrs Simpson across her face, Mr Simpson came into the day room and knocked Edna on the floor and kicked her. She was then sent to Countesthorpe.

Months went by before they saw her again.

As a special treat for Easter, Ma took the girls to the pictures to see 'Song of the South.'

'Zippadee doodah, zippadee ay,
My oh my, what a wonderful day.'

Round the dining table on sewing night, in the bath, down the cellar, once one voice took hold of the ditty, all twelve voices joined in, whatever they were doing. It was only when Ma got so fed up with the 'zippadee doodah' that she suggested she would have to take them to see something else so that they could have a change of tune.

At the hairdresser's, Mrs Cooper's baby, Michael, was now a few months old, and to give them a break Ma let Hazel baby-sit for them while they had an evening out. The baby was very good, and in between feeds Hazel tidied the kitchen.

When the weather was warmer, Hazel took him for longer walks through the park, and as a special surprise, ventured as far as Jerome's photographers in Leicester. The Coopers' were thrilled with the very first photo of their baby son, which she collected the following week. Hazel began to spend most of her time at the hairdresser's, hoping one day to take it up as a job. She kept the cups of tea going for the customers, doing some of the jobs that were usually left until later.

After Holy Communion every Sunday, the girls bumped into Stephen Harvey, he was the acolyte for Father Watson, and a dark-eyed choirboy whose angelic voice they all fell in love with. Stephen's mother and father and spinster aunt also attended church every Sunday and were never far away when they came out of church. Stephen always smiled at the girls when they went up to the altar for communion.

"I saw you at Moat Road last week," said Stephen to Hazel after church.

"We have our cookery lesson there, every Friday," Hazel said quietly.

"Which school do you go to then," said Stephen with his face right close to Hazel, as they squeezed through the door of the church together.

"Bridge Road." The conversation was at an end as they had reached the door of the home. Hazel carried on walking with him.

"Don't you live there?" Stephen's head turned to look at the other girls disappearing down the entry.

"Yes I do, but I can walk a bit further with you. Where do you live?" Hazel asked, striding along to keep up with Stephen.

"Off Evington Road," Stephen was looking back towards the church

"Well I'll come as far as the pillar box," Hazel said, it was the closest she had ever been to a boy, and she liked it. She had dared herself to walk with Stephen that far. "Are you coming to the eleven o'clock service?" Hazel asked.

"I never miss it, my parents will be there so I shall have to walk home with them." Stephen looked at Hazel and grinned.

"What time do you come out of school?" Hazel dared to ask another question.

"We come out at four, sometimes a bit later," said Stephen as they reached the pillar-box. "Meet me here and we can walk up the hill together," he said.

"I'd love to," Hazel said. Her heart was pounding, and she blushed when he suddenly gave her a kiss on the cheek.

Hazel walked back to Ma's waving to Stephen occasionally until he was out of sight. Father Watson had been watching as he came along the road. He gave Hazel an icy stare as he passed by at the entry gate. She ran down the entry.

On Friday, as planned, Hazel was hanging out of the cookery class window that overlooked the boys' playground to see if she could see Stephen. At four o'clock, there he was waiting at the pillar-box, and like two old friends they walked up the hill. Hazel gave him a cake out of her cookery basket.

"What's this I hear about you kissing boys, H?" said Ma at teatime.

"The head choirboy at church," said Margaret.

"Yes, Ma," Hazel said.

"You're supposed to come straight home from school, you know that," Ma said pouring her tea from the tiny teapot.

Still sighing, Hazel wasn't really listening, and just promised not to do it again. She now knew how Olive felt when she raced to the blue-room window when the choirboys came out of church, sitting on the front row in church in their squeaky clean outfits gazing at the starched ruffs and

Day out with the Councillors at Butlins, Skegness, 1949.

the snow white embroidered tops of the young choristers.

The meetings at the pillar-box on Fridays went on for a few weeks until the end of term.

The Superintendent's visit reminded them that they would soon be off to camp again. Edna had been in hospital again, and back from Convalescence she was now living at number six cottage at Countesthorpe. The girls sent her a card for her twelfth birthday - they would be seeing her in a few weeks time.

The girls had all done well at school. One twin was a bit cleverer than the other. Louise in her class at Sacred Heart had come fifteenth, Nipper was tenth, and Winnie at her new Grammar school was twelfth. Ruth had done much better and come sixth, Colette thirteenth, Marie fifteenth. Margaret was top of her class again, and Hazel had come twelfth, Doris was now at the convalescent home in Norfolk and out of hospital.

"You can all give yourselves a pat on the back," said Ma as she looked at the reports on her table.

"Can we all go to see Shirley Temple, please Ma, in "The Little Princess," they all shouted.

"You promised, Ma," said Nipper.

"Maybe," Ma said.

Apart from the rain, the outing to the cinema was a great success. They all enjoyed it, and related to the Little Princess locked away in the attic of the boarding school. There would never be an Indian Prince or anyone like that to come to the rescue of the East Park Road girls.

*   *   *

It was a good camp that year, the weather was perfect. They had all learned from previous years what to expect. There were more organised days' outings to Skegness, accompanied by the Councillors from Leicester. Taking them to nice restaurants for tea.

Edna spent as much time with the girls as she was allowed, she looked very ill, and had been treated badly at Countesthorpe. Hazel asked her why she had run away, and she told her that she had been seen with a boy coming from the park. When she was caught at Market Harborough she was taken to the Receiving Home.

"Them at the Receiving Home asked me if I had been intimate with

282

boys, and I said yes, and I shouted at them. Well I didn't know what it meant so they sent me to Countesthorpe. That Mr Simpson kicked me on the floor," she said.

Hazel felt she had been wronged and told Ma, but there was nothing they could do about it. Sports Day brought the final day of camp to a close, the weather was warm and sunny, and the cameras clicked for several photographs. Once they were back home Edna was sent back to the hospital.

The newest and latest venture of the Superintendent was the Christmas Review. The boys and girls of Countesthorpe were going to be in a concert. Ma's girls now travelled to Countesthorpe for the practice nights, and practised on the top deck of the bus on the way home.

The first week was the throwing out week; anything that wasn't any good was scrapped, as was Hazel's song 'Silver Hair and Heart of Gold.'

At Countesthorpe, they all sat together for the informal sing-along in the same hall that was used for the church service on Sunday.

"What are you doing in it? I think our cottage is doing a sketch," said Laura.

"Eileen King sings lovely, she's singing 'I'll walk beside you through the world today' and Mr Burleys daughter, Kathleen, is singing 'Jerusalem', accompanied by a piano and violin," said Laura who was giving the girls some inside information.

Suggestions were coming in from all angles, and the whole show was being run by a funny little man who looked as if he had no teeth, he was one of the main acts of the show.

Hazel waited at the pillar-box for Stephen; she had bought him a fountain pen from Skegness. Father Watson came along.

"What are you waiting here for?" said Father Watson.

"I'm waiting for Stephen Harvey," Hazel replied proudly.

"Leave that boy alone," said Father Watson, "and you get off home, go on." He waited while Hazel walked towards the home.

Hazel couldn't understand it, what business was it of his she thought, and stared back occasionally to see if Stephen was anywhere about.

On Sunday morning, Stephen wasn't at church, perhaps it was his Sunday for the Wesley Chapel she thought, or he was probably still away on holiday, Hazel told herself.

In August, Brenda and Hazel's new class teacher was Miss Crofts, the Sports Mistress. She was jolly and drove a car to school, she smiled every time she called the register, and the girls all loved her.

It was the job of the fourth year to vote for the Head Prefect, and the Hockey Captain. For the Head Prefect the voting was down to three equal votes. Audrey Bennifer, Rita Robinson, and Hazel Hunt. Hazel could not believe that she would ever be in the last three.

The last vote was counted, and to her amazement Hazel became Head Prefect. It was the same for Brenda, she was voted unanimously as Hockey Captain. The two girls became really good friends.

Miss Tomlinson, the headmistress, congratulated them, and told them what was required of them. Hazel was to have a team of prefects and Brenda was the Hockey captain, and was responsible for thanking the teams after playing in the matches, "Ma I'm in the hockey team," Hazel shouted, as soon as she was in the back door. "Can I play on Saturday mornings, please Ma."

"Well, you'll have to do your jobs first," said Ma.

"How can I do the kitchen and be at Ethel Road, by nine o'clock?" Hazel said, almost in tears.

"You can't can you?" said Ma adamantly.

Hazel slowly returned to the dining room, silently screaming, she had been chosen to be goalkeeper, because nobody else could do it. She would have to try again later when Ma was in a better mood.

"No. And that's all there is to it," Ma snapped at her when she finally asked again.

Hazel had to break the news to Miss Crofts, and waited until after school.

"It's not the end of the world," said Miss Crofts.

"I'll come and see Ma if you like. Don't worry about it."

Sure enough, Miss Crofts visited Ma a few days later and Ma said Hazel would have to do the kitchen on a Friday night. Fortunately for her the Christmas Review practice night had been altered from a Friday because the pianist wasn't available.

Miss Tomlinson announced that the school was to have a uniform and everybody could do a design to see what ideas came from the girls. The school badge was on the heading of the school notepaper and Hazel drew it in her notebook.

They had a week to put in their entries.

The school blazer was just the same, and the tunics were very popular but with fewer pleats. The school summer dress was navy checked.

Hazel had designed her own school beret in the Alderman Newton style, which wasn't a beret but a hat with a brim, and had a badge on the crown. She had the advantage over all the other girls, because of Margaret and Winnie's uniform, plus the fact that Hazel wanted to wear a school uniform.

At night-time in the attic, Hazel embroidered her own school badge, the three bridges were held up like a viaduct, with B R G S across the top of the bridge. Two Leicester white roses sat in the top space of the shield, and blue water ran under the bridges. She stitched it on to her blazer, and was the only girl in the school with a badge.

It was certainly a term for doing things and going places. During the autumn term, Miss Crofts arranged a trip to London.

"Hands up, how many would like to go?" said Miss Crofts.

Everybody put up their hands, including Hazel.

"The train doesn't get back to Leicester until two o'clock in the morning, so you'll have to get your parents to meet you at the Station," said Miss Crofts.

It was just Hazel's luck, Ma wouldn't be able to pick her up, nor anybody else.

All the literature was given out, they would visit the Tower of London, Houses of Parliament, Westminster Abbey, Buckingham Palace, and end up at Covent Garden for the Ballet, 'Swan Lake.'

Hazel took the letter home to Ma, and it was rejected.

"How can you expect to go?" said Ma.

"If I can get somebody to pick me up at the station, Ma, will I be able to go?" Hazel said.

It was Brenda who came to the rescue, she had asked her Grandma if Hazel could stay the night at her house, and they could have a taxi from the station. To Hazel's amazement the problem was solved.

They had a few weeks to save money, Hazel's pocket money had gone up to sixpence, she was now on the same footing as Marie.

Stephen was pleased to see Hazel at the Wesley Chapel on Sunday morning. As they walked home she told him about Father Watson.

"What did he say that for?" said Stephen. "Why should he tell you to go home? I was on holiday."

"Is it because I live in a home?" Hazel said to Stephen bluntly.

"I don't think so, Hazel," said Stephen.

Hazel felt a ripple through her body when he spoke her name. She fumbled in her pocket.

"Well I bought you a little present from Skegness," and she handed the box to him.

Stephen opened it, "Its just what I need," he said, and gave her a meaningful kiss on the lips.

"I haven't been to communion for a week or two, because of Father Watson's accusing eyes, he watches us all the time," Hazel said.

"Don't worry about it," said Stephen "Let's go to the pictures."

One Saturday morning Hazel, went to the pillar-box to post Ma's letter, Stephen's spinster Aunt stopped to speak to her, she had been to church arranging the flowers.

"You have been seeing Stephen, and meeting him out of church," said his Aunt. "We don't want the likes of you going out with him any more," she said.

"We have been to the pictures once, in the afternoon, and I walk with him to Burnaston Road. What harm is there in that?" Hazel said naively.

"It's his Mother's and Father's wish that you do not talk to him any more." The Aunt looked at her very severely.

Hazel didn't answer, she was a bit upset, and promised nothing.

The Swan Lake Ballet was magnificent, the dancers so graceful, and the orchestra so loud, if it wasn't for Brenda's Grandma, Hazel wouldn't be sitting there. The train journey home, at two o'clock in the morning, was wonderful, they had never been out so late. Thanks to Miss Crofts, they had all had such a super day in London. The taxi took them to Brenda's house, and they crept up the stairs so as not to disturb her Grandma, but as Grandmas, do she crept in to say 'goodnight' to the two girls.

The journeys to and from Countesthorpe for the Christmas Review were enjoyable evenings out, travelling on public transport with all the street lights on, lots of people still out and about. The girls were thrilled by the outings, more so than the concert.

The sketch for the East Park Road girls was called 'A penny stamp, please,' and was a bit of a washout at the rehearsal.

"It's all to do with timing, you have to come in at the right place," said Mr Payne.

The Christmas Review was eventually open for the public to see, and at the Co-op Hall in Belgrave Gate the audience packed themselves in.

Backstage, it was just like a mad house, the makeup was put on a bit thick as someone had said to put plenty on because of the glare from the lights. They were laughing and giggling, trying to put the lipstick on straight. Nipper had peeped through the curtains and came to tell them that the Lord Mayor was sitting on the front row. Nobody cared about their lines any more.

"A penny stamp, please," said Doris. "That's all I have to say."

"Well don't forget to come on the stage," said Winnie, who was sitting behind the counter at the post office holding a conversation with Margaret.

Ruth came on stage to start the ball rolling, she was posting a parcel.

"Is it for your Aunt?" said Winnie to Margaret as she took the parcel.

"No it's for my sister," said Ruth, "It's her birthday."

"Oh, I didn't know it was her birthday," said Margaret to Winnie behind the counter. What are you buying her?"

"A penny stamp," said Doris who was pushed onto the stage.

The audience got the gist of it, and it was funny as folks were being pushed on to the stage, and just looking blank. The conversation behind the counter got out of hand, and they were just talking amongst themselves until the curtains closed.

Eileen King, as expected, was the star of the show, she had to sing another song before she could go off the stage.

They had all done their best and the Superintendent came on the stage with them all at the end of the show, and thanked everybody for turning out on such a wet night.

They all sang 'God Save Our Gracious King', then made their way back to Ma's on the tram, with all the make-up and eye shadow still on their faces.

*   *   *

Hazel felt everything she did from this point on was for the last time. It was the last time she would be helping Ma mix the Christmas puddings, the last time to help with the trimmings, only so many more times to scrub the kitchen floor.

December eighteenth, after seven years in the homes, she felt abandoned, with both parents dead, and Ted away in hospital. Norman was in hospital and had just had one of his lungs removed. Doris was at the Convalescent Home, and now Edna was back in hospital. She didn't know where their baby, Brian, was, or whether he was still living with

Di. Grandma had been exhausted visiting the hospital and Grandad was making her rest.

Now it was Hazel 's turn to leave Ma's.

"Here's your birth Certificate Hazel," said Ma. "You'll be needing that."

Hazel took the birth certificate, and looked at it again.

"They've put my birthday down wrong, Ma," Hazel said.

"Let me look?" said Ma. Oh you're a bit older than you thought you were," said Ma.

"That means I'm a month older than Marie, doesn't it, Ma?" Hazel sat down. "All these years I have wanted to be the eldest, and I've been the eldest all the time," she said.

"Never mind, H, you've not done so bad out of it," said Ma.

"If I was the eldest there wouldn't have been any fights, Ma," Hazel said and felt like bursting into tears.

Hazel stared at the birth certificate.

"Its been arranged for you to go and live in a foster home on Duncan Road, H, your social worker is coming to see you," said Ma.

The 'social worker' arrived and Hazel was taken to Duncan Road, to meet the new 'foster parents'. They were an elderly couple, much older than her own Grandma and Grandad. Hazel wasn't too bothered as Duncan Road was quite near to Grandma's house, just off Saffron Lane. Hazel was told to go to their house after school had finished. She didn't want to go into a foster home.

There was no welcoming party, when they first arrived at Ma's, and there was no farewell party now that she was leaving.

The doll that her mother was making when she died had been entrusted to her Grandma. Hazel had personally hidden it in Grandma's bedroom drawer, for safe-keeping. On her latest visit, Hazel asked Grandma if she could look at it. Grandma was very sorry, but she had given the doll away to some crying child.

With her school satchel, school reports, the surprise birth certificate, and three pairs of knickers, Hazel walked up the entry - she was free!

THE END
* * * * * * * * * *

About the Author

Donald Imrie is a writer, musician and author of the brand-new Primal series. A lover of fantasy and all things mystical, the Anglo-Scot seeks to immerse the reader into a world of magic in his debut novel. When the dog enthusiast is not trekking across the countryside, he can be found in the company of friends and family, in his home county of Lancashire.

Primal: Volume I

Donald R. Imrie

Primal: Volume I

Olympia Publishers
London

www.olympiapublishers.com
OLYMPIA PAPERBACK EDITION

A CIP catalogue record for this title is
available from the British Library.

ISBN: 978-1-80074-231-4

This is a work of fiction.
Names, characters, places and incidents originate from the writer's
imagination. Any resemblance to actual persons, living or dead, is
purely coincidental.

First Published in 2022

Olympia Publishers
Tallis House
2 Tallis Street
London
EC4Y 0AB

Printed in Great Britain

Dedication

To my family and friends. Thank you for making the magic possible.

Acknowledgements

As with any author striving to leave their mark of imagination on the world, it would be remiss to go without thanking the many people responsible for their assistance in my debut novel.

The concept of the *Primal* has been with me for many years, and while I have often struggled for the right words, with support I have been able to fulfil a lifelong dream. The journey of Emrys and his struggles mirrors my own in some cases, and I have drawn many of the characters from experiences and conversations held with friends, family and loved ones. But it is with pride that I am able to bring something new into the world, and the first thing I would like to do is appraise the individuals without whom I could not have achieved this.

To Mum. Thank you for being the first one to read the novel, the first to offer advice and the first to encourage writing even when the going got tough. I cannot thank you with words enough and I only hope I can make you proud, despite my many misspellings, grammatical errors and typos.

To Caeron. Thank you for your support and importantly your challenges to the story. Without your innovations, thoughts, and without the opportunity to amend the novel, I would not be in the position I am. This is down to you mate and I shall not forget it. I will always have time for you, you cocky Welsh so-and-so!

To Magda (the only person I know who manages to get stuck in Peru). Thank you for your enthusiasm and joy for my book, you do not know how much it meant to me. Thank you for being so eager to read my writings, and offering your wisdom to my cause. Your efforts have been greatly appreciated and I even managed to sneak you your own character in there!

To Kaz. Thank you, my old friend. You are without a doubt the fastest of readers out there. You've gone above and beyond the call of duty, with your unwavering assistance in reviewing, spot-checking and advice for the story. Thank you for everything you have done.

To Nadia. Thank you. You are a most talented artist and I cannot thank you enough for creating the map and bringing the world to life. Without you, there would be no reference for the readers, and I want you to know how important your efforts have been to the production of this novel. Thank you Nadia.

Next, I would like to turn my attention to Olympia Publishers. There are several individuals working for this publishers and notable people I would like to thank for their assistance. To begin with, there is James, my commissioning editor. Thank you for spotting my work and offering me the chance to publish with Olympia. You were kind, attentive, and gave me just the courage I needed to agree a publishing deal. Next, there is Kristina, my production coordinator. I must have annoyed you something rotten in the beginning with my many irritating questions and queries! That being said, thank you for your patience, encouragement and diligence throughout these many months of production. Furthermore, I would like to thank the design team for their efforts in my cover, the editors for their proofreading and amendments and finally my thanks go out to you, the reader. Thank you for taking the chance and reading the first *Primal* novel. I only hope that you have enjoyed my imagination and have taken something from it. Work is well underway on the sequel and, with luck, I hope to bring this to you as soon as possible. Thank you once more for undertaking this journey, now go, enjoy Emrys' journey instead!

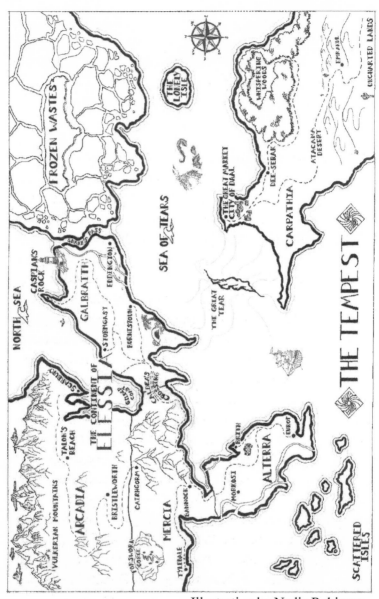

Illustration by Nadia Robinson

Prologue:
Mage Law (Twenty Years Ago)

BOUND with manacles on his arms and legs, Hal struggled forward with his fellow mages as they were led through the streets of Talon's Reach. It was the capital city of Arcadia, the Empire to the North of the Elessian continent, and a place that had been once been home to the Circle, the highest order of mages. He was an apprentice sworn to the Circle from an early age and gifted with magical abilities. Not that it mattered. As he looked around and saw the despair and anguish on the faces he knew as family, he knew there was no hope, no magic to save the day. Mages had been corralled as if they were cattle and abused for almost a fortnight. There had been hangings, burnings at the stake, drownings and all manners of cruelties had been bestowed upon his kind. Screams rang out across the streets, echoing down the cramped alleys and alcoves as crowds formed and hurled abuse to their once friendly counterparts. Hal kept his head down as they all did. The cold cobbled stones had turned his bare feet numb on the walk from the dungeons. The chill in the air swept through his bones causing him to shudder with each passing gust. Armed knights clad in black surrounded them, their armour shining in the moonlight. They walked weapons in hand, ready to strike out at any act of defiance from Hal's group. Slowly they limped on in silence. No-one dared utter a word and each mage kept their heads down and away from the fierce gazes in the crowd around them.

They were brought forward to Griffon Square, the centre of Talon's Reach. As Hal looked around, he realised he had never seen a bleaker setting. The streets were awash with muck and blood and all of the colourful features that had once graced the area had been stripped away, leaving a soulless square in its wake. Three huge pyres lay in waiting and as the crowd parted, he could see there were nooses at every entrance with limp bodies being wrenched down. A platform in the midst of the chaos around them housed Emperor Harold Valyris, the ruler of the Arcadian Empire. He was a small stout man with a quickly receding hairline and a face crueller than Hal had ever seen. Emperor Valyris was dressed in golden armour which twinkled as the flames of the pyres flickered around him. Behind him and the pyres stood the Temple of Gallico, the home of the Circle, and Hal knew within himself, this was the last time he would see its like. The crowd continue to pelt their group with rotten food and vitriolic abuse until the emperor raised his hand and they stood to attention. "Arcadians!" he boomed, stepping forward into the light. "We are at an impasse. For month after month, we have all suffered. The one known as Caulder has ravaged our lands again and again! Our fields of wheat have been scorched so much so that we will never sow our crops again! Our livestock slaughtered and riddled with disease that spreads so easily we have had to strangle our pigs, lambs and horses! Our people, fathers, mothers, sons and daughters who are innocent have either been killed or corrupted! Corruption as you have all seen is a fate worse than death! Arcadia has suffered this plight of the Corruption alone, and who is to blame for this?"

"MAGE-FOLK!" the crowd angrily boomed as they

stomped their feet, waved their torches and pelted Hal's group with rocks. One of them caught him square on the temple and he fell to his knees as the pain throbbed and blood gushed down past his ear. A guard promptly beat him and forced him back to his feet as he shivered and huddled close to the other mages. *How had it come to this?* Hal puzzled. He cast his mind back six months ago when mages were revered and well-respected in Arcadia. Collaboration between the townsfolk and mage-folk had never been greater and they had shared in era of peace, music, arts and all manner of creativity that had made Arcadia the nation at the forefront of technological advances. Then the Living Death, or the Corruption as the Arcadian called it, swept across the land with Caulder as its bearer.

"Yes, you're right!" Emperor Valyris continued, "The mages are to blame for our hardships! Without them, none of this sickness would have come to Arcadia! So what should I, as a responsible Emperor of Arcadia, do?"

Cries of 'Kill them', 'Hang them' and 'Burn them' filled the air as Emperor Valyris smirked. He was enjoying himself, Hal noted and felt a burning anger swell within him. The emperor held his hand up once more, "I agree," he said pulling a scroll from his pocket. "We should kill them but I have decided that we should do *more* than that. After all they brought this plight to us, so it is fitting that they deserve their share in the suffering! Because of this I have enacted a new law, one which I call Mage Law."

He waved the scroll high above his head as the crowd drew breath in anticipation. To Hal's side, his friend Kalin began to cry and he reached an arm around him for support. "I Emperor Harold Valyris," he started to read, "of the Arcadian Empire, from this day forth hereby outlaw the use of magic on our lands. Mages are to be culled and exiled for crimes against our great nation. Any person who has information pertaining to a mage's Awakening will be greatly rewarded. But let it be known, any person aiding and abetting mages shall be executed without trial or forced into a life of servitude as penance for their sins. The Temple of Gallico is to be stripped of its wealth and all knowledge of magic is to be burned on the pyres you see behind me. Men! To arms! BURN THE TEMPLE OF GALLICO!"

Hal joined his fellow mages in their outcry as the gleaming Temple that stood as their beacon in Talon's Reach was ransacked by hundreds of armed soldiers. Books containing centuries of knowledge were cast upon the fires as men cheered and his people wept. Torches were carried into their home and before long a raging fire consumed most of what they had known. Defeated, he slumped to his knees in the puddled water beneath him. As he looked at himself, he barely recognised the raggedy man in his reflection. He was malnourished, dirty and thin to the bone as his black matted hair stuck to his forehead. Blood continued to pour down to his chin where it dropped into the puddle, clouding the waters in claret. As he looked to his left, Kalin was in floods of tears and buried his head in his hands. Hal stretched his arm out. "Kalin we must be strong," he weakly said. "We will find a way to survive without the temple."

"Why are they doing this?" Kalin squealed as he rose his voice. "We defeated Caulder and rid the land of the Corruption, not them! We saved Arcadia!"

"Oi!" A nearby guard overheard them. "Pipe down mage or I'll gut you now!"

Hal attempted to calm the situation and held Kalin close

but his friend became growingly agitated and restless as he clawed to be free. "Kalin don't," Hal hissed. "Please don't!"

"No, I will not take it any longer!" Kalin shrugged him off and leapt to his feet.

Hal helplessly watched on as Kalin's eyes began to burn crimson red and jets of flame emerged from his hands. The other mages around them backed off as the guard took a swing of his sword. Kalin caught the blade in his flamed hand and Hal watched as the metal melted instantly and liquid trickled down the hilt to the ground. Bursting forward Kalin spewed flames from his hands at the guards who backed off into the crowd. "We saved Arcadia!" Kalin bellowed bringing a silence to the noisy square. "Why do you torment us so? We saved you all from Caulder and the Living Death!"

Emperor Valyris did not move but smirked and rolled his eyes flippantly. "Lies!" he dismissed. "Archers kill him!"

"NO!" Hal screamed as arrows whistled through the air and Kalin's body slumped to the cold ground. He scampered over to his body and sobbed as he cradled his wheezing friend in his arms. Hal was distraught. Kalin was his closest friend. They had grown up together in the city from poor beginnings, and they had spent nearly fifteen years at each other's side. His curly blonde hair was unmoving as he twitched and blood frothed in his mouth. The lad who had been a bundle of life with laughter and kindness was no more, and Hal clung to him desperately wishing it was not so. The guards kicked him away before they carried Kalin's body to the pyres and threw his corpse onto the flames. "Do you see now?" Emperor Valyris called out. "Do you see what threat these mages pose? It was not they who defeated Caulder but us! They would have you believe their lies that magic is good and kind. But what was

Caulder if not magic? What was the Corruption if not magic? Guards! Bring forth half of that group there. We will exercise Arcadian justice!"

Hal watched hopelessly as his friends and colleagues were rounded up and flung onto the pyres. A few resisted to no avail. Arcadian Knights wore armour shielding them from their magic and before long the resistance was quelled. Their shrill shrieks and screams echoed through the square as their flesh melted to the approval of the baying mob. Less than ten of them remained. Of those left, there was Magnus an Illusionist, Asher a Conjurist, Solanta a Healer, Dagmar an Enchanter, Ferah a Seer, Eorfric a fellow Arcanist and Mitkal a Necromancer. They were all in various stages of grief and anger, yet it was Solanta who centred them all. "Stay with me," she whispered to the group. "For as long as we live, the Circle survives. Do not give them the satisfaction of your death."

Hal had always admired Solanta. She was as beautiful as she was wise, and when she took his hand she gave him the briefest glimpse of hope through these disastrous times. Emperor Valyris continued to applaud the fire as the Temple's foundations began to give way to the flames. A loud crash erupted as the roof caved in and dust poured through the square. As it settled, the emperor dusted himself off and addressed the crowd once more.

"The Temple is no more! Rejoice!" he said. "But that is not all my loyal subjects. For I have another announcement to make. Bring forth the prisoner."

A horse cart bearing a steel cage was brought along the cobbles with a man inside who Hal did not recognise. He was brown of hair and wore clothes alien to that of Arcadia. His trousers were stitched leather, and on his tunic there was an embroidered Oak tree that Hal could swear he had seen before somewhere. "Oh no…" Eorfric piped up. "I know who that is…"

The cart came to an abrupt stop and three guards threw the stranger to the ground before the emperor. "Ladies and Gentlemen," Emperor Valyris said. "Allow me to introduce you to the brother of King Terrys of Galbraith, Prince Osyris!"

The crowd promptly booed Osyris who barely seemed to notice them. He seemed to scan the square, almost as if he was evaluating his options of escape until he locked eyes on Hal's group. His blue eyes flickered when they saw Solanta and he promptly shook his head with a fierce gaze. Hal noticed that tears began to flow down her cheeks as she started to nervously tremble.

"*Prince* Osyris," Emperor Valyris said mockingly. "You stand accused of harbouring mages and escorting them from Arcadia to your Kingdom of Galbraith. How do you plead?"

Osyris merely looked at the emperor and smirked. "If you're looking for someone to blame," he said. "Why do you not start with looking in a mirror?"

Emperor Valyris' cheeks flushed red in anger and he motioned to a guard who promptly beat Osyris sending him to his knees. "You dare speak out of turn to me?" he spat. "Let it be known to you all that Prince Osyris here has indeed been ferrying mages from our Eastern shores. We have proof and testimony to accord of this. Now comes…"

"Magic is not and has never been your enemy!" Osyris interrupted. "Do not allow yourselves to make it so! What happened was not the Circle's fault! It was the responsibility of one mage and yet you seek to snuff out the very tribe of peoples that saved Arcadia, nay Elessia from certain

19

destruction!"

Guards continued to pummel Osyris to the floor until he spat out fresh blood and strained as he dragged himself to his knees.

"Magic has no place in Arcadia any more," Emperor Valyris said. "We have destroyed their temple, enacted Mage Law and we shall hunt them down like the rats they are."

"Then you are a fool," Osyris coughed. "Know this *Harold,* Caulder may return and if that happens, you will need magic to save you."

"I have heard enough from you!" the emperor shouted. "I find you guilty of aiding mages and sentence you to die."

"Kill me," Osyris replied, "and you will be at war with my Kingdom."

"Precisely," Harold replied coldly and turned his attention to the crowd. "Galbraith has not been touched by the Corruption. Its ground has not been poisoned as ours has. Its air is still fresh and the flora flourishes under King Terrys. Why should we not claim it by conquest? This is an Empire! The strongest nation in Elessia and I will see to it that we claim what is rightfully ours!"

"You're insane," Osyris said.

"Far from it, *Prince* Osyris," Emperor Valyris hissed. "You will die here and now Galbraithian. But because you are royalty, I will let you choose your fate. Death by fire or death by noose?"

"Surprise me," the prince replied defiantly.

"Fire it is," the emperor laughed. "Let this serve as a warning to Galbraith! Mages will be brought to justice!"

Solanta burst into a full flood of tears as she watched on. Hal hugged and attempted to console her as he turned her head away from the pyres. "I am sorry, Solanta. Do not watch him die," he whispered as she sobbed into his shoulder. "We must leave, and leave quickly. Magnus distract the guards around us quickly! With luck we shall escape."

Magnus nodded before muttering a few words to himself and his eyes became aglow with a blue hue. The guards around them seemed dazed with many of them closing their eyes and giggling to themselves. Each one of them failed to notice as Hal's group crept by and away from the square, away from their slaughtered family. The rowdy crowd continued to watch Prince Osyris' execution unfold and as Hal looked back for the final time, he felt the lump in his throat grow. The prince leapt onto the pyre willingly and with a roar of flames he disappeared from view. "Farewell Osyris," he whispered. "Your death will not go unavenged."

Chapter One
The Children of Galbraith

ON a midsummer's day in his fourteenth year, Emrys Galbraith was sparring with his siblings in the garden courtyards of Stormgast as their Master-at-Arms, Rheinar, looked on. He was the second Prince of Galbraith, the Eastern Kingdom whose lands stretched as far as the Gilded Coast to the Frozen Wastes. His brother, Tyris, was next in line to the throne and his younger sister, Lymris, the sole Princess. The three Royals were honing their sword-skill beneath the shade of the Great Oak, a tree which had stood longer than anyone could remember and was the very heart of Stormgast. It was the warmest summer Emrys could think of. The flora surrounding them in the gardens had flourished under the red suns, and if he concentrated, he could hear the low humming of happy bees swarming the exotic flowers by the pond. Beads of sweat clung to his brow as he stepped forward to face his older brother. Tyris, the eldest by two years, stood a good shoulder above Emrys and as his brother stood towering over the young Prince, the scale of the challenge dawned on him. Rheinar signalled for them to begin with a simple nod and Emrys hurried forward with a wild slash towards Tyris' midriff. His brother caught the blade with power, disarming him, and sent him hurtling back with a sweep of his leg. Emrys landed face down in a puddle of mud and coughed up the remnants of his late breakfast. Tyris swung the sword over his shoulder and laughed. "Little brother, how many times have I told you, don't eat so soon before training?" he said.

His sister, Lymris, joined in the laughter along with a few of the lord and ladies watching on by the garden benches. Emrys swept the mud from his eyes and rose to his feet gingerly, feeling a rising wave of embarrassment flush over him.

"Not much of a warrior, am I?" He coughed and stumbled over to retrieve the dulled blade before finding a seat to catch his breath. It was true. Emrys knew he would never be the swordsman his brother was and envied him his speed and quick mind for battle. They had been training this way for nearly two months now and Emrys had made no progress in wiping the smug grin from his brother's face.

"We all have our strengths little brother," Tyris beckoned his sword in Emrys' direction. "You're the thinker, the bookish kind who ponders over maps, discusses literature and poetry. I'm the swashbuckling fighter who…"

"And what am I then?" Lymris interrupted, drawing her sword. "Care to test your craft against your baby sister?"

Emrys admired his sister's courage. Lymris, often nicknamed 'Lym', was less than a year younger than him but could not resist a challenge and held skill of her own with a blade. The two were extremely close, not only in age but in bond. They had been inseparable as younger children and together they would always speak of the adventures waiting across the lands when they came of age. Tyris now had her attention and chuckled as he paced a circle around her. "Would you like me to take it easy on you, sis? Spare your blushes and tears from these lords and ladies?"

Lymris fixated her emerald eyes on Tyris, her gaze

unfaltering. She smirked and bowed, "That's cute, I'll try and do the same."

Raucous laughter echoed through the courtyard and Emrys too was lost in the moment. That was enough for Tyris as his blood boiled and lunged forward. Enraged he angled an overhead swing chopping down for Lymris' head. She quickly darted left and spun herself behind him, slapping the flat of the sword against his backside. The laughter continued and Tyris sped forward once more. The two swapped blows and parries as the eldest began to take control of the fight. Lymris was losing ground and edged slowly backwards towards the pond where Emrys had sat down. Lymris flashed a jab which Tyris caught and sent a riposte into her arm, disarming her. Before Tyris could land a finishing blow, his sister had leapt forward onto his torso, her arms and legs locked in grip, and sent the pair of them tumbling into the water behind them. It was at this point that Rheinar had seen enough and wandered over to stand by Emrys who was breathless with laughter. The siblings surfaced and gasped for air. They glanced at each other with serious, stone-like faces. Lymris was the first to crumble and burst out laughing, shortly followed by Tyris whose foul temper had relented.

Rheinar applauded and smiled at the three. He felt a sting of pride with how the children of King Terrys handled themselves with and without the sword. True they were teenagers, spats and arguments were a constant in their time together, but they never forgot their sense of family and duty to care for one another. It had been difficult for them since their mother Althea had been taken by a fever two years ago, but Rheinar knew she would be proud of her children. Tyris was almost as tall as his father, and tufts of stubble had begun to settle in as he came of age. He was brown haired, as they all were, and had begun to bulk out from the vigorous training the King had enforced this summer. Lymris also took more after Terrys, though was much more slender, than her older brother, and seemed the most fearless of the three. Emrys was the only child who reminded Rheinar of their mother. He was smaller than his two siblings but had eyes of amber with speckles of blue, just as Althea did. He was not a great swordsman but showed an eagerness to learn and was regarded as highly intelligent by the library scholars. Rheinar pulled Lymris and Tyris out of the pond effortlessly and sat them down by their brother. "On a note of form," he said kneeling before them. "Lymris, good provocation. You took your brother's rage and used it against him but remember to keep your feet moving against a stronger opponent. Tyris, as ever, great motion with the sword but do not allow yourself to be taunted and lose your head. Emrys, sword-skill may not be your forte but you are improving, keep your chin up and never take your focus away from your foe."

Emrys was comforted by Rheinar's words and looked to him as he met his smile. He was a large man of darkened skin who had served his father for nearly twenty years. He had a large scar across his face that stretched from his chin to his crooked nose which Emrys guessed had been broken multiple times. Stormgast's Master-at-Arms had a fearsome reputation as a warrior and over the years had become known as 'The Storms Fury' for his ferocity and prowess in battle. "Now you three," Rheinar said grinning. "Enough for today. I believe the King wishes to speak to you all. Tomorrow we've got young Tyris' wedding and there is much to be said."

Tyris blushed as his siblings nudged and teased their older

brother. The wedding had been the talk of the city. Nobles from across the land had been arriving for a fortnight and the excitement in Stormgast was palpable. The bride in question was Elette Valyris, the daughter of Emperor Harold Valyris of Arcadia. The Empire to the North was arguably the most powerful of the nations in Elessia, and the union was seen by many as necessary to bring an end to the war which had raged the continent. Emrys was certainly curious to meet his sister-to-be but most of all to seeing his father once more. As the war had continued on through his childhood, he had seen him less and less as demands of the King rose. When his mother had passed away two years prior, his father had closed himself off in grief and Emrys could no longer remember the warm smile he had looked upon as a small boy. He was hopeful that today at least they would share kind words once again as a family.

The three siblings left the courtyard with Rheinar in tow and turned their attentions to the castle of Stormgast. Preparations for the wedding had taken the best part of a month but the efforts of the city-folk had been worth it. The walls of the castle were lined with the maroon and golden banners of Galbraith, florists had lined the streets with Aurelian lotuses, a sweet-smelling plant indigenous to the Kingdom, exotic foods and spices and many gifts from nobles and common folk alike were sat awaiting the new Princess' arrival. As they walked along the cobbled stones, the twangs of harp and string carried a jovial tune from the bards practising nearby. Emrys noticed how Lymris, a lover of music and the arts, skipped along with a spring in her step as they approached the oaken door of the Great Hall. The guards posted at the entrance nodded in respect of the Royalty and wrenched the heavy doors open.

The hall was dimly lit but squinting Emrys could see his

father locked in debate with Mikhael, his most trusted advisor. The Great Hall had been refurbished with new tables and benches yet still the most striking feature were the roots of the Great Oak, entwined within the foundations of the keep. His father had often told the three about their great grandfather who had built the fortifications around the Greak Oak as a symbol of their duty to nature. As the years had passed the roots had grown further and stretched across the floor and walls with some even reaching the roof itself. The largest of them, which spanned the north wall behind the throne, was etched in the names of their forefathers, and past rulers of Galbraith. The doors swinging open had broken his father's and Mikhael's focus, and turning to face them, Mikhael walked forward smiling. He was a small man famed for his art in magic, but in recent years his age had begun to catch up with him. His hair was all but white nowadays and he seemed to have fewer and fewer teeth as every summer passed by. He now wore huge spectacles and adorned a grey robe masking the dark blue tattoos covering his body. Grinning toothlessly, he patted Tyris on the shoulder. "Are we all ready, young Prince?"

Tyris hesitated and Emrys could see the nervousness that gripped his older brother. Smiling weakly, he said, "I am ready to do my duty for the Kingdom, though I must admit I am nervous about meeting Elette."

"I am sure she feels the same way, Tyris," Mikhael retorted. "But you and she both know that by going through with this you will help bring an end to this bitter war between Galbraith and Arcadia."

"I would feel a lot better with you there by my side." His brother angled a plea in his father's direction, who frowned and looked away.

The request brought pain to Mikhael who took a step back and looked at his feet. "We've been over this, your father and I agree that my presence there would only seek to antagonise the emperor. He has no love for my kind and I do not wish to be the cause of more hostility." Swirling his hand in his air, he muttered a few words under his breath. All of a sudden, his eyes were aglow before an ethereal sphere emerged hovering before him. Smiling once more he said, "Never fear though young Prince, I will still be watching. Now though, I believe your father has words for you all, we will take our leave."

Bowing, Mikhael and Rheinar left the hall leaving only the family of Galbraith. Emrys looked at his father as he took a seat on the throne. He was a tall man bearing the same eyes as his siblings and had long threads of hair tucked back behind his ears. He was wearing a maroon tunic embroidered with the Great Oak of Galbraith and still bore the oaken ring bestowed to him by his mother at their wedding many years ago. Atop his head sat the Crown of Thorns, the oldest relic in the Kingdom of Galbraith. True to its name, it was a woven crown plucked from the very thorns of the Great Oak itself and was rumoured to have blessings of old magic upon it. His father looked back at him and smiled briefly before asking the three, "How is the training going? Rheinar isn't working you too hard I trust?"

All three teens shook their heads but did not speak. It was awkward, no one could deny it. In his absence, Terrys had lost a closeness to his children that was once unthinkable and his children shifted around in uncomfortable silence.

Breaking the silence the King said, "How are you feeling, Tyris?"

"I am nervous Father, but keen to meet Elette. Is she truly as beautiful as Rheinar suggests?"

Terrys laughed heartily, a sight Emrys had not seen in a long time. "You're marrying the daughter of our sworn enemy and you're worried she might not be pretty?"

Tyris laughed along with his siblings. "I would rest easier safe in that knowledge, yes."

"Even if she's not beautiful," Lymris chipped in, "it would do us some good to have some more female opinion in this court."

"Lym speaks the truth Tyris." Her father smiled, "But don't worry, Mikhael showed me through his sphere the emperor's carriage travelling today. She is truly a sight a behold and you are a lucky prince."

Tyris seemed comforted by the words as his siblings giggled beside him. Terrys himself grinned for a brief moment before getting back to the matter at hand, "I called you three in today because we need to go over our etiquette prior to the Arcadians' arrival today and to perhaps explain more about the emperor's family."

"If I might ask," Emrys said. "Why would the emperor propose this marriage between Tyris and Elette? We've been at war since our Uncle Osyris was killed."

Terrys chose his words carefully, "This is true but the emperor is an old man now, and as we get older fear creeps into your every thought. I believe he's worried of losing his Empire's hold in this world and Arcadia has many enemies."

"Enemies, Father?" Tyris asked.

"Aye," he replied. "While we pose the greatest threat to Arcadia, there are the Mercians to our West who have no love for Harold, there are the Alterrans who refuse to bow before any machine, and let us not forget the Carpathians to the South."

"Why would the Carpathians be an enemy of Arcadia, Father?" Lymris asked. "They are on the other side of the continent and far beyond the Empire's reach."

"Carpathia houses the one remaining Circle of Magic. Indeed, it is where Mikhael came to us from and if the reports I have read are true… I do not believe it is long before Carpathia rises to take action."

Emrys was stunned by his father's revelation. It seemed the continent was after Arcadia and he asked, "What do you know of the Arcadians, Father?"

Terrys stroked his beard and said, "They are a proud people and their technology has no rival. Their war machines billow black smoke that chokes every battlefield before them. I believe they are even currently attempting to build a new machine capable of flying in the air. That would certainly be a marvel to see, wouldn't it? So long as we remain on their friendly side that is."

Rising from his throne, King Terrys walked over to the siblings, "While we hope this arranged marriage will put an end to hostilities between our two nations, we must do nothing to aggravate or demean our guests. They need this marriage but so do we. I cannot ask the people to continue to fight an endless war. Now, I expect the emperor's son will be looking for weaknesses or even attempt to goad you into a fight. I have been told he's very hot-headed and unwavering on his hatred of magic. Do not rise to any bait. You all represent Galbraith and I expect you to handle yourselves as royalty. Be proud. We are the Storm."

"We will not let you down, Father." Emrys proudly stated

with his siblings nodding in tacit agreement. Terrys clasped a grip on his shoulder and grinned into his eyes. "I am sure of it. I want you all to know how proud I am of you. Things haven't been easy since your mother's death and I apologise for my part in any suffering you have been through. I, like you, have been lost without her. With hope, after the wedding we will have more time to be the family we were and honour your mother's memory together."

Emrys could feel himself welling up and bit his lip to stop it from trembling.

"Now I'm not going to lie," his father said stepping away from them and picking up a blade near the hearth fire, "Rheinar has told me you are becoming decent swordsmen. I would like to see what you have learned."

The three stood stunned and matched gawping looks to one another. They had barely seen their father and now he stood waiting to test their abilities in combat. Gulping, Tyris stepped forward and drew his own, "Are you with me Lym? Emrys?"

Brother and sister nodded and pulled their swords in synchronicity. "We're with you," Lym said and adopted her stance.

King Terrys unhooked his cloak and threw it on the floor. "Prove to me you are the children of the Storm!" he shouted and launched himself forward.

Chapter Two
Awakening

EMRYS stood beside his family beneath the gates of Stormgast as the emperor's carriage came into view. He was dressed in his finest attire and stood proudly, as instructed by his father. The spar between them had gone as expected and beneath his clothes fresh bruises had begun to throb, bringing the occasional wince when he moved. The three siblings had failed to land a single blow on their father despite their numbers and Emrys doubted the outcome would be any different should a second bout be on the cards. Looking on at the approaching column he noticed the machines of Arcadia and realised his father had not spoken in jest. They truly were a marvel and completely alien to the lands of Galbraith. The emperor's carriage was a large war cart, forged in metal, pumping out a trail of black smoke that could be seen for miles. The bodywork was lined with spikes and Emrys seriously doubted any arrow could pierce its hull. In tow of the lumbering machine were the Knights of Arcadia. Dressed in blackened armour atop large steeds, they bore banners of black and gold embroided with the Griffon of Talon's Reach. His father had often spoken of Talon's Reach, the capital city of Arcadia which sat deep in the Vulkerian Mountains, and said it was the crowning jewel of the nation.

The drums and fifes announced the Arcadians arrival as they reached the gates. Stepping forth from the war cart was

Edmure, the son of Emperor Valyris, and another man who Emrys did not recognise. Edmure was short in stature and had trimmed hair, matched with a goatee of jet black hair. They were both dressed in black tanned armour and the young ruler straddled a longsword plated in gold and rubies. He was youthful and Emrys estimated that he was only a few years older than Tyris. As they descended the stairs of the carriage, King Terrys greeted them with a smile and spoke first, as tradition dictated, "Welcome to Stormgast Edmure, son of the emperor, we have awaited your arrival."

"Thank you, King Galbraith," Edmure retorted softly. "Your Kingdom truly is a sight to behold."

Emrys noticed the emperor's son had a strange accent he was unaccustomed to, and seemed to roll his 'r's' and 'l's'.

"Allow us to use this union as a chance to learn about each other's nations and build a lasting peace that will rain prosperity on us all," his father said with the lords behind nodding. "Might I ask where is the emperor?"

The emperor's son seemed unfazed by the words and leant an ear to the stranger whose voice was but a whisper. Acknowledging this, he paced from side to side and said, "We have brought you a gift in view of the wedding."

A cart pulled by horses was beckoned and pulled up short of his father. From its rear two soldiers emerged pulling a chain. Emrys looked at Lym and Tyris as their expressions changed from one of curiosity to horror. A group of around twenty people bound to each other were led out. They looked extremely malnourished and it was clear to see that many had been abused with lashes. They were all adorned in dirty rags and shivered as the night's wind swept by, bringing a stale odour of sweat and blood to Emrys' nose. King Terrys was outraged and stepped forward snarling, "What is the meaning of this?"

Edmure smirked, "We caught a few rats on the way here and wished to present them to your justice."

"Of what crimes do you hold these people?" his father snapped. "And by what right do you subjugate the people of Galbraith?"

"These are mages," Edmure laughed. "They are not people. We decided it would be best to deal with the pest problem that seemingly plagues your lands. But please King Galbraith, they are a gift, they are yours to deal with."

King Terrys gritted his teeth. Emrys could see the emperor's son was testing his father's patience and this whole ruse was designed to bring a rise out of him. His father calmed himself and beckoned to Rheinar, bringing the Storm's Fury to attention. Speaking sternly he said, "Rheinar, unbind these people, give them food and see to it they are bathed and given clothes befitting the people of Galbraith."

Rheinar saluted the King and strode past and ripped the chain from the grips of the soldiers. He comforted the first person leading the group, a limping woman in tears, her mouth caked in blood and snot. Terrys' attention turned back to Edmure who stood clearly amused with himself as Rheinar moved past, evidently disgusted with the actions of the emperor's son. "To you I ask again," the King spoke, "where is your father, Harold?"

"Is my company not enough?" Edmure asked with arms outstretched. "My father and sister are both asleep inside. Bless him, he is getting old and such travel is weary on him. She is getting her beauty sleep in for tomorrow's main event."

"Then I will see him tomorrow at the wedding, for now

farewell," his father said turning to leave. "Is that all King Galbraith?" Edmure smirked. "And here I had heard such great things about the hospitality of Galbraith. Must I be treated like an animal?"

"We do not tolerate such abuse in this land, Edmure, son of the emperor," his father spat. "If you behave like an animal, then you will treated as such."

Edmure flew into a rage and cursed and barked orders at his men when the Galbraiths and Galbraithian lordship departed. Emrys was still coming to grips with what he had witnessed and prayed Mikhael had not seen the barbarity with which the mages had been treated. As they walked along the main square his father noticed his children's shocked demeanour. When they were out of earshot he said, "Do not let it get to you, my children. I will speak with Harold, he would never have allowed Edmure to insult us on arrival, but there is nothing I can do to change their minds on mages. They have more cause than most to be distrusting of magic. For now, rest, we have a big day tomorrow and you will all need to play your parts for Tyris' wedding."

"Who was that man with Edmure, Father?" Tyris asked.

Terrys shook his head, "I do not know and that concerns me. I shall consult with Mikhael. For now, rest."

***

AS EMRYS rose on that fateful day he felt very strange. He could feel a pulsating throb in his heart that made no sense and almost as if the Great Oak was calling to him. Stretching out a trembling hand, he reached for the window where one of the roots grew. As he touched it he heard screaming and vivid images flashed through his mind as if the roots of the tree were swirling around him. He was pulled from his bed flying high into the sky atop the branches. Up above he could see all of Galbraith in its glory. The bustling streets of Stormgast, the waves slopping to the shores to the North and the lightning as it crashed through the sky. But all was not well. Squinting he could see a large black cloud forming across the sea which raced towards Stormgast. At the front flew a skeleton-like figure with eyes of amber adorned in a tattered robe. As the figure touched the Gilded Coast the land became scorched and the animals burned where they stood. The cloud moved further and faster, breaching the city gates before consuming the people of Galbraith. Emrys could hear nothing save the screaming of the people below. The smog climbed up through the clouds and reached Emrys before long. Emrys looked on in horror as the black cloud burned through his flesh and screamed as it coursed and consumed his body. The figure was soon floating in front of him, cackling as Emrys felt his skin rot. "Primal," it hissed and dragged Emrys towards him with a wave of its hand. Up close the unnatural figure was gaunt and rotted. Emrys could see that huge chunks of its skin were missing and only a few wisps of hair remained on its head. The figure seemed to be inspecting Emrys as he screamed and writhed in pain. "Primal," it said once more with cruel intent in its eyes.

"Who are you?" Emrys asked breathlessly as his energy was sapped from him. "I am Caulder, the Bringer of Storms," it replied, "This, my Corruption, will spread and devour this world. And you will not be able to stop me." Caulder drew a small knife from its robe and licked its lips as it brought the blade above Emrys. "I will find you Primal," it said. "And drive this knife through your heart."

Emrys felt a grasp on his shoulder as he was pulled down from the clouds racing back to his room as the world seemed to unravel before him. Caulder screamed in fury as it disappeared along with the black smog which had choked his lungs and blackened the sky. Mikhael was knelt beside him chanting with his eyes aglow. Emrys shivered violently in a cold sweat as Mikhael carried him back to his bed. "Emrys?" he asked. "Are you okay?"

Weakly Emrys said, "What was that? Was that real?"

Mikhael, visibly disturbed, shook his head, "I did not see what you saw, I only felt the magic coming from here, from you."

Emrys was shocked. "I am not a mage, Mikhael. I cannot do magic." Mikhael drew a glass of water and passed it to Emrys. "Small sips, my Prince. What I am going to say may shock you but you need to know this."

Emrys sipped the water and felt his strength slowly returning. Mikhael sat down at the foot of the bed and locked eyes with Emrys. "Mages are not born mages, Emrys," he said softly. "Each of us has been through what we call an Awakening. A stirring of magic within us that unlocks our abilities. While this may be difficult to hear, you have Awoken; you are now a mage."

Emrys could not fathom Mikhael's words and sat there stunned. "This can't be," he said desperately.

"It is true, my Prince," Mikhael replied. "I would not lie to you. Mages can sense other mages, the magic and Ether which flow through them. You are a mage and I am sorry to be the one to tell you."

Tears welled in his eyes as Mikhael attempted to console

him. He, the second Prince of Galbraith, was a mage. Emrys sobbed into a pillow as he came to terms with what Mikhael had said. Looking up with bloodshot eyes he asked, "What will this mean for the Kingdom, Mikhael? I do not wish to be the cause of another war with Arcadia."

"That will not happen," Mikhael said authoritatively. "Once your brother marries Elette we are bound to Arcadia, and them to us. What we must do is keep this hidden until after the wedding and then we can discuss what happens next."

"What caused this, Mikhael? I don't even understand why I had this Awakening."

"An Awakening can happen to anyone at any age," Mikhael said. "For most it happens in their late teens, early twenties. Myself I did not have my Awakening until I was nearly thirty. I have to be honest, I have never seen one happen to someone as young as you, Emrys. What this means? I do not know. All we can do is try to understand what happened. What did you see?"

Emrys struggled to recall the chain of events that had happened. "When I woke, I felt as if the Great Oak was speaking to me. A language in my head that I did not understand. I touched the root by the window and I was above Stormgast, atop the very tree itself."

Mikhael seemed confused by Emrys' account. "You said the Great Oak spoke to you? This is most peculiar. Awakenings are visions of the person's past and nothing more."

"I'm not lying!" Emrys shouted, startling Mikhael. "I was at the top of the tree and saw this huge cloud sweep over the land killing everything it touched."

Mikhael stroked his beard as if lost in his thoughts. "This cloud killed everything?" he asked.

"It was if the lands were scorched by its touch," Emrys replied. "Even the grass burned as the animals wailed and children screamed."

"I have never heard of a killer cloud before," Mikhael shrugged. "That being said, was there anything else? When I pulled you back, you were screaming."

"There was a..." Emrys struggled to find the right words, "thing that led this and spoke to me. It called the dark smog its Corruption."

Mikhael's eyes widened and he stood up, pacing the room. "I've heard of this Corruption once before but it can't be..." he said still pacing. "This thing, was it a person?"

Emrys tried to recall how it looked and said, "It wasn't a man, nor was it a woman. It looked... dead, like a skeleton. It was rotting and its eyes were glowing yellow."

Mikhael stopped dead in his tracks. Slowly he met Emrys' eyes with a look that made him nervous and asked quietly, "What did this thing say to you?"

"It called to me, and said Primal," Emrys responded. "It called itself Caulder, the Bringer of Storms. It said its corruption would devour this world and that it would kill me!"

Mikhael was speechless for a minute or so as the colour from his face ebbed away. "That's impossible," he said dismissively. "Caulder died twenty years ago."

"Who is Caulder?" Emrys asked. He noticed that a faint tremor had gripped Mikhael, and his demeanour had changed to one of fear.

"It can't be..." Mikhael muttered to himself. "I need to return to my study, Emrys. I need more knowledge. Promise me that you will not utter a word of what we've discussed to anyone else, even Lym. You cannot reveal yourself as a mage before the time is right. The Kingdom depends on this."

Emrys was lost for words. Clearly, he had unsettled Mikhael but he had more questions than answers at this point. "What's the matter, Mikhael?" he asked.

"Think nothing of it," Mikhael smiled weakly. "Promise me that you will not tell another soul."

"I promise," Emrys said resolutely. "Before you go, please tell me. Who is Caulder? And what does Primal mean?"

Mikhael shook his head and looked at his feet, "It's not important right now. Get yourself dressed, the wedding is all we need to focus on. Remember, don't tell another person."

The old mage departed Emrys' bedroom bringing a draught of warm summer air, and leaving the young Prince's mind racing with a plethora of unanswered questions.

Chapter Three
The Wedding

EMRYS struggled to come to terms with everything that happened the morning of the wedding. He was now a mage and feared the reaction he would receive when the news became common knowledge. Emrys had always loved the tricks Mikhael had put on for him and his siblings, but as the years went by and the war raged on, his father had asked him to keep his abilities to a limit with the growing resentment of mage-folk across the land. True, Arcadia had an unflinching stand towards their kind but even in Galbraith, mages suffered tough lives in the towns and cities. But most of all he feared his father's disappointment. He knew that this would hurt him and could undo all of the work the wedding might bring.

"Are you okay, Emrys? You seem deep in thought," his sister asked as she swayed towards him in her silk dress. She had made a lot of effort for the wedding which had not gone unnoticed as the younger lords ogled her when she passed them by. Her arms and neck were painted in golden roots and she had her long hair tied back by a golden thorn, complimenting the family colours with her maroon dress. By his own standards, Emrys did not look half as impressive but still wore his favourite tunic embroidered with the Great Oak across the chest. He had brushed his hair behind his ears and bore an oaken dagger on his hip, a symbol of Royal lineage. They stood in the Great Hall between a myriad of lords and ladies awaiting the arrival of the prince and bride-to-be. Their father, Terrys, was not yet present, nor too were the emperor's party.

"Emrys? Hello?" His sister persisted snapping her fingers between his eyes, "What's the matter?"

"Nothing," he mumbled and avoided her gaze.

His sister smiled kindly, "Emrys you may be shit with the sword but you are even worse at lying. Are you worried about Father? He'd never say it but I think he's worried this whole wedding and peace treaty will fall apart."

"Yes, I'm worried about Father, Lym," Emrys retorted. "At the same time, I'm worried about Tyris, what if he's marrying a gargoyle?"

Lymris punched him hard in the arm several times as Emrys giggled and backed away.

"For your information," she said, relenting, "looks aren't everything, you shallow prick! Besides I spoke to her this morning, she seems to be a lovely person."

"You spoke to Elette?" Emrys asked. "What is our new sister like?"

"She's quiet but kind," Lymris smiled. "But don't worry, once they are married, we will have all the time in the world to get to know her, and I'm sure she'll open up."

Lymris' words hit Emrys like a dagger in the chest. He wanted to know Elette more than anything but if Mikhael was right, things in his life were about to change drastically. King Terrys strode into Emrys' vision, alongside Rheinar and Tyris. His arrival brought with it a silence as the lords and ladies broke up their chatter and bowed as he passed them by. They were all dressed in their finest clothes though Emrys could not help but chuckle when he saw Rheinar. The towering beast of a man looked incredibly uncomfortable and his bulging clothes looked ready to burst as they tightly wrapped his body. No sooner had his father taken his place on the throne, Emperor Harold Valyris burst through the door with his armed guard. He was a small man who limped as he walked, resting his leg on a golden cane with each step. He had next to no hair atop his head and Emrys thought he looked tired above all else. The crowd parted to let him pass with a few disgusted faces leering on and others turning their backs to the emperor who had caused Galbraith so much grief.

"Welcome, Emperor Valyris," King Terrys said sternly. "I am pleased we could bring about a union to end the war."

The emperor acknowledged his father's words and bowed accordingly. "I am pleased also," he said. "Let it be known that the Kingdom of Galbraith and the Arcadian Empire have put aside their differences in the name of peace. Now I would like you to meet my daughter, Elette."

Behind his outstretched arm came forth the soon-to-be Princess of Galbraith, one of the most beautiful sights Emrys had seen in his fourteen years. Unlike her father and brother, Elette was blonde of hair and a pale-skinned beauty. She was adorned in a long green dress and carried her hands together beneath the cuffs. Her pale blue eyes were striking and she carried with her an aura of grace with each gentle step as she made her way into the Great Hall. Skulking behind her was Edmure with the stranger who stopped and leant on the door eating an apple. Emrys noticed his brother's glazed expression as Elette came into view and he nudged Lymris in his direction. Together the pair of them muttered and giggled at their older brother as he stepped forward eagerly.

Drawing a long breath, he met her gaze and said, "I am

pleased to meet you, Elette. My advisor had spoken of your beauty, I know now that his words were a mere fraction of the woman I see before me."

"Thank you, Prince Tyris, son of Terrys," she said softly, blushing as she met his older brother's smile. "I do not know the ways of Galbraith. Perhaps with our union, you can teach me more about the beautiful land I have seen for these past weeks."

"I am pleased to meet you also Elette," King Terrys said as he rose from the throne. "These are my other children, Prince Emrys and Princess Lymris."

Emrys and Lymris stepped forward in unison and bowed before Elette.

"We are honoured to meet you," Lymris said. "It'll be a treat to have another woman in this court."

A small ripple of laughter echoed the hall as Elette smiled and greeted the two siblings. By this point Edmure had strode into the Great Hall and met some equally disgusted looks, like his father Harold had received. "So any chance this wedding will be over soon? I had hoped to go hunting before the day is over."

Emperor Valyris lost his composure for a moment and smacked Edmure across the cheek with the back of his hand. "Learn your place boy!" he spat. "Don't think I haven't heard about your theatrics yesterday. You disgrace the Valyris name with your childish antics."

Edmure did not seem hurt but Emrys could see the look of anger and embarrassment in his quickly welling eyes. He stormed off out of the Great Hall with a small retainer of guards and barked orders to them while he clutched his face.

"My apologies, King Terrys," Harold said calmly. "He is

too much like his father and wishes to war as I once did. How age changes things."

"It is quite all right," Terrys responded. "But I do not forgive his entrance yesterday. We do not consider magic a crime within Galbraith. I expect our guests to honour this and be respectful of our laws."

"Well said. But may I ask, where were you when Caulder raided our lands?" Emperor Valyris asked.

His father seemed irritated by the question, "Here in Stormgast."

"Ah," Harold nodded. "Because you see Caulder nearly destroyed everything Arcadia was. You sit there and preach about magic being good however you have not seen the evil I saw. A plague swept across the land taking everything with it. Crops and towns burned, and the very air was reek with the rotting flesh of the animals and peasants. Then an army came out of the darkness, without remorse, without reason and slaughtered thousands. While Galbraith sat by, the children in Arcadia were screaming."

The tension in the Great Hall gripped Emrys and he could see that the lords and ladies of Galbraith had stiffened up at the mention of this Caulder.

"You executed my brother," King Terrys stated through gritted teeth. "Pray tell, if the tables were turned would you have done any differently? If I'm not mistaken the Circle were the ones to dispatch Caulder to the next plane."

Emperor Valyris snarled at the statement, "And that was the last time mages were freely allowed to roam Arcadian lands. Their kind have caused us enough suffering. Magic and mages may be permitted here but they will never be accepted in Arcadia."

A silence fell upon the Great Hall that seemed to last indefinitely. In the corner of his eye Emrys noticed Mikhael's ethereal sphere high up in the rafters looking on the scene and wanted more than anything to question him about his vision and learn more about Caulder. The mere mention of the name had brought enough discomfort around the hall to scare him.

"Enough," his father spoke. "We are here in peace and to build for the future, not argue about the past. Everyone, please proceed to the courtyard gardens and we can see my son and Elette wed."

A fanfare of music greeted Emrys as he and Lymris slithered out of the Great Hall amidst the lords and ladies. It was a beautiful summer's day in Stormgast and the whole city was out to celebrate, people lining the streets, cheering in anticipation. It had been built up as a memorable event and certainly lived up to its expectation. Banners were strewn across the buildings and folk from the city applauded as soon as the procession made its way through the streets. Edmure had rejoined his father, humbled as King Terrys led the procession and walked proudly as he waved and greeted the onlooking crowd.

"Today is proud day," he shouted. "My son is to be wed and the war between Galbraith and Arcadia shall be over! Rejoice and know that our bitter times are at an end!"

A large eruption of cheers drowned out the music and thunderous applause echoed along the street. The procession started moving again with Tyris and Elette nervously edging forward side by side. Once they had reached the courtyards beneath the Great Oak, Lymris commented on the size of the wedding preparations before them. She was not wrong. A large tent had been erected which spanned the length of the gardens, shading them from the summer's heat. Freshly picked flowers formed an aisle to the newly built podium which stood a mere foot from where Emrys and his siblings had been sparring for months. In the middle of the podium stood a twisted altar, formed from the roots and barbs of the Great Oak. Emrys and Lymris joined their father at the front as Tyris and Elette waited together. Rheinar, ever-present, stood by on guard and shadowed Tyris' every movement. Once everyone had found their seats, his brother and his bride-to-be moved up the aisle in linked arms, greeting the smiling faces as they passed by. When Elette reached the Galbraith family she looked up and met Emrys head on, and for a moment he thought he saw a look of shock as they met each other's gaze.

"Welcome everyone," the Priest of Thorns said stepping forward, "to the union of Prince Tyris of Galbraith and Empress Elette of Arcadia. May this union before the World Tree bless the lands with fertility. May this union bless the waters with life, and may this union bring about peace in our time."

The old man hobbled forward and placed his hands on Tyris' and Elette's arms. "You stand beneath the World Tree," he continued. "Long has this tree stood over us, a blessing from nature which has provided us with shelter in our darkest times. Its roots go deep beneath the ground and course within our very blood, Prince Tyris. Do you promise before the World Tree that you will love and cherish Empress Elette as long as you may live?"

"I do," his brother said and met a small smile from Elette as the priest turned his attention to her. "Empress Elette, you are not of this land and I do not know which gods watch over you in Arcadia. Please be assured that you will always find hospitality beneath the World Tree and protection so long as you may need it. Do you promise that you will love and cherish Prince Tyris as long as you may live?"

"I do," she replied, and the priest shifted backwards to the altar.

"Both of you step forward please," he asked and drew a long thorn from his robe.

Tyris and Elette moved as one and held their arms together as the Priest of Thorns wrapped the thorn around their arms. The thorn cut into their arms and when Elette winced as fresh blood began to trickle down her arm, his brother comforted her with a reassuring smile.

"Let it be known that Prince Tyris and Empress Elette stand together as one. The thorn is a symbol of their vow to each other and the World Tree. To break apart from a thorn is not easy, and with it one cuts oneself and the other with it. Do you both understand the vow you have taken to each other and before the World Tree?"

"We do," they replied as their blood met and dripped down onto the altar.

"Then I ask of the World Tree to receive this union and shelter you in peace and prosperity. Protect Prince Tyris and Princess Elette from those who would harm them. Guide them through the dark in this world and into the light. Let them be true to one another and let their grace shine down and bless these lands."

The Priest removed the thorn from their arms and turned them to face each. "Kiss now and let the Gods witness your eternal love for each other."

Tyris and Elette leant in and as their lips touched, a wave of raucous applause and cheers erupted that carried on out of the grounds and into the city. Tyris and Elette smiled and waved and held hands as they met each other's eyes. Emrys and Lymris whooped as their father smiled sadly and turned away.

"What's wrong, Father?" Emrys asked.

"Today is a great day for our nation, but it also reminds me of your mother, Althea," he replied. "We had a beautiful wedding here beneath the Great Oak and made our vows that our love would be eternal. I wish she was here to see this."

Lymris heard the last comment and comforted him. Emrys had always thought of his father as strong and untouchable. Looking on now he could see his father was lost in grief and yearned for the days they could be together again. In the corner of his eye, he could see Edmure watching, with a smirk that made Emrys hate the son of the emperor in an instant.

Chapter Four
Celebration

THE suns had set as Emrys stumbled into the Great Hall to a crescendo of music and dancing. He was already quite drunk and staggered forward, goblet in hand, in search of his family. His father and the emperor appeared to be locked in debate by the throne with Tyris and Elette eagerly listening on but Emrys could see no sign of Edmure or the stranger. His sister was sat with a handful of ladies on a table in the corner of the hall and she burst out laughing when Emrys fell onto a lord's table sending food, goblets and ale flying high.

"Emrys come and sit down," she laughed and kicked a chair in his direction. "Been on the old ale, have we?"

"Yes, I have," he slurred as his eyes appeared to wander on their own accord. "Have you not been drinking Lym?"

"I have," she replied. "Just seem to be handling it a bit better than you right now. Ladies, let's go and grab my brother a drink of water. Besides Miranda, that Lord by the door hasn't taken his eyes off you and I think we need to muster up his courage to ask you to dance."

A few of the ladies giggled as they passed Emrys but Lymris shushed them and patted him gently on the shoulder as they disappeared from view. Emrys closed his eyes and felt the whirling of the world disappear for but a moment. He was drunker than he had been before and felt the gasses in his stomach hiss as he massaged it. The day had been beautiful and a kind reminder to the summer they had witnessed. Yet even now the summer was beginning to ebb away, and Emrys knew it would not be long before the storms raged and Elette was given a true introduction to life in Galbraith. He had always loved watching the storms crash against the Gilded Coast, a past-time he shared with his siblings at Caspian's Rock. In particular he took to watching the daredevil Stormchasers as they sailed through the chaos.

"Might I join you?" a voice asked stirring Emrys from his thoughts.

Opening his eyes, he could see it was in fact Elette, the new Princess of Galbraith, and the recognition alone was enough to coax that last little bit of sobriety into the fore as he sat to attention. "Of course." He cleared his throat and tapped his hands on the table, "I am sorry for my current state. I do not often drink, nor drink as much as I have tonight."

"It's fine," she smiled with a smile that made Emrys feel at ease. "I have been around my father and brother when they're drinking. Between you and me you're handling it better."

"You're too kind." Emrys smiled and finished his goblet.

"I don't have long to talk; I know what you are Emrys," she said hastily and quietly.

Emrys met her pale, blue eyes and felt a cold sweat take over him. "I don't know what you mean," he stuttered struggling for breath.

"I know you are a mage because I am a mage," she said fearfully checking her shoulders to ensure no-one else had heard. "You can sense that surely?"

Through his drunkenness Emrys was not sure he could sense anything but concentrating on her eyes he did for a moment feel a flicker of light shining back at him. He was unsure of Elette and did not know if this was a trap.

"I am not trying to trick you, Emrys," she said snapping his focus back to her. "I have been hiding this from my family for several months. You've seen what they think of mages, imagine if they knew one was in their own family?"

"When... When did you have your Awakening?" he asked nervously.

"Not long after my seventeenth birthday, I saw a vision of my childhood, a memory I did not know I possessed. I must have been around five years old during the early years of the war. My mother was so frightened and pleaded with my father to sue for peace but he would not relent. He said Arcadians do not back down nor negotiate, then it's all a bit blurry. Like something's missing from the memory. Gods you have no idea how good it is to talk about this. I've been so alone with my thoughts."

It was in that moment that Emrys felt pity for the new Princess. She had clearly struggled in keeping her secret hidden and it had taken its toll. Even now, during her revelation to Emrys she was still paranoid and spoke at a hush whenever anyone walked by.

"Thank you for listening to me rant on," she said looking away.

"You have nothing to fear here. You know that don't you?" Emrys said. "My family will accept you, Tyris will accept you. May I ask you something that's been troubling me though?"

"Yes, of course." She met his eyes again.

"Who is that hooded man who follows your brother? I've asked Father but none of us seem to know anything about him."

Elette seemed to be hesitant but said, "That is Mathas. He only appeared in Arcadia roughly a year ago and my brother swept him into his service. He rarely leaves his side now. Rumours have it that he promised my brother…"

"What are you two talking about then?" his sister interrupted and placed a jug of water in front of Emrys. "Nothing embarrassing I hope."

"Actually," Elette spoke clearing her mind, "Emrys was just telling me funny stories about Tyris."

"Of those we have bucket-loads," Lymris smiled. "Now come with me sister, I want to introduce you to the other ladies of the court. There's not many of us so we have to stick together!"

***

EMRYS had sobered up remarkably quickly following his discussion with Elette and several cups of water as he sat with his sister for their father's speech. King Terrys had spoken well about his hopes for the future, and thanked his Arcadian counterparts for their role in ensuring peace would rule the lands. Elette had spoken next about her excitement to be in Galbraith and promised to learn all she could about its culture and customs. His brother had eloquently complimented Elette and before long the two were carried off to their room amidst the celebrations. Emrys had laughed as Tyris nervously scampered away before Rheinar one-handedly whisked him under his arm and kicked the door open. Now that the bride and groom were bedded, and the emperor and his guards had left, the dimly-lit Great Hall seemed sparse. Only a handful of lords and ladies remaining were known to Emrys, however now the crowd had parted, he could see that Edmure and Mathas were sat on the opposite side of the hall. A retainer of guards were littered about them as they shared in the feast and laughed as Edmure began carving a message into the roots beneath the table. Emrys could feel each strike of the knife as if it was piercing his body and gritted his teeth to stifle the pain. Edmure sat back once completed and chuckled to himself before firing a quick look at King Terrys and spitting.

"Did you see that, Lym?" Emrys exhaled breathlessly, still reeling from the pain he had just experienced.

"I did," she replied angrily. "And I'm going to have a little talk with our extended family."

Lymris stormed across the hall before Emrys could stop her and threw the contents of her goblet over the emperor's son. No one at the table spoke as his sister threw the goblet down on the ground in fury and stared at Edmure. The noise of the metal cup crashing against the floor rose caught her father's attention.

"What are you doing, Lym?" he demanded.

Without turning she said, "This *boy* has done nothing but disrespect our culture, customs and King since his arrival. I refuse to take it any longer! This should be a happy occasion and yet this *boy* continues to mock Galbraith."

Edmure looked furious. Even from across the hall Emrys could feel the hate emanating from him as his guards sat there stunned. Mathas did nothing, not even move. A small grin gripped the corner of his mouth for but a second before disappearing once again.

"Call me boy once more I dare you!" Edmure spat rising to his feet.

"You are a *boy,*" Lymris coldly replied. "And if these past few days have shown me anything, you would make for a poor ruler, Edmure, son of the emperor."

"Enough!" his father yelled enraged. "Lymris, leave the Great Hall at once."

His sister looked up at King Terrys in disbelief as Edmure dried his face and smiled cruelly.

"But Father I…" she protested.

"Now, Lymris!" his father insisted. "I will speak to you shortly."

Lymris scoffed and shook her head. She stormed past a table of onlookers and knocked a goblet flying with an outstretched arm in defiance. King Terrys took his seat once more and fired Emrys a glance to warn him from misbehaviour. Mathas once more whispered to Edmure who now gazed at Emrys, sending shivers up his spine. "Please forgive my daughter Edmure," his father spoke sternly. "That said, only those of Galbraithian descent are permitted to carve onto the Great Oak. These roots stand as the history of Galbraith and are marked by the ancestors of old. My ancestors. Do you understand?"

"Of course, King Galbraith," Edmure quipped fighting a smug grin. "My apologies."

"Good," King Terrys replied. "Then with that I will take my leave."

His father strolled past the remaining lords and ladies as they bowed and followed his departure. He stopped at Rheinar, before gesturing orders and holding his shoulder. Rheinar acknowledged this and stood behind beside Emrys, who barely noticed Rheinar's arrival as he sat there troubled in his thoughts. None of the events during the day made sense to

Emrys. He could not believe that in a such a short space of time not only he had his Awakening, his new sister revealed herself to be a mage in secret. He would have to consult with Mikhael and see what could be done to protect Elette. Then there was his father dismissing Lymris for standing up to Edmure. She was quite justified in Emrys' eyes with her response given the lack of humility that had been shown since the son of the emperor's arrival. Where Elette had grace and kindness, and showed an interest in the lands she would inherit, Edmure seemingly provoked the Galbraiths for his own amusement. Emrys could not be sure that these actions were uncalculated. Every move that Edmure made, Mathas was ever-present, whispering in the ears of the young successor.

"You there," Edmure called out to Emrys. "Care to join me? I feel its time I got to know the second son of King Terrys."

Emrys was lost for words as the table of Edmure looked on, awaiting a response. To turn it down would make him seem weak but above all he did not want to speak to the young man he had quickly grown to despise. Rheinar tapped him on the shoulder and whispered, "I will not leave your side Emrys."

It was settled. Emrys rose feeling his knees ache and began to move to the table. He remembered his father's words *Be proud, We are the Storm.* The words gave him a gust of confidence and he rose his chin and shoulders to stride like his father, his every step echoing in the now-emptied hall. The guards at the table moved away with a wave of Edmure's hand as Emrys shoulder barged through the grunting men. As he sat down, he realised this was the first time he had seen Mathas up close. He was impossibly pale and slender, and even sat down Emrys could judge that he was a tall man. Beneath his hood lay a huge scar blinding one of his eyes. The other was one of hazel and unflinching as he met the young prince's eyes.

"So I suppose we're family now," Edmure smirked and reclined making Emrys feel uneasy. "Tell me, what do you think of my sister? I saw you too deep in conversation earlier. It looked like quite an important chat."

"She's lovely," Emrys replied clearing his throat. "She was asking me questions about our lands and the storms on the Gilded Coast, nothing more."

"Maybe," Edmure nodded dismissively. "I thought she was perhaps telling you she was a mage."

Emrys froze at the word. He tried his best to appear emotionless as Edmure examined him for his response. "You do know that, don't you?" Edmure asked leaning forward.

"I do now," Emrys responded. "Besides what does it matter, we do not persecute mages in Galbraith."

Edmure sipped his wine and said, "It is true. Galbraith has always been kind to the mage-folk. Perhaps that's why she asked Father for a suitable match here. She's in the ideal place I would surmise, no?"

"Elette asked your father for this wedding?" Emrys asked baffled.

"She did. Somewhat convenient that she should flee our lands on her becoming a mage. However, it's played right into my hands. You see Emrys, I could never persecute my sister in Arcadia. There would be an uproar. A mage in the emperor's family? But she now belongs to the Galbraith family. There is now a mage in *your* family. Arcadia and Galbraith have been at war for twenty years. Who's to say after my father leaves this plane, there won't be another?" Edmure finished his glass and nodded to his men, "Take him."

Suddenly Emrys felt a shuffle behind him as Rheinar was pounced on by five guards and pinned down. Even the brute strength of his Master-at-Arms could not break through as he was dragged back with a knife at his throat. He turned to face Edmure but in an instant his head was cracked into the table and pinned down as the son of the emperor held his head down in a vice grip.

"Now," Edmure spoke closely to his ear, "we can speak plainly. Take a good look at what I carved earlier."

Emrys struggled to no avail, he could not move his body or indeed head from the table. His eyes looked down in horror to the root Edmure had been carving on earlier.

It read: *Arcadian Eastern Territories; The former Kingdom of Galbraith.*

"You see my father and your father sue for peace and that doesn't sit well with me," Edmure tutted. "Arcadia stands above other nations for one reason, we're better. Once my father is dead, I will destroy the Galbraith you know, burn my mage sister at the stake and put the heads of your family on spikes atop the pyre. I'll even use this big tree you're all so fond of for firewood."

"Why would you do this?" Emrys pleaded struggling for breath.

"I was promised the world!" Edmure spat. "I will be the emperor and the only ruler. I will take it by force like my father should have done and none shall oppose me!"

"Galbraith will always oppose tyranny!"

Emrys screamed out in pain as Edmure pushed him further into the table, "You may have you sights on the world but you will not get past us."

Edmure laughed heartily, "Galbraith is nothing, you hear me? Nothing! Besides after your sister's show tonight I have plans for her. I might keep her as a slave once my men have had their way with her."

Emrys could take no more. His anger consumed him and he screamed out in fury. In his desperation he pleaded with the Gods, anything and everything to put an end to his torment. Once more he felt a strange sensation, the same feeling he had earlier that morning. The Great Oak was calling to him. A throb in his heart grew larger and larger until the sound drowned out the boasting of Edmure above him. Slowly he heard a faint whisper, *Primal...* The word repeated itself over and over growing in sound. He felt strong, stronger than he ever had before. In the corner of his eye he looked at the roots and saw a flicker of movement. The whisper returned once more. *Take control...*

In an instant Emrys' eyes burned with a green hue emanating and illuminating the Great Hall. He summoned the roots which ripped themselves through the stone and pulled at Edmure's men as they panicked. Ensnared, their feeble attempts to cut the roots proved fruitless and within a few seconds they were all bound head to toe. Emrys clenched his fist and the roots crushed through every man's armour, and he could hear as their bones snapped under the pressure.

"You're a mage!" Edmure spat and pulled a concealed dagger from his pocket down upon his head. The very root he had been carving on leapt to his defence and wrapped tightly on Edmure's forearm causing him to squeal in pain. Mathas leapt across, blade in hand, but Rheinar was on him in a flash and held his longsword to the advisor's throat. Emrys stood and turned to see the man who promised such evil. "I am no mage. I am the Primal," he said speaking in a voice that did not belong to him.

Emrys tightened his fist again and every bone in Edmure's arm audibly shattered as he screamed in agony. His exertions came to the fore and Emrys could feel his legs weaken. The grip he had on Edmure relented as all the roots fell and slithered back beneath the stone floor. He felt woozy and stumbled as Rheinar leapt to catch him. His eyes rolled back and the green light that had filled the room diminished. Mathas grabbed a wailing Edmure under his arm and the two scurried off out of the Great Hall and into the night.

"Emrys! Emrys! Can you hear me?" Rheinar asked as the world slipped from view and faded into black.

Chapter Five
Aftermath

RHEINAR stood over an unconscious Emrys as Mikhael burst into the Great Hall. He was beside himself with worry, and shame. Worry for the prince of Galbraith and shame for his inability to protect him. He berated himself for not seeing it sooner. The guards had placed themselves behind him but his sole focus was on Emrys and he kicked himself for his negligence. The would-be-Emperor Edmure was visibly troubling the young Prince and Rheinar admitted to himself that even he was disturbed by the manner of his revelations. He would have to warn King Terrys, of course, but how would he explain the events that followed? Rheinar had seen Mikhael use his abilities in battle but never before had he seen the raw power Emrys bestowed upon his attackers. Behind him he examined the carcasses left behind, mangled beyond recognition. They looked like islands of flesh in a tide of blood that swept the floor. Then there was Edmure himself. Emrys had destroyed his right arm with a mere clench of his fist before he collapsed into his arms.

"Is he okay?" Mikhael hurriedly asked Rheinar snapping him back into attention.

"I don't know. There's many things I do not know after tonight," Rheinar replied. "Emrys is a mage, Mikhael."

Without turning Mikhael compressed Emrys' head with a cold flannel and nodded, "I know Rheinar."

"What?" Rheinar exclaimed grabbing Mikhael by the shoulder and spinning him to meet his eyes. "How could you not tell us?"

"Because I only found out this morning," Mikhael replied placing his hand on Rheinar's. "I came down from my study and Emrys was experiencing his Awakening. The Awakening... It's an act that awakens a mage's abilities. We both agreed that we would keep it secret until after the wedding so as not to jeopardise the marriage between Tyris and Elette."

Rheinar was staggered. There was much going on that he knew nothing of and Mikhael's explanation did little to sate his curiosity.

"There's more, Mikhael." He calmed himself. "Emrys pulled the roots between the stone. He crushed the men behind us and crippled the emperor's son. I've never seen anything like it. Roots racing through the air and all Emrys did was close his fist. He spoke in a strange voice and called himself the Primal. Please tell me because I don't understand anything I've seen tonight, what the fuck's a Primal?"

Mikhael looked worried and stroked his beard, clearly struggling with his thoughts. "We must move quickly if we are to prevent a war. I will call King Terrys from his slumber."

His eyes burned a bright blue and he muttered to himself for a moment. Rheinar looked once more on Emrys. He was in a cold sweat and twitched occasionally as Rheinar met his hand with his. Kneeling before him he said, "I am sorry I failed you, my Prince. It will not happen again."

Mikhael had stopped chanting and began pacing the room deep in thought. The two stood in silence occasionally looking at each other but were stumped for words. Minutes passed by but they felt like years as Rheinar thought how he would tell the King everything he had witnessed. He would start, of course, with Edmure's plans for the Kingdom and his attack upon Emrys. That would be the trickiest part for him he knew. He had failed to protect the prince and feared King Terrys' wrath upon him. He also hoped Mikhael would help explain Emrys' abilities but the two of them knew they would not be able to predict how the King might take this news.

The doors swung open and before them, in his rags, stood the King. He looked understandably tired during this late hour and had done little to fix his appearance. Terrys was observing the area and spotted the crumpled heap of bodies. Upon seeing Emrys laid upon the table he frantically ran across the Great Hall and rushed to comfort his son.

"Emrys! Emrys! Are you okay?" Terrys pleaded. "Mikhael, Rheinar, what's happened to my son?"

"Calm down, my King," Mikhael reassured him. "He will be fine. There is much we need to tell you and we must act quickly or risk another war."

"War?" Terrys replied. "War with who?"

"Who else, Arcadia," Mikhael folded him arms across his chest. "Rheinar, please explain the situation to the king."

Rheinar stepped forward and felt uneasy as he met King Terrys' gaze. He knew the king was an honourable man but he was fierce when he needed to be and Rheinar worried about how the king might react to this news.

"After you left the Great Hall, Edmure summoned Emrys over to his table to 'get to know him'. I stood by the prince's side and acknowledged I would be there with him. Edmure claims his sister Elette is a mage and that by coming to Galbraith he can now deal with her as Arcadians do with mages."

"Elette is a mage? Mikhael is this true?" The King replied. "I have not felt a presence of her magic but that might be because I haven't been looking for it," Mikhael shrugged. "I will check this claim in the morning."

Terrys shifted his attention back to Rheinar and insisted, "Go on, Rheinar."

"Everything happened quickly," Rheinar continued. "I was jumped by five of Edmure's guards and pinned back with a blade by my throat. Edmure had slammed Emrys' head across the table there and went on to claim that once his father is dead, he will invade Galbraith and destroy the Kingdom. He plans to stick the Galbraith family heads on spikes while he burns his sister at the stake. He said he wants to enslave Lymris after her actions tonight."

King Terrys rose to his feet and circled the table. "That fucking Arcadian!" He snarled, "When I get my hands on him there will be no heir to the emperor. He will answer for his crimes."

"There is more, my King." Rheinar went on, "Emrys screamed out in fury, his eyes burning brightly and all of a sudden the roots of the Great Oak swarmed around us. He effortlessly crushed these five guards you see before you and he crippled Edmure's arm with the roots below our feet."

King Terrys stopped in his tracks. He appeared motionless before looking down at Emrys then back at Rheinar, "My son... My son is a mage?"

"He must be. What I've seen tonight I will not soon forget. I do not lie to you," Rheinar bowed before him. "I am sorry I failed you my King. I swore to protect him, and I could not."

King Terrys sat down beside his son and took his hand.

"The failure is mine and mine alone Rheinar," he said. "I never should have left him with that poisonous monster."

The room was filled with an eerie silence as Mikhael and Rheinar stood, awaiting his response. King Terrys was speechless. Rheinar looked on but knew there were little words of comfort to be said at this time. Everything the King had worked for could be undone with the events that had transpired.

"My King," Mikhael mustered his courage, "I must be honest with you. Earlier this morning I witnessed first-hand Emrys' transformation to a mage."

"You knew!" King Terrys bolted upright and launched himself forward. Rheinar stepped between the two and kept the King from shredding Mikhael to pieces.

"Emrys and I agreed to keep this hidden until after the wedding," Mikhael floundered. "We did not know that Edmure would torment him! That this would force his powers to manifest and strike back. This morning he revealed to me that he had a vision of Caulder."

King Terrys repeated the word, "Caulder."

"The very same." Mikhael stepped forward. "In his vision he claims Caulder appeared before him and called him Primal. I've spent nearly all day pouring over the books and what I've learned is twofold. First, Caulder is alive or will return. I don't know how and I certainly don't know what the grand scheme is, but I fear what Emrys saw was a premonition for the future. In his vision he saw a black cloud suffocating Galbraith. Emrys was threatened by Caulder and I fear he has a role to play in the events that will follow."

"Wait," Terrys stopped, "Caulder raided Arcadia but the Circle killed him didn't they. What makes you think he would come for Galbraith?"

"Caulder is neither male or female," Mikhael corrected the King. "I believe the Circle banished Caulder but I cannot be certain. Emrys claims that Caulder will spread its Corruption and devour this world. I do not believe nations are of a concern to The Bringer of Storms. I think it views Emrys as a threat and that's why I believe it will come for him."

Rheinar looked down at Emrys. He could not believe it. "Emrys is barely fourteen and does not have a grasp on his abilities," he said. "How could he be a threat to a being that even the most skilled mages across the world could not kill?"

"That leads onto my second discovery," Mikhael said and shoved his arm into his robe. From it he withdrew a tattered book with an ineligible title and flipped through it before presenting it before Terrys and Rheinar. "Look at this, my King."

The three gathered around the page and Mikhael brought their attention a paragraph near the bottom which read:

A Primal, to my best knowledge, is unique among those with magical abilities. Where other mages mimic the elements or can conjure up illusions to baffle the most brilliant minds, the Primal stands alone with their ability to commune with the world around them. The trees, the sky, the ocean, there is no apparent limit to the reach of their abilities. I also note that animals are fond of the Primal, and will often flock to their aid in times of need. They are the only mages I have witnessed that can bring life from nothingness and as such are highly revered among the mage-folk. To many at the Circle, they are often referred to as the Nature's Pupil, the bridge between humanity and nature itself...

Rheinar allowed himself a moment to absorb the

paragraph in its entirety. According to this account, a Primal has command over the forests, oceans and sky. He felt a slight hint of fear catch him as he looked down at Emrys, and he doubted the young Prince would be ready for such power.

"The Nature's Pupil?" Terrys puzzled, "Who wrote this book Mikhael?"

"It was a scholar by the name of Drayton," Mikhael replied. "That's the thing, my King. This account was written more than two centuries ago. The Primal in question was an Arcadian woman by the name of Elysée and there has been no recorded sightings of a Primal since."

"But what part could a Primal play in stopping Caulder?" Rheinar asked, baffled by the thought of an Arcadian Primal. "If this Corruption spreads it will kill everything we know."

"I do not know," Mikhael shook his head. "But one line of this paragraph took my interest... *can bring life from nothingness*... If this is true then somehow Emrys might be the key in stopping Caulder for good."

"So you're saying my son is this Primal," Terrys scoffed. "He's only a boy and one that's never even left the Kingdom. No. My son deserves better. A peaceful reign beside his brother when my time comes to pass. That was the plan. All of this mysticism and magic? I cannot make sense of this."

The three stood in tacit silence for a while they grasped the gravity of events. Emrys, by Mikhael's reckoning, was to be hunted by Caulder and the fourteen-year-old prince still lay there, unaware of the revelations happening above him. Rheinar was concerned mostly about the troubles that lay at their door. Emperor Harold Valyris was not known for his forgiving nature and the ramifications of Edmure's injuries could be severe for Emrys and indeed the Kingdom.

"My King," Rheinar spoke breaking the silence, "I cannot speak for Caulder because I do not know anything of magic, but we need to act fast on how to deal with the emperor."

Terrys muttered to himself for a moment before saying, "Hell's teeth this is a horrible situation we find ourselves in. The options available to us are few. Rheinar, place extra guards around the Valryis family, we may have to snuff out the threat they pose before they act."

As Rheinar moved to leave Mikhael stood in front of him. "No Rheinar, stop," he spoke plainly. "Terrys, you will not kill the emperor and you will not kill his son. I know you too well to know you are not privy to such cruelty. Althea would not want that."

"Althea is dead, Mikhael," Terrys slammed the table with an open fist. "We have to consider today's threats, not tomorrows. Rheinar is right, as soon as the emperor hears of the injury to Edmure he will demand Emrys' head or worse. I will not surrender my son to the cruelties of Arcadia. We've all seen how they treat mages, imagine how they'd treat Emrys? The prince of a nation they've been at war with for nearly twenty years?"

"No, Emrys will not be subject to that," Mikhael spoke resolutely. "I have another idea in mind, my King," He moved closer and spoke with a whisper, "It will be hard on you, Tyris and Lymris, but it will be even harder on Emrys."

Chapter Six
Consequences

THE SKY whipped with lightning and roared with thunder as Emrys stirred from his slumber. He opened his eyes slowly and saw that he was now back in his room, lit only by a single candelabra by the door. His head throbbed painfully and his throat was desperately parched, bringing on a hoarse cough that shook his body. He squirrelled an arm across his bedside table in pursuit of water and nearly knocked over a jug before downing its contents. Breathing harshly, he tried to recall what had happened but found himself only thinking of the wedding and the warm smile his brother had given to Elette. His legs were trembling as he brought them to meet the cold stone floor and launched himself upright dizzily. Flashes of lightning occasionally lit the dark room before the boom of thunder shook the very floor beneath him. Rising to his feet, he moved gingerly to the door but upon turning the handle, the door remained wedged shut. He tried a second and third time to no avail before banging on the door. "Is anyone out there?" he asked weakly before banging several more times.

A single knock came from the other side followed by a stern voice, "By order of the King you are to remain in your chambers and await judgment. I will say nothing further."

The sound of footsteps retreating gave Emrys little hope of a second reply. What had happened? He closed his eyes and desperately tried to piece the images jumbled in his memory.

It was no use. He let out an exasperated sigh before slumping by his window and staring out at the Kingdom. The winds had not yet rose, but streaks of lightning crashed beyond the Gilded Coast, illuminating the darkness across the land, ever followed by a low rumble of thunder. He recalled a story his mother Althea liked to tell him and his siblings when they were children. It was about the Gods of Lighting and Thunder. They had once been close friends and rang out together in harmony. But Lighting wanted to race beyond Thunder's clouds. Jealous, Thunder set out to catch Lightning and trap him in the clouds they had once called home. But Lightning was too quick. And so they remained in the skies trapped in a cat-and-mouse chase for eternity.

He chuckled to himself as he thought of better times and closed his eyes to remember his mother's loving smile and warm embrace. Some small twigs rustled above him and clipped his ears as they fell to the ground below him. Looking up he squinted and saw the faint silhouette of his sister climbing down the branches before stopping to meet his gaze. "Move over Emrys," she whispered as Emrys receded into his room. Seconds later Lymris was stood on the windowsill and climbed down quietly. The two stood silently for a moment before Lymris rushed forward and embraced her older brother in a hug. "Lym, I can't breathe," Emrys said breaking the lock between the two.

"Are you okay?" she replied running her hands down his face as if she was checking for wounds of abrasions.

"I'm okay Lym," he said. "What are you doing? I've been locked in and Father will pitch a fit if he finds out you're here."

Lymris stared at him bluntly, "Like that would stop me."

Emrys was moved. He could always rely on Lymris to be

there for him, and now in his time of confusion, she stood there smiling at him. He hugged her again for comfort before they both sat down on his bed. Emrys needed more information, and so he asked, "Do you know why I've been locked in? I can't remember anything Lym. I remember the wedding and then... blank."

Lymris responded in an instant, "You've broken Edmure's arm," she said. "Well crushed actually. That bastard won't be wiping his arse anytime soon."

Emrys sat there gormlessly, his mouth hanging open stupidly at his sister's latest remark. Closing his mouth and stumbling for words he said, "Wait, what?"

"You're a mage, Em," Lymris stated. "Don't worry, I don't mind that you didn't tell me. Mikhael just came up and explained the situation and I think he's gone to tell Tyris as well. After Dad kicked me out of the hall, you and Edmure got into some discussion that ended with him threatening you and the Kingdom. You killed his men and from what I've heard you've crippled him."

Emrys wouldn't accept it and shook his head in defiance. "No," he dismissed. "How would I do that?"

"Mikhael said you called upon the roots of the Great Oak. How can you not remember any of this?" she asked. "Rheinar was stood by your side the entire time, he saw everything. He even said you called yourself Primal."

The word echoed a few times in his mind and jogged remnants of memories Emrys did not know he had. Staring back at Lym, it clicked. He remembered.

"I remember..." he said unmoving. "I remember Edmure's men pinning back Rheinar and then he pinned me down. He said such horrible things, Lym. About you, about me, about the king, but mostly about his sister. He's not after peace, he's after Elette because she's a mage! We need to warn Father, he'll burn the Kingdom to get to her!"

Emrys leapt to his feet and began banging on the door voraciously until his hand throbbed in pain.

Lymris pulled his arm back and attempted to console him. "They won't open the doors, Em," she said, looking away. "They will come for you at first light."

"To do what?" Emrys asked fearfully and noticed his sister was now biting her lip.

"Mikhael said… I need to get ready," Lymris looked up, her eyes glistening with tears. She hugged Emrys tighter than before which brought deeper worry to the young prince. He struggled to ask more, partly out of fear and partly because he knew whatever happens next would not be good for him.

＊＊

A KNOCK on the door came in the seventh hour and as the door swung open, Mikhael stepped forth from the folds of darkness. He looked tired, more tired than usual, and seemed enveloped in an aura of sadness as he met Emrys at the foot of his bed.

"My Prince," he bowed. "I am sorry but you must come with me wearing these."

From his robe he pulled a set of manacles and an escort of guards entered the room behind him. "The Arcadians want your head," he continued softly. "But I've found a compromise. You need to be brave, Emrys. Can you do that for me? For your family? For your Kingdom?"

Emrys sat staring at his feet and was already fighting back

the wave of tears. He calmed himself and turned to meet Mikhael. "What will happen to me, Mikhael?"

"I am sorry Emrys, I truly am." Mikhael shook his head and looked away, "Your father must be the one to pass judgement and I cannot be the one to take that from him. Know that what happens next must happen. For as long as I live I will stand beside you. Now, are you ready?"

Emrys rose to his feet and stretched. The guards moved swiftly and locked the manacles around his arms and legs, bringing a shiver upon him as the metal kissed his skin.

Mikhael led the escort as they moved down through the castle and out into the streets of Stormgast. The clouds remained from the night's brief storm and the ground was still fresh with the rain that had followed. The townsfolk had gathered along the high street and were muttering to themselves as Emrys marched past. He would pay no heed, he told himself, but could not fight the urge to view their shocked faces as they witnessed their own prince walking by in chains. Mikhael led them to the garden courtyards whereupon a retainer of guards let them pass to the lords and ladies. The tent had not yet been taken down from yesterday's wedding though its set up looked remarkably different. There were no joys of flowers, nor banners which gave the gazebo an unwelcoming, colourless atmosphere around the once pretty gardens. Guards were upon every inch of sight as Emrys looked on and he could see the Arcadians keeping their distance, hands pressed to their blades should a fight become necessary. As he moved slowly into the crowd he felt as if a thousand eyes were upon him and was too ashamed to meet anyone's gaze. As he looked up he could see his brother, sister and Elette on one side of where the altar had stood, and to the other Emperor Valryis without

Edmure or Mathas present.

Emrys came to a halt at the foot of the steps and awaited his father's arrival. As he looked on at his family, he was met with a sadness that coursed his veins and looked away in shame. A silence had gripped the gardens. None of the nobility muttered a word as they grasped the gravity of the situation. Emrys had not intended for any of this to happen and he wondered if the peace between Galbraith and Arcadia could survive this. He refused the urge to look at Emperor Valryis and suddenly felt very grateful for the litter of guards between them.

"You!" Emperor Valryis boomed. "I will see you dead for what you have done to my heir!"

"Enough," his father stepped forward and placed himself in the middle of the two families. "The judgement for Emrys' fate comes to me and me alone."

"He has mutilated my son!" Harold protested as the guards on both sides shifted nervously, "Never again will Edmure write or hunt!"

"And I am sorry to hear that," his father replied appearing to attempt to defuse the situation. "But it has come to my attention that Emrys was provoked by your son. Rheinar, if you will."

Rheinar stepped to attention and looked at Emperor Valyris. "Emperor Valyris, I was present when your son's men held me at knifepoint and he himself attacked Emrys. He pinned him down on the table and made wild accusations that upon your death, he seeks to invade Galbraith and kill every single Galbraith. He made some vile claims regarding Princess Lymris and it was at this time that Emrys lost control and wounded Edmure, defending himself."

"You lie!" Harold spat while Rheinar stood unflinching. "Mages have been itching for a chance to kill Edmure and they almost succeeded last night."

"And that is why I have come to a decision on what must be done to uphold the peace between Galbraith and Arcadia," King Terrys interrupted. "I want nothing more than for the war to be a dark spot in our shared histories. It is because of this I have determined the punishment appropriate to appease Arcadia."

His father turned to look at him. In his eyes he could see the same sadness shared by his siblings. As he looked closer at the king he could see his arms were trembling, as if the weight of such a decision was tearing him in two. Silence fell again as King Terrys weighted his words carefully.

"Emrys," he said. "In light of the events following the wedding yesterday, I find myself in the unenviable position of having to determine the fate of my son."

"Father, please I…" Emrys pleaded.

"No, I will not hear more," his father stopped him. "Rheinar and Mikhael have told me enough and it is with their advice I have made my decision. From this day until my last, you are hereby banished from the Kingdom of Galbraith. You are stripped of your Royal Lineage and cast out to whatever future you may find."

The words hit Emrys like a dagger to the chest as he fell to his knees and sobbed uncontrollably. His sister ran down the steps and comforted him as Tyris sat down with his head in his hands. Elette stood in a daze as she contemplated losing her brother a day after meeting him. Cries of anguish erupted all around Emrys and there were overlapping shouts of nobles pleading in his name. King Terrys stood still amongst the chaos and with a stiff upper lip hushed the crowd, raising his arms above his head. "I do this with a heavy heart," he said faltering to tears. "If I must lose my son to keep the peace, better that he should have a chance of a future than be killed for crimes outside his control. I am sorry, my son."

Emperor Valyris' nostrils flared and he stepped forward, facing King Terrys. He offered an outstretched arm which his father took and with a nod of approval, he and his men departed. There were still nobles flocked around Emrys attempting to console him but they too knew his fate was forever sealed. In the space of a day, they had gained a princess and lost a prince. Rheinar had joined Emrys and grabbed him by the chin. As tears streamed down his face, Emrys squinted up at his Master-At-Arms who looked down not in sadness, but with a kind encouraging smile. "This is not the end, Emrys," he said softly. "Only the beginning of a grand journey that you and I shall take together."

"What?" Emrys spluttered wiping a snotty nose on his sleeve.

"You didn't think your father would just leave you to fend for yourself now did you?" Rheinar said rising to his feet. "You still need to train and I'm not going to be happy until you can fell me. The world has other plans for you Emrys, former Prince of Galbraith." He extended an arm to Emrys which he took, and his mentor pulled him to his feet with ease. It was the first time in the day that he had felt a glimmer of hope. Rheinar would be his guide, and teach him the ways of the world outside of his own bubble of Galbraith. His father looked on besides Tyris, wiping the tears from his eyes and embracing him in a cuddle Emrys envied. His sister stood by his side and held his quivering hand as he composed himself to speak to Rheinar.

"What happens next?" Emrys asked sniffling.

"Next," Rheinar clapped his hands on his shoulder. "We find out what all this Primal nonsense means and there's only one place for it."

"Where's that?" Lymris asked in her brother's stead.

"Carpathia lass," Rheinar replied. "Your brother and I are off to see the Circle."

Chapter Seven
The Aurelian Road

"ARE you ready Emrys?" Rheinar asked as he mounted his horse. Emrys had spent the rest of the morning gathering provisions with his sister and Rheinar. He was told to wear his plainest clothes so as not to attract attention and had picked enough fruit to last several weeks. The butcher, Finn, and herbalist, Grace, had been the first of the traders to shun the former prince, and sheepishly he had asked his sister to gather some dried meats and herbs for the journey. Retrieving his horse had been a similar affair until Rheinar stormed into the stables, threw insults at the stablemaster and dragged his mare out into the street. His mare, who he had named Elmyra, whinnied at the sight of him and he felt a strange sensation with how the auburn beast met his gaze. Rheinar had packed the mare himself with a short sword, two bows and a quiver, and the remainder of food that he had not managed to pack onto his stallion, Shrieker. As for his own equipment, the Master-At-Arms straddled a huge shield on his back with a gilded longsword nestled across his waist. He wore plated armour and a helm which obscured his features from view.

Emrys' farewells to his family had been brief, awkward encounters. Tyris had hugged him but appeared in a state of shock at losing his younger brother so soon after his wedding. Lymris wept inconsolably and pleaded with him not to leave. Seeing his sister had hit him hardest. They always wanted to journey across the world together but now he knew they would be lucky to see each other again in their lifetimes. His father had barely spoke when it came to their goodbye. He had avoided making eye contact with Emrys and soon found an excuse to leave as his son broke down again.

"Yes, I'm ready," Emrys replied sadly as he reflected on his heart-breaking morning.

He took one last glance at the castle towering above them. He had always felt behind its walls and felt a tinge of fear pass over him as he thought on facing the unknown. He could see Tyris and Elette both raise their arms to him high inside the castle but could see no sign of his sister or father. Even now he could feel the Great Oak call his name and wondered if anything could ever make this sensation leave him. Sniffling and dabbing his raw eyes, he turned away and met Rheinar's pace as they moved to a trot down the high street. Many of the townsfolk had formed a guard of honour and threw wreaths and flowers before them. Emrys felt touched that so many of them would remember him and stopped to thank those he could.

A billow of smoke from the gates told Emrys the emperor's carriage was getting ready to depart and return to their homeland. Upon seeing the former prince, the guards had drawn their weapons, shouted abuse and spat at his arrival. He had still seen no sign of Edmure and eagerly looked out for him as they passed the carriage by. It was to no avail. Emrys met only the cold eyes of Mathas who never took his eyes from him, and panicked as the advisor grinned evilly in his direction. Several of the guards made threats on his life and shot arrows at their horses' feet, causing Emrys to wince to the chorus of laughter.

"Pay no attention," Rheinar spoke sharply. "The Arcadians want to see you cower. Give them no such satisfaction."

Clearing the gates, the pair broke into a gallop and began making their way south along the Aurelian Road. The lotuses across the plains smelled sweet in the cool air as storm clouds circled above them. Emrys tried to match Rheinar's pace as best he could but soon found himself dawdling behind. It almost seemed as if Elmyra was resisting his calls and tugs, and the young mare outright refused to move in a straight line. Up ahead Rheinar had noticed this and slowed the pace. He pulled Shrieker to a halt as he waited for Emrys.

"Emrys," he snarled angrily and grabbed him by the cuff of his shirt. "We do not have time to take things slowly. Stop messing about."

"Why not?" Emrys protested, "My family's abandoned me! I have no home and I'll never see this land again!"

"Things are tough lad but you're still alive," Rheinar responded. "We need to move quickly and flee these lands before you become an even bigger target!"

Emrys was shocked by Rheinar's admission. "What do you mean a target? I've been banished and the emperor himself agreed with my father's judgement."

"You're a fool if you believe Emperor Valyris will let you go," Rheinar shook his head. "Even now, as we're talking, I'd wager Harold is placing a large bounty on your head, sending word to all corners of the continent."

"But father wouldn't allow it…" Emrys dismissed.

"Your father cannot protect you any more!" Rheinar shouted, his patience wearing thin. "You are no longer a Prince of Galbraith, Emrys. Only I stand between you and any would-be-assassins. We need to be smart, which means getting as far away from Arcadian influence as possible. First, we ride to Burnistoun in the South, take a ship to the Great Market City of Daal and from there we work our way through Carpathia."

"Why Burnistoun?" Emrys asked as the two began moving again. "Surely Eddington is closer and we could catch a ship from there?"

"You're correct," Rheinar acknowledged. "However, there's a Captain in Burnistoun I'd trust with my life, and he owes me a favour. With good weather and a steady ride, we should make it there in about three weeks."

As the two continued along the road, Elmyra continued to disobey Emrys' commands and he cursed in frustration as she took him from the path and onto the plains. "Mikhael told me something about you Primals," Rheinar laughed. "Apparently you have an affinity with animals, why not try asking Elmyra to behave?"

Emrys chuckled himself and considered it a folly of a request. Nevertheless, he duly concentrated his thoughts and pleaded with Elmyra to act as Shrieker did. The results were astounding. Not only did Elmyra rejoin the path, she met the black stallion on the path and rode with him side by side. Even Rheinar looked gobsmacked as the young man, hopeless in horsemanship, matched his skill effortlessly.

"Not bad." The warrior grinned. "Now let us make haste."

The remainder of the day passed by fairly uneventfully. A couple of times they met strangers on the road but their conversations were fleeting as each party rode forth on their respective paths. Twice they were offered trinkets by travelling merchants, yet as eager as Emrys was to browse their goods, Shrieker had broken into a canter, forcing Elmyra to follow. To pass the time the pair practised sparring on horseback. Rheinar led the instruction and encouraged Emrys to plant his feet like stone to the stirrups for balance. They used dulled blades, as they had done in the courtyard gardens, yet Rheinar's tutelage seemed much more brutal than over the past few months. He was less forgiving of Emrys' mistakes and no longer held back his immense strength, forcing difficult parries from the young man. Emrys cried out in pain after a sweeping blow connected with his shoulder and caused him to drop the blade. Rheinar ordered him to pick it up and continue to practice through the pain several times over.

By the time it was dusk, the pair dismounted and set about their tasks of making camp a couple of fields over from the Aurelian Road. Emrys was exhausted and fell from his horse without grace causing Rheinar to laugh as he gathered firewood. He directed Emrys to bring water from the nearby stream, and tie the horses to a tree surrounded by grass which they began to wolf down almost immediately. Emrys massaged his shoulder which had taken a beating through the trip. Rheinar had targeted it with every strike and continued to remind Emrys that in battle, always go for the weakness. The former prince had spent an entire summer looking for his Master-At-Arms' vulnerability yet had not found anything of the sort. He was faster than he looked, strong as a country ox and cunning in his craft.

As Emrys returned from gathering water, Rheinar sat by the fire cooking ham and chewing on fruits they had picked earlier. He passed Emrys the first slice which melted like butter in his mouth and brought a strength back to his bones. "We've made good progress today," Rheinar said as he chewed through an assortment of berries. The fire crackled as the two ate in silence and for the first time in the day Emrys felt a hunger for home. He missed the comforts of Stormgast, the busy streets and the kind nobles with whom his family held good standing. Yet nothing compared to how he missed his family. He could barely begin to think on how this was affecting them and fresh tears welled as he thought on their final moments together. His sister, he should have hugged more. His brother, he should have had a joke with. Elette, he should have reassured. His father, he just wished he could understand more about the man.

Turning to face Rheinar he asked, "So how did you and my father first meet?"

Stoking the fire, Rheinar replied, "Your father and I met many years ago in a land far from here. I was enslaved, you see? Enslaved to the fighting pits of Daal. Terrys and Althea were making a tour of the world in the years of peace when your grandfather Tymos ruled. They came to the Great Market City and bought my service."

"Why did they buy your service?" Emrys leant in, "What did you do to catch my father's eye?"

"I never caught your father's eye," Rheinar responded. "It was your mother who sought to give me my freedom. One day I was pitted against a trio of gladiators unarmed. The slave-master Denrick was a cruel man and cruelty was his sport. Many of my friends had died in similar ways but I told myself I would not die at his command. I defeated the gladiators without killing them, took a sword and threw it at Denrick. I missed the bastard. If I get the chance, I won't miss again."

"So my mother bought you from him?" Emrys asked.

"She did," Rheinar nodded. "She always told me she was moved by how I fought the oppression and defied the slave-master. She gave me my freedom then and there. I ran to the slave quarters to find my wife and son. When I got there, all I found was death. Amarint's body lay in front of me, her throat slit. There was no sign of my boy, Jakob."

It was the first time that Emrys had ever heard this story and he was moved by Rheinar's plight. He had lost his wife and son years before he was even born. Rheinar sat there emotionless, like the years had taken their toll and the loss was a distant memory that happened to someone else.

"I'm so sorry, Rheinar," Emrys said. "I never knew you had such a horrible thing happen to you."

"You need not apologise," he replied. "Your mother gave me a new life. A good life with her and your father in this foreign land here they called Galbraith. They gave me the name Rheinar when I first came here and taught me the Elessian language. Each night I dream of Amarint and Jakob and I long for the day I can see them again. It's why I understand how you feel about exile. You've lost your family as I lost mine. We've all lost something Emrys, but in your case we might find something new and beautiful."

"I'm scared, Rheinar," Emrys said softly. "I'm really scared."

"I know, lad," he replied as he lay back on his bedroll. "But I am here with you, and I will die defending you if it comes to it. Now get your rest, you'll need your strength for tomorrow's ride."

***

AS the morning suns rose, the chirping of the birds stirred Emrys from his sleep. He had slept soundly and nodded off almost immediately after Rheinar told him about his wife and son. The story had scared him and made him pity Rheinar. As for his brutish mentor, he was already up and handed Emrys a plate of fruit as the he met him by the smouldering fire. They ate together in silence and once done, Rheinar beckoned Emrys to free the horses. Within minutes of packing up, they were back on the Aurelian Road. The morning suns warmed Emrys as they rode and he smelled the sweet dew as it rested on the grass around him. His thoughts were interrupted once more as Rheinar threw a dulled sword to him and the two began sparring as they had yesterday. The road had been quiet, all morning. They had yet to see another person, but Emrys could now see why they called Galbraith the Storm Lands. He passed perhaps a hundred felled trees as lightning had struck and ripped them root and stem.

"The storms here are a magnificent sight," Rheinar noted. "As long as you're not on the receiving end. There's a town beyond those trees. Poor bastards."

After speaking Rheinar stopped and glanced a look behind them. He looked perturbed and motioned Emrys to carry on trotting, keeping a hand fixed to his sword. "Emrys, don't panic," he said. "We're being followed."

Emrys froze still. He fought the urge to look over his shoulder at what Rheinar had seen and awaited further instructions. "Do you see the ravine over there?" Rheinar nodded in the direction. Emrys saw it and acknowledged this with a slow nod. "We ride hard when I say, drop below there and set up an ambush. Ready your bow."

Emrys frantically grabbed the bow to his right and gripped it so tightly he was sure the oak would bend. "Now!" Rheinar shouted as the two fled to the clearing from their unknown pursuer.

Chapter Eight
Threatened

PANIC gripped Emrys as he shifted in the undergrowth. The ravine they had jumped into reeked of mould and other smells he did not want to know the origins of. Stifling himself from gagging he drew an arrow and nocked it back awaiting Rheinar's command. His mentor was to his side, blade in hand, with his other clutching a rock to launch himself forward if needed. The pair heard a third horse clumsily enter the area and footsteps when the rider had disembarked. Whoever it was, they moved quickly, Emrys thought. Small tiptoed movements gave little sound away. It was only the occasional crunch of a twig underfoot that let him know there was someone else with them.

"Keep your arrow steady Emrys," Rheinar whispered. "I'm going up."

Rheinar gripped the rock and with a fluid leg kick disappeared from Emrys' view. He could see very little to begin with. A small gap protruding to his right allowed him to see the horses but beyond that he was very limited in what he could do. A rustling between trees erupted above him followed by a smattering of swords as they clashed in battle. "Emrys come up, it's okay!" Rheinar shouted as he heard him sheathing his sword.

Emrys placed the arrow back in its quiver, threw the bow over his shoulder, and grabbing roots by the nearby tree vaulted himself over the mound. Rheinar stood by a hooded figure sprawled out in the mud. "Who is it?" Emrys asked as he walked over.

The figure pulled back their hood and Emrys was overjoyed by what he saw.

"Lym!" he said as he ran to his sister's side. She was covered in mud, head to toe, and using her sleeve wiped a huge chunk from her face. "Think you could leave without me big brother?" She laughed as Rheinar rose her to her feet. "I'm sorry, Princess," Rheinar said kneeling. "I did not know it was you. What are you doing here?"

"I made a promise to Emrys that we'd adventure the world together. What better time than now?" his sister said, dusting herself off.

Emrys felt honoured by his sister's presence and angled a desperate plea to Rheinar to allow it. "No," he said stubbornly. "Go home, Lym. Your father will be worried sick. Many dangers face your brother and I."

"Which is all the more reason for me to stay," Lymris piped up. "He's no good at fighting but I've got skills with sword and a bow."

"I cannot put another Royal in danger," Rheinar turned away deep in thought.

"Well, there's two choices then," Lym said frustated. "Either I ride with you or I ride a day behind you. There's nothing left for me in Galbraith. I want to see the Great Market City of Daal and visit the gardens of Carpathia with my brother. Tyris is the heir, not me, so I can do what I will. Please let me travel with you rather than behind you."

Rheinar muttered a few curses to himself and threw his arms out in frustration. "You're as stubborn as your father," he said, gritting his teeth. "Very well. But what I say goes. I will protect you both with my life but do not make me give it up for nothing."

Emrys and Lym nodded in unison, failing to hide their glee as they hugged before their Master-At-Arms. Rheinar signalled them to mount up and continue along the Aurelian Road. Lym had brought her mare, Styria, who whinnied as Emrys rode past. He was overjoyed his sister was with him and the two began taking turns winding up Rheinar and racing each other as they made their way down the open road. Emrys had given her the better of his two bows. He had seen Lym practising throughout the summer and knew her natural talent would serve them better than if he had kept it. She shot down a couple of apples from trees above and passed them out to her brother and Rheinar. Rheinar grumpily munched his down before passing the remnants to Shrieker who swallowed the fruit in one huge gulp. Lym explained she had been following them from the moment they had left Stormgast and she had hoped to surprise them in Burnistoun. Rheinar appeared a little unsettled by how his sister knew where they were headed but dismissed it and asked how Tyris was doing.

"He's okay," Lymris said mid stride. "He misses Emrys but he's absolutely besotted with Elette. I hope if anything they get to have a happy life together."

Emrys had been keeping Elette's secret but in light of recent events he thought the people closest to him could be trusted with it.

"Elette's a mage, Lym," Emrys said and noticed how both companions stared at him in disbelief.

"You mean to say," Lymris frowned, "the daughter of Emperor Harold Valryis, the Mage Slayer, is in fact a mage?"

Emrys nodded as Lymris and Rheinar laughed. "What?" he stated. "It's not funny!"

"It's pretty ironic," Rheinar chuckled and elbowed Lymris who was breathless with laughter.

"I wouldn't worry about her," Lymris said wiping a tear from her eye. "If she's a mage she'll have the finest tutor in Mikhael."

His sister spoke well. Mikhael was a calming influence and could be exactly what the new Princess of Galbraith needed. Emrys envied her, in fact. Whereas he would be forced to travel to a different continent, she would be instructed by the Galbraith's closest family friend.

"So what of your powers, Emrys?" Lymris asked. "What makes you so different to other mages?"

"I don't know," Emrys shrugged. "I feel strange most of the time. Like something is calling to me. Before it was the Great Oak but even now, I can feel a voice whisper. Primal. It's saying it over and over again. It's doing my head in."

"Have you tried speaking back?" his sister puzzled.

"No, I'm too afraid to," Emrys said embarrassed. "I don't want to lose control and hurt someone."

"You never lost control," Rheinar chipped in, "I saw the whole thing. The power you have is frightening but you saved me and yourself with a flick of the wrist. You also taught that bastard Arcadian a good lesson at the same time."

Emrys could not feel the same way Rheinar and Lymris felt about Edmure. He pitied him more than anything and felt sorrow that he had brought further sadness to the emperor's son. Elette had explained very little about how the pair of them had been brought up in Arcadia. Their father, Harold, was known for being a stern ruler yet from what Emrys saw he had a strained relationship with Edmure. Neither seemed to listen to the other and he remembered when Emperor Valyris publicly humiliated his son moments before the wedding.

As night fell on the party, they set up camp faster than the previous night with the added help of Lymris. They camped this time beneath a huge cliff that rose from the road and provided them shelter from the elements should they appear. It was Emrys' turn to cook and he set about with a few chicken legs and vegetable leaves Lym revealed from her stash. Not long after their meal, the exiled prince received his instructions from Rheinar. He would take the first shift of guarding the party before waking Lymris, who in turn would wake Rheinar. As the suns finally set, Emrys began pacing the camp. His sister and Master-At-Arm were soundly asleep at this point and as the cool winds whistled past, he could hear the faint snoring from his mentor. Thunder rumbled in the distance and Emrys felt excited about the night's entertainment.

He was not disappointed. The lightning and thunder tonight were majestic, so much so that for a moment Emrys felt he was back at Caspian's Rock with his family. He loved going to the rock with his siblings, mother and father. It was the best thing about the summer ending and the start of their stormy season. Once when he was small, Lymris was petrified of the storm which raged around them and bawled with tears as the booms of thunder roared around them. Whereas his mother Althea liked to tell them to story of the gods, his father told a very young Lymris a different story. He had said that there is nothing to fear. That the thunder and lightning are merely dancing through the sky for our entertainment. Lymris had never cried about a storm again, Emrys noted. His mother may have been quick with words to his heart but his father clearly had the same effect for his sister.

Emrys shook his sister's shoulder as the moon reached the middle of the sky. She woke unhappily but duly rose to her feet and let out a huge stretch before sitting down where he had. He took the bedroll, let out a huge sigh, and within moments fell into a deep sleep.

***

PRIMAL. Emrys heard in his dreams. The voice was different and louder than the usual one pestering him in his consciousness. From the darkness of his imagination appeared a grassy plain, the likes of which he had never seen. A lone figure dropped down from the sky planting its feet into the ground and in an instant Emrys froze with fear. Caulder stood there, its yellow eyes glaring back at him. The robed figure cackled deafeningly as it walked around, circling Emrys.

"Primal," it hissed. "It is good to see you."

Emrys froze with fear. As he looked on at The Bringer of Storms, he had never seen anything so vile and repulsive. Forgetting the rotting flesh which stung his eyes with its stench, Caulder seemed to have a necrotic touch. With each step the being took, the ground beneath it perished in a flash replaced by black scorch marks and maggots. Emrys reached for his sword but there was nothing there. No bow was tied behind his back and he knew then he was defenceless.

"What are you?" Emrys asked slowly backing away.

"I was once like you," it said matching his pace. "Until I left this pitiful world and discovered a new plane of existence. I came back years ago to bring my new paradise and share it with the peoples of this world."

"What paradise do you speak of?" Emrys shouted frightened. "You're killing everything you touch!"

Caulder laughed again as worms spat out of its mouth. "There is more beauty in death than there is life Primal," it said mockingly. "Your kind and mine are complete opposites in our approach. But you are just a scared little boy I see. Killing you will be fun and I look forward to it."

"You are a monster," Emrys said his courage faltering. His hands were trembling now and each step seemed to sap him of energy.

"Yet to me, you are the monster," it replied. "Can't you see that what I bring with me is beautiful?"

Caulder raised both its arms as its Corruption spread over the grassy plains. From the dead grass ethereal beings rose that Emrys believed were only in children's stories. Wraiths, hooded figures of the dead circled the pair of them, their numbers beyond counting. Through the veils of their hoods appeared red eyes. Ghastly moans echoed in Emrys' ears as he cupped them to stifle the pain.

"These wraiths came with me back to this world," Caulder said. "They are my vessels of hope. Life is a misery, but death is a comfort I can give each person. We shall go from world to world, starting with yours, Primal."

Emrys screamed as his ears began bleeding profusely. He stumbled forward and fell to his knees, his hands sinking into the earth.

"I will start with your homeland, shall I?" It began to boast, "Galbraith. A Kingdom of fools. Their only wise move was that they never sought to challenge me. I will scorch the lands with my Corruption and make an abomination of the World Tree. The last time I was here I raided Arcadia in the same manner. Those filthy people with their technology were no match for me..."

"But the Circle was!" Emrys screamed, bringing a still silence as the Wraiths stopped floating to observe the scene. Even Caulder too had stopped mid-sentence as he looked down on a defiant Emrys. Emrys felt a surge of power restore his confidence. "I may not know everything. Anything about what is going on with me," he said rising to his feet. "But one thing I do know, I will do everything I can to stop you!"

"Brave words, Primal," it laughed in response. Caulder pulled the same dagger Emrys saw in his first vision. "I made you a promise." Caulder walked forward. "And it is a promise I mean to keep. I will find you, and I will kill you with this knife. Rest well, Primal. For soon I will carve this world with your blood."

"EMRYS WAKE UP!" Lymris screamed stirring him from his nightmare. "YOU'LL BRING THE CLIFF DOWN ON US!"

The ground was shaking as if an earthquake had hit, and Emrys could see Rheinar holding a shield above him and his sister. Boulders crashed down all around them, smothering the fire and Emrys could hear as the horses bolted from their slumber. As for him, his eyes were aglow once more, burning a green reflection against the tower shield that illuminated the ground beneath him. "Emrys!" Rheinar shouted as several large rocks hit him and the shield. "Take control! You must calm down!"

Focusing his mind, he tried to calm his emotions. Seeing Caulder had sent him racing into a panic and he struggled to hold his rage and fear from consuming him whole. His sister let out a shriek of pain as a chain of rocks crashed against her shoulder and Emrys could see a fresh trail of claret flowing from her neck. "Emrys, think of Mum," she cried. "She wouldn't want to see you like this."

He did as his sister asked and found a speck of serenity to hold onto. He could see his mother's face, a kind face that always made him feel at ease. Slowly he could feel the tremors in the earth begin to subside as he floated back down onto the bedroll. Rheinar ditched the shield and ripped a piece of cloth off his trousers to stem his sister's injury.

"Emrys, what happened?" she asked tearfully.

Chapter Nine
Burnistoun

THE GROUP'S journey south across Galbraith passed by largely uneventfully for the next fortnight following Emrys' loss of control. His sister's injuries had healed well and she could now fire a bow and swing a sword without any issues. Emrys had struggled to explain the bond between him and Caulder to Lymris and Rheinar, and still had no answer to why it plagued his every move. Rheinar in particular seemed rather concerned about Emrys, who whilst unconscious, had nearly buried the three of them under the cliff. He had sustained injuries himself but whenever Emrys or Lymris offered to look at them, he dismissed their concerns and carried on. Rheinar had also made sure that they camped on open plains to avoid seeing a similar situation occur. Emrys was able to use his newfound abilities to call the horses back to them after they had bolted on the night of the incident. Shrieker and Styria seemed particularly cautious when they were around Emrys, and he could always feel their eyes upon them as he brought them food in camp. The group had seen fewer and fewer travellers on the Aurelian Road as they galloped South. Wandering merchants were few and far between and for the first time in his life, Emrys could see the full extent of damage for people living in the Storm Lands. Whole villages to the West had been wiped out completely, either by stray waves or floods that had washed towns down to the shore. Lymris and

Emrys had wanted to explore further into their father's lands but Rheinar had forbidden it. They needed to get out of Galbraith he had reminded them, and before long they cast their eyes upon the new sight of Burnistoun as it rose beyond the horizon.

"Emrys, Lym," Rheinar said once they had all clapped eyes on the distant city. "We will need to be careful in this city. You cannot use your names. Many people of poor and rich backgrounds could seek to ransom a prince or princess. Emrys, we'll call you... Bertred."

"Bertred?" Emrys exclaimed as Lymris giggled to his side.

"It's a common enough name," Rheinar said grinning. "Shouldn't raise any suspicions. Lymris we'll call you..."

"Can I use my mother's name?" Lymris interrupted as Rheinar and Emrys looked at each other.

"Very well," their mentor nodded. "Now let us make haste, we'll need to stay a night or two until I've spoken to an old friend."

"Who is this friend?" Emrys pondered as they started moving again.

"His name is Velstadt," Rheinar replied. "He used to command a fleet in your father's navy. Until captaining a group of brigands and pirates became his new normal. But I trust him and no man knows the Sea of Tears better than him."

"Why did he leave the navy?" Lymris chipped in.

"There's more money to be found in pirating than serving a King," Rheinar chuckled. "But he is a man of honour, if such a thing is possible. No more chatter. Bertred, Althea, let's go."

As the suns reached their peak heat late in the afternoon, they found themselves trotting to a stop in front of the city gates. They were less impressive that Stormgast's, Emrys and Lymris agreed, and now they stood close to the city, they could smell the faint odour of freshly gutted fish wafting through with each gust of wind. The guard at his post allowed the three into the port city without a fuss and stumbled back as the gates swung open. As they moved through the street Emrys couldn't believe how impoverished and dirty Burnistoun was. Beggars lay strewn to either side of him and almost every building was coated in a thick layer of mud and salt. The road itself was bog-like and he could feel Elmyra struggling to grip and move through it. Almost every person he clapped his eyes on was wielding some form of weapon and a great deal of mistrust was cast between the townsfolk as they went about their business. The manners he had grown accustomed to within the palace were non-existent in Burnistoun, and he heard curses thrown around like greetings. "This is an interesting place Bertred," his sister leaned in.

"Aye, you're not wrong," Emrys said baffled as a tavern door swung open near them.

A half-dressed man came bursting out as a prostitute came hurtling after him. The man slipped and fell into the road as the jilted whore began to throw punches, prompting widespread jeers and laughter to the onlooking crowd.

"Let that serve as a reminder to you both," Rheinar grinned at the stunned royals. "Always pay a whore her dues."

Rheinar continued to lead them through the crowded streets and signalled left as the road forked between the taverns and the port front. They pitched their horses at a stables, shortly after turning left, and Rheinar took them through the doors of The Trickling Trout, Velstadt's regular ale house. As the doors opened, they were greeted with the stench of stale beer and patrons sat on benches in mixed consciousness. Rheinar's stomping through the creaking shack alerted a few drunkards who clearly cowered at his sight, ducked their heads and returned to their drinks. As he approached the bar, the barmaid turned with a flagon in hand. She was a comely girl, Emrys noticed despite the dirty rags she adorned.

"What'll it be?" she asked of Rheinar.

"A room for the three of us for two nights please," Rheinar muttered. "And the whereabouts of Captain Velstadt. I'm an old friend looking for passage across the Sea of Tears."

"Haven't seen him in a while," she said scrubbing a few goblets. "He was at sea last I heard. Some of his old crew are in here though, might be best off asking them." Rheinar thanked the barmaid and ordered the three of them mutton for dinner. He pointed Emrys and Lymris in the direction of an empty table in the far corner, and when they had taken their places, he walked around the room canvassing patrons for information on Velstadt. As the two siblings sipped their water, a band of violinists began playing a few tunes as the conscious patrons clapped their hands and stomped their feet. A pretty girl appeared as if from nowhere and jumped from table to table as she sang a shanty that proved popular to the locals. Emrys saw his sister smiling happily as she tapped her fingers off the table rhythmically. "This place is nothing like Stormgast," she said before joining in with the patrons, grinning from ear to ear.

An older couple began to dance in the middle of the pub and as Emrys watched on amused, he felt a tug at his throat dragging him to his feet. The pretty singer was before him, her lips pursed and her amber eyes shining like fire in the candlelight. She took his hands and together they danced around the room as Lymris, Rheinar and the locals cheered them on. For the first time in his journey, Emrys was truly enjoying himself and found himself smiling stupidly in all of the fun. As the song came to a finish, the girl pecked him on the cheek and bowed before him, bringing a hot flush and rosy cheeks to him. He staggered back over to the table with weak knees before crashing down besides his sister. "Aye, I like Burnistoun." He blushed as his sister teased him.

Rheinar joined them at the table with a huge flagon of ale and sat opposite the two siblings. "So I've got good news and bad news, Bertred and Althea," he said taking a huge swig as the beer tricked down his chin. "Velstadt is not currently in Burnistoun but he arrives back either tomorrow or the following day."

They had learnt so little about this captain his mentor had spoken of, that Emrys felt compelled to ask: "How did you meet Velstadt?"

"We met during the war," Rheinar nodded. "Galbraith has always had control of the seas. Arcadia sought to end that dominance and failed miserably when Velstadt and the navy defeated them at the Battle of Caspian's Rock."

"Father ever only spoke briefly of that battle," Lymris said fascinated. "What happened?"

"The Arcadians attacked during the veil of night," Rheinar continued. "A surprise attack that favoured us. Velstadt fired ten ships and set them towards the approaching navy. In the midst of the chaos as the Arcadian vessels burned, he took a command of ships and sank almost all of the ships Arcadia had dared send. Very few Galbraithian lives were lost that day thanks to the cunning of Velstadt."

"You said, he owes you a favour? What is it?" Emrys

asked eagerly.

"I saved his life during that battle," Rheinar replied taking huge gulps of ale. "His ship was at the front of the charge and I was placed on it at your father's command. As our ship was crashing into one of theirs, we were boarded by a group of Arcadian Knights, just like the ones at the wedding. One of the knights launched himself at Velstadt and I... interrupted him. How else do you think I got this scar?"

Rheinar pointed at a long slice which ran the length of his arm. "Now since we've only just arrived," he continued, "why don't I show you around the city?"

The two siblings nodded and finished their waters as they rose to their feet. The pretty girl blew Emrys a kiss and smiled, causing him to blush uncontrollably and stumble into another table. Embarrassed, he did not turn to see if she had seen it and sheepishly left the premises after Lymris and Rheinar. The three headed West towards the docks down the littered streets and fresh gusts brought the smell of the sea to Emrys' nostrils. It was now late in the afternoon and the suns had begun to dip, both in heat and light, casting shadows of cold throughout Burnistoun. The docks themselves were huge oaken platforms raised higher than the ground to sustain big waves, Rheinar had told them. He had also explained that the fishmongers in Burnistoun were acclaimed for providing the freshest of fish and that they would have to try the local delicacy, the Skarpa Trout, before they embarked on the Sea of Tears. More than ten ships were docked and sailors frantically paced the docklands gathering their essentials before the next tide rose. The path from the docks led them further into Burnistoun and before long they were at what Emrys assumed was the city centre.

A huge marble arch rose above them and a once pretty garden, now covered in mud and unmentionables, lay before them. In the centre of the gardens was a chiselled statue of his father, King Terrys. The likeness of it was quite remarkable and Emrys took a moment to appreciate the woodworking skills of his countrymen. As he stepped closer, he could see the resemblance as if his own father were before his eyes. His locks were perfect, the beard immaculate and they had even made the Crown of Thorns to match his proud stance. His admiration was quickly interrupted by the thundering clap of boots underfoot as people flocked towards the square. Citizens began pouring out of every crack and crevice around them. They encircled the square and Rheinar hastily urged the two siblings to back out of the way of the impending stampede. Men carrying torches appeared leading the charge and almost bundled Emrys over as they marched past, unaware of his existence. As the dust settled and the trio were at a safe distance they looked on as a few peasants brought forth a box. A man from the crowd stepped forward to huge cheers and applause before standing on the box to address the people. He was well dressed, sporting a sapphire cloak, a rich cotton tunic and a feather hat to boot.

"My friends!" he shouted raising both arms. "I'm glad you have come today. For I have news from the capital."

He pulled a scroll from his pockets and cleared his throat before saying, "Following the wedding of Prince Tyris of Galbraith and Empress Elette of Arcadia, I regret to inform you of a traitor to the Kingdom of Galbraith. Our very own Prince Emrys sought to assassinate the emperor's son, Edmure, in a twisted act to reignite a war which has plagued this land for so many years. What's more, this *Prince* is a mage! Defiling the very Great Oak of Stormgast, he brutalised the peaceful Edmure in defiance of the wedding! Fear not my friends, The *Mage Prince* Emrys has been exiled from the lands under pain of death!"

A huge roar from the crowd sent panic running through Emrys, and he hastily pulled his hood up obscuring his sweating face. The crowd were silenced once more as the well-dressed man began to speak again. "Let us ask ourselves a question my friends," he said. "Did we choose the Galbraith family to lord over us? Did we enslave ourselves to their whims of our volition? Did we choose to live in poverty while they live in glamour and riches beyond our imagination?"

'No' rang out all around them and as Emrys looked at Rheinar he noticed he had stopped watching the speaker and was now keeping a ready eye on those in the crowd.

"We have a lot to learn from the Arcadians," he continued. "They may be our enemies of old, but they used to have a King. It's true. They had a bastard of King who abused his subjects and allowed mages into their lands! Mages who brought about the very abomination of Caulder! When the people could take no more, they rose up! They overthrew the monarchy and chose an Emperor for themselves! Emperor Harold Valyris rose to serve the people, for the people! And now, we have our *Mage Prince* who attempts to take the life of the son of the man whom Arcadia chose to lead? Ask yourselves who's the real enemy in this?"

"THE GALBRAITHS!" The crowd boomed back several times as Emrys and Lymris nervously shuffled behind Rheinar. Even Rheinar looked gobsmacked as he looked on at the scene unfolding before him.

"The time is coming my friends!" the man said. "A time

where we must choose where our loyalties lie. Is it with the Galbraiths? Or is it with the Valyrises?"

"VALYRIS!" chanted the crowd once more.

"Down with the Galbraiths!" The man cried and motioned orders, "And down with the mages!"

The men with torches at the front moved forward and set his father's statue ablaze to the roar of many. The flames caught the statue easily, and his father's well-sculpted features began to blacken as the Crown of Thorns fell from his head. Emrys felt a tug at his arm as Rheinar gripped him tightly and began to move from the square.

"The two of you, back to the Trickling Trout," he said urgently. "Go."

"Where are you going?" Lymris asked panicked.

"I need to find a bird and warn your father," he replied once out of earshot. "Before he has a civil war on his hands."

Chapter Ten
Captain Velstadt

EMRYS barely slept a wink that night as he tossed and turned, fearful of what he had just witnessed. The mob had scared him and to see them burn his father's statue was a crime he could not forgive them for. They called him *The Mage Prince*. Emrys couldn't shake the name from his head and wondered if all Galbraithians thought he had tried to assassinate Edmure. It was a shuddering thought and one that sent chills up his spine. The way they had spoken about his family was even more upsetting. His father had made tough decisions in Galbraith but he was not a cruel man, and he was certainly not intent on bringing further suffering to his people. The man leading the mob clearly had it in for the Galbraith family, but Emrys could not help ponder if the man in question was perhaps a spy paid for by Arcadia. Rheinar had spoken very little when he returned a short while after sending Emrys and Lymris back to The Trickling Trout. He was clearly agitated, and neither he or his sister wished to rile him with further questions. Instead, they made a compromise that in the morning they would try Burnistoun's delicacy as Rheinar suggested earlier in the day.

As morning rose, Emrys rubbed the sleep from his eyes and groggily dressed himself before heading downstairs. The pub was vacant, save for the barmaid who set about cleaning and setting up the tables. When Emrys stepped on the ground floor, which creaked violently, she turned to greet him with a smile and said: "Did you sleep well?"

"Yes, I did, thank you," Emrys politely responded, lying to himself and to her. "Is there any food for breakfast?"

"Certainly," she replied jumping over the bar, "Take a seat and I'll bring some bread and cheese through."

Emrys splashed his face in the water by the bar. He looked tired, that much was for sure. Large bags appeared beneath his blue eyes and his brown fuzzy hair was in dire need of a good clean. His fringe now nestled just above his eyes and he wondered if he had time to visit a barber while they were here. Lymris skipped down the stairs before long and the two sat patiently as the barmaid returned with their morning food. Rheinar was the last to rise and he grumpily stomped over and munched his food down in silence.

A few minutes later, after much persuasion on Emrys and Lymris' part, Rheinar agreed they would go out and try the Skarpa Trout for lunch. He expressed his hesitance to staying in Burnistoun any longer than needed and disappeared after breakfast to assess the threats in the city.

"I hate seeing Rheinar like this," Lymris sighed. "Do you think that mob really hate the Galbraiths?"

Before Emrys could respond, the barmaid leaned in, "That mob are riled by anything, I would pay no notice."

"But they burned the King's statue," Emrys protested, trying not to seem too interested. "They'll hang if he finds out."

The barmaid shrugged, "Maybe, maybe not. By the sounds of it, the King has far more pressing matters than an angry group burning his statue. Can you imagine, your son a mage and a traitor? I wouldn't know what to do if that was my boy. I never asked, what are you three doing here in

Burnistoun? Can tell from your accent you're not from these parts."

Emrys started to panic and flashed his eyes at Lymris for support. His sister looked calm and collected as she spoke, "We're from Eddington. My name is Althea and this is my older brother Bertred. Our parents were killed by the fever, so we're being escorted to family in Carpathia."

The barmaid seemed to believe it and rested a hand of affection on Lymris' shoulder. "I'm so sorry for your loss," she said. "My mother passed the same way recently, so I understand what you're going through."

Lymris embarrassedly embraced her hand with her own and the two shared a kind smile in grief. Rheinar returned roughly half an hour later just as some of the locals began entering for their daily drinks. The two siblings wolfed down the remains of their breakfast and joined him as they walked out into the morning suns. Light pierced Emrys' vision and for a moment he saw beauty in Burnistoun's surroundings. The way the sun hit the roofs around him made it seem like the city was aglow with an amber hue. It lasted all of ten seconds until reality sunk in and he saw the Burnistoun he was accustomed to. The three travellers moved down to the docks and took their caution in making their way there. Last night's events had clearly troubled them and they were all keen not to draw attention to themselves. As they approached the docks a fresh breeze of sea air greeted them along with several ships coming in with the tide. Sailors were issuing orders between each other and huge loads of fish and good were being dumped all around them.

"Shall we try the Skarpa Trout?" Lymris asked of Rheinar.

"Why not," he grumbled with the briefest of smiles.

Rheinar asked them to take a seat on a nearby bench and he moved away to locate a trader. Several minutes later he came back with three plates of the local delicacy. Its presentation was not of the highest standard, but from the moment the fish touched Emrys' tongue he understood what Rheinar had meant. The fish melted like butter and brought an exotic blend of spices to the roof of his mouth. Despite being from the sea it was not salty, and Emrys lapped up every slither of meat like it was his first meal in a month. "This is incredible," he blurted out as Lymris nodded in tacit agreement. "They need to take this to Stormgast."

"The fish doesn't travel well," Rheinar replied as he wolfed his down. "Three days on the road and this meal is ruined. But you're right, Stormgast could learn a thing or two from Burnistoun with this meal. Hang on…"

His mentor rose to his feet at the arrival of a large ship with red sails. The ship, which dwarfed every other ship there, came into dock in front of them and sailors all around them joined together to pull the ship in. As it was pulled in, Emrys noticed the name blazoned in gold letters on the stern, 'THE CRIMSON TEMPEST'. Ten minutes later a plank was lowered from the deck and from it emerged a group of pirates dragging a huge netting of loot onto the dock. They were laughing and joking with one another and cheered once they touched dry land. They were weather-beaten, tanned to a man and wore the same blend of blue and red outfits each. Some of them wore earrings which glimmered in the morning sun causing Emrys to squint as they moved closer. At the tail of the group stood a lone figure, caped wearing a hat of admiralty. He was dressed more ornately than the others and had crossed cutlasses embroidered onto his chest. As he moved across the plank without looking, he scanned the horizon of the docks and when he clapped eyes on Rheinar, he stopped still in his tracks.

"As I live and breathe," the stranger said. "I never thought I'd see you again old friend."

"Captain Velstadt," Rheinar replied with a grin. "It is good to see you, my friend." The two embraced in a scuffle as if they were ten-year-old children fighting over a beloved toy. Laughing they hugged and Emrys could tell from their demeanour this was the first time they had seen each other in years. Both men were sizing each other up for changes in their appearances and now that Velstadt was closer Emrys could see his features as clear as day. He was a smaller man than Rheinar but just as bulky with darker skin. He had huge dreadlocks which were emblazoned with golden trinkets and a beard which dwarfed that of Mikhael's. Despite his rugged appearance from a long voyage at sea, he walked with an air of grace and Emrys could tell he had spent his time with nobility from the way he spoke. He was blind in one eye, with one green eye glistening in the midday suns.

"So still robbing and looting the high seas, are we?" Rheinar asked.

"Of course," Velstadt replied with a smile. "Still cleaning up after the Royalty's mess are we you big bastard?"

"Sadly I am." Rheinar smiled back and outstretched an arm to the two Galbraiths, "I have two people I need to introduce…"

Velstadt moved forward and said, "I know who they are Rheinar. I may not know their names but I know their faces. The face of their father is looking right at me."

Velstadt moved close to inspect the two before surprising

them both and kneeling before them. "My Prince, Princess. It is an honour to meet you."

Suddenly Rheinar ripped Velstadt up from his focus and held his arm in a grip as he leant into him. "It's not safe," Rheinar said scanning the docks. "Things have changed and we need to talk."

Velstadt nodded in approval and smiled at the three. "Well whatever needs to be said I'm sure it'll be much sweeter with a beer in the belly," he said and turned to his men, "Right lads! Who's for a pint?"

His men and women cheered and once they had stowed their loot, joined Velstadt as they headed back for The Trickling Trout. Several people in the street stopped to pay their respects to the Admiral and Emrys couldn't believe how popular he was around Burnistoun. Velstadt seemed to limp as he walked and supported his weight occasionally on a walking cane. As the doors of The Trickling Trout burst open, an empty mug came hurtling over Emrys' head and knocked the hat from Velstadt. From the gloom emerged the barmaid, with her arms crossed and a face like thunder. "Three months!" she spat. "You bastard! You promised me you'd only be gone one, or two at the very most!"

"Helga," Velstadt replied as he repositioned his hat. "You know how it is at sea, lass. Besides wait until you see what I've brought home." From his pocket he pulled a ruby the size of a fist and offered it to Helga. She relaxed her arms and stared straight at the crimson gem. She snapped out of her awe and huffed as she motioned for the brigands to enter. A couple of them chuckled when they saw Velstadt lean in for a kiss only to be met by Helga's hand slapping him across the face. When the brigands entered, all of the locals quickly downed their drinks and hastily made their way out. Velstadt pulled up a chair and issued orders for his crew to give Rheinar, Emrys and Lymris their peace.

"So now we can speak freely," he said stroking his beard. "I already know them, but I'd like to hear from you both. What are your names?"

"My name is Lymris," his sister replied. "And this is my older brother Emrys. How did you know we were our father's children?"

Velstadt pointed at Emrys and Lymris as he took his hat off. "Easy," he said. "Spent enough time around Tyris to notice his features. You both share a lot of looks with your old man. Speaking of the King, how is he? How'd the wedding go?"

Rheinar shifted uncomfortably and the smile that had once graced his face disappeared in a flash. He filled Velstadt in on the situation starting with the wedding itself, the attack on Edmure, the mention of Primal and the journey so far. At the end of the tale, Velstadt's lone eye ogled Emrys with curiosity and Emrys feared how he would react. Earlier that morning he had seen how Helga had reacted and spoke of him as a traitor.

"So you're this Primal then?" Velstadt asked sipping his pint.

"I guess so," Emrys shrugged. "Truth to be told I don't really know a lot of what is happening to me. It feels like I'm torn. Half of me is the prince I always was and the other half is this being which frightens me. I can feel a voice inside my head that is not my own and it scares me beyond anything."

"You've been dealt a shit hand, lad." Velstadt clasped his shoulder, "But look on the bright side. You've got the best warrior in the land and your wee sister by your side through this."

Rheinar and Lymris both smiled at him briefly before Lymris asked, "So what is life at sea like?"

"Tough, hard work for all of my laddies and lasses," the captain nodded. "But honestly, when you're out in a blue horizon, as the waves come crashing around you, and the morning suns greet you with their smile, you've never felt so alive."

"Velstadt," Rheinar spoke. "We need your help. I must get the boy to Carpathia and then meet with the Circle. We both know the sea can only take us as far as Daal. Please assist us."

The captain downed his pint and signalled Helga for another. He tapped his hands on the table and looked up at Emrys. He held the stare in silence for a few moments, his concentration broken only when Helga arrived with a fresh pint.

"Aye," he said as Helga moved back to the bar. "I served your father for many years and fought alongside him. He's a good man, a good ruler and he respected my decision to move south, freeing me from my oath. Rheinar, you're one of my oldest friends and you saved my life at Caspian's Rock. I wouldn't be here without you, and Helga would be complaining to some other pirate. I promise I will take you to Daal so you can understand what this Primal business is about. We will cast off with the next tide in two days so chin up lad, exiled or not, you are still my prince. Be certain that my crew will serve and die for you if needs be."

"Thank you, my friend," Rheinar said clasping the captain's hand and squeezing firmly.

Emrys and Lymris both thanked the captain who held his hand over his heart and bowed his head to the young Galbraiths.

"There is one condition," Velstadt grinned revealing a gold tooth.

"What do you need?" Rheinar asked. "I have money if that's what you're after?"

"No, I've got money, I need a favour," he laughed heartily. "You'll have to tell Helga. That woman's got a right temper on her and if I tell her she'll probably take my other eye."

Chapter Eleven
The Sea of Tears

"RAISE the sails and anchor!" Captain Velstadt barked to his crew as Emrys slithered onto The Crimson Tempest.

All around Emrys hungover pirates darted around the deck, adjusting and fastening ropes as if a whip was at their very heels. It impressed Emrys to see how they carried themselves. Each man and woman were direct and precise as they went about their tasks, and there was a unity about their collective that he had to admire. The morning weather was fair and there was a strong Eastern wind that blew into the sails. As The Crimson Tempest edged away from the docks, Emrys looked back and saw Helga stood alone in tears as she worried for her husband. What Velstadt had said came to pass when Rheinar broke the news to her days before. She had flown into a rage and Emrys feared what she would have done to the old captain had Rheinar not stood between the two.

"How dare you?" she screamed as the pub silenced and pirates turned their backs in silent embarrassment. "First time I see you in months and you're heading back out again?"

"My love," Velstadt said weakly. "I must do this. Rheinar saved my life and I owe him this. One simple trip to Daal and I will return I promise."

The words had done nothing to lessen her anger and as they ate that night, she slammed their food on the table, plate by plate. A sharp look that Velstadt and Rheinar shot between themselves highlighted the trouble the captain was in.

Back on The Crimson Tempest, Lymris was climbing the riggings and testing her balance against the gusts of wind. She seemed to be having a whale of a time and beckoned Emrys to join her as she raced up to the weather deck. Emrys was not so graceful and sparked some laughter from the pirates below as he nervously edged upwards. As he reached the weather deck Lymris extended an arm which he gratefully took and she helped pull him up. Standing with the wind in their face, the two siblings looked on at the blue horizon. Save Burnistoun behind them, all they could see was the vast ocean called the Sea of Tears. It was a beautiful sight. As the sun touched the waves, the sea glimmered in its light and it looked as if it was a sea of gold from side to side. "Why do they call this ocean the Sea of Tears?" Lymris shouted over the wind. Emrys shrugged. He did not know. The two made a pact that they would question Velstadt on it later that day. For the time being, the siblings enjoyed their view and waved goodbye to Burnistoun as it slowly crept from their sight. Half an hour later a sprightly pirate climbed the rigging at remarkable speed and joined them on the weather deck in no time at all.

"You two, get down on deck," he said. "The captain wants a word."

As Emrys and Lymris reached the deck after an arduous climb, Velstadt stood before them grinning. He was back in his finest uniform and stood to attention as if he was still commanding his father's naval fleet. Rheinar was sat nearby watching as he took audible bites from an apple.

"Prince, Princess," Velstadt said stepping forward. "How do you like The Crimson Tempest?"

Emrys had been so preoccupied with the vast sea he had

barely taken any time to observe his surroundings. The ship had lived up to its name. Red sails and scarlet-soaked oak made up the deck. Gold and black lines shot across it and lined the stairs to the helm. The wheel, whereupon the first mate stood, was one of gold and carved runes ran along its circumference. "It's marvellous," Emrys said. "Captain Velstadt…"

"Please, my Prince," Velstadt interrupted. "Just Velstadt."

"Velstadt," Emrys nodded and continued. "Lymris and I were wondering. Why do they call this ocean the Sea of Tears?"

"It's a very old story and a tragic one at that," Velstadt sat and beckoned for the siblings to do the same. "Years before Galbraith was formed, or indeed before any of the Kingdoms were born, a tragedy befell the world around us. Without warning a huge whirlpool formed itself off the coast of Daal. Years later we would know this as the first Tear. It swallowed every ship, fishing boat and creature within thirty nautical miles. Whole families, nobles, peasants, it made no difference. They disappeared into the Tear and it was as if they had never existed. Even the coastline was sucked in, and inch by inch Daal crept towards the Tear."

"That's awful," Lymris shook her head. "How was this stopped?"

"They say a mage sailed out alone and sealed the Tear at the cost of their own life," Velstadt said. "Others say it sealed itself. Each account differs to who's telling the story."

"What do you believe happened?" Emrys asked.

"Personally," Velstadt pondered for a moment, "I'm inclined to believe a mage sealed the Tear. As you've probably guessed from the name of this sea, there is more than one Tear.

Some have been taken care of, others we need to avoid entirely. It's a good thing you've got a captain such as myself to navigate these treacherous waters. But I do believe magic is the key to stopping the Tears. I've seen mages do some remarkable things over the years. Hell's teeth, that Mikhael has a trick or two on him."

"Velstadt," Emrys asked again. "Why are mages treated so badly across the lands? I hear about these great things they've done and yet they are treated like scum."

"It's not an easy thing to answer," the captain nodded. "I've travelled the world and there are few others than the Carpathians who are true to mages. Honestly? I believe people are scared of mages. Take Arcadia. Do you believe all of the people there hate magic and mages?"

"Surely not," Lymris replied.

"Aye, you're spot on," Velstadt continued. "How could they? Most of the citizens will never see a mage in their lifetime. The difference is Emperor Valyris, the ruler of Arcadia, detests magic. He organises rallies, lynch mobs and has inquisitors who preach his word on the streets. The truth is that mages saved Arcadia, and yet Arcadians believe the lie that mages caused all of their problems. But you cannot blame them for it. If you hear a lie for a long enough time, eventually you'll take it as the truth."

"We saw a disturbing scene in Burnistoun," Emrys reflected. "A mob burned down my father's statue and accused me of trying to assassinate the emperor's son. I would never…"

"I know lad," Velstadt said calmly and spoke with logic. "But you've been marked as a traitor and you will have to accept that no-one is going to take your word at face value.

Not in Galbraith at least." Emrys allowed the words to sink in. He would never be accepted in his homeland. For the rest of his days people would believe the lie that he had tried to kill Edmure. Only those close to him knew the truth but he felt anger when he thought of his father. His father had thrown him to the wolves and a deep burning of resentment ate away at his soul. He wanted to be at home with his family, not sailing further and further into the unknown.

For the next few weeks Velstadt instructed Emrys and Lymris as he would his crew and barked commands as they scurried about their tasks. He had not spoken in jest. Life on The Crimson Tempest was tough work, and each morning their rope beaten hands were always fresh with blisters. Lymris had taken the time to get to know the crew. There was a woman, Capilla, with whom she built an instant rapport and the two could often be heard joking when the time allowed for it. As for Emrys, he had grown close to two pirates, Balion and Baster, two brothers who always seemed in high spirits despite the bleak outlook of the day. A few of the other members, Dwayne, Keilley and Sidley were quieter than the rest. They spent most of their time together but in mutual silence as they harkened to Captain Velstadt's orders. It had been smooth sailing for the first week, but by the time the second week had arrived, the waves swelled larger and larger and the skies had blackened as the rains ensued. It was at this time that Emrys and Lymris got their first taste of sea sickness. As the ship was battered by the crashing waves, and rocked from side to side, the two siblings failed to keep their breakfasts from re-appearing. This took several days to subside and the crew had cheered once they had become acclimatised to the open sea, and their buckets were no longer filled with sick. Sleep had become difficult, and throughout the night Rheinar would have to wake the royals in their cabin to help out with tasks in the dead of night. As for their skin, the salt water and long exposure to the sun left it cracked and they were tanned more within those three weeks than they had been in their entire lives.

Yet despite how weary Emrys and his sister were, they thoroughly enjoyed being part of Velstadt's crew. Their nights were filled with songs and at the times they were required to man the oars, they did so in unison and felt part of a group larger than themselves. Captain Velstadt always looked in his element. As he stood proudly by the helm, he would always know the right words to say to his crew. If they were upset, he would speak to them in jest; if they were tired, he would let them rest; and if they were bored, he would hold fights among the deck to keep them battle-ready. Not that they needed to be over those weeks Emrys had noted. They had failed to see another ship save a few fishing boats on the horizon. Velstadt boasted often that The Crimson Tempest was one of the fastest ships to grace The Sea of Tears and that he longed for another vessel to chase them. He claimed he would simply wave as they passed them by and then ambush them further down the sea. As for Rheinar, he spent much of his time calming the horses. On one rare occasion that he came onto the deck, the crew begged for him and the captain to spar. Spurred on by Emrys and Lymris, the Master-At-Arms duly obliged, and a great melee ensued. Velstadt was clearly a gifted swordsman, but there was no finer warrior than Rheinar. Velstadt spent the entire fight on the backfoot, and while he had put up a valiant display, it was their mentor who came up trumps convincingly. Groans around Emrys signalled the crew had clearly wagered quite a bit of money on their captain, who grinned and pocketed his share.

On a cool night in their fourth week of voyage, while Emrys was trying to catch what little sleep he could, he felt a sharp tug at his shoulder.

"Emrys," a voice in the darkness said. "Get up, you'll want to see this."

A lone candle illuminated the face enough to see it was the captain staring down at him with his lone eye twinkling as the flame flickered. Emrys stretched out the pain of his bones and rose gingerly to his feet. He rubbed his hands together over the callous that had now formed and grabbed his cloak to hide him from the cold winds that awaited him. Yet he was mistaken, for tonight the sea was calm. The moon shone down its cool light and there was no breeze to speak of. Velstadt led him to the bow of the ship where Lymris and Rheinar stood groggily and rested his hands on the side. "Look down there," he said and pointed.

As Emrys looked on to the depth of the sea he could nothing of mention. Then he saw it. A huge beast probably fifty times the size of The Crimson Tempest slithered beneath them. It's width alone would swallow the ship whole ten times over and Emrys could fail to see how long the beast truly was. It was scaled and as the moonlight touched it, for a second it became luminous, lighting up the sea around it. He could see huge scars running along the beast's body and there were so many harpoons stuck in its tail Emrys lost count. The long slender serpent moved quickly and without so much as a ripple on the water above.

"My word," Emrys said, staggered. "What is this beast?"

"We call it the Serpent of the Sea," Velstadt replied. "But

this ancient beast goes by another name, Leviathan."

"It's enormous," Lymris said bewilderedly.

"It is the ancient guardian of the seas," the captain continued. "You should feel honoured. It is very rare for travellers to clasp eyes on Leviathan."

"How old is Leviathan?" Emrys asked.

"No-one knows," Velstadt shrugged. "Legend has it Leviathan was here when time began. Using his huge claws, he carved the seas from the earth and brought life to the land beneath. A few weeks ago, we spoke about the mage who closed the Tear didn't we? In that account it was Leviathan whom the mage rode and even now sailors pay homage to the Serpent of the Sea. They believe he is the one who closes the Tears. Sometimes fools looking to make a name for themselves try to hunt Leviathan. It probably goes without saying, they are never successful."

Emrys thought on the huge serpent before them. He closed his eyes and felt a strange sensation wash over him. He was no longer on the ship, stood beside his sister, Rheinar and Captain Velstadt. He was moving fast through the water, slithering from side to side, hurtling at a speed that seemed impossible. Then he saw it and stopped. Above him a lone ship sailed slowly through the dark of night. He felt a power he had not felt in a long time, dropped further into the darkness of the midnight sea and vanished.

"That's odd," Velstadt commented snapping Emrys back. "He's gone."

As Emrys looked on, the captain was right. There was no sign of the huge serpent in the water beneath them. It was at that point they could hear the horses whinnying, a sound echoing through them all. The smooth voyage turned into a nightmare with huge waves rising and sloshing around them. Velstadt stumbled towards the main mast and slammed the bell, screaming orders to his sleeping crew. The very floor of the deck groaned and as the ship rocked from side to side. As the crew emerged and scrambled to keep them buoyant, they all stared up in horror. Leviathan, the Serpent of the Sea, emerged spraying a wave of water across the deck that knocked each person to the floor. As Emrys rose and pulled his sister to her feet, he watched as the crew looked on the monstrous serpent helplessly. None had run to their weapons while a few had dropped to their knees and began praying to their gods. Leviathan came to a stop and towered above the Crimson Tempest. With a sharp intake of breath, it bellowed sending ripples across the water. As the crew backed away, Emrys felt strong. He had spent most of his journey in fear, but today he would not allow fear into his heart. The Mage Prince stepped forward, as the serpent's green eyes glared back at him.

Chapter Twelve
Makta

"EMRYS! What are you doing?" Rheinar shouted and sprinted forward to hold him back. "Let me go, Rheinar," Emrys replied and brushed his hand off. "I must try this."

Leviathan growled, sending vibrations through his body as Emrys moved closer. Beads of sweat ran down the young prince as he edged closer and closer. Now the monstrous serpent was clear of the water, Emrys could see that its scales were purple and its teeth were as large as houses. Mustering what concentration he could, Emrys called out for help once more. He begged with everything and everyone he could think of. *Please calm Leviathan, we mean him no harm.* Nothing happened. Exasperated Emrys tried again. *I am the Primal, please calm Leviathan.* Nothing happened for a second time. The third time of asking Emrys approached with a different tact. He stared long and hard into the eyes of Serpent of the Sea. He could feel its gaze upon him. Emrys did not feel fear. He felt as if the Serpent was familiar to him, an acquaintance from an age past. Leviathan's teeth disappeared from view as it looked on at Emrys. It was a look of peculiarity, as if the Serpent were sizing up the young prince for his worth. As Emrys met the stare, he called out again. Not to the Gods, not to Mikhael or anyone else. This time he would call out to Leviathan himself. *Leviathan, I am the Primal. We mean you no harm.*

Primal. Emrys heard back. *It has been a long time since I have spoken with a Primal. Your magic is old. Almost as old as I am. And there I had thought the days of Primals were long since past.*

"Emrys what's going on?" his sister asked as the Serpent slithered forward.

"We are speaking from mind to mind," Emrys replied quietly. "Stay back, Lym."

What are you doing out here? Leviathan asked.

We are on our way to Carpathia, Emrys replied. *We are seeking out the Circle to learn what we can about this Primal. I am still in the dark about what is needed of me. Do you know anything useful?*

Leviathan circled the ship with frightening speed and addressed Emrys from the stern. *A Primal is the vessel of the world. They are called upon by the earth, wind and seas when the planet is threatened. You, Primal, stand as the first and last defence for whatever lies ahead. Long ago, when the great threat was the Tear, a young Primal by the name of Makta fought by my side to save this world. We succeeded but at the cost of her life. More than a thousand years have passed since then and so much has changed.*

What was the Tear? Emrys asked.

The Tear was a rip in the fabric of this world, Leviathan replied. *From it came demons of the Underdeep. Demons who devoured everything, pulling the lands into that soulless plane of existence. Even a God such as I was no match for them. Yet Makta was strong. Stronger than anything I have ever seen in my long life. She destroyed the Tear and sent the demons back to whence they came. She healed the crack in the world at the expense of her own life. Every being alive today owes her a debt that cannot be paid.*

Hearing Leviathan talk about Makta made Emrys think on his own power. Back in Stormgast he had pulled roots from the Great Oak through stone; he had almost brought a cliff down in his sleep; and he could communicate with animals and even gods like Leviathan, yet he did not believe for one second, he could accomplish such a feat as Makta. She had fought demons, impressed a god and closed the Tear to another realm of existence.

Can I trust you? Emrys thought as he saw the crew still paralysed with fear, *We mean you no harm.*

I doubt that, Leviathan replied. *Even now, with dulled senses I can feel the men and women on your ship reaching for harpoons. I will not become a trophy.* Leviathan moved forward and roared. As he did, he let out a huge wince of pain and recoiled.

"Drop your weapons!" Emrys shouted at the crew, "He means us no harm!"

What is the matter? Emrys asked.

I am old. Leviathan responded. *Too old for this world. Men and women used to revere and respect me as a God of the sea. There were temples laid with offerings and I was honoured to receive the blessings of men. But the memories of men are short, and what was once an honour turned into a nightmare. The temples were abandoned and fleets of ships came after me time and time again. I was once loved and revered by the peoples of this world. Now all they see is a bigger target for their nets. A trophy with which they want to boast of.*

Leviathan nodded down below the water at the harpoons lodged in his side. Claret leaked from the wounds and dissipated into the salt water as it rose. Emrys felt pity for the ancient Serpent. As a mage he felt and understood what it was like to be hunted. He did not know of the age Leviathan spoke of, but he would not sit by and allow this cruelty in his own.

I do not know what power runs through me, Emrys thought, *But if I can, I will help you.*

Closing his eyes, he searched the ocean with his mind. He could feel the prongs and serrated blades as if they stabbed his very own side. He cried out in pain as their minds melded and dropped to his knees. With an outstretched arm he mentally pulled at the harpoons. Further cries of pain were echoed between Emrys and Leviathan. Lymris, Rheinar and Velstadt rushed to his side speaking words that were muffled from his hearing. Slowly he tugged on the poles feeling each one as it ripped through the Serpent of the Sea. With a roar of anguish, Emrys went for one big pull and passed out.

***

"EMRYS?" a voice said above him. "Can you hear me?"

Groggily he opened his eyes and saw the chiselled face of Rheinar staring back at him. He was still on the deck as were the others, and with the helping arms of his mentor, he was brought back to his feet. Some of the crew ogled him with awe. Others looked upon him in fear at what they had witnessed. *Thank you, Primal,* he heard. Looking up he saw Leviathan staring at him, stretching as if he had not been able for countless years. Rising from the deeps of the water were harpoons. Hundreds of rusted sticks glistened in the moonlight and it dawned on Emrys the feat he had accomplished. As he staggered forward Lymris took his arm and supported him to the stern. As their minds met again, he could still feel the pain with which the Serpent of the Sea felt.

I am not finished yet. Emrys thought and immediately held his arms in the direction of the open wounds. His eyes glowed brighter and brighter matching the emerald glare of Leviathans' as he felt the pain subside. The wounds laid bare were closed by his magic and once complete he fell into Lymris' arms exhausted. The toll it had taken on was speechless. He was sapped of energy and spoke with but a whisper.

"It had to be done," he whispered to Lymris. "Too long has Leviathan felt the cruelty of man. I'm sorry to ask Lym, please can you get me something to sit on."

"Of course big brother," Lymris held him. "I trust you."

Rheinar moved him to a nearby barrel just as Emrys struggled to catch his breath. His vision was blurry and no amount of water he drank could stop the dizziness he felt swirling in his head. Velstadt, silent through this whole ordeal clasped a hand on his shoulder. "You're a crazy wee bastard, aren't you?" he said. "How did you do that?"

"I don't know," Emrys said breaking out into a cold sweat. "I just willed it."

"Well remind me not to piss you off," Velstadt chuckled and slapped him on the shoulder a few times.

Leviathan meanwhile had submerged. A few seconds later he burst from the ocean and shot up high into the sky a few hundred yards away. A screeching roar followed as the Serpent of the Sea splashed beneath and swam back to The Crimson Tempest.

I can move freely again and my senses are returning to me, Leviathan thought, *Young Primal, words do little to thank you for what you have done.*

I would do it again in a heartbeat, Emrys replied, *I felt your pain as if it was my own. I may not be Makta but I do not want to see cruelty befall you.*

You are kind Primal. That is gift enough, Leviathan thought, *What is your name?*

My name is Emrys, the former Prince of Galbraith, Emrys replied.

Well, my Emrys, Leviathan responded, *I will remember your name and your kindness. Know that whatever you may face, you will not face it alone. If you need me, call on me.*

Thank you, Serpent of the Sea, Emrys nodded with a weak smile, *I will do all I can to protect this world.*

Leviathan bowed and turned to submerge. Suddenly the Serpent stopped, turned back and with a twitch sniffed the air. *I smell deceit Emrys,* Leviathan snarled. *One person on this vessel means you harm.* The Serpent of the Sea leapt forward sending a fresh wave sweeping across the deck. He leant in on the quivering and drenched crew and stopped his snout at Caphilla. The black-haired woman who was close with Lymris was shaking like the others and bit her lip as she met the cold eyes of the Serpent of the Sea.

Are you sure? Emrys asked.

My senses do not lie, Leviathan replied. *She is an imposter, posing as a friend who makes deals with an enemy.*

"Rheinar," Emrys said weakly. "Leviathan has warned me. Caphilla has ill intentions towards me."

Without hesitation, his mentor and Velstadt unsheathed their swords and roared at the crew as several members staggered back. "Caphilla," Velstadt said. "You have been on my crew for two years and I trust your word. Do you mean to harm the prince?"

Caphilla stood there exasperated. She angled a plea to Lymris who now frowned at her and folded her arms as she stood by her brother. Flicking back her hair she said, "The reward for his capture, you should see it, Captain! Enough for us all to retire from the toils of the sea! All we have to do is deliver him to Arcadian spies either in Burnistoun or Daal and we'll be set for life!"

Emrys looked on to see the reaction of the crew. Some pondered what Caphilla had said, others backed further away, some moved to position themselves between her and him. As for Velstadt, the man stood still. He looked over his shoulder at Emrys, a lone eye twinkling in the moon. "I thought better of you Caphilla," he said as he began to pace the deck. "What is a person if they cannot keep their word? We all spoke as one when we agreed to give safe passage to Prince Emrys. An exiled Prince or not we keep our word. A crew is only as strong as its weakest member, I guess that means it's you Caphilla."

Enraged she reached for a sword, screamed in curses and ran in Velstadt's direction. The captain spun on the spot and with an outstretched arm sliced the onrushing Caphilla in two. Blood splattered across the decking as she fell where she stood. Gasping for air she looked up at the crew and let out a huge sigh before succumbing to her injuries. Velstadt grimaced. Emrys could see it had hurt him to enforce a killing blow on someone close to him. The captain reached down and took her hand in his own before sheathing his sword. "I'm sorry, Caphilla," he said kneeling, "but I cannot abide treachery in my own ranks. Forgive me, Emrys. I did not see this coming to pass."

Emrys was still struggling to form coherent thoughts but dismissed Velstadt's apology. He did not hold the captain to blame. Searching his thoughts, he spoke once more to Leviathan. *Thank you for saving me.*

Consider it a courtesy Primal, Leviathan replied. *You saved me and I will always return the favour. The journey before you is long and you will face more endeavours along the path. Know this, be true to your nature and nature will be true to you. Farewell and know that you have a friend in the seas.*

Leviathan submerged and with a flash of speed, disappeared from sight. Baster and Balion grabbed Caphilla's corpse and had thrown her overboard and set about mopping the deck. The crew, still visibly shaken from what they had witnessed, looked on at the weakly Prince. He still struggled to stand and the colour from his face had drained. "Can I get you anything?" Rheinar asked.

"A bed would be perfect," Emrys smiled weakly. "I am spent."

Rheinar carried the young Prince down the stairs and placed him in a hammock inside Velstadt's cabin. The shivers took hold of Emrys and no manner of blanket gave him comfort. He was shaking uncontrollably as Lymris and Rheinar attempted to comfort him.

"You are very brave," Lymris said holding his hand. "We all thought we were done for when the Serpent rose from the waters. What did you speak about?"

Emrys chose his words carefully before he spoke. "He spoke of another Primal, a young girl who saved the world in an age long since passed."

"What was her name?" Lymris asked.

"Makta," Emrys said. "Her name was Makta."

Chapter Thirteen
Morale

EMRYS awoke the following day and as he rose, he felt some of his strength return to him. He had spoken to Rheinar and Lymris the previous night regarding his conversation with Leviathan who expressed their awe in witnessing such a feat. He wondered how the crew would react to him. Velstadt had rushed to his defence yet they had still lost a crew member in Caphilla. Her death and betrayal had hit Lymris hard. For the past few weeks, they had been inseparable, and even as they spoke during the night, Emrys could see that the thought alone was tearing her in two. Stretching he lowered himself from the hammock and felt the bones in his ankle crack as he slowly stood. The dizziness had subsided which had been replaced with a burning hunger that knotted his stomach. Rising from the bowels of the ship he could begin to hear the stomping footsteps above as the crew set about their morning tasks. The blinding sunlight made him squint as he rose up and met a shadowy figure stood above him.

"How did you sleep, my Prince?" Velstadt asked and offered a hand to the clambering Emrys.

He duly took it and was now rubbing his eyes as they adjusted to the light. "I slept well, Captain," Emrys replied. "I never said, thank you for yesterday. I'm sorry it came to losing a crew member. I hope you and the crew can forgive me."

"You have nothing to apologise for," Velstadt shook his

head. "Without you, I doubt The Crimson Tempest would still be afloat. Caphilla's death was hard on us all, yet she betrayed you, and by extension us. I will not allow insubordination on my vessel. We made you a promise that we would get you to Daal. Besides, we are not far from it now, a couple days voyage and we will be at the Great Market City."

"What can we expect there?" Emrys asked as they walked towards the helm. Some of the crew were bowing as he passed, and others smiled at him before returning their attention to their jobs.

"Well for starters don't expect Rheinar to be in a good mood," Velstadt warned. "He's suffered a lot of pain in that city and I don't think he ever wanted to return."

As Emrys scanned the deck he could see Rheinar sat alone staring out to sea. Velstadt handed him some pieces of dried meat which he lapped up and made his way to his Master-At-Arms. As he approached Rheinar, his mentor gazed back at him and nodded before casting his eyes back to the blue horizon. "My Prince," he said. "How are you feeling?"

"I'm fine, Rheinar," Emrys replied. "Tired but I'll survive. How are you?"

Rheinar looked at him taken aback. It was at this point Emrys realised that this was the first time on their journey he had asked his mentor how he was feeling, and felt shame wash over him. Had he been so self-involved to ignore the pain around him?

Rheinar did not answer his question and rose to his feet, "I must look to the horses, they haven't been fed yet."

"Rheinar, please I..." Emrys said.

Rheinar span on the spot and raised his voice, "What do you want me to say? That I'm happy? That I cannot wait to return to Daal? With each passing day we get closer and closer to that bloody city. A place I was born and should've died a slave! I lost friends in the arena, killed friends in the arena, and do not forget I lost my wife and son due to the cruelties of one man! One man who treated it as sport."

Emrys stepped back and held his head down. He had never seen Rheinar like this. His mentor usually held his emotions in check and responded with logic and reason. Now he could see the scars of his past cutting deep. Rheinar feared Daal, that much was plain to see, but there was so much pain in his voice. Emrys felt his cheeks grow flush with embarrassment as Rheinar frowned on. His mentor took a deep breath and calmed himself once more.

"I'm sorry Emrys," he said. "I have so many bad memories of Daal I would not know where to begin. I do not want to spend a second longer in that place than is deemed necessary. Now forgive me, I must see to the horses."

Rheinar disappeared from view as Velstadt smiled sadly and nodded to Emrys. Emrys set about helping on the deck with Balion and Baster who acted differently around him since the events of the previous night. They would still joke about but he could see they were restraining themselves. Emrys wondered if they looked at him, and were scared he would react badly to something they did, but they kept themselves friendly enough to enjoy a little banter. His sister sat alone at the bow of the ship. She was carving her name into the side of The Crimson Tempest, an act Velstadt had allowed her. By the side of her name was Caphilla's, which had been crossed out along with several other names Emrys presumed were dead members of the crew. "Emrys," she said walking over. "Are you going to carve your name as well?"

"I don't know if it's appropriate," he said shyly. "I am exiled after all."

"Ha! All the more reason to put your name down," she smiled and placed a knife in his hands. "Most of the crew will be able to boast about sailing with the Mage Prince and Princess of Galbraith. You can't deny them that anecdote!"

Emrys chuckled himself and replied, "Aye, why not."

As he dug the blade into the grooves of wood Lymris sat on the side and continued their conversation. "Do you think Rheinar will be okay?" she asked. "He's been getting grumpier and grumpier on this voyage."

"He's afraid of Daal, Lym," Emrys replied. "And I'm forcing him to go back there."

"Rheinar made his choice, as I did," Lymris took his arm. "He does not blame you for any of this, you do know that don't you?"

Emrys nodded unconvincingly and finished carving his name on the bow. Now he was closer he could see so many names overlapping each other, and many of these names were stricken off.

"Do you think the crew will forgive me for Caphilla?" Emrys asked.

"I don't know," Lymris shrugged. "Each member has to have a year's service under their belt before they are granted permission to join the ship's log. Caphilla was loved but she also betrayed her Captain. The crew, they follow Captain Velstadt. He is on our side Emrys and swore us safe passage across the Sea of Tears."

"And do you forgive me?" Emrys asked of his sister.

"I never blamed you," Lymris replied. "I only blame myself for being blind to not see her betrayal. Do not fret on it big brother, soon we will be in Daal and another place for us to explore."

His sister had made a lot of sense yet still Emrys felt uneasy whenever he would clasp eyes on one of Velstadt's pirates. Hushed voices whispered in the night and stopped altogether when they saw him move across the decking. He had never felt more exposed than he did that day and despite brief conversations with Baster and Balion, he spent most of it alone.

***

THE cool winds howled that evening as The Crimson Tempest dimmed its lights for travel by night. The sea had calmed for the most part, yet Velstadt had warned everyone they were now entering the most treacherous part of the sea. Each man was called to the oars and hushed orders were passed down the ranks by Velstadt and his first mate. Emrys, Lymris and Rheinar were rowing close to the helm. His hands no longer held the blisters of previous weeks, and as the gloomy night set in, the callous shone back at him as he picked at the dead, hardened pieces of skin. Looking up he saw in the distance lights from the stern of a ship, several nautical miles away.

"Fools," Rheinar said as they matched the strokes of oars. "Whalers you'd imagine."

"Why are they fools?" Emrys asked naively.

"Because there are more pirates than us skulking these waters," Velstadt interjected as he strolled down from the helm. "Stop on the oars lads. I fear this night is about to get dangerous."

Suddenly several blasts of cannons lit up the night sky

with flashes of fire and sparks. The sound reverberated across the ocean rippling the sails with the slightest gust of wind. The crew had stopped rowing as they turned to look on. To their sight, the lit ship was being attacked by another hidden in shadow, yet from the sound of cannon after cannon, they could tell its armament was many. The main mast had snapped and cracked into the ocean as the screams of wounded sailors echoed through the night. He could hear children crying below deck and the clashes of swords in the nearby battle.

"We have to help them!" Emrys shouted at the captain. Rising to his feet he drew his own sword and reached for the bell at the main mast. Before he could reach its handle, a gloved hand from the dark wrenched him back and pinned him against the mast.

"Keep your voice down!" Velstadt hissed. "Or we'll be their next prize."

"We can't let them die," Emrys pleaded, his voice breaking. "It's not right."

"Aye it's not right at all," Velstadt replied. "Many sailors will lose their life tonight but we must allow it. Why? Because you are a prize larger than any whale or trinket that vessel could hope to contain. The Arcadians would parade you around the street as their new toy. They would torture in ways that goes against nature. Can't you see Emrys, you must not get captured."

"He's right," Rheinar stepped over the oars and joined them. "Sad as it may be, we cannot get involved. Our quest is to get you to Carpathia. We cannot help them Emrys."

Velstadt moved his hand and Emrys walked slowly across the deck. He could see fires spreading on the deck and the flag on the helm was ablaze, showing the shadows of pirates as they ran below deck. The screams continued for a long time and eventually it was his sister that broke down.

"Please we have to do something!" Lymris said tearfully sinking to her knees. "This is evil."

"We cannot Lymris," Velstadt said consoling her. "You are a Princess of Galbraith. Most if not all pirates will never meet a Princess in their lifetime. How do you think that crew would treat you? With respect as my own has? They would sell you to Arcadian slavery along with your brother. Edmure, I hear has taken a liking to you. I do not want to think of the depravities that young man would bestow upon either one of you."

The brief battle was coming to an end as the lights were snuffed from the ship and the fires smouldered. A roar from the ship erupted to signal a surrender had been given followed by the screams of women, children and men as they were taken to the other ship. Velstadt ordered the anchor to be dropped. He would not risk a voyage so close to enemies and ordered, that linen sheets were to cover anything which could glint in the moonlight. Emrys helped in wrapping the cannons, cannonballs and torches in linen while Rheinar moved below deck to soothe the nervous horses. Within a few hours of nervous anticipation, eventually they could hear laughter from the ship closer than it had been before. "Easy now," Velstadt ordered as the bow of another ship came into view. "Take positions by the broadside cannons, just in case." The crew scampered silently around the deck and lay down beneath the covered cannons. The ship was closing in on them, one hundred metres, the First Mate had whispered to the captain. "They're going to pass us lads," Velstadt hushed. "Keep your silence and we're out of the woods."

Emrys poked his head through a gap in the wood and looked on the ship. It was much larger than The Crimson Tempest and everywhere he looked he could see members of its crew. Black sails were pulled along by a soft wind and it became clear this ship was designed for night ambushes. There were men, women and children tied up to the masts, the riggings and even the cannons. A man from the mast was dragged forward to a plank and wrapped in chains. "Get going then," a voice said in the darkness.

Emrys and the entire crew could hear the man's pleas for life. "Please, I have a family," he had said. "We know you do," the voice replied. "And we'll take *good* care of them. Now off you pop."

Emrys covered his ears and looked away as he heard the muffled screams of the family and man as he was pushed into the Sea of Tears. Several other sailors were thrown to their doom and the laughs from the pirates made his blood boil with anger. To his side Lymris was in tears as Velstadt grimly looked on. The ship passed them by before long and Velstadt signalled to the crew to raise the anchor. He walked over to Emrys and Lymris as they sat in despair.

"Come on you two," the captain said pulling them up. "We've got a hard night on the oars yet."

Lymris sniffled and wiped her eyes as Emrys welled up himself. Rheinar returned from below deck and comforted Lymris as she cried. "It's a terrible thing," he said, "to see such cruelty. It is harsh lesson to you both."

"What lesson is that?" Emrys asked.

Rheinar met his eyes and for a second thought he could see a tear. "That even with the purest intentions," he said, "you cannot save everyone Emrys."

Chapter Fourteen
Quashing a Rebellion

TYRIS galloped down the Aurelian Road alongside his knights clad in golden armour with maroon cloaks. He had been sent by his father to inspect Burnistoun upon receiving a disturbing message of rebellion from Rheinar. Their Master-At-Arms had warned a mob of angry civilians burned his father's statue to the ground and chanted for the Valyris family. Even now, during these uncertain times, Tyris strugged to believe it. He missed his brother, he could not deny it, but his mind raced to pressing matters across the nation. Ever since Emrys had left for Carpathia, his father had been watching him with greater scrutiny than before and took to testing his capabilities as a ruler. This ride to Burnistoun was to check his resolve, and Tyris told himself he would not let his father down. His father barely spoke of Emrys. Whenever Tyris brought up the subject King Terrys would change topic hastily or leave the conversation altogether. Tyris knew it was shame which forced his father's hand. He had not wanted to exile Emrys but saw no other choice in keeping the peace. In the two months since his brother's exile Tyris had grown a full goatee of hair which snagged away at him in the mornings. His hair was now in locks like his father, which he pinned back behind his ears when the wind raced through it. As Rheinar was no longer with them, he had taken to training with one of his protege's, a young lad about his age named Petra. Though nowhere near as fearsome in stature as Rheinar, the lad held himself well with a sword and provided Tyris with a brand-new challenge whenever they fought. The lad had blonde matted hair and a beard that made people think he was far older than he was.

"Ever been to Burnistoun, Petra?" Tyris asked of his warrior.

"I have, my Prince," Petra replied. "Begging your pardon, but it's a bit of a shithole." Tyris laughed heartily at Petra's admission along with several of his knights. Elette had not joined them on his journey which was a disappointment. He loved her. When he thought on her beauty, he could see her long blonde hair flowing from her shoulders, and her smile that brought a weakness to his knees he had never known before. As beautiful as she was, it was matched in her kindness to the people of Stormgast. Already the people there loved her. She had sanctioned shows and musical events along the streets, and the townsfolks' cheers and jubilations could be heard all the way to the Palace Gardens. But a fortnight ago when Tyris had asked her to join him, she refused to leave Stormgast.

"I have work to do with Mikhael," she had said in the morning of his departure, much to his dismay. The words still rang in his head. *What work could they possibly be up to in Stormgast?* Casting the thought from his mind he prepared himself mentally for the challenge ahead. He would have to round up the civilians and press them for information. His father had warned him not to be too hard on them, else they would have an entire city in uproar. Instead, he should aim to inspire and debate freely. Punishments will of course be handed out but saved only for the leader. Tyris had read the note over and over again, *the man in the feather hat ...* that was who he needed to look out for. Mikhael shared his suspicions that he could be an Arcadian spy, a claim that if true, would be treason. Tyris hoped this was not the case.

When the suns were at their peak Tyris' party of twenty warriors approached the gates of Burnistoun which were sealed shut. The stench of rotten fish rushed through Tyris and he gagged as they approached the guards. One of them walked forward and held a hand out. "No admittance."

"You will open the gates for the Crown Prince Tyris of Galbraith!" Petra called out.

The guards' smirks had receded as they saluted and hastily called out for the gates to open. As they opened, the winds came with it, ripping some of his knights' cloaks straight off. Slowly, Tyris and his men moved down the high street which was near enough vacant. The main street, alcoves and side streets were all empty, and a shared look of disbelief between Tyris and Petra signalled something was wrong. It had taken several minutes for them to spot anyone and when they did, they realised it was a blind beggar holding a cap aloft in his hands. "Spare a coin, sir?" he said weakly.

Dismounting Tyris walked over to the man. "Of course," Tyris replied and duly put several gold pieces in his cap.

"You're very generous, gods bless ye sir," said the blind man who obscured the coins in his clothing.

"Could you tell me where everyone is?" Tyris asked.

"They're in the main square but tread carefully," the man whispered. "Something strange is happening around here. People have been going missing and fewer and fewer of them are returning. Can you smell it?"

"Smell what?" Tyris replied. "Death. Death is all around us boy," the man hissed. "Tread carefully."

Mounting his horse again, Tyris bid farewell to the old man and the escort continued along the main road. Many shops along this road were barred up and others had been looted entirely. Then Tyris saw what the man had warned them of. There were bodies of men, women and children rotting in the street as blood trickled down the muddy slope. "Swords!" Tyris called out to the singing of metal as his knights drew their weapons. Several turns later they found themselves staring at the main square of Burnistoun. The square was clad with people and guards alike and a small podium had been erected at its centre. Squinting Tyris could see the wooden remains of his father's statue. Someone had removed its head and tied a noose around a tree where it was left hanging. Such disrespect. He would have someone's head for this. Tyris ordered his men to sheathe their swords and listen in on the rally. To the right of the square, he could see several pyres being built and feared what was to come. Several chants of 'Valyris' later, a man fitting Rheinar's description stepped onto the podium. He was well dressed and sported a fine tunic that would rival that of the lords in Stormgast. His short hair was obscured from the large feathered hat which drooped over his unblemished face. As he stood there with arms aloft the crowd applauded and cheered him before he hushed them and spoke.

"My friends!" his voice boomed throughout the square. "We have more traitors to execute. More people loyal to the tyrannical rule of King Terrys. Bring forth the prisoners!"

A group of people in rags covered in excrement were led forward as the crowd spat and attacked them. They were joined in chains and dragged by their necks towards the podium, subject to both verbal and physical abuse along with way. Tyris couldn't believe he was witness to such barbarity, in Galbraith no less. The mob were bloodthirsty and cries rang out to butcher the men and women dragged forward. Once on the podium the well-dressed man stepped towards them and grinned evilly. "Now," He said, "We offer all prisoners the same choice when they are up on this podium. Death by fire or death by noose?"

The first prisoner met his gaze and said, "You can't do this! King Terrys is a good man! An honest ruler!" Appealing to the crowd he continued, "Can't you see what's happening! This man is an Arcadian! Sent to stir up rebellion in the heart of Galbraith!"

"What nonsense!" The man laughed towards the crowd. "If you won't choose allow me to choose for you. Death by noose."

"You won't get away with this, Dolgier!" the prisoner said as he was pulled to his feet and a noose was thrown over the tree behind him. As one of the mob wrapped the rope around his neck, Tyris had seen enough. He was angrier than he had ever been to see such scenes, and with a fist gesture he and his mounted knights moved closer to the crowd.

"Bow in the name of your Prince!" Petra bellowed startling those at the back of the crowd. The sea parted allowing the men to pass and some civilians knelt as soon as they clasped eyes on Tyris. He paid no attention. His eyes were fixed upon the man they called Dolgier. Dolgier met his gaze and stroked his chin as they approached. "What in all madness is going on?" Tyris shouted as he approached the podium.

"We are executing those disloyal to Galbraith, Prince Tyris," Dolgier replied flippantly, showing no respect to the Crown Prince.

Tyris dismounted and launched himself onto the podium

beside Petra. He was stood a few yards from Dolgier and the prisoners. The prisoners looked up at him with tears in their eyes. They had been maltreated, starved and abused under this Dolgier's watch. "Under what crimes do you hold these Galbraithians?" Tyris demanded. "And under whose authority do you serve?"

"I serve the people, for the people!" Dolgier replied defiantly. "We're taking Burnistoun back, away from the Galbraith family who have brought nothing but misery and death to this great city! I will never bow before a prince or king in your family!"

A smattering of applause greeted his statement and Tyris flashed a quick look at the crowd. Most were stood in anticipation as they watched Dolgier take on the Crown Prince. Tyris calmed himself and took in everything. *Dolgier does not sound like he is from Burnistoun, or even Galbraith*, he thought. "Pray tell," Tyris asked, "From where do you hail Dolgier? You are clearly not from Burnistoun."

The question stumped the rabble-rouser. A nervous flick of the eyes to the crowd alerted Tyris. He had Dolgier right where he wanted him. "I'm from Eddington…" Dolgier replied without conviction.

"That's interesting," Tyris said as he circled the man. "You see Petra here is from Eddington. What do you think Petra, does he sound like he's from Eddington?"

"No, he does not," Petra snarled stepping forward, his hand glued to the hilt of his sword.

"Then that means we have a liar in our midst," Tyris continued. "Tell me, why do you spread hateful lies about my family to the good people of Burnistoun? Why did you organise a mob to burn down my father's statue? Why have you been executing innocent people as sport!"

Tyris yelled the last question as Dolgier quivered on the spot. The man found some courage and spoke with hate. "Is it not true that your own brother is a filthy mage?" he asked.

Tyris drew his sword and held it to Dolgier's neck. His hand was steady and he could fell this wicked man with but a stroke of his weapon. "My brother is a mage," Tyris said with gritted teeth. "But magic has never been outlawed in Galbraith. You speak as a man from Arcadia, only there is magic banned and mages hunted."

"Arcadia will rule this land!" Dolgier yelled in defiance, "You will all be Emperor Edmure Valyris' subjects by love or by force!"

Turning, Tyris addressed the crowd as he spoke: "And there we have it, people of Burnistoun! This man would have you betray your King to serve a warmongering Emperor! My father, who bled as you all did! And what respect does he get? His own statue burned and turned into a smouldering ruin!"

As he looked on at the crowd many held their heads in shame and avoided the prince's gaze as they thought on their own roles in this treason.

"I do not know what you believe," the Crown Prince continued. "Nor do I know what you hold true to your hearts. When I speak, I speak for the future of Galbraith. Burnistoun is the heart of Galbraith! Which city sees the most trading with the lands to the south? Burnistoun! Which city provides the land with the most food? Burnistoun! And which city provides the most ships for our navy? Burnistoun! Throughout this war with the fucking Arcadians, we have lost our families, our friends and our faith. Faith that there is something bigger than ourselves. That we Galbraithians stand for more. That we stood against the tyranny of Arcadia! Do not allow yourselves to hate as this man would have you! Join me now in forging a new future for Galbraith! One that will stand tall and proud against tyranny!"

The last word echoed through the silent square as the crowd listened to the Crown Prince. Applause began to resonate before people began cheering the young ruler. Raising his sword above his head Petra chanted, "PRINCE TYRIS!"

His men followed suit before the whole square chanted his name back to him. The hairs on his neck stood up as he looked on at the spectacle. A crowd that was ready to execute people not ten minutes ago, now chanted his own name as they watched the scenes unfold. Dolgier attempted to make off in the excitement but Petra pulled him back and bound his hands. "Cut free the prisoners," Tyris commanded. "They are no longer subject to Arcadian cruelty."

The prisoners looked up at him and thanked him several times before Tyris shook his head and held their hands. "Do not thank me," he said. "I am sorry that we failed you. That we allowed this poisonous man into Burnistoun."

Turning his attention back to the crowd he held his hands up for silence. "Now though," he said, "People of Burnistoun. We must decide what to do with Dolgier."

Boos rang out from the crowd with cries of 'Murderer!', 'Hang him!' and 'Burn him!' echoing through the square. Tyris stroked his chin and then, moments later, he had an idea of poetic justice.

"When I came into Burnistoun," he said, "I saw something horrible! Shops looted and boarded up, and the bodies of men, women and children littering the streets! This man has caused untold suffering to many! What is justice for the people of Burnistoun?"

More cries of 'Hang him!' rang out as Tyris chose his words carefully.

"This man, Dolgier," he continued, "Dolgier, who would have Burnistoun bow to Arcadia, executed anyone who disobeyed his command! When I entered the square, I saw him offer a choice. A choice that he offered to the prisoners. In the name of justice, I would like to extend his own choice to him."

Dolgier was in full tears now and his futile attempts to break free from Petra grip proved fruitless. "Please don't kill me," he begged of the Crown Prince.

Unfazed Tyris stared back at the man who had inflicted so much pain in the name of Arcadia. "I will offer you a choice Dolgier," he hissed. "Death by fire or death by noose?"

Chapter Fifteen
Trade in Blood

"EMRYS!" his sister shouted down. "Come and see this!"

He duly ran up to the deck and was amazed by the sight of it all. They had arrived. Daal was merely a few hundred yards away and the view was something to behold. The scorched brickwork of sand and orange sparkled in the sunlight and the heat boiling down from the sun was palpable. Every inch of the dock was littered with small merchant stalls and fishermen flogging their latest catch. They were a few hundred yards away but the hustle and bustle of the traders while they shouted over each other was audible even on The Crimson Tempest. The language, Emrys had heard nothing like it before, and could not make out what the people were discussing.

"What language is that?" he asked of Rheinar.

"That is Carpathi," Rheinar replied. "My mother tongue. Hard language to pick up but I can teach you a few phrases. The most important words I'll tell you now. *Zeet* is 'yes' and *Fuf* is 'no'. You'll need *Fuf* when we're navigating the streets."

"Why do you say that, Rheinar?" Lymris asked. Rheinar chuckled lightly and matched Velstadt's grin as he looked on. "You'll see," he said.

As the ship came into dock Rheinar ordered the two siblings to wear loose clothing or suffer the desert heat. He was not lying. Even down to his rags Emrys was sweating buckets and was always handy to his water as he attempted to wash the heat away. Every breath he took was harsh as he struggled with the warm air filling his lungs. His sister was in the same condition and her hair was a tangled mess of sweat and sea water as she doused her face in cold water. "This heat is unbearable," she said as she wiped her face and neck.

"Aye," Emrys breathlessly replied. "And I thought we had nice summers in Galbraith."

The two siblings checked their luggage to their horses and brought them above deck once Velstadt's crew had lowered the anchor. Elmrya whinnied as she stepped onto the docks and almost lost her footing on the narrow wooden beams. As soon as Emrys touched dry land he felt his feet move like jelly. It must have been amusing to watch, he had no delusions about that. As he awkwardly shifted around like a crab running along a shore, Rheinar strode past him with Shrieker. Lyrmis, Velstadt and his crew followed suit and set about bringing their belongings ashore.

"Emrys," Velstadt called and clapped his hands on his shoulders. "It's been an honour travelling with you."

Emrys' heart sank. "Are you off already?" he asked.

"We're here for a couple of days but, aye, we will return to Burnistoun," Velstadt replied. "I just wanted to say it now in case we don't see each other after this. Despite your exile, never have I see a truer Prince of Galbraith. You will always have a place on The Crimson Tempest."

Emrys bit his quivering lip and avoided the captain's gaze as he became flooded with emotion. "Chin up, lad," Velstadt grinned. "Besides you've yet to see the streets of the Great Market City. Brace yourself."

Emrys could not understand what Rheinar and Velstadt

had meant by moving on the street, yet ten minutes later he knew exactly what they warned him of. As the group moved from the docks, they entered a main square filled with hundreds of civilians, traders, soldiers and sailors. The noise was deafening as people haggled and shouted to each other. Within an instant Emrys was in love with the chaos of it all. Fine silks were paraded around the streets, the air was fragrant with the rich smell of exotic spices, and golden trinkets were held aloft by-passing traders vying for attention. Everywhere he looked he saw a new trader approach him and offer their goods, speaking quickly in the language he knew nothing of. The word he had learnt a mere fifteen minutes earlier, *fuf,* was used a lot as they walked along the narrow alleys crammed full of people.

Lymris grabbed Emrys' hand and the siblings walked together in tandem as they followed Rheinar. She was evidently alarmed by the frantic nature of the people around them, and she gripped his hand tighter and tighter as they barged through the crowded streets, past the merchants and souks. "Who rules Daal, Rheinar?" Emrys asked as they found a clearing in the road.

"No one," Rheinar replied. "Money is King here. There is no ruler, just merchants looking to make their gold, and protect it."

"But surely someone would just invade and claim Daal for their own?" Emrys protested.

Rheinar nodded, "Many have tried. You see those alleys down there? Whole armies have marched through those chasing the mercenaries the merchants bought. Those alleys go on for miles and miles. It is the largest labyrinth I can think of. Invaders or would-be-rulers by the thousands have marched through and none were ever seen again. The following day, their armour and weapons would be on sale throughout the streets."

As Emrys passed through the small streets he began to understand how armies would fail to succeed in Daal. The turns between the alcoves and alleys were small and popped up without warning as people streamed from them. There was little to no cover from the small doors lined up and down the alleys, and ambushing an onrushing group would be easier here than in woodland. It would be a folly to march an army into such a maze, Emrys realised.

Velstadt and Rheinar had agreed that morning that they would stay for a night in the Den, an inn for travellers near the centre of the city. Emrys judged they must have walking through the city for hours and his feet had begun to throb as tiredness set in. The sunlight had dipped beneath the stacked roofs and he felt a slight reprieve from the sweltering heat which he had endured throughout the morning. As they approached the Den, Emrys and Lymris looked on and laughed as they realised where they were staying. The Den was its name, but any fool could ascertain it was a whorehouse with the clambering ladies and men alluring people from the upstairs windows. As they moved into the dimly lit establishment, a group of men emblazoned in golden trinkets rose from their seats and barged past Rheinar and Velstadt. They stank to high heavens of sweat and blood, and wore grim faces as they left The Den. Rheinar immediately spat on the ground and gritted his teeth. To Emrys it looked as if he was restraining himself, and he shared his thoughts with Velstadt. "Of course he's restraining himself," Velstadt said as Rheinar approached the bar. "Those *people* you just saw were slavers."

"Slavers in here?" Emrys asked.

"Slavers are everywhere in Daal," Velstadt replied. "They bring slaves from every corner of the world. Every colour, every creed, every religion. I saw your face earlier today as we strolled through the streets. Yes, there is a lot to buy here, some wonderful artifacts, spices, and food to purchase, but do not forget that everything, and I mean everything, including lives, has its price in Daal."

"It's despicable," Lymris interjected.

"It is," Velstadt nodded sadly. "But the merchants of Daal have been around a longer time than you or I. They are set in their ways and for many their commerce is blood."

***

EMRYS had found it impossible to sleep that night on a bed instead of hammock. He had grown accustomed to the sway of a ship and it was a testing challenge to drift off into a peaceful slumber. His attempts to ask for a hammock had proved fruitless as no-one, save the party, seemed to speak Elessian. He had thought about asking Rheinar or Velstadt, but decided his own discomfort was a small price to pay for their help in this city. Velstadt had explained the blood that ran through this city, and it served as a constant reminder to Emrys how difficult it must be for Rheinar to be back. His mentor barely spoke that evening, and once he had wolfed down his dinner, he made his excuses and went straight to bed. As Emrys rose and dressed himself, he splashed water on his face and went downstairs. He was the only one up, and as he opened the front door, he could smell the early morning tide as it swept to the shore. He decided he would have a wander. Not too far. But at least see the city with his own eyes as it rose for the day. The streets were dead, save for a few fishermen racing to the docks. Now the stalls had been dismantled Emrys could see first-hand the poverty stricken around. Homeless people were strewn about the place and it dawned on him that the traders must have been working above the bodies. The thought sickened him as he weaved his way through the alley.

Eventually he came onto a clearing where a few people stood by a well, locked in a deep conversation. As he approached, one of them looked up at him and instantly he regretted his decision to walk the streets. *Slavers*, he thought. They were not as richly dressed as the ones in The Den the previous night, but their demeanour could not be mistaken. They had chains wrapped to their belts and eyed Emrys up and down as a wolf would eye its dinner. His arrival broke up their discussion and they all turned on the spot to look at him. There were three men and a woman fully robed and staring at him with cold dead eyes. Emrys stopped in his tracks. He sensed a shiver running up his spine and his legs turned to jelly as he stood frozen in anticipation. One of the group moved closer, and smiled at Emrys. "Tor ka'deel val malbrek?" he said and grinned. "Daal erkladi ist senta volla."

Panic raced through Emrys' mind. "Fuf," Was all he could muster, as his voice broke.

"Fuf?" The slaver replied as the group laughed and stepped forward. The man held out his arm and gestured towards Emrys. "Forr telki per bladarki."

His hand was now pointing towards Emrys' sword.

"Fuf," Emrys replied. "No, you can't have my sword."

The group spoke between themselves for a moment then they all turned their attentions back to him. The woman, who had remained silent until now pulled back her hood revealing auburn hair and a scarred face. "You... be from Elessia?" she said in broken Elessian.

"You speak my language," Emrys replied taken aback.

She cackled with laughter and drew her sword. "With us come... boy," she snarled. "Or die."

Emrys fought the rising tide of fear and wished he'd never decided to take a walk this morning. As he edged away they matched his pace and all four slavers had now unsheathed their swords. He was outmatched. Even if he was as good as swordsman as Tyris, he felt this fight would be beyond him. Turning, he spun his legs as fast as they could carry him and began to sprint down the alleys. He could hear their shouts to one another as they chased closely behind, he would pay it no attention. *Get to The Den*, he thought. In his confusion he could not be sure he knew the way. The alleys looked the same and he could not tell if he had been through this part of the city before. Panicking, he leapt over a cart and knocked it over sending fruit spiralling into the air. A few grunts and a crash from behind let him know he had hit one of the slavers, but that was the least of his concerns. He knew he was now lost. He had never seen this part of the city, nor its grey stone walls as he ran along. A fork in the path appeared and he chose to run right. He whimpered as he looked ahead, and realised he'd chosen the wrong path. There he stood, facing a dead end as his heart sank to the floor. A few seconds later he was surrounded by the slavers, growling at him and speaking among themselves in Carpathi.

Emrys drew his sword. Outnumbered or not, he would not die or be enslaved without a fight. He drew harsh breaths as his lungs pained from his run. The slavers moved forward together and Emrys edged further away until he was almost touching the wall behind him. "I'm sorry Rheinar, Lymris, Velstadt," he muttered to himself. Gripping his sword tightly, he shouted and ran forward at the first slaver. To his amazement he caught the slaver off-guard and before he could defend himself, Emrys had sliced the blade into his right arm. The slaver howled in pain and dropped his sword as Emrys wrenched the sword free from the exposed bone. Blood poured from the wound and he fell back as Emrys repositioned himself. The other slavers looked shocked, as if most of their victims had never fought back. This time the female slaver moved forward and with several lunges put Emrys on the defensive. She was incredibly quick with her scimitar and did not relent as Emrys struggled to parry each blow. Her last blow was a two-handed swing which knocked the sword clean from his hands. The slaver held the blade to his throat, pinning him back against the wall. The other slavers had taken the wounded member in their arms and were hastily tying the bloodied arm. The female slaver pressed the blade down on Emrys' throat and he could feel as it slowly pierced his flesh and pain seared to the wound. She hissed at him revealing a forked tongue among the strange ornaments enveloping her face. "You fight," she said leaning in closely ripping his silver necklace from him. "None fight. I impressed. Name?"

Emrys squealed in pain as he felt the blood from his neck trickling down to his rags.

"Bertred! My name is Bertred!" he begged pressing his hands between the blade and his neck. "Let me go!"

The female slaver did not relent. She pressed the blade harder and his calloused hands began to bleed as they held it back.

154

"We have place for you," she hissed again. "We take you to Kelpis Magna."

"Kelpis Magna?" Emrys howled in pain as the blade pressed deeper and deeper. "What is Kelpis Magna?"

She laughed in his face and pressed her face up to his. "Arena," she smirked. "There you fight or die, Bertred."

Chapter Sixteen
Lost and Found

LYMRIS groggily stood up and stretched. She had slept well and was fully appreciative of a feather bed after their hard voyage. She had loved every minute on The Crimson Tempest, save for the battle she had witnessed and which continued to haunt her thoughts. She felt such pity for the sailors who were ambushed and dreamt of having an armada at her command to deal with such cruel thugs. The journey as a whole had been exhilarating and terrifying at the same time. She had seen some amazing things during her travels but the scenes at Burnistoun and the cliff almost crushing them still haunted her. She missed her father and brother too. Yes, she was on her adventure, something she had always wanted to do, but she grew more and more homesick the further they rode from Galbraith. She missed the palace gardens and longed for the summer sparring with her siblings, but she knew deep down those days were now in the past and never to return. Daal was strange to her. She had never felt such heat than in the boiling pits of the city, and she had promised herself she would come back here one day to admire the trinkets strewn across the markets and souks. Dressing herself, she strode over to Emrys' room and knocked on. There was no response. "Emrys? Are you decent?" she asked as she turned the handle. To her surprise the room was empty and her brother's stuff was missing. She shrugged and assumed he must be downstairs having breakfast. As she walked downstairs, she could hear the faint noise of the bustling markets outside building to a crescendo and rising whenever the front door was opened. In the corner of the room by the bar she could see Rheinar and Velstadt with several members of the crew relaxing on the benches nearby, but there was still no sign of Emrys which worried her. "Morning you two," she said smiling sitting next to Rheinar and Velstadt.

"Good morning Pri... Lymris," Rheinar said correcting himself while Velstadt nodded and grinned. Velstadt slid across a plate of bread and cheese which Lymris began wolfing down. "Where's Emrys?" she asked between mouthfuls, "He's not in his room."

"Wait, what?" Rheinar said dropping his bread.

"I've just been through," Lymris said. "He's wasn't in his room, I thought he'd be down here."

Rheinar rose to his feet and began searching the brothel. Occupied rooms or not, he barged into each one looking for Emrys. Lymris started to worry. It was very unlike Emrys not to be at breakfast, after all it was his favourite meal. Velstadt joined Rheinar in his search as Lymris nervously began chewing at her nails. Several minutes later the two men met by the stairs. "He's not here," Velstadt said. "Lymris, did he say anything to you? Anything he might want to do or go somewhere?"

"No," she said scanning her memory of the previous day. "He said nothing."

"Then we have to assume he's either gone out this morning or he's been taken." Velstadt frowned and turned to his crew, "Right lads! Lasses! Get up! We need to find Emrys! Search the city, ask around, bribe, threaten, I don't care, see it done!"

Rheinar held his head in his hands and punched the wall sending tremors through the building. He looked devastated, and for the first time in Lymris' life, she saw he was afraid. He looked lost and paced in thought as he deliberated on what action to take.

"Rheinar snap out of it!" Velstadt barked at her Master-At-Arms. "We must act quickly. My crew will scour the city and we must do the same. Lymris. Stay with Rheinar at all times. We've already lost one Galbraith, we must ensure we do not lose another."

Velstadt grabbed his weapon and burst out of the door with his crew. Rheinar gritted his teeth and his expression changed from one of fear to unbridled anger. "Lymris," he said. "Let's go."

The streets were as busy if not more so than the previous day. Rheinar's patience had snapped and any merchant foolish enough to try to stop him was cast aside or kicked to floor as Rheinar soldiered forward. The search was frantic. They stopped the merchants they could but no-one had seen or even heard of Emrys. Panic set in. They had spent all day searching to no avail and Rheinar was becoming visibly distressed. He lashed out several times during their journey and nothing could seem to calm him down. Lymris looked on and worried for him. He looked disjointed, unorganised. It was something she was unaccustomed to seeing in her Master-At-Arms. By the end of the day, they returned to The Den and awaited news from Velstadt and his party. Lymris was tired, more tired than she realised. As she sat down, she massaged her throbbing feet and searched in desperation for food. The crew came back in dribs and drabs with little news to lift the spirits of Lymris or Rheinar. Velstadt was the last to return and he had no information on the young Prince. Together they shared a meal in silence and thought on their next plan of action.

"We should try again early in the morning," Velstadt reasoned. "Emrys disappeared then. It would be wise to check the streets and see if anyone has noticed."

"I'm afraid," Rheinar replied, "afraid for what comes next. If I find the people responsible for his disappearance... Forgive me, Lymris. I will not hold back."

Lymris nodded towards Rheinar. She felt the same way he did. If she got her hands on whoever took Emrys she would ensure they did not live to see another day. She was angrier than she had ever been and found it difficult to vent her frustration. She took her leave from the meal early and prayed to any of the gods that would listen for Emrys' safety. As she drifted off to sleep that night, she wondered if her prayers would be answered.

Dawn broke and Lymris was woken up by Rheinar. They skipped breakfast and headed South, further into the city centre. The streets in the early morning were vacant, she noticed. In a few hours they would be clad full of people, but for now Daal almost seemed peaceful. Save the cries of the birds, the city was asleep and she could hear her own footsteps echoing down the cobbles for the first time since they had reached the city. Moving down through the twisting and winding streets they came upon a square with a well in its centre. Surrounding the well were a group of armed people who noticed their arrival. There were three men and a woman and Lymris could not help but notice one of them bore an injury to their forearm. One by one they turned to look on at Rheinar, Lymris and Velstadt. "Be careful," Rheinar whispered. "These are slavers."

They were very dirty. Their clothes were awash with sand and Lymris could barely see any teeth among the four of them. Then she saw it. A glint of morning light pierced through the dawn sky and sparkled off a necklace from the woman in the group. The necklace was made of silver and carved and styled to the roots of the Great Oak. There could be no mistaking it. This was Emrys' necklace. Without hesitation Lymris drew her sword and marched past Rheinar and Velstadt, putting herself within six feet of the woman in question. "That is my brother's necklace!" Lymris shouted, "Where is he?"

A second later Rheinar and Velstadt were both at her side, swords in hand. The group looked on shocked by what they were witnessing. Eventually they drew their swords and squared up to Rheinar and Velstadt. The woman was ogling Lymris with a grin. She had not yet drawn or sword or responded to the princess' question.

"Answer me!" Lymris spat again. "Where is my brother?"

"Sold," the woman hissed. "He fetch good price."

Enraged, Lymris launched herself forward with a wild slash. The woman dodged it with ease and pulled a dagger from her waist. Countering she went for a stab towards Lymris' midriff who jumped out of the way in the nick of time. Rheinar and Velstadt had engaged the other slavers. With one huge swing Rheinar had decapitated one of the slavers and knocked down another for a killing blow. Velstadt was toying with his combatant and after each flick of his sword, a trail of blood streamed down onto the cobbles below. Upon seeing the death of her fellow slavers, the woman kicked Lymris back and attempted to flee the square. "Rheinar! She's trying to run!" Lymris coughed as she gingerly rose to her feet.

From his pocket Rheinar pulled a small dagger and threw

it with venom at the woman. He did not miss. The dagger pierced the back of her knee and with a curdling cry she fell to the floor. Velstadt had now finished off his opponent and began cleaning his sword. Rheinar was unflinching in his conviction. He stomped over to the woman and stood on the dagger forcing a squealing scream from her. He then spoke in Carpathi as Lymris and Velstadt watched on.

[In Carpathi] "Where is the boy?" Rheinar shouted. "Tell me, and you will live. Refuse and I will paint the streets with your blood."

"We caught him yesterday morning," she cried. "He wandered through here and when I heard he was from Galbraith I thought we would get a good price selling him on. Foreign slaves always make more. He attacked us when cornered so we decided we could sell him on as a fighter."

Velstadt stepped forward and it was at this point Lymris realised he too could speak Carpathi.

[In Carpathi] "To whom did you sell Emrys?" the captain asked.

"To the slave-master at Kelpis Magna," she replied shuddering from the pain. "He'll be fighting in the pits later today."

Velstadt and Rheinar looked at each other with serious, worried faces. Rising to his feet Rheinar scratched his chin and paced the square, evidently troubled by something.

"How do you know that he'll be fighting today?" Velstadt asked.

"Because the slave-master was boasting about it," she squealed as she ripped the dagger from her leg. "He said he has some rare beasts coming in from Alterra and he wants to pit them against fresh slaves."

[In Galbraithi] "What monster would pit slaves against beasts?" Velstadt said and shook his head.

"It's Denrick," Rheinar replied without looking back. "That bastard must still be alive. It used to be one of his favourite sports. Cat against mice he used to call it. Even if anyone survives against these beasts, he'll shoot them down himself with arrows and laugh. He was always laughing at his own cruelties, and because he's friends with the richest merchants in the city, he's untouchable. They even fund his *sport*."

"Who's Denrick?" Lymris asked now she could understand again.

"My old slave-master," Rheinar said. "And he will not live for long if I have my way."

The woman had begun to crawl away from the square but Velstadt quickly put an end to that and pinned her clothing down to the cobbles with another dagger. Rheinar turned back to face her. The two shared a look with the woman angling a plea from him to no avail. "You said I would live if I told you everything," she protested.

"I lied," Rheinar replied. "You took the prince of Galbraith and made him a slave. You then sold him to perhaps the worst person alive in Daal and you expect me to spare you? No. I will not. This, this is justice."

Lymris turned away, she had seen enough death for one day. The pleas from the woman came thick and fast under a crunching blow from Rheinar's sword as it plunged through her chest. Lymris would never be able to forget the sound of her ribcage cracking open as the blade split the slaver in two. The square was a bloody mess. The bodies of the slavers were strewn across it with a pool of blood forming at the base of the well. Lymris felt a bit weak at the sight of it all, and trembled slightly as she looked away from the square. "We must regroup with the crew," Velstadt said. "We'll need every able-bodied ally we can get if we are to storm Kelpis Magna."

"I never thought I would have to return to that place," Rheinar said glumly. "Lymris, whatever happens please do not judge me too harshly."

"Why would I judge you?" Lymris asked.

"Because I did many evil things while I was a slave there," Rheinar replied. "Things that still haunt me. But I only did so to stay alive, you must know that."

"I do not care for your past Rheinar," Lymris said shaking her head. "Only for your present and future. Whatever you did or may have done it was a lifetime ago."

"Thank you, Princess." Rheinar bowed his head as Velstadt flicked his dreads back.

She returned to the bloody mess Rheinar had made of the female slaver and with a quick hand wrenched the necklace from her corpse. Within half an hour, the party of three had returned to The Den just as the crew began to stir from their dreams. Velstadt tipped the innkeeper to give them privacy, and within moments The Den was vacated, save for the crew of The Crimson Tempest. Velstadt called a meeting by the bar and spoke to the group as one.

"Right all of you," he said. "We know where Emrys is. He's been enslaved to the fighting pits of Kelpis Magna. We have it on good authority that he is due to be blooded in the arena later this afternoon. We must not let that fight happen. I need all of you to be brave, for what I have in mind requires courage and sacrifice. Emrys is the Primal. I do not know what the fuck that means, but I know that he's more important than we are. We all saw what happened with the Serpent of the Sea. He's destined for bigger things, which means we're the ones destined to save him! Whatever happens now, know that it has been my honour to sail with you all. Never have I had a finer crew than you, the crew of The Crimson Tempest!"

His men and women let out a cheer for the group and began banging their goblets against the bar. Lymris joined in and cheered the captain's fine words. Velstadt downed a pint and smashed his cup off the bar. Drawing his sword and raising it to the roof he shouted, "Get yourself ready lads, lasses! For today we fight! Today we free the Primal!"

Chapter Seventeen
The Pits

EMRYS shivered violently as he was bound in chains and led down deep into the bowels of Kelpis Magna. Since his capture that morning he had been tied up, stripped down to his rags, beaten and masked in a hood which obscured his view. The blood in his throat tasted of iron and his lips were so parched each breath was a harsh croak. He had not been fed or even granted water. He desperately needed something to drink and whenever he spoke out, he was either promptly beaten or laughed and spat at. His shivers grew more constant the further he was led down into the bowels of the arena. Below the boiling city of Daal was the freezing cold and damp stone he felt beneath as he limped bare-footed into the unknown. He was not the only slave being carted down. His chain was tugged at now and again and the faint whimpers of slaves behind and in front of him could not be ignored. Slavers barked orders at the group and if they were not adhered to, a quick whip of a lash saw to any disobedience. Emrys could hear as an iron gate was wrenched open before more orders in Carpathi were howled in his direction. Once he stumbled over the gate, his mask was removed and he shuddered at the sight in front of him.

Almost a hundred slaves from every culture he could think of were bound, either to each other or to the cave walls surrounding the large caged room. There was barely any light and as the guards wielding torches walked in, some of the slaves clambered over each other to hide themselves from its fiery embrace. One by one, Emrys' group was led off and chained to the wall. As Emrys was tugged along he could see there were corpses among the slaves that had been left to rot and the stench was unbearable. He gagged as he moved past one in particular, to which the slaver saw and grinned evilly. "Dor tell mink skekosi?" he asked and pushed Emrys' head down to within an inch of the maggot-ridden corpse. Emrys could not fight the wave of bile which emerged as the slaver's laughter echoed through the cave. He was thrust down to the nearby wall and kicked as the slaver lashed his chain to the wall and bolted it down to the cave floor. "Mor deit Elessi," the slaver spoke again before spitting on him. As the slavers turned to leave, they threw a handful of mouldy bread in the centre of the room and a few cups of water which spilled almost instantly. What happened next was horrible to witness. Emrys looked on as starving slaves fought tooth and nail for the slightest crumb or drop of water, oblivious to the mocks of the slavers. As the final slaver stepped out of the gate a man in a robe came forward.

The man was old, dark-skinned like Rheinar and had frazzled hair that was tied back with a golden hairpin. He spoke a few words to the slavers before he grabbed a nearby torch, stepped over the gate and entered the room. He addressed the room in Carpathi to the cries and wails of many. Emrys noticed that most of the slaves were fearful of him, and avoided meeting him eye to eye. He shifted around the room as if he was in a marketplace and was always smiling as he spoke. He had a gentle voice but even Emrys, who could not speak a word of Carpathi, knew there was malice behind every word. As the man walked past, he stopped when he reached Emrys and looked down at him. Up close Emrys realised he was a short, stout man with many sovereign rings on his hands and bangles adorning his arms. He smelled sweet, almost as if he had been bathed in jasmine. Kneeling down to meet his face, the man stared long into his eyes with cold precision. "Ors eik ball telkire?" he asked as the torchlight flickered in his face.

"I don't speak Carpathi," Emrys hoarsely croaked, spluttering as he said so.

"Ah, an Elessian I see," the man replied softly. "Tell me, what is your name?"

"Bertred," Emrys lied. "What is yours?"

A firm back of the hand greeted Emrys' cheek and he felt fresh blood circulating in his mouth as his cheek throbbed.

"Slaves do not ask questions here, Bertred." the man said. "But since you will probably not live more than two days, I will answer you. My name is Denrick, slave-master of Kelpis Magna."

Emrys knew the name and froze in horror. The man before him was the same man who had caused so much pain to Rheinar. He thought back on what his mentor had said to him. This man had abused him for years, killed his family and treated slaves as if he was a butcher in an abattoir. Emrys shrivelled as Denrick looked on, smiling from ear to ear.

"Now since you don't speak Carpathi," Denrick continued, "allow me to explain what I have just said to the group. Tomorrow you and a handful of others of my choosing will fight against beasts I bought from an Alterran trader. I doubt any of you will survive against these monstrous abominations but after all, it is my favourite sport. If you survive, well done. You will come back here and fight, again and again until finally you breathe your last breath in the arena. I own you now Bertred, and I will squeeze every last drop of blood, sweat and tears from you."

Emrys plucked what courage he could from his quickly emptying morale and said, "You are a fucking monster."

A second slap greeted his other cheek and Emrys spat out blood as Denrick giggled, giddy like a child. "Slaves do not speak back to their masters," Denrick replied and gripped Emrys by the neck. "But you will learn as they all do. I will see to that. The slavers who brought you in tell me you have a bit of fight in you. I want to see it tomorrow." As Denrick rose to his feet he slammed Emrys' head off the wall behind him and the young mage cried out in pain as his vision went blurry and claret began pouring down his neck. Squinting he saw the slave-master smiling down at him and he felt unbridled rage rising up through him. Denrick blew him a kiss and waved delicately as he swaggered from the room leaving with the only source of light. Darkness swallowed the room and as the gate was locked shut Emrys curled up into a ball and began to sob. He missed his family, Rheinar, Velstadt, even the crew. The abuse he had received during the day was like nothing he had every witnessed before, and slowly but surely, he could feel his spirit breaking apart. He had only wanted to see Daal, perhaps pick up a trinket for his sister but he was now enslaved to Kelpis Magna, and Denrick, the cruel slave-master who tormented Rheinar for years. He was more scared than he had ever been in his life and kicked himself for his stupidity in heading out alone on the streets of Daal. He tried to summon what powers he could but failed time and time again. As tears streamed down his face, he prayed to the gods for his swift rescue from the hellish place he found himself in.

***

THE iron gate swinging open woke Emrys from his chilly slumber. It was freezing in the cave and his constant shivering had kept him from barely having any rest as he tossed and turned searching for warmth. Even deep in the bowels of Kelpis Magna he had been able to hear the fighting above along with the cheers and chants of the crowd as the day passed by. He had no concept of time and could not tell if he had been down here for an hour or twelve. From the gate emerged a sole man caked from head to toe in blood. He was led over to Emrys and pinned down next to him. As he strolled over Emrys saw how huge he was. He would probably rival Rheinar for his height and build and he reckoned the man could fit his whole head in one hand. Emrys estimated the man was in his mid-twenties, despite his shaven head giving him an older look. When he sat down the slaver handed him meat and a jug of water which he took a huge swig from and exhaled sharply. His hands were twitching quite badly and he punched the wall a few times to settle himself. At this point he had looked down between mouthfuls at Emrys and asked: "Vei kiliar vor tei mussen?"

"I'm sorry," Emrys replied weakly. "I do not speak Carpathi."

"Well, you are in luck," the man replied. "For I speak Elessian."

"How?" Emrys asked flabbergasted. "It is not common-place to find another who speaks Elessian this far away from Galbraith."

169

The man chewed away at the fat on his mutton as envious eyes watched on in the darkness. Not that those eyes would worry him. This man was clearly a battle-hardened fighter and most of the others dare not even cast a wrong glance in his direction. Every now and again as a slaver bearing a torch passed them Emrys could see the scars rippling across the massive muscles on his arms. Forking his teeth with his nails he replied, "I once fought side by side with a Galbrathian. A good man and an even better fighter. Cillian was his name. He taught me everything I know with the sword, axe and spear, and he even taught me the language of his forefathers. It helped when he used to shout commands and carried me through the toils of Kelpis Magna for many years."

"What happened to him?" Emrys asked.

"What happens to everyone in the arena eventually," the man replied sadly. "He died fighting an impossible challenge."

"I'm sorry for your loss," Emrys shook his head. "He sounded like quite the man."

"That he was," the man said nodding. "Are you hungry?"

Emrys felt the pain of his knotting stomach writhe at him and spluttered. "Yes," Emrys replied weakly. "But I'm more thirsty, than anything. Since I was captured, I haven't had a drink."

The man handed him the jug and Emrys took a big swig revitalising a sap of his strength. He felt as the dry blood in his throat was washed away and coughed several times after he handed the man his jug back. "Thank you for this kindness," Emrys gasped.

"Now tell me," the man continued. "Are you any good in a fight?"

Emrys could see now the man was judging him and his

response. From the flicker of torchlight, he felt his brown eyes angling him for lies. Emrys felt his best option was to be truthful. "My Master-At-Arms back in Stormgast trained me as best he could," Emrys replied. "I know a bit of fighting with sword and bow, but I have a lot to learn."

The man nodded and seemed satisfied with his response. "Eat this," he said. "You will need your strength for tomorrow."

Emrys gratefully took the meat and it went chewed it quickly. His bloodied mouth pained with each mouthful but he was grateful nonetheless. "Is that your blood?" Emrys asked. "Are you injured?"

"No," the man replied. "This is not my blood. Some pirates trying to make a name for themselves attempted to best me in the arena. They failed."

The man continued to watch him as Emrys poured his mind over his next question. He wanted to learn more about the stranger before him, the only kind person he had met since he was brought to Kelpis Magna.

"How long have you been fighting in Kelpis Magna?" Emrys asked.

"For as long as I can remember," the man replied. "I was taken as a child when my father disappeared and my mother was killed before my eyes. My father, Jerreko, fought here. He was one of the finest warriors Kelpis Magna has ever produced. Denrick enslaved me to the Pits when he disappeared and I've been fighting ever since."

"What happened to your father?" Emrys quizzed.

"Your guess is as good as mine," the man shrugged. "Some say, he was killed in the streets of Daal, others say he joined a Lord's service. It does not matter. I have never known the man."

"That's awful." Emrys shook his head. "I'm sorry."

"You do not have to apologise," the man replied. "All you have to do is fight, and fight well."

"What are these beasts Denrick speaks of?" Emrys asked.

"I do not know but I have heard rumours from the slavers," the man replied. "They say Denrick paid a handsome fortune to a trader from Alterra for vicious cave-dwelling beasts. I have seen many beasts in my time but their descriptions sound strange. They say the beasts have three heads, wings and can breathe fire. We will have to be quick on our feet."

Emrys felt a flutter of fear cross over him. He had never heard of fire-breathing beasts before and wondered exactly how he would go about facing such monsters. He clung onto a tiny spark of hope that he could speak to them as he did with Leviathan, but even in this place he could feel his strength dwindling away like light from the suns. He needed the power, the strength of the Primal, which he felt ebbing away. He felt hopeless without it. Emrys shuddered and fresh tears ran down his face. He felt the strong grip on his shoulder as the man gripped him as comfortingly as his huge hands could muster. "No tears boy," he said. "We do not cry in the face of fear, we rise up to meet it head on. Cillian, your countryman, taught me that when I was your age."

Sniffling Emrys wiped his nose on his rags and finished the meat the stranger provided to him. The two sat in silence for a short while before the man addressed him once more.

"Tomorrow we fight, boy," he said. "I need to know, will you obey my commands? Follow me when I say, strike when I say?"

"I will," Emrys sniffed and met him head on.

"Good," the man nodded in approval, "Now tell me, what is your name?"

Emrys felt he could trust the man, and he was tired of lying about who he was. He needed to trust someone and he knew the man had been open and honest with him from the start. "My name is Emrys of Stormgast," he said. "What is your name?"

"It is good to know you Emrys," he replied. "Jakob. My name is Jakob."

Chapter Eighteen
The Beasts of Morkosi

EMRYS squinted as he, Jakob and a party of eight slaves made their way from the Pits below. The suns were blinding, as if he had never seen their bright glow before and he hid his eyes from the strain of their heat. He could not believe his luck in who he had spoken to the previous night. Jakob, Rheinar's son. It had to be, but Emrys never knew he had another name before it was Rheinar. Jakob had explained his father was called Jerreko but he could neither confirm nor deny if this was his Master-At-Arms. Rheinar was extremely secretive when it came to his past before he came to Galbraith and only spoke of his time in Daal with a tone of shame. What would he even say to Jakob? That he knew his father? He had only just met the man and could not judge if he had Rheinar's anger in him. What if he had lashed out at Emrys? He shuddered at the thought and dismissed it as soon as he thought it. As they moved, Jakob was striding proudly up the stairs to the rhythm of the crowd above. The sound was staggering. There must have been thousands of voices cheering, chanting, clapping, stomping and jumping as they called forth the next challengers to the arena. As the morning had passed, group after group of slaves had been taken from the Pits to fight above and so few had returned. The ones that did were covered in cuts, scrapes, bruises and spoke not a word of the horrors they faced above. A deafening horn was blown by Emrys' right ear causing him to roil in pain as the slavers unhooked their chains. He and most of the other slaves were handed short swords of questionable quality and a small shield that had all but rusted over. "This sword is all but dull," Emrys said to Jakob.

"Focus Emrys," he replied as he took in his hands a spear and shield. "Remember do as I command and you stand a chance."

The crowd roared as the group made their way into the arena. It was a huge circular pit fitted with bloodied sand and spikes lining its circumference. Opposite of their entrance stood a huge gate, above which the richest of Daal could be seen feasting and drinking as they eagerly awaited the next event. They made their way to the centre as Emrys gawped at the people above. There were so many faces in the crowd and above them archers who lined the towers surrounding Kelpis Magna. A second horn was sounded as they reached the stone centre silencing the crowd as a man in the rafters stepped forward. It only took a second of Emrys squinting to see it was Denrick who walked forward with his arms aloft as the crowd applauded. He was wearing a blue robe and hood which he pulled back as he shouted to the crowd in Carpathi: "People of Daal! Are we having a good time?"

The crowd squealed in excitement and applauded the slave-master. "I am glad! I am glad!" He continued, "But the fun is only starting! For I have a special event for you. Your champion, born of Daal and the greatest warrior of his generation, Jakob will lead a party of fresh recruits against a pair of abominations! I have paid a hefty fortune to bring this joy to you all. From the mines of Morkosi in Alterra I bring to you a pair of magnificent horrors of which you've never seen the like! They feast on the blood on any fool to enter their domain. They have not been fed since they arrived, so you can imagine how hungry they are for the brave souls you see before you! Bring forth the three headed beasts! Bring forth the Chimeras!"

The pounding drums kicked in around them sending vibrations through Emrys' body. Ahead of them the huge gate was wrenched open slowly as two large shadows lurked in the darkness. Snarling breaths spewed embers which lit up their features for only a second before they disappeared back to the dark. One of the slaves dropped his weapons and sprinted back to the entrance to the boos of the crowd. "Please," he pleaded. "I have a family! I don't want to die!" He began climbing the gate and the archers in the towers shot him down with no hesitation as the bloodthirsty crowd cheered. "Hold and stand firm!" Jakob shouted at the nervous ranks of slaves around him. He raised his spear and addressed them all, "We stand together! We fight together and we die together!"

The drums stopped promptly as the gate reached the top and the crowd grew silent as they waited for Denrick's command. "RELEASE THE CHIMERAS!" He screamed as the drums resumed and the crowd whooped, baying for blood. Chains snapped forward as Jakob grunted and raised his shield and spear in anticipation. Emrys gripped his sword tightly and fought the tremors in his legs to stand firm as the warrior beside him commanded.

From the darkness emerged the Chimeras and Emrys could not believe his own eyes. The towering beasts, which stood before him, were about ten feet tall and had the heads of a lion, dragon and what appeared to be a face of snake at the end of a coiled tail. The dragon spat forth flames that jumped twenty feet causing panic among the ranks as they slowly edged backwards. The lions roared in unison and Emrys could feel the pain behind it. The reason for the pain became apparent when Emrys saw the lacerations spanning the Chimeras' bodies as they were beaten into submission. He could not see a calm beast before him, only ones that were consumed by rage. There was to be no communicating with these tortured monsters and Emrys' hope of calming them faded quickly as they slowly crept forward. The roars continued as the tail snapped in their direction revealing two huge fangs the size of their swords. Suddenly one of them broke out into a sprint and jumped at them. Jakob reacted quickly and screamed commands as the group split into two, one either side of the beast. For the most part they had avoided the leap except one of the slaves who was caught by the whip of the tail, and was strangled above the Chimeras head. His head burst and neck snapped under the pressure as the crowd howled and applauded the bloody spectacle. Emrys stood by Jakob as he leapt forward in a feint attack zig-zagging from side to side. The dragon head spewed a fresh trail of flames towards him at which point he slid under the Chimeras' belly and pronged his spear into its side prompting fierce howls from the lion. "Emrys attack now!" he shouted spurring the young Prince into action.

He ran as fast as he could and slashed twice at the beast's rear leg. Suddenly the tail whipped back around and he ducked just enough to avoid it. Using the momentum as his legs sprang back into action, he thrust his sword against the tail. To his surprise he serrated the tail and its snake head and eyes rolled back limp as the Chimera dragged it along. In its fury it jumped on the spot and snarled a mere foot away from Emrys. He froze in the lion's gaze as it growled and showed its fangs. Behind it, the dragon inhaled once more and Emrys knew he would have to be quick. As a jet of sparkling flames headed his way, he jumped prone under the belly of the beast. Jakob at this point jammed his spear into its side, and before ripping it clean, propelled himself to stand on the Chimera. He dug the spear once more into the beast and gripped tightly as it bucked around, trying to throw him from its back. The other group were not faring well at all to the other Chimera. Emrys glanced over and saw three charred remains from the four as the last slave attempted to flee its embrace. "Go for its throat, Emrys!" Jakob shouted again.

Drawing upon his courage Emrys dodged the lion's bite and sliced its throat with as much strength as he could muster. Warm blood sprayed his arms and the Chimera stumbled around in a daze as the rest of the slaves charged. Within moments the beast was down and further cheers erupted from the crowd. Of the ten that entered the arena, Emrys, Jakob and three others remained. The final slave from the other group howled in agony as the other Chimera disembowelled him with a slash of its razor-sharp claws. It turned its attention to the group of five and Jakob instructed them to surround it. One of the slaves broke formation, and charged it prompting a fresh jet of fire, which engulfed the poor woman, setting her ablaze. Her curdling screams sent daggers of fear into Emrys' heart as he nervously awaited Jakob's orders. Jakob, he noticed, had dropped his shield and moved behind Emrys. "Do you trust me Emrys?" he asked tapping him on the shoulder.

"I do Jakob," Emrys replied as the beast feasted on its freshest victim.

"Then draw its attention to you!" he shouted. "Scream as loudly as you can."

Emrys obeyed and shouted as loudly as he could, demanding the beasts' attention. It snarled and cast its fiery eyes at him. It broke out into a sprint and leapt at him. "Emrys roll forward!" Jakob demanded. He did so, and as the beast flew over his head, Jakob forced a two-handed thrust straight through the lion's head in the centre of the beast. Its eyes rolled back and even as strong as Jakob was, the beast toppled over, crashing down on top of him. "Jakob!" Emrys shouted and dropped his weapons. He ran over to him and saw the beast was pinning him down. "You there!" Emrys shouted to the other survivor. "Help me get this beast off him!"

It was not easy work but the two of them managed to wrestle Jakob free from the Chimera's weight. Jakob spluttered a dash of blood and pulled himself to his feet, coughing sand with each harsh breath. Wrenching the spear free he turned to Emrys and clapped his shoulder with a strong hand. "You did well," he said. "There's a warrior within you yet."

The crowd continued to chant Jakob's name as he raised his spear aloft and cheered. Emrys and the other slave cheered with him and threw their arms up into the air. A large toot from the horn silenced the crowd once more as Denrick strolled back out onto the veranda. The gate ahead of them was half closed and dust continued to swirl around the arena. Denrick did not look pleased yet licked his lips and smiled an evil grin Emrys did not trust.

Hushing the crowd and speaking once more in Carpathi he said: "The Champion Jakob delivers once more! Yet, I think that was too easy, don't you agree?" The crowd burst out into cheers once more as Denrick continued: "The trader with whom I bought the Chimeras also sold to me something else his people found further into the mines of Morkosi. They went deeper and deeper, right into the bowels of the watery cave. From it they found a truly horrifying creature. One that has already claimed the lives of twenty of my slaves as they hopelessly struggle to control it." Jakob shuffled back to retrieve his shield and warned Emrys: "Be brave, we will need to be strong."

"It is my absolute privilege to bring to you all, THE HYDRA OF MORKOSI," Denrick shouted as the gates began to re-open.

Suddenly the half-opened gate was ripped apart by the sheer weight and size of the reptile in front of them. Emrys gasped in shock as he looked at the Hydra. The scaled emerald serpent towered above them and had teeth half the size of Jakob. Its scales glistened in the sun, blinding Emrys whenever he looked at its reflecting light. The monster had two tails and five heads that snapped at each other almost as if they were play fighting. The crowd had gone from cheers to sounds of disbelief and some were even booing the unjust challenge before them. A few of them had run for the exits as it slowly dawned on the crowd, the slavers and archers were in no control of the huge monstrosity. The Hydra roared in fury. It was a deafening sound and both Emrys and Jakob dropped to their knees muffling their ears with their hands. The beast stomped forward sending ripples through the sand, stands and walls around them. The archers had nocked their arrows and nervously awaited the outcome below. The third survivor attempted to run past the Hydra drawing its attention to him. With one swift bite the monstrosity swallowed him whole with its third head while the two behind snapped at each other's throats.

"We're doomed," Emrys cried out as the monster turned its attention to him and Jakob.

A voice from behind him spoke boldly, "Not yet, my Prince."

Turning on the spot Emrys saw the huge body of Rheinar standing tall and felt tears welling in his eyes. Jakob looked at Rheinar as if he had seen a ghost but quickly averted his eyes to the danger lurking ahead. An arrow flew over Emrys shoulder and hit the centre head in one of its glaring purple eyes. Jumping down from the parapets was Lymris, her hair swishing through the air as she nocked another arrow. From all sides of the arena came the crew of the Crimson Tempest, rappelling down into the arena. Balion and Baster leapt down from opposite sides with grappling hooks and set about pinning the beast to the spikes on the sides of the arena. Dwayne, Keilley and Sibley all jumped down too, with harpoons and stuck them squarely into the beast as it squealed in pain. The rest of the crew joined in a mix of axe and sword as they began slicing the Hydra's body. Then Emrys saw it. From above, Captain Velstadt jumped down and with a huge swing of a broadsword, sliced one of its heads clean off. The Hydra roared again in fury as it charged forward ripping itself clean off the spikes to its rear. Balion and Baster were dragged through the air clinging onto the hooks for dear life as the rest of the crew scurried from its path.

"Emrys! Lymris! Get behind me!" Rheinar commanded as the siblings met. Lymris fired another arrow and hit the middle head square on its throat causing it to gasp for air. Rheinar ran forward and dodged two head snaps before sliding beneath the beast. With his sword upturned he sliced the Hydra's belly apart causing all manner of disgusting guts and bodily fluids to spray out in all directions. Emrys could not believe his eyes. Rheinar had done the impossible and killed the beast in emphatic style. The Hydra stumbled wearily before crashing down to its side. Baster had no time to evade this and with one slam, he was crushed beneath the huge serpent. "Baster!" Balion screamed and ran over to the Hydra's twitching corpse. No manner of strength could lift its corpse and Balion wept inconsolably sat in the sand. The crowd that remained cheered but only for a few seconds before a hail of arrows rained down on the arena. Baster, Dwayne, Keilley and Sibley were all filled with arrows as the remaining crew grouped together in the centre. Velstadt screamed in anguished fury as he saw the beloved members of his crew shot down before his very eyes. "SHIELDS UP!" Rheinar demanded as they formed a tight unit from the aerial bombardment. The volleys of arrows continued to rain down on the shields for several minutes as the group huddled up. Once the arrows came to a halt, Emrys peered out from a gap behind the shield wall. He saw Denrick step back out onto the veranda, who was stood applauding and smiling at the group. "Jerreko!" he boomed. "I'm so *very* happy to see you."

Chapter Nineteen
Family Feud

SILENCE fell upon Kelpis Magna. The crowds had returned to an arena littered with blood and corpses. Emrys looked around at the crew. So few remained. Balion and Baster, his two closest friends on the Crimson Tempest, were gone. Dwayne, Sibley and Keilley too were spluttering blood as they crawled and grouped together. They shared one last look between one another and linked their arms together as they breathed their last. Velstadt was noticeably trembling beside him. Whether it was rage, sadness or the two emotions entwined, Emrys could not be sure. The gates behind them opened as heavily armoured slavers and soldiers began to pour into the arena. Within a minute they were fully surrounded by a glistening shield wall as it sparkled in the sun. Beneath their own shield wall, the stifling heat was unbearable. Emrys was a sweaty mess, and a trail of perspiration trickled down to his chin as he wiped his face on his rags. Rheinar had still not responded to Denrick's call. He glanced a look over to Jakob who puzzled over the man before him. "Jerreko!" Denrick shouted once more in Carpathi. "You can come out! I won't shoot you down."

"And how could I ever trust you?" Rheinar boomed back. "When you fired without warning before."

"Very well," Denrick smiled. "Let the people of Daal be witness that I command the archers to stand down. Put your bows away so that your former champion may reveal himself."

"I don't like this Rheinar," Velstadt interjected as he tapped Rheinar on his shoulder. "He's up to something."

"Denrick is always scheming," Rheinar growled. "We're surrounded with no way out. We have no other option than to play this out. Emrys take my shield. It's heavy so use both of your arms to hold it up. Do not for a second stick your head out."

Rheinar passed his shield to Emrys as he shifted to the right and despite the initial struggle, he was able to hold it aloft. The weight was staggering and Emrys could not believe Rheinar carried this on his back let alone one arm. Rheinar stepped out of the shield wall which formed up after his exit. He walked forward and held his arms out to his sides. "So what now, Denrick?" he asked.

"Now," Denrick licked his lips. "We have a game on our hands! The former champion will fight the current champion to the death!" The crowd roared its approval as Emrys and Lymris looked at each other worryingly. Rheinar grimaced as he turned to meet his son's eyes. Jakob, who had remained relatively quiet throughout this encounter, stood up and returned his father's gaze. They both looked sad, as if they were thinking of the time together that had been robbed from them. Rheinar turned back to Denrick and shouted, "No! I am done fighting at your whim! I will not fight my son!"

As the news sank in around Kelpis Magna, groups of the crowd started chanting for their release.

Denrick raised his arms to hush the crowd once more and said: "My decision is final! Fight now Jerreko, or I will kill you all!"

The guards surrounding them backed off to clear an area.

A few of them began dragging one of the Chimeras' corpses from the stone to the sand leaving behind a thick trail of the beast's blood. "What say you Jakob?" Denrick continued. "This is the *father* who abandoned you! He killed your mother and fled like a coward!"

"That's not true, Jakob," Rheinar reacted as the crowd began to boo and curse him. Jakob looked furious. So furious in fact that his jaw was locked stiff as he stared on at his father. His eyes were unflinching as he gripped his spear and shield as if he was gearing himself up. "He left you for dead!" Denrick spat. "You would be so had I not brought you into my service!"

"You killed my mother!" Jakob screamed. "You left me for dead!"

"No, I didn't Jakob!" Rheinar pleaded. "He is lying to you! Can't you see that?" Jakob couldn't. He paced around, spat on the ground and announced to the crowd: "I WILL FIGHT!"

It was met with huge cheers as the crowd backed their favourite fighter. "Throw the coward his sword," Denrick commanded. "May the best fighter win!"

Jakob screamed with a fury Emrys had never seen before as he leapt forward. Rheinar dodged the first few attacks easily but even now Emrys could see that his son was far faster than his mentor. He skipped around him with a speed Rheinar had no chance of matching, and were it not for the skill of his Master-At-Arms, he would already be dead. Rheinar made no attempts to attack Jakob. He parried and dodged where he could but refused to strike at his son. Jakob continued to thrust his spear until Rheinar caught it and snapped it in two. "Son," he said panting. "I did not know you were alive! I returned to our quarters where I found your mother dead!" Jakob, unbelieving, dropped his shield and picked up two of the swords from the dead slaves. Spinning forward he unleashed a relentless assault that put Rheinar squarely on the back foot. He was desperately and frantically blocking the blows he could but Emrys could see blood pouring from his right arm and left leg.

Emrys felt a tug at his shoulder. It was Lymris, who looked on at him with tears streaming down her face. "Please Emrys," she said, her voice breaking. "You must do something."

"What can I do?" Emrys asked defeated. "I cannot do anything."

"You can do everything," Velstadt looked at him intensely. "We believe in you. Trust in yourself and trust in your abilities." Emrys closed his eyes and tried to find a moment's peace in all of the chaos around him. He hushed the crowd and he silenced the twangs of steels as they clashed in the air. He had felt despair, pain and hopeless in his struggles so far. Ever since he had arrived in Daal he had been overwhelmed by the sights, the smells and the cruelties of this soulless place. He felt his anger rising, higher and higher until he thought his head would explode. He was angry at his father, angry at the slavers who caught him and angrier still at Denrick, the man who continued to torture his mentor even now. Then he felt it. He dropped Rheinar's shield and put his hands on the ground. His sister's warning was but muffled complaints to the strength of what he could hear. The vibrations. He could feel and hear everything. The steps of Rheinar and Jakob, the harsh breathing of the guards in the sand, the panicked heartbeats of the crew, Velstadt and Lymris around him. He screamed under the noise of it all. In an instant his eyes were aglow and the sand from the arena flew up into the sky and whirled around them as if it was a tornado. They were caught in the eye of the storm and the spar between father and son came to an abrupt end as they looked on at the swirling vortex around them.

"Now's our chance!" Velstadt shouted to his crew, "Clear a path and make for the gate! Rheinar, we need to move!"

Rheinar approached his son who raised his weapon agitatedly. "Jakob," Rheinar said as softly as he could muster. "I swear to you on your mother's life, Denrick has lied to you. I had nothing to do with her death."

Arrows began whizzing through the air to the centre as Velstadt engaged a few guards who had ploughed through the sand. "Please," Rheinar continued as tears began to form in the corners of his eyes. "Come with me and protect Emrys. I swear I will explain everything to you." Jakob was unmoving and disbelieving of his father's words. "Please, Jakob," Emrys spluttered. "I can't hold this for long."

Jakob stood there dazed for a moment before he nodded, "I will help you," he said. "But only for Emrys, not for you."

Emrys continued to maintain the vortex as cover, straining as the mental effort took its toll. Slowly he waddled behind the group as melees erupted around them. Lymris was loosing her arrows in all directions, while Rheinar charged the front rank knocking down four guards with one huge swing of his sword. Slowly but surely, they made it to the open gate, and once they were clear of it, with a tug of his mind, Emrys scattered the vortex in every direction. The puff of sand spread across Daal as far as the eye could see, covering it in a thick mist which fell down, cloaking the deserted city. They could barely see through it, nor could they see friend or foe. Weakened, Emrys stumbled to catch his breath before Lymris slid her hand into his and guided him away from Kelpis Magna onto the dusty and cramped roads ahead.

***

NIGHTFALL fell by the time the group had made it clear of the city. Velstadt and others from the crew had returned to the city to retrieve the horses and arrived late on in the evening just as the suns began to set. They had encountered little resistance as they stumbled through Daal. The cloud of sand had only started to part and most of the merchants they met were scrambling around to cover their trinkets from the sandstorm or thieves. Once clear of the city Emrys spluttered and coughed for what seemed an hour. The sand had sunk deep into his lungs and no amount of water washed it from his breath. Seeing his family and friends again however had brought back his spirit. He was defeated, distraught in Kelpis Magna, yet even now as he watched his sister fashioning arrows, he felt happier than he had ever been. But he could not shake the sense of guilt when he looked at Velstadt. His cries in the arena haunted him still when the captain saw five of his crew killed before his very eyes. Balion, Baster, Keilley, Sibley and Dwayne. Emrys promised himself he would never forget their names, nor their sacrifice to save him. When Velstadt returned with the horses and supplies for their journey, Emrys saw him take his remaining crew and clasp hands on them in a circle. He muttered a few comforting words to them all as they nodded in silence and held swords aloft for their fallen comrades. Rheinar and Jakob were locked in a deep discussion far away from the others. When Emrys rose to his feet to investigate, Velstadt walked over and pushed him back down.

"No," he said sitting by his side. "Rhienar and Jakob need to have that chat alone."

"But I can help," Emrys protested. "I can…"

"You cannot Emrys," Velstadt shook his head. "They haven't seen each other for a long, long time. Jakob believes Rheinar abandoned him and killed his mother, and let's not forget he's been enslaved to Kelpis Magna just as his father was before him. There's very little either of us could say to ease either of their sufferings. What they need, they need to get from each other."

Emrys slumped back down and twinged from the pain in his ribs. The fighting in the arena had caused a myriad of injuries across his body, and he felt the back of his leg sizzling with pain. He could not remember getting hit by the Chimeras but when he saw the red blistered skin on his calf, he knew he had been kissed by their fire. Velstadt stoked the fire at the camp and began cooking some meat he brought from Daal. Emrys could not stand it any longer and felt he needed to apologise to Velstadt about his crew. "Velstadt," Emrys started.

"Don't, Emrys," Velstadt said without looking. "My crew knew the risks but every single man and woman on the Crimson Tempest would die for you without a moment's hesitation. Why? Because we believe in you. None of the crew could ever forget what we saw that night when you spoke to the Serpent of the Sea. We have travelled the high seas and seen the wonders and mysteries of the world, but in that moment, we agreed that what we were seeing was special. Unique even. I have never cared much for destiny nor fate, but it must be your destiny to fix the wrongs in this world. There can be no greater sacrifice than to die for such a cause."

Velstadt's words moved Emrys more than he could mention. The crew listened to his words and nodded in turn as they looked on at Emrys. They were loyal, even after their friends had died. He could see their eyes staring back at him as the campfire flickered in the night, and felt comforted he was in such good company. Rheinar and Jakob returned about an hour later and sat down as the food was handed out. They ate in silence and shortly after the meal Velstadt and his men began packing up their things. "Are you leaving?" Rheinar asked between mouthfuls.

"Yes," Velstadt replied. "Our place is with the ocean. We are going to head back to Galbraith after a slight detour and see if we can recruit some new members of the crew."

Emrys had grown so accustomed to seeing Velstadt to his side that he looked on at them in shock as they gathered their things. "Please don't go Velstadt," he begged, prompting the captain to turn and look at him. Velstadt offered him a kind smile and knelt down beside him.

"I have to, my Prince," he said putting his hand on his shoulder, "You remember Helga? If I don't return soon, she'll have my head, make no mistake about that. But I do have something for you."

Velstadt slid one of his many rings from his left hand. It was silver and shimmered in the night sky. Wings were carved around its circumference and runes ran parallel to them almost as if they were telling a story. "What is it?" Emrys asked.

"No idea," Velstadt shrugged. "I won it from a mage a few…"

"When you say won," Rheinar interjected, "you mean stole."

A few of the crew chucked and Velstadt broke out into a big grin. "I count that as a win," he said. "But nevertheless, it's yours Emrys. You're off to see the Circle, I'm sure they'll be able to tell you more about it."

"Thank you for everything," Emrys said rising and looking around at the crew. "Thank you all." They smiled at him and held their arms across their hearts as they bowed to the exiled Prince. Velstadt gave him a hug and ruffled Emrys' shaggy hair from his eyes. "Go and save the world kid," he said smiling.

Rheinar stood up to say his farewells and struggled for the right words. "You have been a true friend," he said. "How can I thank you?"

"Get Emrys to the Circle," Velstadt replied. "There's nothing more important my friend. No doubt our enemies know we were in Daal so be careful out there. There're more than slavers to worry about when you reach Carpathia. Fair winds, Rheinar."

"Fair winds, my old friend," Rheinar replied as the two companions shared a gaze for a few seconds. They said no more to each other, as if more words would make their separation harder. Emrys watched as Velstadt and his crew walked off into the darkness, and prayed he could turn around and go with them, back to the Crimson Tempest.

Chapter Twenty
A Storm is Brewing

TYRIS' return to the capital had been well attended and he received a rousing reception as he jumped down from his horse. The Crown Prince had returned home and the lords and ladies took no hesitation in meeting him in the streets of Stormgast. He had been riding with his warriors for two weeks after restoring stability in Burnistoun. The scenes he had witnessed there were a great cause for concern and he promised himself he must warn his father before the day was out. He had felt no remorse in his execution of Dolgier, far from it. He had enjoyed it more than he dared to believe. As the crowd watching on chanted his name in Burnistoun, he had even smiled as the traitor scurried like a rat fleeing to its hole. He had left ten of his men to report back to him on events in Burnistoun and he prayed they would not be needed in the coming months. It was the middle of the afternoon, or at least he thought it was. Since the storms had arrived in Stormgast, the time of day always became harder to judge as huge clouds darkened the sky and hid the suns. The temperature was dropping. Tyris knew he would have to be quick about his business if he was to flee to shelter before the winds whipped through the streets, the rain thundered down and the sky cracked with lightning.

At the top of the stairs afore the Great Hall stood a smiling Mikhael and Elette. She was a sight for sore eyes. Her flowing golden hair swept in the wind and her pearly smile made Tyris feel warm in face of the bitter cold. He matched her smile as he walked up alongside Petra. As they reached the top Elette ran forward and hugged Tyris with a strength he did not know she possessed. She smelled like fresh flowers on a meadow and as they stood there in each other's arms, Tyris felt giddy like a child. He had missed her more than he realised. They kissed and Tyris felt his shoulders relax as he stood there bound by love. "My Prince," Mikhael said stepping forward. "Welcome home. You have been missed."

"It is good to be back," Tyris replied with a nod and looked down at Elette.

"You need a good shave," Elette laughed tugging at his stubble.

"Aye I do," Tyris chuckled itching his beard. "We've been riding for a good few weeks, haven't we Petra?"

"We have, my Prince," Petra said. "We would do well with a warm meal and beer in the belly."

"That we would, my friend," Tyris nodded. "But first I must speak with my father. He must hear about Burnistoun. Where can I find him Mikhael?"

"He's in his study," Mikhael motioned. "Find me afterwards, my Prince. There are things that need to be said."

Tyris nodded his approval and kissed Elette on her cheek as he departed. Turning to the palace he opened the doors and began climbing the spiral staircase to his father's study. King Terrys was always in his study of late. He spent hours poring over maps and sending correspondence to the furthest reaches of the Kingdom. Since his brother's exile, Tyris could count on one hand the number of times he had seen his father outside or in the Great Hall. Their conversations had been brief, and

King Terrys always seemed distracted, as if something else was playing on his mind. He reached the top of the stairs and gasped to catch his breath as the fire in his legs cooled. Composing himself he knocked on the door and waited for his father to speak.

"Enter," the voice behind the door boomed.

Turning the handle Tyris entered and was completely unsurprised by the sight before him. The study was a small room, filled with piles of books, scrolls and parchment in huge stacks from the floor to the roof. There were bookshelves, of course, however most were cobwebbed and undisturbed for the most part. A lone table was sat in the far corner of the room with candles providing the only light in the windowless study. It was at this table his father spent most of his days and a huge map of the continent sat beneath his arms as he poured over scroll after scroll from spies and friends. The room was smokier than usual today and huge puffs of smoke spread across the study as his father smoked his pipe.

"Welcome home, Tyris," his father said without turning. "Come and take a seat."

"Father," Tyris said as he walked forward. "I am pleased to see you."

King Terrys stopped writing and turned to look at his son. The King's beard had grown along with his hair which sat as a matted mess across his face. He looked gaunt, as if he had not seen the suns warmth for several days and huge bags hung beneath his eyes. He did not smell fresh either and covered his nose as discreetly as possible. His face was thinner than he remembered and he wondered when his father last ate a warm meal. "Are you okay, Father?" Tyris asked as he sat beside him. "You look like you need a good rest and I don't think a meal would be amiss."

"I am tired, Tyris," Terrys rasped and coughed. "Always tired. But I cannot rest for there is too much to worry about, and my worries extend beyond our own borders. How did you fare in Burnistoun?"

Tyris poured a cup of wine from a nearby jug and passed it to his father. "It went well," he said as he sat back down. "But I was concerned by what I saw. Executions in the streets of our lords and ladies. It was despicable. They were either hung or burnt at the stake. Bodies were strewn across the streets and your own statue was burnt to cinders by the time we got there. At the front of the movement was one man. An Arcadian by the name of Dolgier. I executed him as he executed so many of our countrymen and I'm ashamed to say I took pleasure in it."

His father looked at him and scratched his beard. He did not respond. Instead, he turned his attention back to the map and a note he fiercely clutched with his right hand. "Is Burnistoun under control?" he asked as he lit several candles.

"It is, Father," Tyris replied. "I have left ten of my men to serve the Lords and to ensure this does not happen again."

"Good," King Terrys nodded. "You've done very well Tyris. I'm proud of you."

Tyris felt a flush of warmth flow over his cheeks and he sheepishly avoided his father's gaze. Turning the topic, he looked down at his father's hand and asked: "What's in the note? Do we have more word of Emrys?"

"Sadly not," King Terrys replied. "The last we heard of Rheinar and Emrys was in Burnistoun. But there is good news. I received a second message while you travelled South, your sister is with them now."

Relief washed over Tyris and he chuckled along with his father. "I swear Lym and Emris should be joined by the hip," he said jokingly. "But of course, I am glad she is with them."

"So am I," his father said. "But I would've appreciated your sister to have left more than a note of her intentions. This note, however, details something entirely different yet all the more concerning. Here, take it."

King Terrys passed the note and Tyris poured over the words. It read:

Bad news, my King. Emperor Harold Valyris' health has taken a turn for the worst. Upon his return to Talon's Reach the emperor was struck down with a sudden illness and has scarcely been seen from his bed for more than a fortnight now. His son, Edmure, has been ruling in his stead. He appears to be taking advice from his advisor Mathas and as such has raised a large army which is set to move South...

"South?" Tyris looked up at his father. "But that would take them to Mercia."

"Indeed, it would," his father growled. "I fear Arcadia is itching for another war. We must warn your aunt in Mercia of this news. But I do not trust this message to be sent by bird. We must see this delivered this to Queen Eremea by hand."

Since his mother died, Tyris had never heard his father speak of Eremea. She was the ruler of Mercia, the Kingdom to the West and the homeland of his mother's people. King Terrys and Queen Eremea had always had a frosty relationship which had certainly worsened in the two years since Althea's passing. Tyris struggled to remember what his aunt even looked like and could not recall the last time he or his siblings had spoken to her, let alone seen her.

"What of the emperor's illness?" Tyris asked. "Do we

know anything more on that?"

"According to our spies he was healthy on the journey," King Terrys replied. "But we do not know more than that. We must hope he makes a speedy recovery or the peace between Arcadia and Galbraith could be over before we know it. Now allow me to show you something."

King Terrys cleared the table save for the huge map and candles lighting its features. He drew his fingers across the map as he laid out the plans before Tyris. "We're here," he pointed. "Arcadia lies to the North West, and Mercia to our West. We control the seas between us and Arcadia. Arcadia knows this and if they have any sense, they would not risk a naval battle. But if Arcadia takes Mercia, then they have a direct land route to Galbraith. We must ensure Mercia does not fall. Do you have anyone under your command who you trust with your life?"

Without hesitation Tyris replied, "Petra. He's a strong warrior, smart too. I would not question his loyalty nor his honour. He'll be able to make the journey to Cairngorm."

"Then I would have you deliver this to him." King Terrys placed the note in his hand and pulled another from his pocket, "And this as well."

The maroon envelope was sealed with their family crest and wrapped in strings of leathers. Judging from the writing, Tyris ascertained this was written by his father's hand. "What is this?" he asked.

"A last resort son," Terrys replied frustratedly. "Hopefully it will not come to it. Do not mention this to anyone, and that includes Mikhael."

"Father, I do not understa…" Tyris protested.

"Just do as I say!" his father shouted slamming his fist

down to the table. "I will not be around forever Tyris, and before long you will inherit my mistakes. My enemies. Galbraith is standing but only just. If we cannot rally Mercia to our side then I fear for our survival. Edmure *will* be Emperor, and I do not doubt he will destroy everything in his path unless we plan accordingly."

Tyris stood as still as he could. The venom he had seen in his father's eyes scared him and he gulped down the remnants of his fear as he chose his next words carefully.

"Father, I will see this done." He bowed his head. "But you must get out of this room. The lords, ladies, commonfolk, they have not seen you for weeks. I hear them whisper. Would you like to know what they call you? They call you The Absent King."

King Terrys dropped his head in shame. Tears welled in the old king's eyes as he shuffled through his papers and avoided looking at Tyris directly. "I exiled my own son," he said weakly. "Emrys is a good boy. A kind boy. He did not deserve that cruelty and yet I did it because I am weak. Because I feared Arcadia more than I loved my son. How can I face my people? The lords and ladies who look up to me to set an example?"

Tyris had never seen his father like this before. It was if he had given up hope since Emrys had left Galbraith and it was evident enough to see how his father tormented himself for it. "You did what you thought was best," Tyris said calmly. "Emrys, intentionally or not, injured the son of the emperor. You acted because you wanted the peace between Harold and Terrys to mean something."

"And yet it will mean nothing when Edmure rules," his father dismissed. "I made an error. Emrys should be here with his family, not half a continent away, chasing shadows."

"Father, he is the Primal," Tyris said. "Mikhael's explained it to us all. He needs to be with the Circle if he is to realise his power, whereas we need to tackle the problems at our door. And for that we need you, strong and just. Not a feeble man pouring over maps in a dark room. We are feasting tonight, please do not hide in this study any more. Elette barely know you. She's not seen you since Emrys' banishment."

His father looked up at him and took the Crown of Thorns from his head. His matted hair barely moved from its greasiness and his father stabbed at the prongs of the crown as if he was a scolded child. "I could do with a bath first," his father said sour-faced.

"Aye," Tyris nodded smiling. "You smell like shit. I will hand these notes to Petra. Knowing him, he'll be out of Stormgast within the hour." As Tyris turned to leave, King Terrys gripped his arm in a vice grip and tugged his arm. "Thank you, Tyris," he said. "You are a good son, and you will be a greater king than I."

Tyris held his father's arm and smiled briefly before leaving the dusty study.

Tyris handed the notes to Petra under strict orders to discuss his business with no one save Queen Eremea of Mercia. As he watched his friend ride off into the night, he prayed to the God of Nature that his journey be swift and his path be true. Later than evening a feast was brought forth in his name as he, Elette, Mikhael and several Lords and Ladies sat down to dine. The spread was magnificent. A hog roast laden with herbs and spices was diced and passed from plate to plate. Fruits and vegetables were there in abundance and Tyris' particular favourite, the spiced apples, were brought out last. The doors of the Great Hall swung open and as silence spread from table to table, King Terrys emerged from the dark of night. He looked fresher than he had for months and his presence brought smiles on faces all around him. The lords and ladies began to rise to their feet before his father ushered them to sit and smiled at them all. "I am sorry I have been absent of late my friends and family," he said. "No more. Let us raise a flagon to my son and my daughter, the Crown Prince and Princess of Galbraith. Let's hear it for Tyris and Elette!"

The Lords and Ladies duly obliged as cheers rang out around the hall. Tyris and Elette, hand in hand, smiled back and bowed before their King. Terrys looked back at him and merely winked with the corner of his eye. Mikhael approached his father, and with a few mutterings of words, the smile on his face dropped in an instant.

Chapter Twenty-One
Back on the Road

EMRYS tossed and turned in a cold sweat as he slowly drifted into a dream under the night sky. He could see Caulder again yet he remained obscured from its view. Caulder was seemingly oblivious to Emrys' existence as it moved through the strange woodlands. The Bringer of Storms was gliding through the glade, spreading its Corruption as it strangled every blade of grass, tree and plant in range. Fresh scorch marks lit up the ground like fire and from its cinders rose horrific beasts and deathly creatures, each more vile than the last. Wraiths circled the spectacle as undead beasts clawed their way to the surface snapping at each other in unbridled rage. One creature rose that Emrys could not unsee. It cast an odd resemblance to Caulder's ghostly figure yet wore a headdress caked in blood. Unlike Caulder, it had no hood, and its features were easily visible. Its pale skull was covered in mould and its icy breath formed snow crystals in the air around them. It had a long slender body that was covered in scars which oozed a strange green liquid the likes of which made Emrys' skin crawl. With each drop, otherworldly skittering creatures grew from the blobs and ran over the course of its body. The ground beneath them began to shake as Caulder held its arms aloft. From the ruined earth rose a huge rotten platform made from bone, covered in barbs and spikes. It carried on climbing, higher and higher into the night sky and eventually stopped when it reached the high treeline. The platform boasted two huge plinths, one on either side, and glowing runes emanated from its base when Caulder stepped onto it. Caulder turned on the spot and drew its attention to the summoned creature rising from the ground.

"Siska," it said. "I am glad you have risen for I have a task for you. Find me the Primal. Do not kill him, not yet. Bring him to me so the work can be completed. Fly now and do not rest until he is with us."

Siska shrieked on the spot and from its body, bones of blood poured, ripping themselves from its very spine. Ghastly wings caked in the same green liquid formed from the bones and with a simple stretch, the winged beast took flight. Caulder turned back to the platform and began laughing maniacally. "I see you, Primal," it hissed without turning. "Siska will find you, of that, I am sure. But do not fear. Soon you will be with me and we will do wonders to this world."

All of a sudden each of the wraiths, beasts and creatures stopped in their tracks. They all turned to look at him. A thousand eyes pierced Emrys' very soul as he stood there shivering in fear. They made no sound. They made no movement. Their eyes began to glow and with a snap of Caulder's fingers, they screamed in unison at the young prince.

Emrys screamed as he jolted upright from his dream. The sound was enough to awaken Lymris and Jakob as Rheinar leapt to his side. "Emrys," he said. "What's wrong?"

"Caulder," Emrys squealed as he struggled to catch his breath. "I saw Caulder."

Lymris and Rheinar looked at each other and with a nod of his head, his sister ran down to the river to fetch some water. Emrys felt cold, as if the blood in his veins had been frozen over. Jakob said nothing, but as Emrys met his gaze he could tell Rheinar's son had many questions for him.

Lymris returned a few moments later and passed some water to Emrys. "Drink this," she said as she held him and wrapped him in a blanket. Emrys downed the water but could not shake the shivers as he clutched the blanket tightly. "What did you see?" Rheinar asked as he began to cook some meat on his shield.

"Caulder was in a forest," Emrys said as his sister cuddled him. "It summoned these nightmarish beasts from the ground and spoke to one of them. It called it Siska. I've never seen anything like it. It had huge wings and oozed a green liquid from its body. Caulder ordered Siska to find me and take me to it."

Jakob at this point began pacing around the area, almost as if he was searching for a fight. He'd drawn a sword and clearly decided he was best served guarding the party. Lymris continued to hold Emrys for warmth and after a few minutes, his shivers had receded. Rheinar stoked the fire deep in thought. "Do not fear, Emrys," he said. "Caulder does not know where we are and even if it did, we will protect you from this Siska. Isn't that right, Jakob?"

Jakob outright ignored his father. Their relationship was frayed at best. Since Velstadt left the previous night, Emrys could not recall a time he had seen Jakob and Rheinar talk. It was a difficult situation for them all to be in. Whenever they had travelled, two groups had always formed. During the previous day, Emrys had hoped Jakob and Rheinar would hunt together. It did not happen. Instead, Jakob disappeared for half of the day before returning with two hares tied to his waist. Rheinar did not speak again that night. He cooked the meat and passed it to Emrys who wolfed it down before they returned to sleep.

The next morning as the embers of the fire dwindled, he was woken up by his sister and they began to pack up their belongings. Emrys was over the moon to be back with his sister and Rheinar following his enslavement to Kelpis Magna. He had found new joy in the simplest of things like feeding Elmyra, fetching the water for the camp or even fletching arrows with his sister. Rheinar pulled a map from Shrieker's pouch and showed Emrys the route they must take. "We're here," he pointed. "We need to follow the road as far as Dee-Sarak and from there make our way East, crossing a small portion of the Atacama Desert."

Emrys was shocked. "You never said anything about a desert?" he protested. "Is there no other route?"

"No," Rheinar shook his head. "If we go too far south, we run the risk of running into the tribes. And if that happens there's very little Jakob or I could do to stop them taking or killing us all. If we cross the Atacama then we stand a chance. After the desert we get to the Whispering Woods, somewhere beyond there we will find the Circle."

"Somewhere?" Emrys continued. "We don't even know where the Circle is!"

"No one does," Rheinar said calmly. "There's strange rumours surrounding the Circle, and more importantly how they remain hidden from the world. We will search for as long as it takes Emrys, do not worry."

But Emrys did worry. How long before Caulder or this new threat Siska would find them? Emrys knew his days were numbered and he desperately needed to get to the Circle to understand his role as a Primal. He thought about what he had learned of Carpathia and questioned the risks of travelling South. Rheinar had explained to Emrys and Lymris that while Carpathia was one of the largest lands on the continent, it did not have a ruler. Instead, warring tribes swapped ownership of farms, lands and even towns to the South in a conflict he described as never-ending. It was the same tribes that would sack Daal occasionally before retreating South once more. Heading in that direction would be inherently risky and he understood Rheinar's concerns. They no longer had the numbers of Velstadt's crew to support them and their journey was putting them all under strain. Lymris looked like she needed a good rest but still she soldiered forward, ever smiling. Emrys admired and envied her courage in equal measure. She looked up at him as they set off and began pulling faces at him to cheer him up. It worked and Emrys laughed as the horses trotted down the road.

***

"AGAIN!" Rheinar commanded as their language lessons continued. Emrys was paired with Jakob, while Lymris sniggered at his attempts. Carpathi was tiring work. So many words could be misconstrued or misinterpreted for similar sounding words. Emrys noticed that the word for 'I love' and 'I hate' were so close in sound and pronunciation, it made no sense to him.

"Ti Berre," Emrys muttered as Lymris stifled her laughter.

"No, that's not it," Rheinar shook his head. "It's Ti *Berra.* Ti Berre is hate."

"Well, I'm starting to hate you for these lessons," Emrys quipped.

Rheinar chuckled and even Jakob cracked a smile as they rode on into the afternoon. The language seemed to come easy to Lymris and by now she was having brief conversations with Jakob. Rheinar called them to a halt when they located a clearing and ordered Emrys to tie up the horses. His legs ached when he slid off Elmyra. It had been one thing experiencing the rope burns on the Crimson Tempest, it was an entirely different story with the seemingly endless horse trek before them. He chafed in places he didn't know was possible to chafe and his already blistered feet throbbed with each step. Sitting down on solid ground was a relief, and one he took with blissful comfort once the camp was set up. He closed his eyes for a moment's rest in the baking sun and leant back on a tree stump to relax. A few minutes passed by when suddenly a shadow loomed over him. "Defend yourself!" a voice commanded.

Squinting Emrys saw the figure of Jakob standing over him with his sword in hand. Before Emrys could reach down for his own weapon, Jakob cleaved down with a two-handed swing. Emrys barely escaped the blow and heard the crack of wood as the sword split the tree stump behind him. He darted quickly to his feet and dodged a flurry of attacks as Jakob pressed his advantage. Rheinar and Lymris were nowhere to be seen. Emrys scanned his surroundings whenever he could but neither his sister nor his Master-At-Arms were present. Jakob continued to press forward and with a swift kick knocked Emrys hurtling backwards to the floor.

"Jakob, stop please!" Emrys cowered. "I'm tired!"

"Do you think an enemy will care if you're tired!" Jakob barked as he continued the barrage of attacks. Emrys was now rolling on the ground to avoid the blows and scurried like a rat in search of his sword. Finding it, he pressed forward with a lunge which Jakob dodged with ease. With a metal fist curled, Jakob landed a crunching blow to Emrys' face. Emrys squealed in agony as he heard the bone in the nose crack and blood began spewing forth. "JAKOB!" Rheinar shouted mid-sprint. "What are you doing?"

"He's not ready," Jakob said before he spat. "He needs to be ready."

Emrys' nose throbbed as Lymris rushed to his side. "This will hurt," she said before cracking his nose back into place. Emrys sank his head into the ground to muffle the scream as the bone was reset.

"We train together!" Rheinar shouted. "We do not attack each other at camp!"

"Do you think Emrys' enemies will wait for him to be ready?" Jakob said as his voice rose. "That they will allow him time to gather himself? They will slaughter him the first chance they get!"

Emrys stumbled to his feet and spat an ounce of blood from his mouth. He could feel the metal taste on his tongue and teeth as he approached Rheinar. "It's okay, Rheinar," he said. "Jakob is right." Rheinar calmed his fierce gaze as he looked at Emrys. "We have some food by the verge," he said. "Emrys, Lymris, start cooking tonight's meal."

Before the siblings could move to the nearby verge, Jakob held his sword sideways, blocking Emrys' path. "I am sorry for your nose, Emrys. Also, I am sorry for this," he said. "Jerreko. Fight me."

Rheinar looked at Jakob and shook his head. "I will not fight you Jakob," he said.

"Then I will attack Emrys and Lymris until you do," Jakob

spat and swung his sword for Emrys. Suddenly Lymris gripped his clothes and tugged him back from the blow. The two fell over sprawling onto the ground, and a winded Lymris gasped for air as Emrys rolled off his sister. Jakob stepped forward but suddenly flew ten feet to their right as Rheinar slammed his huge shield into him. "Emrys! Lymris!" he urged. "Get behind me and stay there!"

Jakob sprang back to his feet and beat his chest as he reclaimed his sword. As he approached his father, he began to circle him as Emrys and Lymris matched the pace. "So I see you will protect the children," Jakob said. "Where were you when I needed protecting!"

"Jakob!" Rheinar replied. "We've been through this, I believed you were dead! Amarint... Your mother was dead long before I arrived and there was no sign of you. Had I known you survived I never would have left Daal. Please, stop this!"

"For so long," Jakob said as he picked at his sword, "I was told tales of the great Jerreko. The most fearsome warrior in all the lands. And yet you did not even fight back in the arena! Denrick was right! You are a cow..."

"I did not fight back because you are my son and I love you!" Rheinar interrupted.

"Then if you truly love me," Jakob replied, "fight! Prove to me you are the warrior they say you are!" Rheinar nodded and Emrys saw how his mentor braced himself with a steady patience. Jakob jumped forward with frightening speed attempting to sweep Rheinar's leg. The Storm's Fury was wise to this and thrusted his shield into the ground. As the sword connected it repelled off the shield and Jakob was thrust back again. Attack after attack was repelled by Rheinar who did so easily as if he was swatting a fly. Emrys could not believe what he was witnessing. In Kelpis Magna, Jakob had the upper hand as his father held back and did not attack. Out here on the road, Rheinar looked in his element and freely sparred as if he was a cat playing with its prey. The fight dragged on for several minutes until Rheinar flung his shield at Jakob. Jakob ducked but as he did so Rheinar slid from underneath and with the butt of his sword smacked his son across the chin. Jakob fell like timber chopped from a tree and hit the grassy ground hard. Rheinar sheathed his sword and knelt in front of his son. "You have a lot of talent my son," he said, offering his hand to Jakob. "But you have a lot to learn."

Chapter Twenty-Two
Reconciliation

IT HAD been almost three weeks since Lymris watched on as Rheinar and Jakob fought it out between them. Surprisingly it had done wonders for their relationship and almost seemed to clear the air between the father and son. They laughed together, they ate together and they talked whenever the chance occurred. Lymris could see Jakob wanted to know all about his father, learn about his past and what he had done in Galbraith. Rheinar had often spoken of her mother, Althea, and the kindness she had given him in his release from Kelpis Magna. He also regaled tales of his warring days and the times he fought alongside King Terrys in Mercia or with Captain Velstadt on the high seas. Jakob was certainly enthralled to learn about his father's past, yet Lymris could not help notice the sadness resting in his eyes. After each story Jakob reclined further back and looked lost, almost as if he wished to turn back time and join his father on his adventures. They had their own conversations too. Often, they would be deep in conversation and when she or Emrys approached they would happily switch languages to keep their chats private.

The day after the bout Jakob set about making his amends. He had gone off into the woods with Emrys and by the time of their return they were laughing and joking as if nothing had happened. Jakob had also taken the time to apologise to Lymris and spent the rest of that afternoon fletching arrows by her side. He continued to teach her Carpathi, yet she struggled to focus when Emrys was near, as his fruitless efforts to speak the language provided her with a mountain of amusement. Even Jakob had laughed as they carved away at the wooden shafts. Emrys grew increasingly frustrated with his difficulties grasping the fundamentals of the language but Rheinar was ever persistent. He did not relent, nor did he offer Emrys breaks from his education. Occasionally he would ask Jakob to take over and try a different tack but still her brother struggled. Carpathi, it seemed, was not his mother tongue.

Their journey South had been a mixed bag of events. Occasionally there were groups of families fleeing North to Daal. With one particular family they had rushed towards the party begging for any scraps of food they could get. It didn't take long for Lymris to notice how malnourished they were and she hastily shared what provisions she could with them. Rheinar had frowned on this, but Lymris could not allow herself to sit idly by at their misfortune and suffering. The mother had kissed her hand incessantly and the small children had cuddled her as if she was their guardian angel. The family had offered them many of their things in exchange but Lymris could not accept. They had so little to begin with, she would not dare take what they had. When Rheinar jumped off Shrieker to check his hoof, Lymris quickly smuggled some gold away and handed it to them. The tears of joy and hopeful expressions they had, she promised herself she would not forget them.

Then there had been the times where they had to flee raiding parties as they swept along the dusty road. Slavers or tribesmen, Rheinar was not sure. For three days they hid in empty forests while the large warring bands made their way past. Lymris could not believe how close they raided to Daal, and wondered if Daal itself was part of their raid. Then she remembered what Rheinar had spoken of back in the city. It would be impossible to part Daal from its merchants and blood money. After the three days had passed, they rode over a field of bodies. Jakob remarked there must have been a huge fight and Lymris was alarmed at how young some of the bodies were. Children her age with mismatched armour and swords too big to wield were a common sight, and she could not shake the feeling that they were being watched as they made their way further into Carpathia.

Nervously the party made their journeys small and brief, and they only camped once the area had been scouted ahead and behind by either Jakob or Rheinar. Yet even for all of the dangers this land posed Lymris could not help but succumb to its beauty. The sands of Daal seemed like a distant memory to the glades and lush wildlife around them. Staggering waterfalls and huge cliffs which rose like waves were in abundance. Families of deer and elks skipped across the plains while the monkeys in the trees chanted and watched them pass by. Lymris struggled to understand how so much fighting, slavery and injustice could exist in such a pleasant, breathtaking land. In the early mornings, when the suns rose, she could smell the sweet scent of jasmine wafting through the winds. The crescendo of birds singing filled the breeze and for a moment all of the troubles in the world seemed to fade away. She loved the mornings. Lymris rose earlier than the others just to sit for a while in that pocket of peace she found in Carpathia. Yet she understood this would not last forever. Sooner or later the group would have to cross the Atacama Desert and face the burning heat once more. Rheinar had spoken only briefly of the trials they would face in the desert sea, Jakob had said even less. It had become apparent to Lymris that father and son had been discussing the route they would take in secret.

On the third week during the dead of night Lymris was awoken by Jakob shaking her shoulders. "Lymris," he whispered as his face shone in the moonlight. "Follow me and bring your bow."

Lymris wiped the sleep from her eyes and stretched before she crawled to Jakob. He led her through the winding woods before he dropped prone behind a felled tree and motioned Lymris to join him by his side. She crept up as quietly as she could until Jakob pointed to the treeline before them. "See the elk in the shade?" he whispered once more. "Can you see?"

Lymris allowed herself to adjust to the night sky. It was quiet, quieter than any night that they had experienced on the road. She could make out the trees in the distance and saw a few bushes rustling. The sound of water trickling by echoed through and through the moonlight she could see the ripples of water forming as the adult elk drank from the river. "I see it," Lymris whispered as she rose to her knees.

"Nock your arrow," he said quietly. "And await my command."

Lymris did as she was instructed and allowed herself to catch her breath as her back arched with the bow. She was aiming for the centre of mass and at a range of eighty feet she felt confident she would not miss. The elk remained unaware of their existence and continued to gulp down its share of water. "Take the shot," Jakob said. Lymris was ready to loose her arrow but paused at the small shadow she saw creeping up on the elk in the moonlight. To its foot emerged a baby calf as it stumbled around into the water. The adult elk nudged it along to the river bank and helped it take its drink. The baby elk was adorable. Its antlers had barely formed and its doe-like eyes shone towards them. Lymris froze. She couldn't bring herself to kill the beast and she jammed her arrow down into the mossy ground. With a sharp whistle she alerted the elk who grabbed its baby in its mouth and leapt from their sight into the darkened woodlands.

Jakob looked at her for a few moments then smiled, his teeth glistening in the darkness. "Good," he said. "I am proud of you Lymris."

Lymris was more confused than ever. "What? This was a test?" she said frowning at him.

Jakob rose to his feet and offered his hand to Lymris. "It takes skill to shoot a creature from this distance with a bow," he said. "But it takes courage to stay your arrow when you know to kill is wrong. How long do you think that calf would've survived without its mother? Two days? Maybe three? By allowing yourself to feel compassion you have proved yourself stronger than myself or than my father."

Lymris almost laughed at the statement. How could she compare to the strength of either warrior? Rheinar was revered throughout Galbraith and Jakob was the only person she'd ever seen stand up to his abilities. "Nonsense," she said as she stood up. "Rheinar's the finest warrior in Galbraith and you're near enough as good as he is. How could I compete against either of you?"

Jakob's face grew serious as he stared on at Lymris. "Strength is more than physical prowess or skill with a weapon," he said. "Strength of heart is lord of all. My father and I have done a lot of evil in Kelpis Magna. We have killed innocents by the dozens, slaughtered children and done things that haunt us to this day. No Lymris. You are stronger because you *chose* to be. Isn't that right, Father?"

Rheinar appeared from behind them and nodded in silent agreement. Lymris looked at them both in a different light. True they were warriors and fearsome ones at that, yet they seemed broken, almost as if they were at war with their consciences. "Emrys is lucky you have come with him," Rheinar spoke softly on return to camp, so as not to wake her sleeping brother. "He will need your strength more than he needs ours. You must be the one to remind him to do good rather than take the easier option. Courage, Lym. You must teach him courage."

Lymris felt fresh goosebumps on her arms as Rheinar and Jakob watched her. They believed in her more than she could ever believe in herself. "I," she said softly staring at the ground in embarrassment, "I will try."

***

THE next few days passed by without incident as they grew nearer and nearer to Dee-Sarak. Jakob and Rheinar had rode on ahead to check the roads as the siblings trotted behind. As they disappeared from sight behind the trees, Lymris thought on what they had said to her that night. As she looked on at her big brother, she could understand their concerns. He was not a coward by any means, but even now she could see how out of his depth he was. As he rode along the road atop Elmyra, he stared into the distance deep in thought. He had barely spoken to her since his latest vision of Caulder, and of late he had spent meals alone as he played with his own thoughts. Whenever he did speak to Lymris, it was brief and without the same humour they had enjoyed earlier on in their journey. Perhaps his stint in Kelpis Magna still plagued him, she wondered. Most likely, she reasoned, it was the pressure of being the Primal. Emrys had no clue about what or how his abilities linked him to Caulder and twice already she had seen how terrified he was when he woke from his nightmares.

"How are you, Emrys?" she said as she matched his pace.

"I'm okay, Lym," he said softly, though his focus was clearly somewhere else.

"How beautiful is Carpathia?" Lymris asked. "I wish Galbraith had these pretty waterfalls."

"It is stunning," Emrys smiled briefly then looked around in wonderment as though he had not taken in the sights before. "Do you think Mother and Father came down this way when they visited Daal?" He asked.

Lymris pondered the thought and shook her head. "I don't think so," she said, "As far as I'm aware they went east after they stopped in Daal. Who knows. We can always ask Rheinar later."

Slowly but surely the sound of rushing waters left them as they worked their way down a narrow canyon. Small rocks clattering against the upright echoed through the valley. Lymris looked up. The light of day was harder to see down here, and the further they trotted into the chasm, the less light they could see. She turned her attention back to the road and saw Rheinar and Jakob frantically galloping back to them.

"Hold on," Jakob said as he neared them. "There's a checkpoint up ahead. The narrow road is blocked off by a handful of armoured men."

"Is there any way past them?" Emrys asked nervously.

"No," Rheinar shook his head. "This chasm goes straight onto Dee-Serak. We cannot go around and there is no safe route above. The rocks above are prone to collapse and many travellers have lost their lives attempting to cross the valley."

"What should we do then?" Lymris asked as she ogled her nervous brother.

Rheinar stroked his chin and thought for a few moments. "I have an idea," he said sternly. "Emrys, Lymris. You two are mine and Jakob's slaves for this encounter. I need you both to keep your mouths shut and dismount your horses. I'll have to bind your hands and tie you to the back of our horses."

"Why do we need to dismount our horses?" Emrys asked as he ruffled Elmyra's ears.

"Slaves in Carpathia are not permitted to ride horses," Jakob replied. "If they see you on a horse and we claim you are slaves, they will not believe us."

"I don't like this plan at all," Lymris scratched her head. "What if we need to fight?"

"Don't worry," Rheinar said. "I will tie your hands together, but it'll be a loose knot. Now keep quiet you two, with luck we will pass without incident."

Lymris and Emrys dismounted as commanded and their hands were lightly bound to Jakob and Rheinar's horses respectively. As they moved closer and closer, the men they had mentioned came into view. They were clad in blackened armour and Lymris felt a stroke of deja-vu as she looked on at the soldiers. They looked familiar and Lymris could not shake the feeling she was missing something important. Within moments they had noticed Rheinar and Jakob as they walked forward. A few words were spoken in Carpathi as they pulled up next to the soldiers. One of them came around to the back of the horses and sized Lymris and Emrys up. He stank of ale and sweat as he leant into them and Lymris was hoping for the wind to change its direction. Then she saw it and panicked. Emblazoned on the pauldrons of the shiny armour was the Griffon of Talon's Reach.

The Knights of Arcadia, it had to be. She thought back to the wedding and she could remember the rows and rows of Arcadia's finest soldiers. How had they made it here before them? She nudged Emrys and gripped his arm as she drew his attention as discreetly as she could. Emrys' eyes widened and he began breathing harshly as the soldier squinted his eyes at them. Rheinar and Jakob had finished talking with the guards and proceeded to move forward. Lymris felt her heart beating quickly. The eyes of every soldier were on herself and her brother and she was praying they would not be discovered. As they passed by, she turned to look and saw the soldiers shouting at each other as one pointed at them. "Emrys, we need to go!" she said hurriedly and freed herself from the bounds.

Behind them she heard a shrilling cry as one soldier barked, "Seize them!"

Chapter Twenty-Three
Split Up

EMRYS felt his heart thundering to the rhythm of Elmyra's stride as they hastily fled through the chasm. Lymris had grabbed their attentions quickly and they broke into a canter long before any of the soldiers had mounted their horses, and chased them in pursuit. The winding pass was riddled with holes and crevasses, forcing Emrys to pay close attention to the hazards ahead. He did not look back out of fear. There must have been six or seven soldiers posted there and he prayed they were no more ahead. *How could Arcadians be in Carpathia already? How did they know where he was?* Questions for another time he thought as Elmyra whinnied through the stress of the ride. They rode for what seemed an eternity and the gloomy light shining down the cracks in the cliffs was waning quickly. Emrys pulled alongside Rheinar who barely noticed his arrival as they powered forth into the night. "Rheinar, when are we going to stop?" he asked mid-stride. "Elmyra's knackered and she needs a rest."

"We cannot rest," Rheinar replied without looking. "Those soldiers will not, and we do not know if there are more of them. Jakob, I have an idea. When we clear the valley, I want you to take Lymris and head North. Emrys and I will head South for a day then loop back round to Dee-Serak."

Jakob nodded and pulled Styria's reins close to him as the group formed two ranks of riders. Emrys meanwhile shivered as the cold night's wind closed in and howled through the tight chasm. Up ahead they could see torchlight and the shadowy forms of three soldiers sat atop a crumbling wall. "Shit," Rheinar said and quickly drew his sword. Be it the thundering sound of hooves or the mere sight of them, the soldiers leapt to their feet and drew their weapons in anticipation. One of the soldiers blew a horn which was echoed swiftly by another sounded behind the group. Jakob strode past and with a strong arm launched his spear forward. It caught the horn-blower square in his neck prompting a ghastly gargling of blood as he clawed at his throat helplessly. Arrows whizzed overhead as the soldiers counterattacked, one of which flew a whisker from Emrys' ear, rocking him from side to side. Lymris loosed an arrow yet missed when suddenly Styria tripped on a stray rock. The mare tumbled over and his sister was thrown from her saddle. She rolled to within ten feet of the two soldiers and gasped for air pinned beneath Styria's saddle. The armed men turned to face Lymris who attempted to free herself from Styria. "Lymris!" Emrys shouted in panic as Shrieker skid to an abrupt stop.

Jakob launched himself from his horse and with a swift flick of the sword, beheaded one of Lymris' pursuers. "Father take Emrys and go!" he screamed as he engaged the one remaining soldier. Rheinar did not need telling twice, and with a whip of the reins Shrieker and Elmrya sped off onto the dusty road. "We can't leave them!" Emrys protested trying to wrestle his reins free from Rheinar's iron grip.

"Jakob will look after Lymris!" he said snagging the reins back. "For now, we must look to ourselves. Ready your bow Emrys, we do not know what lies ahead."

Emrys turned to look at his sister. Jakob continued to spar

with the armoured warrior as she was helping Styria back to her feet. Rheinar's son span on the spot and sliced the soldier across his gut causing his entrails to spew out onto the road. The distance between them grew greater and greater until he could barely see either of them excepts as specks flickering in the dwindling torchlight. A second blow of horn was sounded not far behind them and Emrys feared the worst as his sister drifted from his sight.

Before long Emrys and Rheinar had cleared the valley and found themselves moving through complete darkness. Rheinar seemed to know where he was going, and once they reached the road he broke off into canter down the right fork. Neither of them uttered a word as they rode along. It was eerily quiet and after all the noise and chaos they had witnessed, both of them keenly listened to ensure they were not being followed. This went on for a good hour or so until Emrys yawned audibly. He was exhausted and Elmyra was too. Her harsh grunts bore witness to the strain in her legs and Emrys doubted she could continue on for much longer. She had been pushed to her limits and even now she swayed from left to right disorientated. Rheinar dismounted and scanned the area for a suitable place to sleep. He disappeared behind a hedgerow for several minutes before motioning Emrys to join him in his discovery. Behind the huge hedges Rheinar pointed at a small cave snug enough for the two of them. Elymra nearly collapsed when Emrys dismounted, before she snorted and rummaged through the ground in search of grass.

"Will she be, okay?" Emrys asked quietly as he patted his mare.

"She will," Rheinar said taking the saddle from Shrieker. "She's tired, nothing more. Rest and a belly full of grass is all she needs."

The cave was cold, damp and full of slimy moss, but Emrys in his exhaustion had no room for complaints. He felt his eyes lolling to the back of his head within moments. Rheinar meanwhile ripped a hedge apart and stuffed it as a cover at the mouth of the cave. "We will be fine, Emrys," Rheinar said as he threw Emrys a blanket. "Jakob and Lymris will be all right. Do not worry for them."

Emrys bit his fingernails nervously and prayed his mentor was right. He worried for his sister and hoped she was uninjured from her fall. "How will they know where to go?" Emrys asked shivering beneath his blanket.

"You can't miss Dee-Serak," Rheinar replied. "You can see it for miles. Now rest. It has been a testing night for us and you will need your strength for tomorrow."

***

AS the birds sang with the morning suns, Emrys felt a light skittering brush across his face. Peeling back his eyelids he saw, to his horror, hundreds of colourful spiders coursing his body and the mossy ground like a swarm of ants. He leapt to his feet in sheer panic and spun on the spot patting down his body as he thrust the critters away. He jumped from the cave and ran in a circle a few times before he found a pond and jumped into it head first without hesitation. Soaked, he pulled himself out and waited for the fear to settle. He hated spiders with a passion. Had he known the cave was full of them he never would have slept. Once he wrestled the blanket free from the cave, he shook it vigorously ensuring no spider was clinging to a single thread on it. As he looked around, he could see the horses were up and feeding by a grassy mound nearby, yet there was no sign of Rheinar. Before Emrys had the chance to venture further, Rheinar emerged from behind a tree clutching a bag. "Morning, Emrys," he said as he sauntered over and placed the bag down. "I've found us some mushrooms."

"I don't like mushrooms," Emrys frowned folding his arms.

"Nor do I," Rheinar agreed. "But it's all I could find so be grateful we have something rather than nothing."

Rheinar opened the bag and passed a handful of fungi to Emrys. They tasted exactly how he expected they would, awful. The slimy texture of the mushroom did not sit well on Emrys' palate, but now was not the time to be picky. Lymris had the vast majority of food in her saddle. In hindsight Emrys realised this was a bit of a mistake, one he would he seek to rectify when they next met. Already, as he disdainfully stuffed down the bitter vegetables, he was entirely enviable of Jakob and Lymris' breakfast.

"What now?" Emrys asked between mouthfuls. "Well," Rheinar replied as he took a seat. "We need to keep heading South. There's a trail about half a day's ride ahead we need to take. It goes through the woods and back to the road we left close to Dee-Serak. With luck, we'll be there by the morning and so will they."

Emrys understood little about where he was and even less about the route Jakob and his sister had taken. "Lymris and Jakob," he asked, "what kind of things will they be facing to the North."

"Their path is somewhat trickier than ours," Rheinar said. "Instead of woodland they will be trekking across plains which makes hiding difficult. But I trust my son to navigate the wilderness. They will be travelling a greater distance than we are but that does not mean they cannot make it to Dee-Serak for tomorrow."

Once the pair had finished their breakfast, they mounted their horses and after Rheinar had checked the road, began heading South. It was the coldest day Emrys had experienced in Carpathia so far. Whereas the journey since leaving Daal had been awash with sunny skies and stifling heat at times, their journey South was proving to be a tricky one. They were whipped and lashed by unrelenting winds and rain and the blanket Emrys used last night was now tied across his body to shield him from the conditions. Yet he was enjoying this spell of weather for it felt like he was at home. He yearned for Galbraith. It's plush countryside and its stormy season, the peak of any Galbrathian's year. He smiled as he met the rain head on and held his arms to the sky. *Thunder. Make me feel at home,* he thought, pleading to the skies. And it did. Storm clouds formed in an instant, and streaks of sapphire-tinted lightning tore across the sky in majestic fashion, as the booming thunder roared its response. Emrys could not help himself, he burst out laughing and whooped as the orchestral sound rang through the sky. "Was this you?" Rheinar bellowed through the wind.

"Aye I think so," Emrys shouted back. "It feels like Galbraith now!"

The weather passed by midday and the day's proceedings went by with Emrys' spirit lifted higher than it had been before. They found the trail Rheinar mentioned and made good progress as they trekked through the woodlands. The route had clearly been unused for a long time and several times the horses had leapt over downed trees. There were plenty of woodland critters watching them. Squirrels scrambled up trees, families of deer skipped through the clearings and they even saw some boars ruffling their tusks against the tree-bark. Rheinar was able to shoot one of the boars which he promptly shoved onto his shoulder and kept it for their tea later. The shelter from the wind and rain was appreciated by both riders who had been shivered for several hours. By nightfall they had reached the edge of the woods and Rheinar made a fire to soothe their soaked bones. He showed Emrys how to gut a boar and used his shield again to cook the meat by the time the darkness had settled around them.

"This is delicious," Emrys said as he lapped up his first mouthful. "How far are we to Dee-Serak?"

"Not far," Rheinar replied. "Beyond that tree line lies the road we left, though we are further South of course. We will rise at dawn and keep a look out for Jakob and Lymris."

"I hope their journey was as uneventful as ours," Emrys said as he warmed his hands by the fire.

At the young prince's request, Rheinar then regaled a story of King Terrys and his storming of Cairngorm some fifteen years ago. The castle which sat atop a huge moat in the middle of the Mercian mountains, was acclaimed to be 'unbreachable', something his father quickly rectified. King Terrys and his most trusted warriors, including Rheinar and his mother Althea, climbed the keep in the dead of night and without a single ounce of bloodshed, opened the gates for his army to enter. It was a master-stroke, a plan of genius which was executed perfectly. Rheinar always allowed himself to be giddy and proud of his part in the plan, and he always smiled as he reminisced on his days as a younger warrior. Emperor

Valyris' troops were routed and ever since then Queen Eremea had ruled in relative peace.

"Of course, she was not the friendliest of allies. Many called her mad, which was true to a point," Rheinar said. "And she *hated* your father."

Rheinar had never spoken of this before and it peaked Emrys' interest. "Why so?" he asked.

"I believe she loved him once," Rheinar nodded. "Then when King Terrys took an interest in her younger sister, I believe the nail in the coffin was set. She never married, your Aunt Eremea. Perhaps she was stuck in clinging onto the past. All I do know is she's not forgiven your father even after he saved Mercia from Arcadia. No offence lad but your aunt is a bit mental."

Emrys could not help but smile. Rheinar was grinning as he looked back and began rolling his index finger clockwise around his temple. As Emrys went to sleep that night he thought about Queen Eremea and wondered if he would ever meet her.

Morning came quickly. The two packed up the camp and made for Dee-Serak at Dawn, just as Rheinar suggested. What Emrys saw he couldn't believe as they cleared the treeline. He had been expecting a town or city from its name, but Dee-Serak was nothing of the sort. A huge column rose from the ground and towered over everything around it. Emrys reckoned it rivalled the size of the Great Oak back home and as he observed the monolith, he could see three runes carved vertically along it. "What do they say?" he asked in awe.

"The runes are Ancient Carpathi," Rheinar explained. "They read 'Truth Lies Within'. Who knows what it means though? It has been centuries since the meaning was lost, and no-one follows the old ways any more. See the clearing to the East?"

As Emrys scanned the horizon he could see the aforementioned clearing. "Aye, I see it."

"We'll wait for Jakob and Lymris there," Rheinar continued. "Hopefully they shouldn't be too long."

Hours passed quickly as Emrys and Rheinar sparred in the clearing. His mentor complimented his movement and appraised his sleight of hand as they continued to train. By the time it was midday they sat and watched the road eagerly for his sister's arrival. Then they saw it. A lone rider appeared from the trees hurtling forward as if hellhounds were chasing it. Atop the steed he saw Lymris, splattered in blood. She fell from Styria when they neared and she cried at the sight of Emrys and Rheinar. "Emrys!" She wailed as she ran forward and hugged him tighter than ever before.

"Lymris, what's wrong?" Emrys asked. "Where's Jakob?"

"They've taken him," she cried. "Please! We need to hurry! We need to save him!"

Chapter Twenty-Four
In With the Tide

"ARE you okay, Tyris?" Elette asked as she walked into their bedroom. It was late at night and even though Tyris was desperately tired, his mind would not settle and continued to race the room in search of answers. He had still not heard back from Petra and was concerned for his well-being but most of all his worries came when he thought of his siblings. There had been no updates for weeks and it was anyone's guess where Emrys and Lymris were. Tyris rubbed his eyes and could feel the strain they were under as he sat down on the plush feathered bed and exhaled.

"Aye, I'm okay," he said softly. "I've just been thinking about Emrys and Lymris. It's funny really, we spent all summer play fighting and taking the piss out of each other. Emrys used to get so wound up. Often he would say, that he hated me and I used to tease him about his swordsmanship. But do I miss that summer? Aye, I really do. I miss them more than I realised was possible."

A comforting arm embraced him around his neck and Tyris felt his neck grow limp as he dropped into Elette's arms. "I did not know your brother well," she said stroking his thick hair. "Nor did I know your sister, but what I did know is they were like peas in a pod. Our entire wedding, they spent at one another's side. One thing you can be certain of, they will be safe and they will be happy as long as they are together." Elette had proven herself to be the most hospitable partner over the past few months. She had a way with words and never failed to find the right ones to soothe Tyris when he worried about his siblings. They lay there in comfortable silence for a moment before Elette smiled and whispered, "I have something to tell you."

Tyris sat up and faced her. She looked more beautiful now than she ever had before and the young prince could feel his cheeks growing redder and redder. Her golden hair flowed down her shoulders and her piercing emerald eyes melted his heart whenever he caught her gaze. When she smiled it always brought happiness to him and he eagerly sat on the edge of the bed awaiting her news. "You can tell me anything," he said gripping her hand in his. "Is it something good?"

"I think," she said gripping his hand tightly and shying away, "I think I might be pregnant."

Tyris was lost for words and stared blankly on at his pretty wife. "Are you sure?" he stuttered and edged closer.

"Yes," she said softly. "I have been late for a month now and the women at the bathhouse were quick to advise it could be pregnancy. Are you all right?" Tyris cheeks grew wider and wider as a huge smile took hold of his face.

"I am over the moon," he said and grabbed her cheeks. "We're going to be parents!" He jumped to his feet and pulled Elette into his arms as he began jumping on the spot. "We're going to be parents!" he repeated over and over as Elette laughed and tears began welling in her eyes.

"What's the matter?" Tyris asked when he noticed.

"Nothing," she said sniffling. "These are tears of joy. I was so worried about what you would think."

Tyris was so excited and could barely contain himself as

he paced joyfully around the room. A boy or a girl, he did not care one bit. He was going to be a father. With all of the heartbreak and sadness that had befallen his family of late, this could the chance to create something new, something brilliant. He wished his mother was here to see it. She would've been the greatest grandmother and Tyris knew that if they had a girl, he would have to call his daughter Althea in her memory. "I must tell Father," he said proudly. "He'll be ecstatic at the prospect of another Galbraith. Then we'll need to tell Mikhael he'll be…"

"Mikhael knows," Elette interrupted nervously. "I'm sorry Tyris but I needed to confide in someone and I've been spending so much time with him… I thought talking with him about this might help."

"I don't mind," Tyris chuckled, shook his head and took her hands in his once more. "Do you know why? Because we're going to be parents! I love you Elette and I cannot wait to be a father with you at my side."

Tyris promised himself that he would never forget the warmth in the smile Elette gave as she looked up to him. She was perfect. As her face shone in the candlelight Tyris knew he would do anything for her. Their child would be their greatest achievement together and when they kissed passionately, he realised he had never been happier than in that moment.

***

TYRIS rose the following morning with a sense of pride he'd never felt before. The euphoria from last night gave him a skip in his step as he walked through to the Great Hall. The weather had been much the same for the last few weeks. Rain, wind, thunder and lightning. The stormy season was in full swing but even the harshest of rain clouds could not dampen his spirits. Opening the doors sent a gust of wind through the Great Hall extinguishing many candles as the lords looked up to greet him. Atop the throne was his father who was deep in discussion with Mikhael. King Terrys had been true to his word since they had spoken in his study. He was ever-present and always made time for his subjects. His renewed sense of duty brought with it a happiness he thought his father had lost. The King smiled greatly and often, and during meals he would take a moment to inspire his fellow lords and ladies with the tales of the Old Kingdom. When Tyris approached his father promptly rose to his feet and greeted his son with a hearty smile. "Tyris," he said stepping forward. "How are you today?"

"I am well, Father," Tyris said matching his father's smile. "Very well and I have some amazing news. Elette is pregnant, Father. Your grandchild and heir to the Kingdom is on the way."

King Terrys clasped his hands around Tyris and hugged him laughing all the while. "That is great news," he said pulling his head close to his. "We must feast, drink and celebrate tonight! Mikhael! My son will have an heir! Ensure we celebrate in true fashion that befits the heir to Galbraith!"

"Certainly so," Mikhael said hobbling over to them. "My congratulations to you, young Tyris! Would you like a boy or a girl?"

"I honestly don't care, Mikhael," Tyris replied shaking his hand. "So long as my child is healthy, and has ten fingers and ten toes."

"Well said." Mikhael smiled and then turned to his father, "I will see to the arrangements, my King."

Mikhael bowed and crept away from the royals. Tyris could not help notice that his frail body seemed even frailer in the colder months. Mikhael had never been sprightly, but in comparison to how he fared in the summer, the stormy season had made the old advisor slower than ever.

Tyris continued to chat with his father through the morning and ate his fair share of fruits and meats as the day rolled by. At midday the doors burst open once more as a pair of soaked soldiers ran into the Great Hall. "My King," one of the said shivering from the cold. "A ship with red sails has been spotted coming into dock."

"It can't be," King Terrys rose to his feet with a look of wonderment in his eyes. "Tyris, grab a coat and join me at the docks."

"Why?" Tyris asked. "Who is it father?"

"Someone I have not seen for an age." His father smiled. "I believe you're about to meet Captain Velstadt."

Tyris remembered the name but couldn't remember why or how. *Perhaps Rheinar had mentioned it?* Regardless, the young prince was curious to learn of this Captain Velstadt and rushed off to his quarters to retrieve his warmest attire. Leaving the grounds of the palace he was blast almost instantly with a harsh wind as it howled through the air. The rain was consistently soaking everything in sight, and within moments he was as drenched as the soldiers who had come to the Great Hall. The marketplace was all but abandoned and the few traders he saw were fleeing indoors to escape the awful conditions. As he looked down to the docks, he saw the waves crashing against the jetties as huge spouts of water flopped back down. He could see the ship the soldiers mentioned. Its red sails were easily noticeable even in this dreary weather and running abreast of the ship, emblazoned in golden carvings were the words 'THE CRIMSON TEMPEST'. Some of its crew were heaving the sails, while others hurried to tie the ship down to the jetties. His father was already stood looking on. He was completely unfazed by the blistering winds and needle-like rain and stood with his arms to his side as he waited for the crews to disembark. Leading the group emerged a large scarred man with dreadlocks soaked by the sea's embrace. He wore a tunic of red and blue with cutlasses emblazoned on its front. As he walked down towards them, he ornately shimmered as the rain splattered from the golden trinkets adorning his attire. His dark skin bore the shapes of many burns, scars and cuts, and Tyris could see that he was blinded in his right eye. The man smiled as he came to stand before them. He promptly dropped to his knee and said: "It is great to see you, my King."

King Terrys approached and pulled the man to his feet with a big smile. "It is greater than you know, Velstadt," he said. "Now tell me, how did you lose the eye old friend?"

"Long story for another time," Velstadt laughed. "Besides we should probably get out of this weather, no? My crew have been drenched ever since we made our way through the Snake's Pass."

"Well before we go any further," his father replied, "please allow me to introduce you to my son and heir to Galbraith, the Crown Prince Tyris."

"It is my honour to meet you as an adult Tyris." Velstadt bowed. "I doubt you remember me; you were only a small child when we last we saw each other. I'll tell you one thing though, you look much more like your father than your brother does." Tyris was shocked and shared a concerned look with his father.

"You've seen Emrys?" he asked hastily. "Is he okay? Is Lymris okay?"

"He's fine lad. They're both fine," Velstadt said calmly. "I'll tell you everything I know as soon as we get inside, agreed?"

Both the King and Prince nodded in unison and walked to the Great Hall with a spring in their step. They had heard nothing of Emrys or of Lymris since they had left Burnistoun and were keen to listen to whatever news Captain Velstadt had to share.

Velstadt and his crew arrived moments later while King Terrys provided blankets, stoked the fires and ordered food to be brought forth. They sat together, the three, by the roaring fire and felt the warmth sinking into their bones. The captain was true to his word. He told them everything, from their first meeting to their last. He explained the difficulties they had faced along the way and Tyris could not believe the tale of Leviathan, nor of the beasts in Kelpis Magna. He had to calm himself when he heard of Emrys' enslavement, and even with gritted teeth, his anger was evident. "We should kill that bastard Denrick," Tyris spat as his blood boiled.

His father shook his head. "No. We kill Denrick and another takes his place. Daal is a different world from the Kingdom, Tyris. Money always wins there and cruelty often yields the biggest profits."

"What of this Leviathan?" Tyris asked of Velstadt. "You say that Emrys spoke to him."

"Aye he did," Velstadt nodded and the sincerity in his

voice was apparent. As Tyris looked at him, he did not believe the captain was a liar nor a fool. "Emrys has abilities that quite frankly I've never seen before." He continued, "He saved the lives of me, my crew, Lymris, Rheinar not once but twice. In the arena he somehow created a sandstorm that swept up through the sky and covered every inch of Daal. The sand took three days to clear and blackened the suns covering the city in shadow. Your son, my King, he is the most magnificent mage I have ever witnessed."

The words seemed to pain his father and he looked away almost as if he was embarrassed. "I did not treat my son fairly," he said. "I hope Emrys does not hate me for it."

"He does not," Velstadt said authoritatively. "He loves and misses you both, even a half-blind man such as I could see. But his journey is only beginning. I left them at Daal, but they have to go cross the Atacama Desert if they are to reach the gardens of Carpathia. There we can only hope the Circle will have the answers he needs."

"What of Caulder?" King Terrys asked. "Mikhael has explained a bit of who it is. Does Emrys know more? Has he been able to learn anything?"

Velstadt seemed to stiffen up at the mention of King Terrys' advisor and he merely shrugged at the question. No one had answers when it came to Caulder and Tyris felt lost whenever his name was mentioned. The rest of the afternoon his father and the captain spent in conversation. Velstadt asked his father for some sailors to replenish his crew, a request the King was more than happy to oblige. Tyris admired the captain. He had an aura about him that commanded respect and he was beginning to see why his father was so excited at his arrival. His crew, though rough and ready in nature, were hanging on his every word and they all seemed loyal to a fault.

The doors of the Great Hall swung open as the skies darkened, sending fresh chills among those inside. Emerging from the hail came Mikhael with his arms tucked tightly into his robe with a panicked look on his face. "My Prince," he said as his mouth quivered from the cold, "Come with me quickly. Petra has returned!"

Without a moment to lose Tyris jumped to his feet and followed Mikhael out into the cold. "What's happened?" Tyris asked. "Why has he not come to see me himself?"

"He's in a bad way my Prince, you will see," Mikhael said sadly as they walked down into Stormgast.

Chapter Twenty-Five
The Storm's Fury

"EMRYS keep up!" Rheinar barked as they galloped away from Dee-Serak. Lymris was still mopping up the blood caking her shoulder, arms and face frantically. Emrys made sure she was unharmed while Rheinar had lashed out relentlessly. He had never seen his mentor this angry. Rheinar had flung curses like sweets and swung his sword time and time again turning a young tree into a carcass of splinters. There was a mixture of pain, anger and despair in his eyes and Emrys dared not to think on what he would do if they caught up to the soldiers. Lymris was shaken yet she still rode well and told Rheinar exactly what happened as they sped away across the plains. Believing they had lost the soldiers in the woods, they had camped for the night. During their breakfast, a hail of arrows rained down as men began storming their campsite. Jakob's horse was shot down before they even had a chance to react. When they did, Jakob strode forward with his spear and cleared a path for Lymris. He had already killed three soldiers by the time he turned to his sister. "Ride and don't look back!" was all he said to her as he slapped Styria on her back end.

She welled up when she recalled her morning and she too was in a mixture of anger, pain and despair. Emrys did not know what to think, and felt numb from the entire experience. Jakob had saved his life and taught him valuable lessons along the way. He did not want to see a friend hurt, nor a friend back in the chains he had spent a lifetime trying to escape from. Rheinar did not speak except to shout orders or speed the group up in their pursuit. He would not allow breaks and forced them all to ride hard into the afternoon. They found the trail of the soldiers easily enough which turned back around to the West, as if they were heading for Daal. Their knowledge of the land in Carpathia was amateur at best, and it could easily be seen they had looped themselves twice over. *A good omen for the pursuing party*, Emrys thought. They were definitely gaining on them. When nightfall crept in, Lymris passed around some dried meats as the horses slowed to a trot for stamina. No one spoke. Emrys was too afraid to ask Rheinar anything. He feared his mentor would blame him for this, *after all why wouldn't he?* This entire journey was down to Emrys. The young Prince only hoped that he could harness his powers as the Primal to some useful end.

In the distance they could see the amber glow of a campfire burning. They were travelling in the cover of darkness and found a small clearing in the woodlands, where Rheinar ordered them to move by foot and ready their bows. "Now listen," he said. "I do not want either of you to be seen. This is my battle. Mine alone. You can help with your bows. Take out any archers you see but remain hidden."

"This is our fight too," Lymris protested. "Jakob saved me, I need to save him!"

"I will tend to Jakob," Rheinar dismissed. "First we scout the camp and ensure he's there. If he's not there then we find someone and make them talk."

"How would we do that?" Emrys asked naively.

Rheinar did not reply. He just stared at him and Emrys immediately understood. No mercy was on the cards tonight and certainly no kindness.

The three crept through the treeline until they were about fifty yards from the camp. Most of the soldiers were asleep in crudely formed tents while three archers paced the outskirts of their dwelling. The fire was audibly crackling and lit up the features of a bloodied man tied up at its centre. "Lymris," Rheinar whispered into the wind. "I am going to make a dash for those bushes to the right. Nock an arrow. If the archer sees me, I need you to take him down. Do you understand?"

Lymris nodded and did as commanded while Rheinar gathered himself. "Emrys," he said finally. "I need you to continue moving to the left. I'll signal you when you're in position. When you are, target another archer, the furthest from us. Remember, be light of foot." Emrys gulped swallowing his fear as he settled his tremoring hands. Rheinar broke from cover and dived down behind the bushes before the archer managed to turn. Emrys continued to circle the camp to the left and as he drew nearer and nearer, he could see that it was indeed Jakob tied up. He had been badly beaten and his features were drenched in a layer of blood that coursed his body. Emrys continued on with quick looks to Rheinar's location for further instruction.

Rheinar eventually held his hand up and Emrys stopped in his tracks. There was an archer approaching Jakob who spoke out to the other two. "Get anything else from this fucker?" he said kicking him square in the ribs. Jakob spat out blood and wheezed before addressing the man in Carpathi. "How many times," the archer replied slowly kneeling down, "I. Don't. Speak. Foreign."

In the corner of his eye Emrys could see Rheinar creeping up on the camp and grounded himself down behind one of the tents. Lymris remained ready and kept a steady aim on her target as Emrys nocked his arrow in tow. "We should just kill him," another man said. "He's hardly going to lead us to the prince if he's tied up. What use is he?"

"We'll take him back to Arcadia," the third said. "See how long he stays quiet then. Besides the prince and princess might be stupid enough to come after us."

"What about the other one then?" the man by Jakob said. "The huge fella riding with 'em."

"We can take him," one said laughing. "What's one man going to do?"

"Let's find out!" Rheinar said breaking cover. "Emrys! Lymris! Loose!"

The siblings loosed their arrows without a moment's hesitation. Lymris' flew square into her target's heart and he dropped dead instantly, his legs twitching on the ground. Emrys hit his archer square in the gut who dropped to his knees and gasped for air. The one remaining by Jakob panicked and shouted, "We're under attack!"

Five soldiers emerged from the tents and armed themselves as they rose from their slumber. They backed away and formed a line behind which the archer dropped behind for cover. "Do you know who I am?" Rheinar shouted. "I am Rheinar of Galbraith, the Master-At-Arms for King Terrys Galbraith! I am Jerreko of Daal, undefeated champion of Kelpis Magna! But you will know me by another name. One which has killed your countrymen by the hundreds. I am The Storm's Fury!"

The soldiers backed away and swapped nervous glances as they held their line. Only the archer remained unchanged and spat on the ground as he nocked an arrow. "Well then,

Storm's Fury," he said, "what's to stop me putting an arrow through you?"

Rheinar smiled cruelly, a look Emrys had never seen before and feared. His mentor looked at the men like a wolf stalking its prey. He was goading them. Rheinar had a bloodlust and he wanted a fight, Emrys realised. "Try," Rheinar hissed.

The archer did not move yet three of his line broke formation and ran at Rheinar wildly. He simply dodged their slashes and countered by sending them flying with a huge shield sweep that knocked all of them to the ground. Using the foot of the shield, he crushed one of the men and stared back at the archer. Trembling, the man released an arrow which Rheinar easily deflected with his shield. Before the two men rose to their feet, he was on them in a flash, and sliced both of their throats in a swift fluid motion. Blood rained down on the scene causing the fire to hiss and smoke.

Rheinar seemed to move slowly and cautiously, yet never did he seem out of place. Emrys began to understand why he was the greatest warrior in Galbraith. He did not rush his actions, he waited for the opportune moment to pounce and strike. A few more arrows flew his way to which he blocked and struck out at the remaining soldiers. Within seconds it was just the archer left and as he stumbled backwards Rheinar strode forward to stand by his son. "If you value your life," Rheinar cast his menacing gaze towards the cowering man, "leave now and never come back."

"You'll never win," the man defiantly spat as his voice broke. "Emperor Edmure Valyris will have that *boy* and his bitch sister before long! Galbraith will be nothing but a ruin by the time he's finished! He'll burn the…"

Suddenly an arrow flew through the air and caught the man mid-sentence square in the chest. Emerging from the darkness was Lymris with venom in her eyes. "I will hear no more," she said through gritted teeth. Emrys could see though that the weight of the deaths had taken their toll on his sister. She seemed rattled, as if she struggled to grasp the morality of killing these men. He had not noticed it before, and berated himself for not seeing it sooner. Rheinar cut his son free and brought him to his feet.

"Are you okay, Jakob?" he asked.

Jakob spat out some blood and grabbed some water. "I'll survive," he said weakly. "We must move. If what these men were saying is true there are plenty of others searching for us."

"How do you know they weren't bluffing?" Rheinar puzzled.

"Because they were boasting about the bonus," Jakob replied as he dressed himself. "How they would hand me over to Arcadia for money. They meant to use me as information to find Emrys and Lymris."

"You didn't say anything did you?" Rheinar asked gently. It was a tender subject and Emrys could see he did not want to aggravate Jakob.

"No," he replied. "My blood attests to no answers. I gave them nothing. I kept reciting gibberish in Carpathi and they certainly didn't like that."

"Emrys, Lymris," Rheinar called out. "Come here."

Both of the siblings approached their mentor and could see he was smiling down at them. "You did well," he said. "You held your nerve and I thank you for it."

"I've never see you like that before," Emrys said fearfully. "You were terrifying."

Rheinar looked down at his feet and pondered for a moment. "I am not a good man, Emrys," he said. "I kill, and that is my existence. But if I can kill to save someone I love, does that not warrant my savagery?"

The question hung over the camp in silence as Emrys and Lymris shifted uncomfortably. They were of the same mind and shared their agreement with a single look. Never before had they seen such cruelty in Rheinar and it cast a different light on the man who had trained and honed them for battle. Lymris was struggling with the guilt in her part as she looked down at the bodies surrounding them. The man Emrys caught with an arrow in his gut breathed his last and fell limp as Lymris walked over. She stumbled over a body behind and when Emrys caught her, she burst into tears and hugged him in despair. Rheinar meanwhile helped Jakob who hobbled over to one of the spare horses and mounted it with great difficulty. "Em, Lym," Rheinar said as he knelt down beside them. "War is cruel. Killing is cruel. I am sorry for what you have seen but I am not sorry for what I have done to defend either of you or Jakob."

"I miss the palace," Lymris cried and tugged at Emrys. He felt it too. The safety of home was a luxury that neither of them had any more, and they felt the pressure of adulthood more now than ever. They wanted to be children and enjoy childish things, yet it seemed those days were a distant memory.

"So do I," Rheinar nodded sadly. "And once we've got Emrys safely to the Circle we will return, I promise. Now get up. It is not safe here and we need to keep moving."

***

JAKOB was nursed to health over the following week as the group soldiered on. His injuries, though not severe, were many. He had lacerations to his face, bruises beyond counting to his arms and legs, and two of his ribs were cracked. Riding horses was out for the time being. On the night they left the bloody camp Jakob had wheezed in pain with every trot the horse mustered. Only in the morning did they realise he needed rest before trying again at a later date. They had found a secluded grove not far from Dee-Serak and set up camp until Jakob was free to ride again. Emrys for the most part tended to the horses while Rheinar and Lymris hunted game in the woodlands. On the occasional off day, he would practice archery with his sister or receive fresh bruising from his bouts with Rheinar. Jakob continued to teach them Carpathi and for the first time since their lessons Emrys felt like he was making progress. He knew how to greet, how to thank and how to ask simple questions. His sister on the other hand was a natural and already had fluent conversations with both Rheinar and Jakob. On the nights where Rheinar and Jakob had private discussions, they had to move far away from Lymris if they wished their talks to remain secret.

By the end of the week Jakob could move reasonably well and despite the pain was keen for the group to get moving again. They made their way East past Dee-Serak and gradually Emrys noticed how the landscape changed. Where before there was rivers, woodland and grass in abundance, its appearance grew scarcer and scarcer. Sand became more prevalent and the horses struggled for grip as they slowed to a trot. "Hold on," Rheinar said calling them all to a stop. "What is that?"

Rheinar pointed to a stretch of land in the distance. It looked entirely out of place and as they cautiously approached

Emrys feared what he saw. The ground was blackened and without wildlife. The grass, sand, bushes and trees were all either rotten or scorched. There were no animals to speak of. An eerie silence haunted the land as though sound had never existed. It spanned to the South as far as they could see and as Rheinar dismounted he stood on the dead grass. With each step the grass came apart like ash from burning paper, and the bewildered look on his face said it all.

"What devilry is this?" he said.

"It's Corruption," Emrys said as he stood next to Rheinar. "Caulder's Corruption. I've seen it before, in my dreams. It spreads across the land and kills anything it touches."

"Does that mean Caulder's here?" Lymris panicked.

"No, I don't think so," Emrys shook his head. "He was in a glade when last I saw him. I fear this is something else."

"Look at this," Jakob said drawing their attention. There were strange footprints covering the land around them. The foot in question was closer to a talon in comparison and Emrys recognised the carvings immediately. His eyes widened and he started to panic. "This is Siska," he said. "We need to leave now!"

Chapter Twenty-Six
The Gathering Storm

"GET him up on the table!" Mikhael shouted as he led Tyris into the infirmary. An unconscious Petra was dragged through on a stretcher by several men. He was shivering uncontrollably, and with each step the men took, a large trail of blood was left in their wake. Removing the blanket he was wrapped up in, Tyris could see two arrows had pierced his right leg and arm respectively. Who had done this? He felt his anger rising and punched the door before slamming it shut, sending ripples through the creaking shack. Instantly he felt guilt and paced the room anxiously as the men worked on treating Petra. Tyris bemoaned himself for not sending additional troops and as he looked down at the sweating, whitened Petra he wished he would open his eyes. He received just that a few minutes later when a heated sword was brought into the room. The men ripped the arrows from him without contest, but the moment the blazed poker struck his wounds and seared his flesh, Petra jumped up and screamed in agony. It took Tyris and a handful of others to pin down the young warrior while he strained through the unbearable pain. He wearily passed out after a short while and the prince turned to Mikhael, snarling like a dragon.

"Who did this!" he demanded of his advisor.

"We do not know." Mikhael shook his head. "He was found unconscious atop his horse as he rode to the gates of

Stormgast."

Tyris inspected the arrows closely. They were not crafted in Galbraith, that much was clear. The stone arrowheads and sapling shafts were badly formed and the feathers were all but non-existent. "Who uses stone arrowheads?" Tyris quizzed rhetorically. "We mine the hills and use the iron and steel for arrows in Galbraith, but I've never seen arrows like these before."

"We must wait until he awakens," Mikhael said limping over. "Then we will know the truth of what happened. Why did you send Petra from your side?"

Tyris kept his father's promise and spoke nothing of the task he had given to him. "I sent him to Mercia to arrange a meeting with my aunt," he lied. "If I am to assume the Kingdom one day then I would very much like her to meet Elette."

Mikhael raised a suspicious eyebrow but said nothing to question the prince's tale. "I will notify your father," he said, making for the door.

"Mikhael," Tyris stopped him. "Alert the city guard. If someone has attempted to assassinate Petra then they may try again. Post a handful of guards by the door but tell them nothing of what is inside. Double the patrols and send scouts to the West along the road. We must take all precautions. I will stay by his side until he wakes. If you see Elette, please tell her not to worry but I must do my duty to my good friend Petra."

"Very well, my Prince," Mikhael obeyed and covered his face with his robe. The door almost blew off its hinges to the arctic wind when his advisor hobbled out into the rain. The thunder roared once more and before the door was closed, Tyris saw the sky light up as the lightning raced through the sky. He sat down by Petra's side. There were a few men and women tending to him but before long it was just the two of them in the candlelit lodge. "I'm sorry, Petra," Tyris apologised as he leant forward. Petra's black hair was a matted mess of mud and moss. His eyes lolled back every now and then when he shivered, and Tyris promptly ripped down a bear pelt from the wall to blanket him further.

The dark of night fell and Tyris lost all track of time as he sat waiting by Petra's side. A few guards came and went with their reports while one scout returned to inform him tracking anything would be impossible given the weather. Tyris shivered himself. The room was not warm and in his idleness the cold had crept in. He briefly considered moving Petra to the Great Hall so they could warm themselves by the fire but quickly forced it from his mind. Only he, Mikhael and a handful of others knew of Petra's location. Tyris promised he would not create a bigger target of his friend to save his own comfort. Mercifully the winds died down later in the night and the constant draught that had plagued their time there was at an end. Tyris could feel his eyes growing heavy under the weight of the day. It had started as one of jubilation and now it would end as one of torment. Each second that passed by Tyris grew more nervous and chewed his nails as he stared longingly at Petra, almost willing him to wake up.

It was not until the early hours of the morning that Petra opened his eyes. Tyris smiled down at him and met his hazel eyes head on. "Welcome back, Petra," he said softly. "How do you feel?"

"Like I've been shot with two arrows and burned," Petra remarked. Tyris loved that about him. He never lied, nor did he hold his words. Petra spoke his mind without apology.

"What happened?" Tyris asked as he poured a cup of water from his bedside pitcher.

"Do you mean what happened with Queen Eremea or why someone tried to kill me?" Petra replied.

"Let's start with the latter," Tyris passed the cup to Petra.

He drank the water and coughed, spluttering water down his chin. "I was riding back from Cairngorm, when suddenly a group jumped me at the Caldea Crossing. I rode as fast I could. The arrow to my leg hit first. It wasn't until I crossed that rocky steppe that the second arrow was loosed into my arm. I made it into Galbraith and headed straight for Stormgast. I rode as fast as I could for as long as I could. I must've passed out somewhere along the way."

Tyris held up the arrows to Petra. "Stone arrowheads," he said. "I've never seen the like. Do you have any idea who attacked you?"

"I don't have an idea," Petra replied pulling himself to sit. "I know who attacked me. Those there are Mercian arrows." The news was dire and hit like a hammer blow as Tyris rocked in his chair. If Mercia attacked a messenger of Galbraith, it would be a break of peace, and one he would not allow to go without retaliation.

"Are you sure, Petra?" Tyris asked, his face a state of worry.

"Positive," Petra nodded. "When I was in Cairngorm, I saw ones just like them being crafted. Cairngorm is full of rubble and few trees. They use the stone because they have it in abundance. That being said the Mercians are pretty rubbish when it comes to fletching an arrow, as you can tell."

"I'm sorry this happened to you," Tyris said. "For Mercia to attack a messenger of Galbraith. This crime will not go unpunished."

"Don't apologise, my Prince," Petra spoke sternly. "I went because you asked me to, what happened on Caldea Crossing had nothing to do with you. But I am sorry, for I have not told you the worst news yet."

Tyris poured himself a cup of water and took a deep swig before Petra continued. "When I arrived at Cairngorm, I quickly realised I was not the first one there. While I was waiting to meet with Queen Eremea I noticed there were Arcadian Knights guarding a carriage at the gates of the palace. From which, that advisor came out. Can't remember his name... The one who advised the emperor's son. He wore a robe and had a big scar across his face."

"Mathas is his name," Tyris remembered.

"Aye, that's him," Petra nodded. "I think he was there for the same reasons I was. To meet with the Queen. He was escorted into the Palace before I was and seen to without hesitation. I had to wait a couple of days there before the Queen would even see me and when I did..."

"What happened?" Tyris asked.

"She told me she agrees with Arcadia and their stance to mage-folk. She's enacted Mage Law in Mercia. Anyone who is a mage or harbours mages will be executed without trial. She also told me she will not stand with Galbraith while there is a mage in the royal family," Petra replied sadly. "The sealed letter you gave to me? She burned it before my very eyes. Unopened."

"What?" Tyris flipped. "Those were my father's words and she dares disrespect him? And what's this about the mage in the family? Emrys has left the Kingdom and is exiled never to return. How can she speak of this?"

"I'm sorry, my Prince," Petra looked up at him, "but she did not mention Emrys. She mentioned someone else."

***

THE following morning as the birds sang and weather cooled, Tyris stood by his bed as he watched Elette sleep. His discussion with Petra had been alarming for a myriad of reasons. Firstly, the peace between Galbraith and Mercia was on a knife's edge. If they freely attacked a messenger with the King's seal then he would have to report to his father. Secondly, with Mercia enforcing Mage Law, Tyris feared how many refugees they would see fleeing East. Galbraith would of course shelter them, however there would be no telling how long supplies in the Capital would last heading into winter. Thirdly, and probably most profoundly, what was Mathas' role in all of this? Was he seeking to create a union between Arcadia and Mercia? This most of all, Tyris feared. Galbraith could withstand attacks from Arcadia or Mercia independently but together was a completely different story. They had control of the seas which neutered the Arcadian offensive but if their troops were freely allowed to cross through Mercia then a different kind of war would be in place. Tyris promised he would call a war council later that day, he had many things to discuss and fyrds to call upon.

Tyris rubbed his temples under the stress of it all. He had barely slept a wink and wondered if his father had the same kind of routine during troubles. He looked down at Elette differently following Petra's revelation. According to him, she was a mage. Looking back on the past few months it did make sense with how much time she and Mikhael spent together. She would rarely discuss what they had been up to and shied away from answering Tyris' questions. He felt anger at her omission. They had been married for months with a child on its way and yet she never thought to consult him that she was gifted with magic like Emrys. The suns heat began to filter through the open window and rays of light came down onto the bed stirring Elette from her sleep. She opened her eyes and smiled when she saw Tyris standing over her. "Good morning, my love," she said rubbing her eyes vigorously.

"When were you going to tell me?" he asked looking away from her.

"Tell you what?" Elette puzzled as she sat up on the bed.

"I know, Elette," Tyris shook his head. "I know you are a mage. Why didn't you tell me?"

Elette froze and panicked. She tried to grab Tyris' hand who swiftly ripped it away and moved back from the bed. As Tyris looked on he could see that she was petrified. She bit her lip nervously and said, "I didn't want to hurt you."

"Thank you," Tyris nodded. "Because it felt *so* much better hearing it from someone else. How could you lie to me?"

"I didn't want to lose you," Elette wailed, "I come from Arcadia and you know what they do to mages. Things are different here in Galbraith but I didn't know if you shared your father's thoughts on mages. He banished your brother."

"He banished Emrys because there was no other option!" Tyris interrupted stunning Elette. He realised they had not argued before and it was a new experience for them both. Calming himself from saying something he might regret, he sat down on the bed and met Elette's gaze. She was welling up and it pained Tyris to see her upset.

"I'm sorry, Elette," he said holding her hand. "I just want you to be honest with me about anything. Has Mikhael been helping you?"

"He has," she sniffed and wiped her nose on her sleeve. "He's been helping me control my abilities. I can do some basic illusions and he's even shown me how to summon a Seeing Orb. I can show you Emrys or Lymris if you'd like?"

Tyris felt completely astounded. Eagerly he nodded and Elette rose to her feet. She muttered a few words under her breath before her eyes began to glow blue. An ethereal sphere appeared as if from nowhere in front of them and she ceased her chanting. "Look into the orb," she said. "And think only of Emrys or Lymris. Concentrate and they will appear."

Tyris stared long and hard through the transparent orb. Several frustrating minutes passed where nothing happened until a drab of colour entered the bottom of the sphere. He could see an endless horizon of sand and beneath it he could see two figures struggling to climb a dune. Their faces were wrapped in linen but even through their covers, Tyris could spot his siblings from a mile away. "Emrys! Lymris!" Tyris excitedly shouted and leant into the orb. He tried shouting again and looked at Elette when they failed to respond.

"They cannot hear us," Elette said. "The Seeing Orb only allows us to view them for a couple of moments."

"It's enough to see them," Tyris said feeling his heart twang with pain. He missed his siblings, that much was true, but to see them and not joke with them, hold them or even spar with them was painful. Behind them he could see Rheinar trudging through the sand and a man who he didn't recognise pulling four horses in tow. The orb continued to show their crossing of the dune and yet behind the group he could see a shadow prowling. A large creature, completely unknown to him skulked behind the dunes and beat the sand from its wings with a single slap. It bore huge talons caked in a layer of frost, and it eeked a strange ooze which tainted the sand black with each drop. "What is that?" Tyris asked pointing at the anomaly.

Elette was puzzled too and shrugged. "I have no idea. But whatever it is, it's following them."

Chapter Twenty-Seven
The Desert

THE heat was staggering. Emrys thought Daal was bad but within twenty minutes of ploughing through the dunes of the Atacama, he realised Daal was nothing in comparison to this. The night prior to their hike, Rheinar had ordered them all to strip down to their rags and ditch their armour. "It'll do nothing except slow us down," he reasoned. "When the suns are high in the sky, you'll thank me that we dropped our plate and leather." He was not wrong. During the peak of the day, Emrys felt strangled by the dry heat scorching his arms, neck and face, and he struggled to breathe with the hot air clogging his lungs. His ring finger itched constantly and as he stared down at the ring Captain Velstadt had given him, he could've sworn the features had changed. The wings lining the ring were in a different place and when he tried to remove it, nothing happened. It would not budge from his finger. Emrys cursed and strained at the efforts before he gave up and tried to distract himself.

Their breaks were short-lived and during them Emrys could see they were all under the cosh. Jakob was still recovering from his fresh injuries, and during any ascent, his vocal struggles could be heard by all. Lymris looked sapped of energy. She emptied her boots of sand incessantly and she swept what sweaty hair she could from her eyes. Lymris hadn't smiled once since they reached the desert and Emrys doubted she would until they left this fiery place. Rheinar, though certainly exhausted by sleepless nights, was the least afflicted to the desert. He sustained burns like the rest of them but always stood proud and kept the group going against their aching bodies. "We have to keep moving," he would say. "There is a lot of ground to cover yet."

Despite the harshness of the land, it was beautiful. Sand covered the horizon and when the suns kissed the ground it looked like a sea of fire beneath their feet. The desert seemed endless. As Emrys scanned from left to right, it beggared belief that they would find a forest beyond such an impressive sight. When night fell the temperature plummeted and to keep warm the group either buried themselves in sand or cuddled together by the horses. One night when Emrys began violently shivering, he felt the warm embrace of his sister holding him in her arms. "It's okay, Emrys," she whispered. "Look to the sky." He did and was amazed by what he saw. The sky was clearer than ever and he could marvel at the stars as they shone down in magnificent fashion. There were so many beacons of light that they were beyond counting, and as the siblings soaked in the view, they shared a brief flicker of hope in this desolate land. "That's some view, Lym," Emrys stuttered sinking his head into Lymris' arms. "Aye," she replied. "We'd never see this in Galbraith. I wish Mum was here to see this. She would tell us some fantastic fables about the stars." Emrys shared her wish. His mother, Althia, was above all else the finest storyteller he had ever known. She would regale fables from her homeland about the giants who formed Cairngorm or the harpies nesting in the mountains ready to snatch away naughty children. They would curl up by the fire as children and listen eagerly to their mother's stories. If they were scary fables, she would comfort them and if they were funny, they would laugh heartily together. Even their father, Terrys, would join in the fun and he was not averse to a good story himself. Emrys always looked back on those days happily and as he lay beneath the stars, he was hopeful that one day he would have a family of his own to share stories with.

The next morning the hike resumed and all thoughts of happiness seeped away beneath the shifting ground. Emrys came to a realisation that he hated sand. No matter how often he cleaned or patted himself down, he would be itching constantly as the sand coursed his body. Rheinar led the group to a huge dune which rose high and above the others around them. The trek to its peak was arduous and none of the breaks truly gave them any reprieve. By midday they were halfway up and the sweltering heat was upon them. Emrys stumbled over and spat out sand when he clambered back to his feet. "I. HATE. THE DESERT!" he bellowed sending ripples of sand racing down the dune.

Rheinar grinned and slapped him on the back. "We all do, Emrys," he said. "Let's get to the top in one piece, eh?"

Emrys dusted himself off and continued the long climb and saw the struggle Jakob had in pulling the horses. They were hesitant to climb and several times he had to calm them down. Lymris had jumped in to assist him where she could but Emrys could see she was exhausted. The strength in her arms waned and her legs trembled with each step.

Atop the dune they could see in all directions for miles. Jakob dropped to his knees, visibly tired from his strenuous climb with the horses. Lymris slumped down by his side and laid back as she gasped for air and began drinking from her flask. Only Rheinar and Emrys remained standing together.

Emrys felt the ring on his finger burning from the inside and winced in pain. As he looked down at the ring, he could've sworn he saw the wings flutter and the carved runes moving. Rheinar noticed his discomfort and looked on concerned. "What's wrong, Emrys?" he said.

"I don't know," Emrys strained. "This ring Velstadt gave me. It's burning."

"Metal does that in the heat of the suns," Rheinar nodded.

"No, this is different," Emrys replied. "It's burning from the inside. Something strange is happening."

"Well allow me to try and take your mind off things," Rheinar clapped him on the shoulder. His mentor pointed to the East and squinting Emrys could just make out a cliff. Rising above the cliffs in the distance there was a treeline, the likes of which he had never seen before.

"That's our target," Rheinar stated. "The Whispering Woods."

"Why is it called the Whispering Woods?" Lymris asked.

Rheinar shrugged and turned to face her, "No idea Lym, there's rumours that…" Their mentor broke off his sentence and barged past Emrys, clearly disturbed by something. "What's the matter?" Jakob asked rising to attention.

"I saw something behind us," Rheinar replied and drew his sword and shield in an instant. "Arm yourselves!"

***

THE group's descent down the other side of the dune was a hasty, messy affair. They had all taken a tumble and even the horses had rolled a couple of times. Emrys was certain supplies had been lost but it was insignificant compared to how worried

Rheinar was. His mentor had a glazed over look on his face and still said nothing of what he saw. Rheinar had only urged the group that they must make for cliffs if they were to stand any chance of survival. Emrys by now was in severe pain and when he glanced down at his hand, scorch marks were burning themselves around his finger. He shrugged off what pain he could muster and continued to help Jakob with the horses as they fled from the dune. Lymris ran ahead and checked the route. She reasoned they should head South before looping back East in order to avoid climbing the dunes ahead. No one was in a mind to contest this and they gladly trusted his sister's navigation.

A shrieking cry burst through the air and Emrys, Rheinar, Jakob and Lymris stopped in unison to turn around. Atop the dune Emrys could see what he feared to see. Siska flapped its wings and stood scratching the ground with its huge talons. Its black slithering body continued to leak critters and ooze as it spat out fresh green liquid. The wind caught its scent and Emrys gagged as he smelled the stench from the creature Caulder raised. Its shallow icy breaths formed snow in the air and to the ground ice formed by its talons. It's skeleton-like body shone in the sunlight and on seeing them it shrieked again ringing pain to their ears. Emrys dropped to his knees and screamed in agony. He was unsure if the others were affected until he saw Lymris screaming as blood poured from her ears and nose. Emrys staggered back to his feet, his vision blurry. Siska at this point shot up into the sky at frightening speed and launched itself down towards Emrys.

"Emrys, get behind me!" Rheinar commanded raising his shield up. Siska slammed into the shield with unbridled strength and Emrys could see the strain Rheinar was under

259

from holding it back. Rheinar slashed a wild swing towards Siska which missed as Jakob came from the side and thrust a spear into Siska's side. Siska squealed before firing strange green liquid in every direction and beating its wings. They were all knocked prone and flew ten feet through the air. As Emrys struggled to his feet he looked at Rheinar. "Rheinar, your shield!" Emrys spluttered as he looked on horrified. The liquid melted through the shield within seconds and Rheinar hastily threw it away before the ooze touched him. Siska, wounded, dropped back as Rheinar and Jakob circled it. Lymris, now standing, fired an arrow which the creature dodged with ease. Siska hissed before it dived beneath the ground and hid from their view. "Everyone group up!" Rheinar commanded as the formed a tight circle. Emrys and Lymris nocked arrows while Rheinar and Jakob scanned their surroundings. "What the fuck is this thing?" Jakob spat, visibly shaken.

"It's Siska!" Emrys replied. "One of Caulder's creatures I dreamt about!"

"Look there!" Lymris piped up drawing their attention to a growing mound of sand.

From the rising mound came a swarm of the crittering beatles, scorpions, snakes and spiders which had been running through Siska's body. The mound continued to grow and grow until eventually the sandy ground was swarming with thousands of slinking emerald creatures which sped towards them. "RUN!" Rheinar screamed as they broke formation and ran further to the South. The horses whinnied and bolted past them leaving a trail of scattered dust in their wake. Emrys refused to look back out of fear and continued to stride through the thick sand as quickly as his tired legs could muster. His finger was in agony and he screamed as though his hand was on fire. They ran for what seemed like an eternity until eventually they reached a plateau of rocks. As the group gasped for breath Emrys sank to his knees and howled in pain as the burn marks on his ring finger spread to his hand. "Emrys!" Lymris panicked rushing to his side. "What's happening?"

"This ring," Emrys wept. "It's burning me. I can feel it all!"

The burns continued to spread as Emrys tossed and turned in writhing agony. Lymris helplessly watched on and attempted to console her brother while Jakob and Rheinar kept guard. "It's back!" Jakob shouted as Siska revealed itself. Using the bodies of the creatures below it, Siska strode forward and froze the ground where it stood. "Release... Primal," it hissed spitting more ooze.

"No!" Rheinar said resolutely. "Emrys is going nowhere!"

"Then... Die!" Siska jumped forward and slashed at Rheinar with razor-sharp claws.

Rheinar rolled backwards and span out of the way while Jakob launched his spear. Siska batted it away with a flick of its wings and spat more liquid his way. Jakob screamed as the ooze landed on his arms and he promptly dropped to his knees shivering. "Jakob!" Lymris shouted as she nocked and loosed an arrow for Siska. The arrow struck the creature where a shoulder should have been and it squealed in pain for a moment. Before Lymris could nock another, Siska was upon her. "Lym!" Emrys screamed as he staggered to his feet. Siska held his sister by the throat and raised her high into the air, choking her. "Let her go!" Emrys panicked as he ran forward.

"No... Closer," Siska hissed again. "Primal... Come... Or... Girl... Die..."

"Em, run," Lymris gasped weakly as the colour drained

from her face. Rheinar moved past Emrys and held his sword to Siska. "RELEASE HER! NOW!" he commanded, his voice echoing through the sandy valley. Siska merely cackled and pulled Lymris closer. Beneath it, the swarming creatures gathered and began snapping upwards to Lymris' heels. "My... Children... Feast," Siska cackled again. Emrys looked on at the desperate situation. He had to do something. Jakob remained on his knees, crippled from the pain as his flesh turned gangrene and melted away. Rheinar stood resolutely but was too far away to save her, nor his son. All Emrys could feel was pain. Pain as the ring seared more and more scars into his flesh. When he looked down at it, he saw his hand was covered in wing marks. He closed his eyes and slowed his breathing to listen. A voice in the recess of his mind echoed like whispers under a bridge. *Please help me*, Emrys thought. A single voice replied. *Release me.*

Emrys took one last look at his ring and pushed the wings together. Everything after became one blur. Flashes of red illuminated the land as rays of colour erupted from Emrys' hand. Siska leapt forward to attack yet when the light touched it, it recoiled in horror and screamed. The light scolded its body and it dropped Lymris by Emrys' side as it staggered back. Rheinar took his chance and hacked away severing its wings. Siska squealed in agony as the light consumed its body and before he knew it, the skulking creature grew limp. Skittering creatures around them began exploding on the spot and fading to dust. The light spread further and further into the sky and took the form of a roaring Phoenix. The marks from Emrys' hand faded and the mythical bird raced through the sky burning Siska to a crisp. It was beautiful to witness, but the strain of it all forced Emrys to his knees and before he knew it, his eyes lolled back and once more the world went dark.

Chapter Twenty-Eight
Swan Song

LYMRIS scrambled to her feet and gasped for air as she felt fresh blood trickling down her throat. She spat out some sand and rubbing her hands around her neck she could feel the lacerations where Siska had grabbed her. The ordeal had terrified her. Hastily she wrapped a cloth to stem the bleeding and observed the scene around her. To her side lay the freshly twitching corpse of Siska. The stench was overwhelming and she spluttered whenever the wind caught its draught. Looking down at it she could see the burns where the light had touched it. *What was that creature?* She puzzled over what she had seen but could make no sense of it. A bird of gold and red, like the Phoenixes from old legends, had emerged from Emrys' hand and consumed the abomination seeking her brother. He himself had been flabbergasted and dropped immediately after the bird dispersed into the air above. "Emrys!" she croaked when she remembered his exertion and rushed to his side. Her brother was unconscious and no manner of shaking would wake him. "Emrys, wake up!" she cried beating on his chest. His breaths were shallow and when she leant her head onto his chest, she could hear the faintest of heartbeats and prayed her brother was not lost.

"Lymris, help me!" she heard behind him. Turning to face the voice she could see Rheinar dragging his screaming son up onto the rocks. As she ran over her heart sank when she saw the damage Siska had inflicted on Jakob. He had lost his right arm to the ooze the monster spat and a rotting stump stood where a strong bicep and forearm had once been. The pain looked beyond excruciating as parts of his arm continued to melt away like pieces of wet paper, dropping onto the rocky surface below. His blood had turned black and spat fresh ooze which sizzled as it dropped onto the rocks and sand. "Hold him down!" Rheinar barked as he rummaged through his pack. From it he pulled a whistle and blew hard twice. A few minutes later Shrieker emerged and Rheinar rushed to his stallion, pulling wood and flint from the saddles. He hastily formed a fire and chucked his sword into the fiery furnace as he sat down and comforted his son. "Don't you quit on me," he said, patting his chest. "Lymris, how is your brother?"

"I don't know, Rheinar." She shook her head, "He's breathing but he's very weak. What was that thing that came from his hand?"

"I don't think it was his hand that did that," Rheinar replied. "The ring he was on about. The one Velstadt gave him. Without that Lym I'm pretty certain we'd be done for…"

Rheinar continued to treat Jakob who babbled incoherently and winced as more of his arm eroded away like a beach during a high tide. She turned to face Shrieker and moved to pull some water from an open saddle. When she approached Shrieker whinnied and reared up in fear. "Lymris get away!" She heard, and when she turned, she could see Siska was crawling forward. She dashed to the right and nocked an arrow as the abomination crawled at a snail's pace in her direction. Rheinar rushed over and hacked its arm off causing it to squeal and spit more ooze from its mouth. "I… Win…" Siska gasped raising a wing in the direction of the fading Jakob.

"What have you done to him filth!" Rheinar shouted.

"Man... Is... Corrupted..." it laughed. "Not... long... now..."

"What do you mean corrupted?" Lymris asked nocking an arrow as anger consumed her.

"Marked... He..." it spluttered, "Will... Turn... Like... Me..."

The words struck Rheinar and Lymris in equal measure as they turned to look at the twitching Jakob. Colour had drained from his face and fresh trails of black blood were forming from his arm and shooting up towards his head. He regained consciousness for a moment and muttered, "Vosh frei kall' o'man kashko."

"What does that mean?" Lymris asked unsure of the phrase as she scanned her Carpathi knowledge.

"Nothing," Rheinar said through gritted teeth. The Storm's Fury turned back to Siska and raised his sword. "My son will live and you will die, monster. Your master will die and all of the evil you spread will end."

"You... are... wrong..." it hissed and thrust itself toward Rheinar. With a simple stroke Rheinar beheaded Siska and kicked its head away from him in frustration as he cursed to the sky.

"What Siska said..." Lymris said approaching Rheinar. "It can't be true, can it?"

"It is not," Rheinar spat. "Now find the horses, Lym. If Shrieker wasn't too far then the others cannot be."

"What will you do?" she asked.

"My sword is hot enough now," he replied pulling it from the fire. "I am going to burn away what I can and tend to my son."

Lymris did as she was asked and began to head to the dune Shrieker came from. As she reached its top, Jakob's blood-curdling screams pierced the sky and chilled her to her very core. They scared her more than anything she had witnessed so far and suddenly she found herself doubting his recovery.

***

IT took Lymris a long time to retrieve the horses after they had bolted from Siska. Styria, Elmyra and Jakob's recently acquired horse were all visibly shaken, and it took almost an hour for her to calm them down. She tied their reins together, cooled them with water and dragged them through the shifting sand as night began to fall. Flickering in the distance she saw the rushed campsite Rheinar had stacked together and as the cold began to set in, she hurried over to the scene. As her shadow grew closer to the campsite, Rheinar drew his sword until her features became apparent. Sheathing his sword he said, "Lymris, are the horses well?"

"They're shook up," she replied climbing onto the rocks. "But they'll be fine. How is Emrys? How is Jakob?"

Rheinar moved to the side revealing a huddled Emrys fast asleep on his bedroll. "Emrys hasn't woken yet," he said pulling a blanket over him. "No matter how much I try to stir him. Whatever that was... Whatever we saw... It's taken its toll."

Lymris walked over and looked down at her brother. His face was pale and covered in a mixture of sweat and sand. Emrys' eyes flickered behind his eyelids but he showed no signs of waking from his deep sleep. When Lymris held his limp hand it felt ice cold, exactly like when Siska had grabbed her. "He's cold," she said pulled the blanket around him tightly.

"The fire's doing nothing to improve it," Rheinar said sadly.

"He'll pull through," Lymris said confidently. "He's capable of more than we know. How is Jakob?"

Rheinar shook his head and did not respond. He merely pointed to the other side of the campsite and held his head in his hands. Jakob was sprawled out twitching and deep in pain. When Lymris approached he looked up at her and held up his remaining arm, "Don't come closer, Lymris," he wheezed. "I can't control it."

"Control what?" Lymris asked and scanned the warrior. Rheinar had burned and wrapped the arm stump on his right side but even under the cover of darkness Jakob seemed different. The bulging veins in his neck and body were jet black and through the flicker of fire she could see the whites in his eyes were non-existent. He seemed to strain with each breath and coughed consistently throughout. Lymris felt fear rising through her and sniffed away fresh tears as they formed in the corners of her eyes.

"You're going to be okay," she said weakly.

"You are kind, but I am not," he replied spitting out black blood which curdled on the ground. "I can feel it changing me. I feel so much hate stirring in my heart. Lymris, I beg you, please kill me."

Lymris staggered back and looked helplessly at Rheinar who still held his head between his hands. "I cannot kill you Jakob," she sniffed. "You are good, you are kind and you are my friend."

"And you are my friend which is why I ask," he cried. "I want to die as Jakob the warrior. The warrior who broke his chains and escaped slavery. The warrior who defended the Primal on his journey. The warrior who reunited with his long-lost father. I do not want to be a puppet for evil. To go against Emrys and the world. Vosh frei kall' o'man kashko."

"What does that mean?" she said as tears streamed down her face.

"It means," Rheinar stepped forward, "honour me with a warrior's death."

Lymris wept like she never had before. Jakob had been a rock to her, a friend whom she adored not only for saving her brother's life but for liberating hers. He had been kind, generous and protected her as though she was his kin. They had laughed, played and fought together and as she looked down on him now, she felt more sorrow than she had known since her mother's passing.

"I will do this for you," she wept. "Know that I love you for what you have been to me and for what you have given for Emrys."

"I gave it gladly," he spluttered. "I do not know the Kingdom of Galbraith, but you and your brother… It has been my honour to serve you as my father has."

Lymris pulled a dagger from her belt and slowly began to walk to Jakob. She felt a tug at her arm and turned to see Rheinar grimacing. "No, Lymris," he said taking the blade from her. "He is my son, and I will honour him."

Lymris crept back and sniffled as she turned to look at Emrys. He had not moved nor had he made any sign that he was with them. *Surely, he can do something*, she thought. Running over she began shaking him violently, screaming down his ear: "Wake up Emrys! Jakob needs you! You can't let him die, you can't!" She cried into his unmoving chest for what seemed like an eternity as time stood still and the heart-wrenching pain stretched on endlessly. When she finally looked up, she could see Rheinar kneeling beside his son and cradling him as if he was a newborn baby.

"I'm so sorry, my son," Rheinar said fighting back the tears.

"You have nothing to apologise for," Jakob coughed. "I have got to know my father after spending years thinking he was dead, and I am not disappointed in the man I see before me."

"I'm so proud of you, my son," Rheinar sniffed. "You are the finest warrior I have known and the greatest son a man could have."

Father and son shared a stare between them and Lymris felt ashamed to be watching their final moments together. Rheinar held his son in his arms one last time as he began to violently twitch. Froth began spewing from Jakob's mouth as his eyes flickered and his legs broke out into a spasm. He began to claw helplessly at his father who kept a firm grip and attempted to comfort and console his dying son. Jakob had left, all that remained was demonic intent. As tears began to run down Rheinar's face he kissed his son's head and pulled the dagger into position. "I love you, son," he said finally as he plunged the blade into Jakob's heart. Jakob's splutterings came to an abrupt end as his head rocked back and his body grew limp. Rheinar cried out to the skies and Lymris tearfully clambered over to hold him. He continued to hold Jakob tightly and hugged him tightly to his chest as his anguished cries filled the night.

"One day," he whispered to Jakob, "I will return to you and your mother, and we will be happy again as we once were a long, long time ago." Rheinar closed his son's eyelids and cradled him for almost an hour.

"I'm so sorry, Rheinar," Lymris cried. "He was a brave man to the end."

"Aye," Rheinar sniffed. "He was. He didn't deserve this, nor did he deserve the abuse he received at Kelpis Magna. It is cruel world we live in Lym, and it is an evil twist of fate that I must now bury my son." He carried Jakob's corpse to the sand and began digging a hole, scooping sand with his sword. Lymris rushed to his side and together they shared the burden in silence. They were both distraught and no words seemed to fit for the grief they shared. They continued to dig until Rheinar was satisfied the hole was deep enough. Using his own bedroll, he wrapped his son up and placed him down the newly-formed trench. As they stood, looking down on Jakob, Rheinar dropped to his knees sobbing uncontrollably.

"Goodbye Jakob," Lymris said. "May you find peace."

She poured the sand over his body bit by bit while Rheinar cried and clawed at the air longingly. Once the grave was filled, she hugged Rheinar tightly and did not let go. He was a mess and understandably so. She tugged at him to stand and said, "Would you like to say anything?"

"No," he replied. "What I have to say to my son, I will say when next I see him."

Rheinar walked away and returned with Jakob's spear. With a large sweep he thrust the weapon into the ground, marking his son's grave. He leant in and kissed the spear symbolically before he motioned Lymris to return to the campfire. Panic raced through Lymris when she looked towards the fire. "Rheinar!" she flustered, darting her eyes in each direction. "Where is Emrys!"

Chapter Twenty-Nine
Family Feud

TYRIS trotted along the crumbling Caldea Crossing with his trusty knights in tow. They left Stormgast a week prior and had made good progress on their journey despite the harsh conditions. Petra's recovery had initially been a poor one until his loving wife Elette had laid her hands upon him. Mikhael explained she was gifted with healing abilities which surpassed his own and Tyris would have disbelieved it had he not witnessed it himself. From the moment she laid hands on him the leaking wounds sealed themselves and he was up and running within a matter of days. Explaining Queen Eremea's betrayal to his father had been another trouble entirely. Even King Terrys' resolve was tested when he heard of the letter burning, and he shifted uncomfortably atop the Oaken Throne. "You must see her," his father said through gritted teeth. "She needs to know who her family is in this world."

"What makes you think she'll see me?" Tyris asked.

"You are your mother's son," his father replied. "Say what you like about the mad Queen Eremea but she did love her sister. You will be granted safe passage, of this, I am sure. But we cannot know the moves Arcadia will make, take with you warriors you trust."

Tyris obeyed his father and before he left Stormgast he was gifted with a surprise visit from Velstadt. The captain smiled when he approached the stables and offered the prince a drink which he declined. "So you're off to Cairngorm, lad?" he said supping a pint.

"Aye, we are," Tyris smiled. "Hopefully I can talk some sense into my aunt before she does something truly damaging between Galbraith and Mercia. What will you do?"

"Come with you if that's okay," Velstadt said grinning with his golden teeth. "My men need to make repairs to the Tempest and I feel like stretching my legs."

"Why?" Tyris asked. "If you don't mind me asking."

"Because I can see the King's children need all the help they can get," Velstadt nodded. "I am trustworthy lad, and handy in a fight if it comes to it."

And Tyris did trust him. As he looked at the weathered captain, he could see no foul intent in his eye and he felt like he could rely on him when the time came. After all, Velstadt was the same man who had ferried his siblings across the Sea of Tears and through the Great Market City of Daal. "I would be honoured, Velstadt," Tyris smiled. "I'll see to it you get a horse."

The Caldea Crossing was completely different to how the Crown Prince had envisioned. The ground was almost entirely made of scree and as the rain thundered down on them, it was evident much of the road had been washed away. Their route took them through a lone mountain path only wide enough for two horses at any time. There were sheer drops to either side and with a thick layer of mist below, Tyris could not see how far down the fall would be. Petra had elected to scout ahead and ensure the road was safe. Tyris admired his gall yet worried constantly when he was out of sight. It was in these rocky hills his friend had been shot down and it beggared belief how Petra had managed to navigate his way back across the crumbling mountainside with two arrows in his side. A signal from his trusted warrior came a few hours later and when Tyris ascended to the summit he could see Cairngorm in all its glory.

The City of Rock lived up to its name. Huge boulders the size of mountains filled the area and carved pillars of stone rose up like pyres in the sky. If Galbraith's speciality was wood then Mercia's was certainly stone. Homes, taverns, even the Palace were all domed and chiselled down to perfection. The craftsmanship behind it all was staggering and Tyris had to admit he was impressed. As they started to descend towards the city, one of the sun's lights broke through the clouds and kissed the roofs of the buildings, with blinding light spanning from their pinnacles. "It's beautiful," Tyris mentioned to Petra. "You haven't met the people," Petra snorted. "There's a reason people say the Mercians have hearts of stone. They…"

"*They* also say," Velstadt interrupted, "that Galbrathians are pompous arseholes. Who's to be believed, lad?"

Tyris laughed as Petra's cheeks flushed and the captain slapped him on the shoulder grinning. "What kind of reception do you think we'll receive?" Tyris turned to Velstadt.

He stroked his beard and pushed his dreadlocks back. "No idea," he said before he pointed down the mountain pass. "Though unless I'm mistaken, I think we're looking at our welcoming committee."

To the foot of the mountain a swarm of guards amassed and awaited their descent. Their armour was of interest to Tyris as he squinted he examined them in greater detail. Each man bore stone helmets chiselled to spikes, clay crafted chest pieces and even their swords seemed to be made of the mountains.

"Well," Tyris said, "it'd be rude to keep my aunt waiting any longer. Best behaviour everyone, we can't risk anything going wrong."

The guard halted the approaching party and a sole rider strode forth holding his hand up. "No further," she said. "Who are you and what are your intentions in Mercia?"

"I am the Crown Prince Tyris of Galbraith," Tyris replied. "And I am here to see my aunt, the Queen Eremea."

"Very well," she nodded. "I will see to it the Queen is notified of your presence. Before you are allowed to pass through our gates I must ask, are you harbouring any mages?"

Tyris frowned at the question and couldn't believe how quickly Mage Law had been administered in Mercia. True, Galbraith had many more mages than Mercia, but he had never known Mercia to turn away the refugees arriving in droves from Arcadia.

"No, we have no mages," he replied through gritted teeth. "How long has Mage Law been in effect in Mercia?"

"Not long enough," the guard spat. "But you will see what welcome they are given in Cairngorm. Follow me."

The group trotted behind the swarm of guards and followed them across a huge stone bridge. The monstrous gates before them shook the ground as they were wrenched open and inside Tyris could see exactly what *welcome* the guard had mentioned. The first thing to hit him was the stench of death. He muffled his nose but as he looked across from his horse, he could see the depravities all around him. Mages, or people who helped them, were nailed to poles either dead or dying. They were beyond counting and Tyris could feel anger boiling inside him. This cruelty was the most horrible thing he had witnessed, and the prince almost wept when he saw a girl no older than ten nailed to a post as well. The densely populated streets were littered with people burning effigies and chanting anti-Mage sentiments. It sickened Tyris to his core. Stern words would be said to his aunt. He promised himself this as he clenched his hand into a fist and trotted further into the city.

***

TYRIS fidgeted restlessly as he sat with Petra and Velstadt in front of the palace audience room. The palace was very plain on the interior and he felt a wave of disappointment wash over him. He had expected more than this. Save for a few golden dishes by the tables there were no ornaments or trophies to be seen and it didn't even seem like a palace, it looked more like a tavern. "Bit plain in here, isn't it?" he whispered to Velstadt.

"Slim pickings lad," he grinned in return. "Pirates like me tend to avoid these gaffes. There's nothing here save for the coffers below ground."

Only three of them had been granted access to the palace. The remainder of his guard were positioned outside so Tyris took with him Petra and the captain. He trusted them both to keep their tongues still while he attempted to negotiate with his aunt. *But what would he say?* He prioritised the peace between Galbraith and Mercia above all, yet with the scenes outside the very doors of the Palace he could barely keep his focus. Never before had he witnessed Mage Law in effect. *Why would Mercia change to this? What had changed in this land to administer such a cruel law?* The questions raced through his mind while he scratched his newly-formed beard.

Half an hour passed by before any movement came from

the audience room in front of them. Two men in robes stepped forward with forced, fake smiles and bowed before the Crown Prince as he rose from his chair. "Prince Tyris," one said. "Welcome to Cairngorm. The Queen Eremea Rothach of Mercia will see you now. Please relinquish any weapons."

"I beg your pardon?" Tyris squinted, "My aunt wants my sword?"

"The *Queen*," the other replied, "will only see people without their weapons. These are the rules of Mercia, and you will abide by them."

"Very well," he hissed and left his sword on the chair.

Velstadt and Petra followed suit and the fake, bitter smiles were upon them once more. They were escorted to the door and with one more bow, the men opened the doors for them. Tyris strode forth proudly and observed his surroundings. The circular hall was huge and through the stained-glass windows around them amber light burst forth illuminating the floor. On it bore the crest of Mercia, a green sash covered in a rockslide. Similar banners rained down from the ceiling and waved like flags in the breeze. Heavily armoured guards stood on the circumference of the room unflinching in their devotion to their positions. By the time Tyris made it to the middle of the room he could see nobles sat behind a large plinth carved into a throne, which cast a shadow darkening half of the hall. "That's close enough," a voice said from the shadows.

Walking forward and taking a seat was, what Tyris could only assume, Queen Eremea. She was tall, had dark auburn hair like his mother yet she was stick thin and almost gaunt looking. Her blue eyes seemed greyer the more he looked at them and huge bags of sleep hung beneath them. She had not aged well. Her skin, devoid of colour, was wrapped tightly around her face, forming a resting frown as she ogled him. She did not look warm nor kind like his mother Althea, and the hopes of a kind meeting faded quickly as watched her take a seat. Regardless, he smiled courteously and said, "Aunt Eremea I am gl…"

"It's *Queen* Eremea," she hushed him. "And it is commonplace in Mercia to bow before a Queen."

Tyris ignored the rudeness and bowed as requested. He could hear some of the nobles behind Eremea sniggering but brushed it from his mind. There were larger things at stake than his pride.

"Queen Eremea," he corrected himself. "I am honoured to finally meet you as an adult. It has been many years since you were last in Galbraith to visit my mother, Althea. Myself and my siblings have missed you."

She did not appreciate the sentiment and Tyris could see her snarling as she gripped her throne. "What is it you want of me, Prince Tyris of Galbraith?" she quipped as her eyes gripped him like a hawk.

"I wish to understand for one thing," Tyris replied. "Why did you burn my father's, King Terrys', letter?"

"Your father's words are not welcome in Mercia," she spat. "When has he ever done anything to help us? Your father is only interested in his precious Galbraith. I tolerated him only because of my sister and now that she's dead I have no interest in dealing with him." Tyris was shocked by her admission and stumbled for the right words.

"My father will not be King forever," he said attempting to take the sting out of situation. "When I am King will you deal with me? Your nephew and Althea's first-born son?"

She seemed to ease at the request and stretched back.

"Perhaps," she smiled briefly. "What can you offer Mercia?"

"I can offer you peace," he said boldly. "Peace from those who would wish to harm Mercia. Galbraith has the largest naval fleet on the continent and one of the best armies going. I would see it that Galbraith and Mercia honour the peace we have held for many years, and stand as allies against any foe."

Queen Eremea and her nobles burst into a laughter which echoed through the hall. "And by foes do you mean Arcadia by any chance?" she grinned.

"Arcadia and Galbraith are at peace," Tyris replied. "I married Elette to unify…"

"Don't you dare mention that witch's name in here again!" Eremea rose to her feet slamming the throne. "We no longer tolerate Mages in Mercia."

"And what changed that?" Tyris rose his voice. "My wife may be a mage but she is a good person. Kind, loyal and capable of wondrous things. Why has Mercia suddenly turned their back on mages? Mages were the ones who joined together and helped create Cairngorm centuries ago! And how do you honour them? There are children nailed to posts out there either bleeding or dead! Mercia has always been friendly to mages in the past, why would that change now?"

"Who are you to lecture me?" Eremea frowned. "Prince Tyris of Galbraith. I only saw you today as a courtesy to my late sister, you and your Galbraithian scum are not welcome here. I have made new allies with whom I share a vision."

"And what vision is that?" Tyris asked through gritted teeth. He could feel Petra and Velstadt anxiously teetering to his sides. The guards around the room gripped their weapons, ready at a moment's notice to hack them down without remorse.

"Why a world without mages of course," she smiled revealing yellowed teeth. "Magic has done nothing except burden the land with torment and anguish. It is a kindness that we rid the world of mages and free ourselves from the plagues they bring. Besides the alliance I speak of will soon be official. I am to be married."

"Married to who?" he asked tentatively, fearing her response.

"You've met him before and he speaks *very* highly of you," she grinned. "His name is Edmure, son of the emperor Harold Valyris."

Chapter Thirty
Guilt

THE winds whipped through the air as Emrys trudged through the night. He would not turn back and brushed the cold from his mind. Fresh tears welled in his eyes whenever he thought of Jakob and he refused to cause any more harm to the ones he loved. He had actually woken up when Rheinar plunged the dagger through his son's heart. The pain in his mentor's voice was chilling when he cried to the sky, and when he saw the anguish in his and Lymris' eyes, he knew what he had to do. He had to complete the journey alone. No more sacrifices would be made in his name and when he reached the rocky cliffs he saw the day before, he began his ascent without looking back. The shame and guilt of it all weighed heavy on his heart. *How could he face Rheinar after this? How could he dare justify Jakob's death as a casualty of his journey?* He had only just been reunited with his son after more than twenty years had passed, and for him to die protecting Emrys was a crime he could not forgive himself. He would miss Rheinar and Lymris more than ever but he could already feel the ghost of Jakob haunting his every thought. Fleeing was his only option.

It took a couple of hours for him to reach the top of the cliffs and his legs throbbed as old blisters cracked and new ones began to form. Catching his breath, he fell to his knees and when his hands touched the ground, he could feel grass instead of sand. The Atacama still bore its mark on Emrys and even now he could feel the itching sand working its way around his body. It was the first time he noticed that his hand no longer burned and the scorch marks around his hand had disappeared. *What had happened?* He tried to remove the ring to no avail and strained under the pressure. The ring burned for a flash causing him to squeal in pain and writhe around in agony. *What are you?* He called out in desperation. Flashes of light erupted from his hand as flames licked the ground beneath him. As he watched on the light joined together at a point five foot in front of him. The shape of phoenix burning brightly emerged in majestic fashion. The light was staggering and Emrys shielded his eyes with his hands.

The light subdued allowing him to observe the majestic bird. Unlike the Phoenixes he had read about, this particular one burned a light blue and its flames flicked silently around its body. It rose from the ground and stood at height of ten foot as its huge talons tugged at the grass. Stretching its wings Emrys could feel its jet-black eyes piercing his very soul. It was as if the bird was in the corner of his mind, reading his thoughts and emotions. "What are you?" he called out fearfully.

"Not many have the power to release me," a voice boomed. "I am impressed."

"What are you?" Emrys asked again.

"I am the Alicanto. Phoenix-Mother and bound to the Atacama Desert," it said as it began to prowl around him. "And you are a Primal, are you not?"

"So people keep telling me," Emrys replied. "Why didn't you help us sooner? Jakob would still be alive if you had!"

"I could not save him, nor could you," she said as smoke

hissed from its beak. "Once corrupted only death awaits you, either your own or someone else's. I felt the pain in your heart when he died. I am sorry for your loss." Emrys sank to his knees and sobbed. The beast moved forward and bowed its head to him. In his mind he could feel an effort of comforting, as if the Alicanto was wrapping its wings around him and cradling him. "It's okay," she said. "He is with his mother now, of that, I am sure."

"How can you know that?" Emrys sniffed.

"I know many things, young Primal," she said. "Things of old, things that man has long forgotten and some things that defy logic. Now let me ask you something, why do you run from those who wish to help you?"

"I cannot face, Rheinar," Emrys shook his head. "I'm responsible for the death of his son."

"You are not," the Alicanto said. "What happened was beyond your control, Rheinar understands this. He does not blame you, he only blames himself. He wishes he had died in place of his son." Emrys wiped his nose on his sleeve and looked up at the flaming bird. It seemed sincere and kinder than he initially believed yet he could not fathom why it pained him so when the bird emerged. "Can I ask," he plucked up the courage, "why do you burn me? Every time you've appeared my hand feels like it's on fire, and I can't remove the ring no matter how much I try."

"We are bound," she replied. "The moment you put the ring on I felt your presence. I have been slumbering for so long now I cannot remember the last time I was awakened. By being in the desert you gave me the strength I needed to appear in your time of need. The pain you feel is necessary for me to leave my mark upon you. For this I am sorry, but there is no escaping it. I was trapped in the ring long, long ago by a curse and bound to the Atacama. I do not know what to do or if I can ever break this spell."

Emrys couldn't believe his eyes nor his ears. A night ago he had been traversing the desert with his sister, Rheinar and Jakob yet tonight he was sat by the side of a beast he had only heard about in myths and legends. "What should I do?" he asked. "Everyone expects so much of me but most of the time I don't know what's happening to me and I certainly understand nothing regarding my abilities."

"You will," she replied as she stretched her wings. "A Primal's duty is to defend nature, the creatures in it and to expel the evil in the world. I do not know of the threat you face but it must be severe if its creatures are corrupted."

"What is Corruption?" Emrys puzzled. "A tale for another time, young Primal," she replied. "Corruption is an ancient evil and I believe you are the only one who can stop it. Now let's get you back to your group."

"I can't go back," Emrys shook his head.

"You must," she urged him. "They love you and you will need their help on your journey. I understand it's hard for you and I can feel that, but it hard for them as well."

Emrys reluctantly rose to his feet and wiped the tears from his face. "What is your name?" he asked.

"Call me Ali," she said gleaming in the moonlight. "I will return to slumber now. Know that the further you stray from the desert, the weaker I become. Find your friends and travel together, the danger is not yet over. Call me when you need me, Emrys."

And with a flash of light Ali disappeared like mist fading on a summer's day. Emrys swallowed the lump in his throat and looked back to the desert. He would return to Rheinar and

Lymris with the tiniest sliver of hope they would be understanding.

***

"YOU selfish bastard!" his sister screamed at him as an arrow was fired at his feet. Emrys shied away from her gaze as Lymris stormed over to him and began pushing him. "Do you have any idea how worried we've been? We've been riding and trekking all night and we've not slept a wink! How could you do that to us!?"

They had reunited at the bottom of the cliff just as the son rose above the sandy peaks, and when Emrys saw his sister approaching he wished he'd never turned back. Emrys had never seen his sister so angry. The veins in her forehead stuck out as she yelled and she spewed venomous words as if she was a snake. She did look tired and Emrys felt guilty that the two of them had been combing the Atacama during the night. "I'm sorry," was all he could muster as he looked on at Rheinar. The Storm's Fury barely seemed to notice him as he looked on at the endless sea of sand. There was sadness etched onto his face yet mostly he looked as if he was in a state of shock. His reactions were off and he seemed more distant to Emrys than ever. "What do you have to say for yourself?" Lymris shoved him back again.

"I didn't want to hurt you any more!" Emrys rose his voice. "Jakob is dead because of me! Siska attacked because of me! What happens when Caulder sends more of his creatures after us? I cannot allow you or Rheinar to sacrifice yourself for me!"

"What gives you the right to decide that?" Rheinar snarled as he approached. Fresh tears welled in Emrys' eyes as he looked at the huge warrior before him. Rheinar grimaced when he saw Emrys crying and looked away as if to stop himself from weeping. "We are here Emrys," he continued, "to ensure you make it to the Circle. That is our quest. That was *Jakob's* quest. I refuse to let you carry on alone in the name of my King, and in the name of my son who died for our common cause!"

"I will second that," Lymris calmed herself. "This isn't *your* quest, it is ours as well. We have to get you to the Circle otherwise none of it, not your exile, not Jakob's death, will mean anything."

"I'm sorry I let you down," Emrys sniffed as he stared at his family.

Rheinar leant down and placed a hand on his shoulder. "Don't be sorry, Emrys," he said. "Be better. We stand with you always. Exiled or not you *are* my Prince and I will die defending you if needs be."

Emrys felt touched by their loyalty and hugged Rheinar fiercely as Lymris joined him. Once they parted Emrys briefly smiled and said, "There's something I must show you. Ali, please come out."

Pain shot up his arm and familiar burn marks reappeared as Emrys bit his hand to stifle the pain. Jets of light burst forth once more and seconds later they were greeted by the glimmering Alicanto who roared into the sky and held her wings out like a fan. Rheinar and Lymris were speechless, their eyes twinkling in unison as they observed the mythical beast. "Hello Lymris, hello Rheinar," she said. "You… talk?" Lymris stuttered and rubbed her eyes in disbelief.

"I do," Ali replied. "My name is Ali, Phoenix-Mother bound in service to the Atacama Desert. I am sorry for your loss. Jakob was a fine man and ill deserving of Corruption."

Rheinar bowed his head and acknowledged Ali with a simple nod. "What is corruption?" Lymris asked.

"Your brother is a Primal, yes? Primals bring life to the world. They are its stout protectors for all things natural and awakened in times of great threat."

"What does this have to do with corruption?" Emrys quipped.

"I'm leading to that Emrys, do not worry," Ali nodded. "Who has been contacting you by your dreams? I feel the fear which courses in your very veins."

"Its name is Caulder, The Bringer of Storms," Emrys shuddered as if it could hear him now. "I've seen its Corruption in my dreams."

"I do not know this Caulder, but this is what I do know," Ali continued. "Imagine if you will a coin. On one face of the coin, you have Emrys, the other is Caulder. Whereas you will bring life, Caulder will bring Corruption. It is an ancient evil which devours anything in its path. Its sole purpose is to eradicate life itself. Creatures born of it bear its mark and once Corruption has touched you, you are enslaved to its will. Caulder will cover the world in Corruption and it is your duty to stop it. Fail, and every living creature will die or worse."

The weight of the words hit Emrys square in his chest and he began to panic under the pressure. *How can I save everyone when I cannot save the ones I love?* He thought. He fell to his knees and gasped for air helplessly and cradled his head in his arms. He couldn't deal with the stress of it. He had seen Caulder in his dreams and each time he had woken in a cold sweat from sheer fear.

"How do you know this if you do not know who Caulder is?" Lymris asked as she knelt by his side.

"This is not first time Corruption has made it to this

plane," Ali retorted as she strolled over to Emrys. "Caulder is merely its vessel. Without the Primal, it is hopeless, Emrys. You must rise up and realise your potential."

"I'm scared," Emrys quivered. "You haven't seen Caulder. You haven't seen what he's capable of, the evil it speaks of."

"No, I have not," Ali leant in and blew warm air which flushed his cheeks. "But I have seen you. I have felt your heart and know it is good. You are stronger than you know and I believe in you."

"We all do." Rheinar stepped forward, "None of this moping will help. Be strong Emrys, for if Ali is right, we will need your strength. Is there no way you could fly Emrys to the Circle? Lym and I can make our way but Emrys must learn more about being a Primal."

"I wish I could," Ali said. "But my power wanes the further I stray from the Atacama. I will do what I can to protect Emrys but you will both be needed before the end."

"What end do you speak of?" Emrys asked as he met Ali's burning eyes.

"A tale for another time, young Primal," Ali mirrored the words she spoke earlier. "The future is not yet written. Now go. You must make haste."

The Phoenix-Mother disappeared in a flash of light and the pain in his arm subsided. Lymris pulled him to his feet and brought Elmyra forward, who whinnied upon his sight and ruffled her head against his. "Thank you," Emrys said. "Thank you both." Neither replied, but smiled and nodded as if his thanks were not necessary. They rode on with the wind at their backs and rushed towards the plush Gardens of Carpathia. Fear and anticipation gripped them all more than they could say. They knew nothing of the world in front of them and even less about the trials and tribulations they were yet to face. Emrys did not share it, but in the recess of his mind he could feel the coldness of Caulder, cackling louder than ever.

Chapter Thirty-One
Irresistible

"LYMRIS, hurry up! Cast your eyes upon this!" Emrys called from ahead. The Atacama Desert was gratefully behind them and Lymris had just managed to free herself from the final bits of sand clinging to her feet. The landscape before them was vastly different. Towering trees were in abundance and their long spiky spires shot high up into the sky obscuring the morning sunlight. The heat, while consistent, was far cooler than the desert had been and Lymris felt thankful the hot air no longer clogged up her lungs. Her brother was standing in front of her, perched on top of a felled tree with a large grin smothering his face. "Look down there," Emrys pointed as she approached. She followed his arm which led down to a sight she felt she had not seen for an age. Below them, merely thirty feet away, was fresh water. A flowing river worked its way through the fauna and the sound of the rushing water filled her heart with joy. She squealed excitedly and ran down to the muddied bank.

"I'm going in," she laughed and threw her weapons down. Atop a rock she dove into the river and felt its cold embrace and laughed heartily as she swam up and down. Emrys stood by the edge and was cupping water which he drank gladly as Rheinar approached and loosed the horses.

"Jump in Em," Lymris said spitting water from her mouth. "It's cold but after that desert it's a welcoming cold."

"No, I'm okay just drinking for now," Emrys smiled.

"Is that so?" Rheinar said standing behind him.

"Rheinar please don'…" was all her brother could muster before Rheinar picked him up by the scruff of his neck and dropped him into the river. Lymris laughed as her brother resurfaced and spluttered from the cold. Rheinar enjoyed a brief smile with her before it sank from his face and he resumed his tasks.

"While you're in there Emrys, see to the horses," he said turning his attention back to the flasks. "They're in dire need of a good clean, plus it's a decent chance to test your abilities again."

Emrys nodded and stood near the shallow end. As Lymris watched on she could see Emrys concentrating as he faced the four horses. One by one, they flocked to his side and stood in the water. Elmyra huffed and motioned to her saddlebag, from which her brother pulled a brush and began to dust the horses off.

"That's incredible how he is with the horses now," Lymris said paddling over to Rheinar.

"Aye," he replied. "I've never seen Shrieker so obedient. Even with me he's a pain in the arse sometimes."

Lymris realised felt flush with guilt and realised she had spoken nothing about Jakob since that night. "Are you okay, Rheinar?" she asked.

"No." He shook his head and exhaled. "But I'll live and more importantly see to my duty. Come with me and have a look at this."

Lymris tied her hair back and dried her face using her bedroll when she pulled herself up. Rheinar poured over the continent map quizzically as she approached. When she viewed the map she could see the various lands of Arcadia, Mercia, Galbraith, Alterra and Carpathia yet much of the detailing left a lot to be desired. Only a handful of roads were clearly marked out and save for the capital cities, little else was on it. Rheinar kept a firm thumb covering the Atacama Desert to the South as his eyes lingered East. "It's hard to judge where we are," he said. "We're definitely East of the Atacama however the woods we're heading into have a reputation."

"What reputation is that?" She asked.

"A reputation for being a bloody maze," he replied. "The Whispering Woods are so thick they blacken the sky and navigation is all but impossible. It is a cruel place to travel so I have heard. Many people have gone in never to return."

"And we aren't in these woods now?" Lymris quizzed.

"No," Rheinar said looking back at the map. "The trees of the Whispering Woods are crooked. If we keep heading East through these woods, we *should* find them before long."

"You said there are myths about the Whispering Woods, what have you heard?" Lymris asked nervously.

"Things I'd rather not believe to be honest," he said. "According to many storytellers the woods earned their name for the whisperings of spirits. Travellers who strayed from the path and lost themselves in the thicket. Others think there is a monster prowling through the trees. A ghastly creation who kills without mercy. Mention nothing of this to Emrys, I do not want him to worry. I want him focused on finding the Circle."

"I won't," Lymris promised. "What do you think is out there?"

"After everything we've seen from Stormgast to this point, who knows?" Rheinar replied. "One thing I'm certain of, we'll find out and we must protect Emrys. We owe that to

Jakob."

Lymris smiled sadly and held Rheinar's hand as he looked away. "Right, Lym," he said. "Please can you help Emrys with the horses? I'll hunt for some game and find a place where we can make camp."

"Are you sure you don't want my help on the hunt?" Lymris suggested.

"No, I need a moment alone with my thoughts," he said. "I will return before long."

Rheinar disappeared behind the trees armed only with a bow and a few arrows. Lymris jumped back into the water and swam over to her floundering brother. The pair of them set about cleaning their horses before agreeing to wash Shrieker together. The giant black beauty towered over the others and there was a silent agreement he would take the most effort to clean. The day passed by quickly as their arms ached and fresh blisters formed and burst on their hands. Their efforts were not in vain and by the time Rheinar returned with food from his hunt, all four of the horses were fresher than they had been in weeks. Exhausted, Lymris slumped by the fire her brother built and looked at him. The sun had tanned him well and he looked bronzed compared to the pale skin he had when they left Galbraith. He seemed much leaner than he had been before and his forearms had grown muscular since he began using a bow. His hair was now overgrown and he was constantly sweeping his fringe from his eyes. Lymris sought to change that. "Fancy a haircut, Em?" she said stoking the fire.

Emrys shrugged. "Why not?" he replied. "I'm sick of not being able to see things."

She pulled her dagger out and began snipping away into the night. She was hardly the greatest of barbers yet she carefully plucked away as if she was malting a dog. "It's a good thing Lym is cutting your hair," Rheinar said as he began skinning the rabbits.

"Why is that?" her brother asked.

"Because if I was cutting it," he replied grinning, "I'd shave it all off. You'd be bald like me."

Lymris laughed, "Well that can be arranged if you'd like dear brother?"

Emrys leapt to his feet and darted away from her. "No, I'm okay," he laughed nervously. "Just a trim off the top will do for me."

She continued to cut away at his hair and an hour later Lymris was satisfied with her work. "Check your reflection in the water," she said tucking her dagger away.

Emrys leant over and tugged at his hair. He turned back and smiled at Lymris, his teeth glistening in the dusk. "It's great Lym," he said. "Just like when mum used to cut it. She'd be proud."

She returned his smile and thought on his words. Lymris missed her mother more than she could ever put into words. She prayed for her guidance that night before they journeyed deeper into Carpathia in search of the Whispering Woods.

***

A FORTNIGHT passed by as the trio wandered further and further into the thicket. Rheinar was right about the Whispering Woods. The trees were warped and twisted beyond reason. It was as if the very roots had been mangled to form crude formations which beggared belief. The silence that creaked within these woods was staggering. Whereas before they had borne witness to birds singing, squirrels chirping and rabbits rushing in the undergrowth, they saw no signs of life anywhere. With each passing day more and more darkness crept into their surroundings. Eventually it became impossible to tell whether it was morning or evening and Lymris was certain Rheinar and Emrys were in the same predicament. All they felt was the cold and damp as the ever-growing mist soaked through their bones. They were forced to huddle with the horses for warmth yet when they awoke, the shivers would not subside. Visibility was questionable at best and they all shared injuries from the jagged thorns which lay hidden from their view. Twice Lymris tripped over branches and cut her arms on landing. Emrys attempted to rest for a moment and leant on a branch which collapsed and he fell straight into brambles. Rheinar grimaced as he watched a thorn rip through his boot and pierce his right foot, leaving a trail of blood behind with each step.

Morale was lower than ever. When they made camp, no stories were told and no laughs were shared. Only silence remained for the group as they ate their small meals as paranoia began to take hold. Lymris felt as if there were eyes upon her and when she closed hers, she gripped her dagger tightly as if ready for a fight. Whenever a twig snapped, she jumped to attention before realising it was one of the horses searching for a late snack. One morning she awoke and rubbed the sleep from her eyes. She was drenched through and shivered as the morning breeze rolled through the woodland. Emrys was curled up next to Elmyra and Styria, while Rheinar slept by Shrieker's side. There was no sign of the fourth horse and Lymris shook her brother awake. "Emrys," she said. "The other horse is missing. Can you try and call her back?"

Emrys shot a frown towards her and groggily rose to his feet. He closed his eyes as Lymris continued to scan their surroundings. A few minutes passed and Emrys opened his eyes and shook his head. "I cannot sense her," he said.

"What does that mean?" Lymris asked.

"I do not know," he said worryingly and woke Rheinar. "Rheinar we've lost the mare."

"Lost?" Rheinar coughed as he stood up. "Well, we need to find her. She has a week's worth of food in her saddle. Both of you, search for her trail, shout me when you've found it. We move together."

Emrys signalled about ten minutes later as they found the trail the mare had taken. They each guided their horses through the thicket as Rheinar took pole position and tracked the hoof-prints. Lymris felt her stomach gurgle and cramps when she thought of the skipped breakfast. They were all exhausted from the stress of it all and this was the last thing they needed. They toiled away for hours as they went further down into a gully. The trail was easy to track and Rheinar made short work of it as he guided Shrieker by his side. Eventually they came to a clearing and they could finally see the sky for the first time since they had arrived. As they entered the light Lymris felt the warm embrace of the suns as it kissed her skin. Ahead of her Rheinar continued to follow the trail until he stopped dead in his tracks.

"Both of you," he said glumly. "Over here."

To their despair they had found the mare. Her corpse was sprayed out across the leafy floor with blood splatters all over the place. Her organs had been ripped clean out and very little, save her head, spine and saddle. "Emrys check the saddle," Rheinar commanded as he placed his hand on a bloody puddle.

"Poor mare, what manner of creature is capable of this? The blood is still warm," he said. "This happened recently. Draw your weapons." Without a moment's hesitation Lymris pulled her bow and readied an arrow. She turned to look at Rheinar who stood there frozen. "What's that?" he asked wide-eyed. "Can you hear that?"

"Hear what?" Emrys puzzled.

"Whispers," Rheinar said ashen-faced. "I can hear whispers."

Surely enough a few moments later Lymris too heard the whispers. It was like a thousand overlapping each other and for some reason she felt safe in their sound. There were young voices, old voices, all repeating the same words *'come to me'.* "I hear them calling to me…" she said as she dropped her bow.

"What are you both on about!" Emrys asked. "There's nothing out there!"

Suddenly the whispers came to an abrupt end. A sole voice sang through the gloomy woods. It was the most beautiful sound Lymris had ever heard and she could feel herself welling up. She had never heard anything like it. "That voice," she said. "It sounds so familiar… So safe…"

"It's so beautiful… Let us find it together…" Rheinar replied. "I think it is coming from there…"

"What are you both doing?" Emrys asked horrified. "Come back!"

"It's okay Emrys…" Lymris smiled as tears streamed down her face. "We're safe now…"

Sound from the world drowned out. The twigs crunching beneath her feet, the wind rushing through the air. All she could hear and all she wanted to hear was the voice singing the melody which pulled at her heart. She was in love with the sound of it and walked eagerly towards it. Her brother tried to stop them but she would not be stopped. His muffled cries and feeble efforts to hold her back meant nothing to her. All she wanted was the song. It was irresistible. She brushed Emrys aside as if he was nothing and continued to stride forward. Elmyra, Styria and Shrieker heard the song as well and joined them as they glided through the trees together, in pursuit of the mysterious voice.

Chapter Thirty-Two
Preparations

TYRIS stood stunned at his aunt, Queen Eremea's, revelation. She had agreed to marry Edmure and join the Kingdom of Mercia with the Arcadian Empire in union. Arcadia had no love for Galbraith and the fragile peace between the two nations hung on the health of Emperor Harold Valyris. The ramifications alone were causing him to sweat and he tried to compose himself before addressing the news. Queen Eremea eyed him curiously for his response and smiled unnaturally as he scanned the room. All eyes were upon him and he knew he had to react in a good manner. Smiling through gritted teeth he said: "Congratulations, I am very happy for you."

"And yet I see no wedding gifts," she replied. "I sent out messengers to all of the nations, surely your father told you this?"

"He did not," Tyris shook his head. "Though I do not believe we received such a message."

"Hmm, strange," she said filing her long nails. "We are to be wed two months from now. Mathas come forward."

From behind the plinth came the familiar ghoulish appearance of Edmure's trusted advisor. His evil stare met Tyris and he bowed half-mockingly towards the prince. "It is *good* to see you, Prince Tyris," he said.

Tyris immediately disliked the tone in his voice but maintained his politeness, "And you also Mathas," he replied.

"Mathas, please could you pass on our letter of demands to Prince Tyris," his aunt smiled. "It is important that Galbraith learns of what is required of them." Before he could move, Petra stepped forward and snatched the scroll from Mathas's outstretched hand that made the advisor rock where he stood. Mathas flashed a frown towards him but Petra merely shrugged and passed the note to Tyris. The Crown Prince broke the seal of the letter and perused the letter with Velstadt by his side:

"By Decree of the Arcadian and Mercian Alliance,

All neighbouring nations from the day of Emperor Edmure and Queen Eremea's union are to uphold Mage Law. The law constitutes that Mages and/or those who assist Mages are to either enslaved or to be executed without trial. Practice of magic is to be banned under pain of death and members of the accursed Circle are to be hunted across the lands. This decree goes beyond the common folk and extends to those within Royal families. Annual fealties are to be paid towards the Arcadian and Mercian Alliance for maintaining the peace and to fund the invasion of Carpathia to destroy the Circle of Mages. Failure to uphold any of the demands mentioned above and swift retribution will be paid. Disobedience towards the alliance will not be tolerated and the harshest of punishments will be allowed to those who stand against the might of Arcadia and Mercia.

Signed,

Emperor Edmure Valyris of the Arcadian Empire
Queen Eremea Rothach of the Kingdom of Mercia"

Tyris could not believe what he was reading, and his shocked face sent smiles around the palace court. "Aunt Eremea is this some sort of sick joke?" he asked no longer hiding his anger.

"*Queen* Eremea," she insisted. "And this is no joke. Once Emperor Edmure and I are wed we demand loyalty and fealty from Galbraith and Alterra. We seek to unite Elessia to a common purpose: To rid the world of magic."

Applause rang around the court as Tyris, Petra and Velstadt watched on flabbergasted. Mathas curled his long fingers back inside his robe and slithered back into the shadow like a nesting viper. Tyris could have sworn he saw his eyes flicker a strange colour but dismissed it from his mind when his eyes wandered back to his aunt. He could take no more. No more insults to his family, no more insults to his nation and no more insults to Mage-folk. "EREMEA!" he shouted bringing a silence to the hall. "This insult to Galbraith will not stand. Long have Galbraith and Mercia stood side by side to protect Mage-folk! Cairngorm! This very city was carved of the mountain by the magic you wish to rid of the world! And you Mathas! The Emperor of Arcadia is Harold, not Edmure! What does Harold say of this decree!"

"You dare defy me in my own Kingdom?" Eremea slammed her hands down and rose with venomous eyes. "Magic must be smothered before it spreads like fire and burns all that we know!"

"Those are not the words of Mercia," Tyris spat. "But the words of your *soon-to-be* husband Edmure! Have you not eyes? Have you not seen the suffering you inflict upon your own citizens outside those very doors!? Children, nailed to posts!"

The words struck a chord with Eremea as her lip began to

tremble. She looked sad and began to quiver as she heard the distant screams as if it was the very first time she had. "Oh no," she said weakly and tears began to form in her eyes. Mathas re-emerged and placed his hand on hers.

"Queen Eremea," he said. "Edmure will be the finest Emperor Arcadia has ever seen with you by his side. Are you going to let this *boy* continue to insult you? To demean the words of the Queen of Mercia?"

Her face bereft of emotion turned to one of anger. "No," she hissed. "Prince Tyris of Galbraith you and your followers are henceforth banished from Mercia. Return, and I will have your heads mounted on spikes!"

Tyris scoffed as his temper soared to boiling point. The lords and ladies of Mercia watched on and he could not be certain if they were looks of joy or horror. He began to step forward and the guards around the hall stiffened. At this point he felt the strong clasp of Velstadt grabbing his arm and shaking his head resolutely. "Not here," he whispered. "We must return to Stormgast and speak with your father."

The three hurried from the palace grounds to cheers and jeers in equal measure. When Tyris looked back at his aunt, he could see a lone tear trickling down to her chin as Mathas grip around her hand grew tighter. Abuse followed as they made their way to the streets of Cairngorm. The word of their banishment spread faster than they could believe, and before they knew it people in the street began to circle and launch rocks at them. Free of the city gates they thundered up the Caldea Crossing until nightfall where they sat under a hastily made camp.

"My Prince," Velstadt approached with a bowl of stew. "Might we have a word?"

"Of course, Velstadt," Tyris sighed. "Today has been a long day."

"Aye it has," he nodded and passed him the bowl. "But I think things are more troubling than you realise." "What do you mean?" Tyris asked.

"I've known Eremea for almost twenty years," Velstadt met his gaze. "Twenty years Tyris. And she didn't even acknowledge me."

"Perhaps she didn't see you," Tyris shrugged naively.

"Tyris she looked right at me," Velstadt said plainly. "But it was almost as if... She saw through me. It was as if I wasn't there, or as if she didn't know who I was."

"What do you think happened in there?" Tyris asked.

"I'm not sure," the captain stroked his chin. "But I know that bastard Mathas has something to do with it. Eremea has always been kind. Mad yes, but kind to her people. She would never have agreed to public executions, let alone the persecution of mages. There's more to this than we know Tyris."

***

THE journey home had been a dejected one and with each day Tyris felt more shame and guilt wash over him. He had been banished from Mercia and knew that he would have to share more terrible news with his father on his return. His knights avoided his gaze during the days and at night he could hear their varied opinions about the Arcadian & Mercian Alliance, and where that left Galbraith. Velstadt and Petra had largely remained silent yet always offered kind words of encouragement to the defeated Prince. Tyris kept the note

Mathas had given to him and clutched it with an anger he did not know he possessed. They had been betrayed, it was as simple as that. Velstadt's words regarding Eremea may be true however Tyris could not look past the cruelty he had witnessed in Cairngorm. He struggled to sleep thinking about it, and his mind drifted back to the young girl he had seen chained to a post mere days ago. The weather had been relentless and two horses were put down after breaking their legs on the ever-sliding scree. The Caldea Crossing was a place Tyris would not miss and during his time there, he spent it alone in his thoughts, trying to work out the right words for his father.

On return to Galbraith, they were greeted by the familiar Great Oak banners at the Western Gate which waved briskly in the whipping winds. By the time they reached the road to Stormgast, Tyris could not believe his eyes and rubbed them vigorously to ensure he was not dreaming. His father had raised the fyrds, and thousands of soldiers could be seen marching to the capital, their armour shining like jewels in the sea. Tyris glimpsed a few battle-mages in their ranks and looked on in awe. He had never seen one in the flesh and the stories he had heard did not do them do justice. Their armour was sleeker than that of the pikemen, beneath which they adorned robes of maroon and gold. They opted for hoods instead of helms and strode side by side with the men and women who would defend Galbraith. One of their ranks looked at Tyris as he trotted past and stopped on the spot. "My Prince," she said pulling the hood from her head. She was probably Rheinar's age he estimated and her face bore the brunt of many battles. Red glowing veins could be seen across her hands, face and neck and she bowed with the grace of a noblewoman. "We will not disappoint you, Prince Tyris," she spoke proudly as soldiers cheered behind her. Tyris responded with a bow and smiled at her, before she fell back into her ranks.

Stormgast was awash with people. The numbers in the crowd far exceeded that of his own wedding and Tyris looked round bewildered to the chaos in the marketplace. People were stockpiling food, soldiers were running drills and lords and ladies flocked towards the Great Hall. Tyris and his party followed suit, and when the doors were opened, he dismounted and entered with Petra and Velstadt at his side. His father was sat on the Oaken Throne in discussion with Mikhael, and when he saw Tyris he practically jumped to his feet. "My son you have returned," he said smiling briefly.

"I have, Father," Tyris replied walking to him pulling the scroll from his pocket. "But I bring bad news from Mercia."

King Terrys examined the note and frowned before he screwed it up into a ball and threw it into the fire. "So Eremea has betrayed us," he said shaking his head. "Velstadt what did you make of her?"

"She was not herself, my King," Velstadt replied. "Eremea has always been strange and wacky, but she's never been cruel. When we arrived in Cairngorm, they were publicly executing mages and those aiding them. Tyris, and indeed all of us are banished from Mercia."

King Terrys exhaled and scratched his head. "Leave us," he announced to the Great Hall. "All of you. Save my son, Mikhael and Velstadt." Thundering footsteps echoed through the hall before the doors slammed and the four of them remained. King Terrys slumped onto the throne and shouted obscenities in anger to the skies. "Father, can I ask?" Tyris stepped forward. "Why have you raised the fyrds?"

"We received this a few days ago," he replied. "Mikhael read it please."

Mikhael cleared his throat and reading from a scroll said, "Emperor Harold Valyris has succumbed to a fever. His son, Edmure, has assumed command of the Empire and readies his troops on the Southern border."

"I had not known of the wedding," his father said irritated. "I read it and thought he was to invade Mercia but this is far worse than I expected. With Arcadia and Mercia joining forces our options are few."

"Should we sue for peace?" Mikhael asked as Velstadt grunted in disapproval.

"Look there," King Terrys pointed to the carved branch. "*Arcadian Eastern Territories.* Do you really think Edmure wants peace? He comes to conquer and that he shall unless we attempt something drastic. Have you any recommendations?"

Mikhael repositioned his glasses and tapped his top lip. "We could buy soldiers from Daal," he suggested. "As I understand it, warriors from the Southern Tribes offer their fealty for gold. We could hire a few companies to replenish our own?"

"That will never work," Terrys shook his head. "Armies that fight for gold will turn on us at the first offer of asking. I think we should perhaps look to other options."

"What did you have in mind, Father?" Tyris nodded.

"Velstadt," his father rose and clasped him on the shoulder. "I would ask for your service one last time. Take my son and his wife to Alterra. With hope they will listen to reason and we unite our forces or else we are all lost."

"You want me to go with Elette?" Tyris interrupted. "My place is at your side father. To whatever end!"

"Should I... should Galbraith fall," King Terrys raised his hand. "We need to ensure the heir to the Kingdom survives. Protect Elette and your child. Attempt to negotiate with King Wulfram. Express the shared peril which lies before us. With luck we can preserve our two Kingdoms. What say you Velstadt? Will you grant me this?"

Velstadt smiled and nodded. "I am at your service, King Terrys," he said grinning. "There's a woman waiting in Burnistoun probably itching to kill me already, so I have no desire to rush back at the moment. The crew of the Crimson Tempest will defend Prince Tyris and Princess Elette as if they were the crew themselves. We will set sail as soon as you command."

"Thank you, my friend," Terrys grinned. "Take what gold, men and supplies you need for the journey. Mikhael would you like to accompany Elette? I know you have been training together and she looks up to you. It is your choice."

"Begging forgiveness, Tyris," Mikhael winked, "but I am too old for travel across the seas. I would be better suited to keeping an eye on things here. Who will look after your father if I leave now?"

Tyris sniffed away a tear and stared at the ground. Everything was happening so fast he could barely keep up with it. His father pulled his head up and stared at him with a smile he would not forget. "I am so proud of you, Tyris," he said warmly. "It is not easy to be the first born but you have excelled where I could not. I wish your mother was here to see the man you have become. Do not hang your head. Be proud of who you are. You represent the best of Galbraith and whatever happens to me, the Kingdom would be safe in your hands. Be safe and protect our legacy."

Chapter Thirty-Three
Nirvana

BE Calm... Emrys could hear Ali calling in the recess of his mind, yet he could not allow himself to falter. He had been chasing after Lymris, Rheinar and the horses for almost three hours and they had not once stopped for a break, nor had they deviated from their course. Panic consumed him. They were unmoved by his pleas of 'stop' and he did not believe they could even hear him. He tried to forcibly stop them but both his sister and Rheinar had pushed him effortlessly out of the way. They were unflinching in their devotion to move further and further into the thicket. Darkness smothered the gloomy surroundings with each step into the Whispering Woods. He had tried to summon the horses over and over again, but they too were deaf to his pleas. *I cannot reach them,* Emrys said to Ali. *I have tried so many times but I cannot even reach the horses. What do I do?*

For now, we follow them, she replied, *but tread carefully Emrys. One false step in these woods and we would scarce see the light of day again.*

Emrys swallowed what fear he could as he trudged after his party. The ground seemed to shift beneath him. Whereas before they were pronged by thorns and stabbed by the harsh woodland, now it seemed the ground was a slimy ooze clad with moss and damp. He lost sight of Lymris and Rheinar several times in his hunt and had to stop to listen for their boots squelching in the distance.

Do not move, Ali spoke sharply in his mind calling him to a halt. *Crouch now and look to your left slowly.* Emrys' breath grew ragged as he dropped to his belly and cast his eyes West. *What is that?* He panicked when he saw what Ali warned him of. He could see the dark silhouette of a creature as it stomped through the woods. Many of its features were obscured from his view but even in the darkness which clouded his eyes, it appeared unnatural. He could not ascertain if the creature was one of hide or scale, yet the putrid stench of its appearance made him gag. Its shallow breaths croaked like the trees in a stiff breeze and it almost seemed to moan as if it was in agony. *Remain still,* Ali reminded him as his legs began to quiver. Emrys closed his eyes and held his breath as the monster crept closer. It sounded as if it was merely feet away from him before its breaths grew distant. Opening his eyes he could see that the creature continued to move forward and appeared uninterested in Lymris, Rheinar or even the horses.

What is that thing? Emrys asked once more.

That is a Zarrac, Ali replied, *an abomination of magic. Something terrible has happened here in these woods.*

What does that mean? Emrys asked as his eyes remained fixated on the moving shadow.

Someone, or something has committed an atrocity against nature, Ali said clearly agitated, *Zarracs are hybrid creatures. Using their knowledge in magic, a mage has melded two innocent creatures into that which remains hidden from sight. They are enslaved creatures, bound only to their master, and every moment of their existence is an agony I would not wish on anyone. It is torture Emrys, torture of the soul. We must hurry, this is far worse than I thought it could be. Keep pace with the group, but remain hidden from the Zarrac. We cannot allow it to see us.*

I'm scared Ali, Emrys thought almost bringing him to tears. *What are we walking into?*

I do not know, Ali replied, *but take heart in the fact that your sister and Rheinar are still with us. There must something we can do. Now go, do not lose them.*

Emrys rushed to his feet and smeared the mud and slime from his hands on a nearby tree. As he touched the trunk, he felt strange. He had not felt this feeling since his Awakening and his mind raced back to when he touched the Great Oak. His heart pounded in his chest as the world around him seemed to slow down. *Primal...* a voice spoke. Confused Emrys asked, *Ali is that you?*

Is what me? the Mother Phoenix replied. *Emrys, you've slowed and we must hurry.* Emrys brushed the thought from his mind and continued to sneak after Lymris and Rheinar. He stalked them for hours. By the dwindling of the light Emrys assumed it must be approaching nightfall, though he could not be sure. The Zarrac seemed to form an escort for the group and Emrys moved carefully so as not to alert it to his location. Ali continued to encourage him along the route yet even Emrys could feel her fear at the unknown. They were alone. Alone only with each other's company and they had yet to find out what had entranced his family.

All of a sudden Emrys could hear shuffling footsteps all around him. He crept beneath a mossy mound and felt as the mud and slime soaked through his clothes. Shivering from the cold, he pulled back the ferns to watch for the source of the sound. He could not believe his own eyes. There were others in the Whispering Woods, hundreds he reckoned. Each one of them was seemingly stuck in the same trance that had taken hold of Lymris and Rheinar. They moved without hesitation, together and in the same direction. Two people stood on his back as they strode forward and Emrys winced and bit his fist causing fresh blood to run down his arm. They had not noticed. Nor had any of them that he even existed. Despite the crowds of people flocking past, Emrys had never felt more alone. Emrys pulled himself back above ground and stood up but no-one seemed wiser to his presence, nor did they even glance in his direction. He started to walk among them and continued to ask himself how this could happen. Faces around him were blank and emotionless. Tears sparkled in the dwindling light like waves in the moonlight. *What have they heard?* he asked Ali. *What are they seeking? They move as if they are under some spell.*

I think we will soon find out, Ali replied. *This is magic, there can be no doubt. Be brave Emrys, for we will need strength for what comes next.*

***

EMRYS followed the droves of people further into the Whispering Woods. He no longer had line of sight of Lymris, Rheinar or even the horses, but if his suspicions were correct, they were all heading towards the same place. His senses were heightened by the absence of light. Though he stumbled through the damp woodland, as they all did, he felt stronger and as though his hearing was better. His eyes had completely adjusted to the dim light and he could now see things ten feet away. The Zarrac was near, of that Emrys was sure. He refused to turn and look for it, but the stench and low growling breaths were ever-present. Before long Emrys could see light appearing in the distance. It was not sunlight, nor was it torchlight. It seemed as if the bright whitened light was shining upward towards the sky itself. That was their target all along he realised. He pushed forward, sliding between the crowd with an agility that would have impressed Rheinar. As the light drew closer and closer Emrys could see that the trees around him were dwindling. The ground flattened out and turned to stone, and the feet of those around him clapped along the surface like rolling thunder. Before long the forest seemed to disappear entirely, replaced by a huge square not dissimilar to that of Burnistoun. A lone tree stood over the scene and stepping from its shadow Emrys could see the sky for the first time. It greeted Emrys and he could see thousands of stars shining down on the scene. The dazzling light, brighter than any star he had ever seen, was coming from the centre of the square.

"My children," a voice boomed from the light.

As Emrys moved closer he could see the light was emanating from a person sat atop a lone plinth. The crowd flocked towards the light and dropped to their knees, resting their hands in worship. Emrys crept forward warily and saw that the person was a woman of remarkable beauty. She was dressed in a long white robe and there was not one speck of dirt on her. She was impossibly clean and her white hair shined with the light that came from her body. The woman was paler than milk and Emrys could not tell if her eyes were green or blue. "Mother," the crowd began to chant.

"My children," she spoke again as her mouth curled into a smile. "Welcome to my Nirvana." *Emrys keep your hand to your bow ready,* Ali alerted him, *this is not what it seems.*

The Zarrac came into the open and under the light Emrys could see in horror how awful the beast was. It was disjointed in every conceivable way. Its very bones were twisted and morphed, forming a skeleton that carried no distinction of the animals it had once been. It had not one, but two heads of a bear while its legs and arms were talon-like. Feathers covered its hide body and a huge tail swept behind brushing trees and people from its way. As it stomped forward, sending tremors through the stone, Emrys could see it was a huge beast that completely dwarfed the onlooking crowd. The light from the woman faded as she rose to her feet and she held her arms out as the Zarrac approached her. "My pet," she said. "Are you hungry?"

A screech resembling that of an eagle roared from the Zarrac and its heads snapped wildly in the air. "Which one of you will be my sacrifice?" she asked looking on at the crowd. Hundreds of people leapt to their feet and began waving frantically, begging to picked by the mysterious woman. "You there," she said, pointing to a woman stood ten feet from Emrys. "You are ready to ascend. Come forth and feel my pet's *warm* embrace."

The woman duly obliged and approached the Zarrac with tears streaming down her face. An unnatural smile was etched upon her face and when she was close enough, the monster snarled, whetting its mouth in anticipation. "Devour," the woman said and snapped her fingers together.

Emrys recoiled in horror as the beast took two snaps at the unmoving woman and blood rained down on the scene. The crowd burst into cheers and raucously applauded as if they were watching a jousting tournament. Emrys felt the fear flutter in his heart and he started to back away from the group.

He could not believe how caught up the people were. They looked at the woman in a state of pure bliss and Emrys could not fathom how this had happened.

He backed into someone and upon turning he could see it was his sister, Lymris stuck in a trance. She barely moved yet rocked just a little from side to side. Her face was devoid of emotion, and though Emrys was stood in front of her, it seemed as if she was looking right through him or couldn't even recognise he was there. He grabbed her shoulders and shook her violently, "Lymris!" he urged. "Lymris, come back to me!" It did not work. She continued to look forward at the mysterious woman unaware to his plight. "Lymris, please!" he begged as his eyes welled and voice croaked. "We need to leave!"

Ali is there anything you can do? Emrys begged internally.

Emrys I cannot break the spell, Ali retorted, *I am sorry but we must find another way.*

"It looks like my pet is still hungry," the woman spoke to crowd once more. "Who else is willing to ascend?"

Lymris practically bundled Emrys to the ground as she came to life and began bouncing on the spot vying for the woman's attention. Noise erupted around them as the people chanted their pleas to the stranger and only when she held her hand up did silence rain down on the crowd. "You there," the woman pointed, "you're a big man, perhaps you will do. Step forward."

Emrys felt gripped by dread. He already knew what was happening and leapt to his feet as fast as his body would allow. Rheinar stood twenty feet to his right and began to stride towards the woman. *Ali what do I do?* Emrys panicked as time seemed to slow down.

We must save Rheinar, Ali urged. *Nock an arrow and shoot the Zarrac, but be ready to run. I do not believe for one moment that it will be without incident.*

Emrys, hands trembling reached for his quiver. Drawing all the strength he could muster from his tired muscles he pulled back on the bowstring and took aim. Rheinar was closing in fast and would be at the Zarrac in moments. Blood drooped down from the hideous creatures' mouth and it felt like everything else faded from the world as Emrys tried to compose himself. "Stop," the woman announced as Rheinar drew nearer. "You have a smell of magic on you, what is your name?"

"I am Rheinar," he replied in a monotonous manner. "Master-At-Arms for the Kingdom of Galbraith."

The mention of Galbraith drew a flicker of interest in her eyes. "You are a long way from home," she continued. "Do tell me more… Rheinar. How did you come to find your way in my forest?"

"I am escorting Prince Emrys of Galbraith to the Circle," he replied without hesitation. Emrys released the tension in his bow and watched as the woman began to circle Rheinar with curiosity. "Well, that would explain the smell," she smiled. "Where is this Emrys now?"

"I do not know," Rheinar said.

All of a sudden Lymris leapt to life and shouted, "He is here!"

Hundreds of heads turned in unison and stared at Emrys blankly. He could not escape, he was at the heart of the crowd and all he could do was tremble where he stood. "All of you move back," she said. "I wish to see this *Emrys*."

The crowd dispersed rapidly as the people receded back into the woodland and fell once more under the cover of darkness. Emrys stood alone with the woman as the Zarrac watched his every move. Emrys could feel her cold eyes upon him which sent shivers racing up his spine. He could hear Ali's voice fading in his mind as he gripped his bow so tightly, he was sure the wood would snap. His breaths were ragged as he watched the woman in an equal mix of fear and disgust. "Hello, Emrys," she said smiling cruelly. "Tell me, what do you think of my forest?"

Chapter Thirty-Four
Primal

"I ASKED you," the woman spoke interrupting Emrys' stunned silence, "what do you think of my forest?"

Emrys looked around. The stone square was bleak yet the view of the stars above was staggeringly beautiful. He felt the hairs on his neck standing to attention as the glimmering sea of a thousand eyes pierced through the dark of the Whispering Woods. The abhorrent Zarrac remained still, poised to attack should the woman command and its anguished grunts were amplified by the silence surrounding them. Emrys could feel the thumping of his heart as he met the cold stare of the woman before him. She watched him closely and awaited his response. "Who are you," Emrys stuttered as he gripped his bow. "How do you speak my language?"

"Uh, fine," she huffed taking a seat on the plinth. "Well, if we're going to go through the whole rigmarole of boring conversation I may as well get comfortable. My name is Aurora, and I am from Elessia, just as you are. Have you any other questions *Prince* Emrys?"

"What have you done to my friends?" Emrys demanded, raising his voice. "Release them from whatever spell you cast I beg of you!"

Aurora giggled and began filing her long nails, "Why would I do such a thing?" she asked. "They came to me. I merely facilitate the lost souls of these woods and give them a new purpose. A *better* purpose."

"You took away their purpose!" Emrys shouted as the Zarrac growled. "You took away their free will! I've been chasing them through the woods for a day and they cannot even hear me!"

"That is because they listen to a different voice now," she said glancing up at him. "*My* voice. Can you not be happy for them Emrys? Look around you. These people no longer care for the troubles of the world. They do not lie, they do not deceive each other. All of their worries have drifted away like a distant dream. They are happy here. Happy in the knowledge that there is only one thing that truly matters."

"What is that?" Emrys scowled.

"Why love of course," Aurora smiled. "They love me more than anything else in the world. They will obey my every command, wish or even fantasy. All I have to do is *whisper* and they consider me family. I am their mother and with it I provide them a mother's paradise free of pain. I treat them well, feed and clothe them, but they are cattle, nothing more. Now tell me Emrys, and do not lie, why do you seek the Circle?"

"I am a mage," Emrys stated plainly through gritted teeth. He felt angrier than ever and struggled to compose himself. Referring to people as cattle riled him more than he could keep concealed.

"Well that much is obvious," Aurora sighed and inhaled deeply. "You are no ordinary mage though, are you? You smell... different." Emrys bit his lip nervously yet continued to stand his ground. He would not run, nor would he flee. Saving Lymris and Rheinar was his only purpose. "No, I am just a mage, you are mistaken," he said.

"You are a poor liar," Aurora smirked. "No mage has ever resisted my enchantment… There's even a mage in this crowd who *loves* me. This intrigues me. Tell me Emrys, what are you? Why have you left your Kingdom of Galbraith? And why do you seek the Circle?"

Emrys considered lying then dismissed it. The Zarrac lingered and with each passing second it become more and more fixated on the exiled Prince. One false move or to aggravate Aurora would end in his swift death. "I was exiled," Emrys said sinking his head. "Exiled for using magic on the emperor's son. My father, King Terrys exiled me as my punishment. Rheinar has been escorting me to the Circle to realise my potential."

"*Realise my potential*," she quoted him. "People are often wrong about mages. They believe them to be capable of wondrous or terrible things. In actual fact very few mages have power. Most of them can perhaps move an object here or there but nothing substantial. You are getting closer to the Circle, Emrys, and I commend you for the journey you've undertaken, but do not look for salvation there. You will not find it."

"You know where the Circle is?" Emrys asked allowing a brief moment of hope into his heart.

"Of course I know where those pompous old fools are," Aurora spat. "I was once part of the Circle, until they banished me for challenging their ways."

"What did you do?" Emrys asked again.

"What all mothers do," she replied pointing to the Zarrac. "I gave birth to my beautiful child here. One day I came across two bears while I was walking through this forest. They were disease-ridden, and in that moment, I knew a painful death was their future. Rather than allow them this death I gave them a new life, together. How did the *Circle* reward me on my return? They cast me out a long time ago! Said that this was an unnatural act of magic, yet they are the ones who dabble with necromancy. The hypocrites! True my child was not born by conventional means but it is still life and one free of pain or death."

"But it is in pain," Emrys stated. "I can feel it. Listen to it. This child of yours longs for death."

"And who will be the one to grant it, you?" she said. "You still didn't answer my question, Emrys. What are you? But before you answer, allow me to give you some incentive to tell the truth. Rheinar, girl, come forth."

His sister and mentor emerged from the shadows of the forest, emotionless yet bound to Aurora's will as she had suggested. They took their place either side of her while Aurora licked her lips and stroked Lymris' hair. "This girl is pretty," she said. "Are you and she inseparable?"

"Please whatever you think I am just a mage!" Emrys protested as he quivered. "They are innocent! Leave them be!"

Unmoved, Aurora looked away. "Rheinar, choke the girl," she hissed.

The Storm's Fury grabbed Lymris by her throat and held her to the sky as his sister clawed at his arm and desperately gasped for air. "You were saying, Emrys," Aurora said casually.

"Please let them be!" Emrys said rushing forward. The Zarrac leapt forward and with a swift flick of its tail sent Emrys hurtling back across the square. Spluttering and winded from the pain he rushed to his feet and viewed the scene. Colour was draining fast from Lymris' face while Rheinar's remained devoid of emotion. Her efforts to resist were growing weaker and weaker with every passing second and her eyes were beginning to loll to the back of her head. *Tell her or Lymris will die!* Ali almost screamed in his mind. "I AM A PRIMAL!" Emrys bellowed. "LET THEM GO!"

Aurora snapped her fingers together and Rheinar dropped Lymris, who coughed and dragged herself to her feet. "Preposterous," Aurora scoffed. "You still dare to lie after everything you have seen?"

"I do not lie!" Emrys protested. "Caulder has returned! I saw it in my Awakening and I continue to see it in my dreams! Please! If you care about this world, you must help me!"

"I think not. I grow tired of your lies, Emrys," she dismissed his pleas and strolled over to the Zarrac. She stroked the beast delicately and finally fired a glance towards him, "Feast, my child."

***

THE Zarrac came thundering forward sending tremors across the square with its long strides. Emrys leapt out of the way of its charge as the beast carried on into the darkly woods. "Aurora, please stop this!" he pleaded as she started to laugh and clap her hands. The Zarrac re-emerged from the shadows and with a crack of its tail swept Emrys flying into the lone tree by the square. The pain was excruciating and he spat fresh blood with each cough as he groggily pulled himself to his feet. The world was spinning and he could barely make anything out with his woozy vision. The Zarrac did not relent and strolled forward hissing and roaring in equal measure. Emrys wiped the blood from his mouth and shouted, "Ali I need you!" Pain shot up his arm as the wing marks coursed his arm. Jets of light shot of his hand as the Phoenix-Mother emerged and came into view. Light coursed over the dark wood and Emrys could see the zombie-like people in their droves watching on with blank faces. "Get behind me!" Ali commanded as she dug her talons into the ground and snarled at the onrushing Zarrac.

Emrys looked at Aurora, who matched his stare, with one of disbelief and anger. The Zarrac charged Ali who beat the abomination away with her wings and roared sending majestic rays of light in its direction. The two continued to a fight in a cat and mouse game, darting between the trees and trading blows as flashes of light lit up the woodland. Aurora rose to her feet, her eyes full of venom, "All of you, get Emrys!" She shouted. A sea of people formed into a tide as they came stampeding towards him. From every corner of the square, they were closing fast, and in his panic, Emrys leapt up and fervently started to climb the tree. When the herd of people crashed into the trunk it almost knocked him off and fresh splinters dug their way into the palms of his hand. He held onto the trunk for dear life as he looked below him. The droves of people were scampering and clambered above one another in a completely chaotic manner. Emrys continued to climb until there were no branches left to ascend. As he wrapped both arms around the trunk he looked down on the square. People continued to flock forward from the shadows, while those at the base slowly crept up the tree. Ali was on the back foot in her duel and Emrys could feel her pain as she continued to engage the Zarrac.

Emrys, you need to get out of there, she urged him. *I cannot defeat this monster. My power is waning quickly. I do not have the strength to hold it off for much longer.*

Where do I go? Emrys replied. *I'm trapped up here with no escape.*

Trust in your abilities Em... was all Ali could reply.

A large thud caught Emrys' attention as Ali's limp body was hurtled to the floor. The Zarrac had ripped through her stomach and it was as if the beast's claws were piercing his own chest. He watched on helplessly in disbelief as time seemed to stand still. "No..." Emrys cried. "No, no, no! Ali!"

There was no response for the young mage. The light that had borne bare the woods slowly diminished and along with it any of Emrys' hope. The Zarrac continued to hiss and roar as Aurora applauded the scene. "Well done, my child," she said grinning from ear to ear.

Emrys wept for Ali as the people below continued to climb. The ring around his finger grew cold for the first time before snapping in two and falling from his finger, down into darkness. He closed his eyes and tried to wish the pain of loss away. "Well, Emrys," Aurora called. "Your pet is defeated, my flock with swarm you, and yet you call yourself the Primal. Primals of old used to face their challengers head on! You are no Primal. Look at yourself... You're just a scared boy rooted up there like a coward!"

Rooted. The word resonated inside Emrys. For the first time he could remember clearly the events leading to his exile. He had called the roots from the Great Oak to his side, to be his shield and weapon. The roots of the tree had burst up through the Great Hall and defended him from Edmure and he felt as though he knew how to call them again. While his heart throbbed and tears continued to stream down his face, he gripped the tree tightly and listened. This tree was very much alive, and very much on his side. They all were. The

Whispering Woods felt like his playground and it was if he was looked on at old friends for the very first time. *Primal*... A voice echoed in his mind. He knew what he had to do, and he had the strength to do so. "No!" Emrys shouted back at Aurora. "I am *the* Primal and your tyranny ends here!"

He dug his hands into the trunk and twisted them as the old tree creaked from the strain. Below him the people gripping onto the trunk were shaken off as the wood span and warped from side to side. His eyes began to glow green and he could now see clearer than ever. He could feel all of the roots beneath him racing and darting between each tree, and they were all his to command.

First, he dealt with the Zarrac. Roots burst from beneath the ground and confined the Zarrac with ease before he curled his hand into a fist and felt as the very spine of the monster snapped in two. In his anger he continued to crush the monster until it was nothing more than a bundle of fur and entrails which spewed forth littering the mossy ground. "NO!" Aurora screamed as she ran towards it. Emrys grabbed the legs of the crowd and swept them from the square. He pulled a wall of roots up surrounding it and Aurora ran straight into it. When she hit the roots, they wrapped themselves around her arms and legs and left her pinned. Emrys called roots to the top of the tree and formed a staircase of sorts leading him down to the square. "You could've helped me," he said as he began his descent. "But instead, you create a monster and enslave my friends!"

"You've killed my pet!" she squealed as she attempted to wrestle herself free. Emrys pulled the roots tighter and she screamed as blood started to pour from her wrists. "YOU KILLED MY FRIEND!" Emrys howled as anger consumed him. "Release these people from your spell or I will end your life here and now!"

He walked towards her and a root wrapped itself around her throat. What little colour there was in Aurora's face drained instantly as the root began to strangle her. She clawed helplessly as Emrys gripped tighter and tighter. "Okay..." she wheezed weakly. Emrys released his grip and watched as her eyes flickered yellow and she began muttering strange words. She snapped her fingers together and said, "They are released from my spell."

"Forgive me if I don't take your word for it," Emrys looked away. He kept Aurora pinned down by roots as he called the wall down and looked at the crowd beyond. They looked confused and disorientated as many held their heads in their hands or stumbled around. He could see Lymris and Rheinar wandered blindly and aimlessly. He allowed himself a brief smile before he turned his attention back to Aurora. "Go now," he said releasing his grip. "And do not return to these woods. They are *mine* now. If I see or hear that you've been doing this again, I will kill you."

Aurora snarled as she mopped up the blood from her arms and legs. "Mark my words *Primal*," he hissed. "You have not heard the last from me."

She turned and fled to the West as Emrys released the roots and his eyes flickered back to normal. "Emrys!" his sister said running to his side. "I'm sor..."

"We don't have time, Lym," Emrys interrupted her. "Get Rheinar, Ali needs our help!"

Emrys raced over to where she had fallen and checked for any signs of life. "Ali!" Emrys begged banging on her lifeless feathered chest. "Please don't leave me..."

"She is not dead," a voice said behind him. "Stand aside."

Emrys turned and saw a hooded man approaching them with his hands ablaze and eyes glowing red. "Stand aside!" he commanded again to which Emrys did in quick fashion. The robed man set fire to the ground beneath Ali. The flames caught the huge bird and turned blue as her body quickly reduced to ash and cinders. "What have you done?" Emrys shouted as he swung in for a punch. The stranger caught his fist with ease and turned him on the spot. "Watch," he said softly. From the ashes crept out a tiny bird struggling in its first steps. It shimmered just as Ali did and was barely the size of a rat. The bird coughed up ash and cutely sneezed as it stretched its wings and waddled forward. Emrys felt tears welling in his eyes once more as he dropped to his knees and smiled. The tiny bird and Emrys met each other's stare and he knew exactly who it was. *Hello again, Emrys,* Ali said.

Chapter Thirty-Five
Renewed Hope

EMRYS ran forward and picked up Ali. The moment he touched her feathers he could feel the warmth running through his fingers as the small bird chirruped and ran up his arm to his shoulder. *You have freed me Emrys,* she said breathing hot air on his neck, *I am no longer bound to that ring, nor am I bound to the Atacama Desert. I am free. Words cannot express my thanks.*

I thought I'd lost you, Emrys replied, *but look at you... You are so young now.*

I will grow and eventually return to my adult size, she replied, *faster than you would believe. But I think you should be having a conversation with the mage in front of you.*

In his joy Emrys had completely forgotten about the hooded man. As he looked on, he could see the man was caked in mud, moss and shrubs, much as they all were. His face was concealed behind the shadows and he remained still as he watched Emrys. "Thank you," Emrys said smiling. "Thank you for saving Ali. My name is Emrys, who are you?"

"My name is Hal," he replied revealing his deep voice. "And it I who owe you my thanks for breaking Aurora's enchantment. You have saved many lives today including my own."

Hal pulled back his hood and for the first time Emrys could see his face. He was a greying man probably about his father's age and bore a wealth of experience on his face. Wrinkles creased his eyes forming crow lines with scars and nicks disrupting what would have been a perfect beard. His tanned face was kind and after one glimpse in his hazel brown eyes, Emrys felt safe speaking to him. Emrys could not explain it, but there was something about Hal that reminded him of Mikhael. Black hair flowed down to his shoulders speckled with white strands and when he flicked his hair from his eyes, Emrys could see a myriad of strange rings on each of his hands. Lymris returned leading Rheinar towards them who remained caught in a daze and unresponsive. "I can't get his attention, Emrys," Lymris urged. "Is there anything you can do? Wait, is that Ali? Who is this man?"

"Which question would you like me to answer first Lym?" Emrys shrugged.

"Allow me to explain," Hal interrupted. "I am Hal, Arcanist Elite for the Circle. I took it upon myself to put an end to Aurora, but I failed in my task. For some reason her power is far beyond what it was and I was caught under her enchantment like everyone else here. Emrys restored me as he restored you. For some, like this man you hold, it will take time to return to normal."

"And the bird on Emrys' shoulder?" Lymris asked.

"I brought the Phoenix back by fire," Hal replied. "The bird took a killing blow as it fought the Zarrac yet Phoenixes are more resilient than you know. Fire restores a phoenix and allows it to be reborn from the ashes. The small bird you see upon Emrys' shoulder is indeed the one you call Ali."

"I am sorry for the rudeness," Lymris shook her head. "I am merely concerned about Rheinar, this man here. My name is Lymris, I'm Em's younger sister."

327

"It is an honour to meet you Lymris," Hal replied bowing and holding his hand over his heart. "It is an honour to meet you both."

"Hal, I'm sorry to ask," Emrys said. "Is there anything you can do to help Rheinar?"

Hal stepped forward and began examining Rheinar. He seemed gormless and a drooping trail of drool ran down the corner of his mouth. Hal clicked his fingers in front of Rheinar and sparked a bit of life into the man who towered over the group. "He will be fine with rest," Hal comforted the siblings. "Now Emrys, tell me. Is it true? Are you a Primal?"

"How do you... How do you know about that?" Emrys stuttered.

"Aurora's spell may have taken my will," Hal replied, "but I was conscious enough to hear the conversation you had. I saw the way your eyes shone. I have never seen green eyes in magic nor the roots of trees attack as weapons for a long time. Are you *truly* a Primal and has Caulder returned?"

"I am a Primal," Emrys watched for his response. "I can't explain it, but it's as if there's always a voice calling to me. *Primal* it whispers. Over and over again. Caulder has returned. I have seen him in my Awakening and in my dreams. I do not lie to you, Hal."

The mage seemed troubled. Hal ran his fingers through his hair and muttered to himself as he stepped away from the group. "So Caulder has returned... I need a moment to collect my thoughts, excuse me," was all he said before disappearing into the woods.

"Can I see her?" Lymris asked smiling at him. She sat Rheinar down and walked over as Ali chirruped and stretched her tiny wings.

"Of course," Emrys said passing Ali to her.

"She's so cute!" Lymris laughed and stroked the baby Phoenix. "I am sorry about before, Em. I couldn't control myself."

"You don't have to apologise," Emrys replied. "That woman, Aurora… She was terrifying. Without Ali there I never stood a chance."

You're wrong Emrys, Ali whispered. *Your powers stopped Aurora and her Zarrac, not me.*

Emrys watched Lymris playing with Ali who ran laps of her arms as she giggled. He was so happy they were safe and even happier that Ali had returned, albeit much smaller than before. How he wished Jakob could be brought back so easily. Emrys walked towards the droves of people. "Els Dier!" a voice called from behind the crowd. Pushing past the people came a teenage boy, no older than he was. "Bersch Els," he said dropping to knees. To Emrys' surprise the crowd followed suit and bowed before him ringing out 'Bersch Els'. His sister brushed his side as she returned Ali to his shoulder.

"Do you know what they're saying, Emrys?" she asked. When he shrugged Lymris smiled and continued, "They're thanking you. You've saved them, big brother. You've saved them all from a terrible fate." Emrys blushed as the hairs on his neck stood on end. There were tears and smiles among the crowd in equal measure. A few people scurried forward and offered him trinkets and jewellery which he waved his hands at and thanked them in reply. He had never felt more like the centre of attention than when the mass of people chanted his name to the sky. There were scenes of jubilation as people enjoyed their first acts free from the Aurora's spell. He smiled as his sister began joining the chant and as Ali chirruped sweetly to his ear. His only wish was that his father and his brother were here to see him at his proudest moment. He had used his powers for good, and with it, saved hundreds of innocent lives.

***

EMRYS, his sister, Rheinar and Hal made camp that night upon the square. Using his call Emrys had brought back Elmyra, Styria and Striker from the woodland and he was overjoyed at their arrival. Elmyra whinnied upon his sight and he ran to hug the mare who had been a constant on his great journey. From her saddlebags he drew some dried meats and passed them out among the group. The vast majority of the crowd had dispersed and made their own way through the woodland. Emrys did not fear for them. He could feel that the woods were safe now and they could return to whatever lives awaited them. Rheinar seemed to be in a better way and occasionally spoke though most of it was incoherent gibberish. He had to be assisted with his food and Lymris continued to spoon-feed him as though he was a child. "He will be fine," Hal reminded him as he tore into the meat. Emrys could not stand the curiosity no longer. He had been given so little information on the Circle and he needed to know more about the group he sought. "Hal," he said. "What can you tell me about the Circle?"

"What would you like to know?" Hal replied putting his food down and wiping his mouth.

"Our court mage Mikhael told me very little about where he came from," Emrys said. "He said almost nothing, when it came to the Circle. What is the Circle?"

Hal nodded and seemed to appreciate his honesty. "That sounds like the Mikhael I've heard about. Well legend goes," he began, "Primals were the first mages to arrive in our world. Using their abilities, they shaped the very world around us. They moved mountains, parted seas, sprouted forests and gave life to the land. They formed the first Circle which brought peace to a world covered in darkness. The Circle now is but a remnant of that past. We seek to bring harmony amongst all people yet it is not so easy. Our brothers and sisters are hunted down by Arcadia and have been for twenty years. Why? Because of the events surrounding Caulder, and according to you, that ancient evil has resurfaced."

"Caulder is an ancient evil?" Emrys asked.

Hal looked at his feet for a few seconds as if it was a look of shame. "No," he shook his head. "Caulder is nothing but a tool for the evil I mention. If Caulder has returned, it will have brought with it the Living Death."

"The Living Death?" Emrys asked again.

"It's more commonly known as Corruption," Hal replied and noticed Emrys' shaken look to the word. "You've seen it haven't you?"

"I have," Emrys nodded. "I've never been more scared in my life. Caulder sent a beast after us. Siska. A winged demon that spat out ooze and created abominable creatures of its own. It was a horrible event. The beast killed Jakob... that's Rheinar's son. He started to turn with the Corruption and Rheinar had to kill him before he was taken by it."

"That's awful," Hal shook his head. "I am sorry for your loss, truly I am. I too have seen the Living Death and the horror it causes. It ravages without relent, consuming all in its path. But the two are one. The Corruption as you know it and

Caulder. Of Caulder... what do you know of his location? His intentions?"

"His?" Emrys asked while his eyebrows frowned with surprise.

"Forgive me, I misspoke," Hal said dismissively. "But what of Caulder's location? What do you know Emrys?"

Emrys closed his eyes and tried to recall the last time he saw the Bringer of Storms. "I saw him in a glade," he reflected. "Caulder touched the ground and from it rose a platform. The platform was... strange. It was made of bone and twisted with barbs and spikes. It had two plinths with glowing runes emanating from its sides."

"I do not know the place you speak of..." Hal replied. "Perhaps Solanta will know."

"Who is Solanta?" Lymris asked as she moved to Emrys' side.

"She is the Arch-Mage," Hal said. "The head of our order and well-versed in the old texts. If any mage is to know of this location it shall be her."

As Emrys looked at Hal he pondered many things. The enigmatic man who chewed down his meat was a true mystery to him, and he raised more questions than he gave answers. He understood little of what Hal said and felt as if the mage was deceiving him. Hal knew more about Caulder, of this Emrys was certain. *Ask him,* Ali spoke in his mind, *I can feel the questions burning inside your mind. Satisfy your curiosity.*

"Who are you, Hal?" Emrys asked. "I may not know much, but you know more about Caulder than you're letting on. What happened twenty years ago?"

"It is not my place to intervene," Hal spoke with almost a whisper. "But I promise you will have the answers you seek when we reach Emrakul."

"What is Emrakul?" Lymris asked.

"It is the home of the Circle," he replied. "Our last bastion since our kind were banished from Arcadia." Suddenly it hit Emrys like a rock to the head. The slight lisp in his speech. The knowledge of Elessian. It could be no coincidence that he sounded like Emperor Valyris or his son Edmure. *"You're* Arcadian?" he spluttered.

"Yes, I am," Hal nodded and spoke sadly. "Talon's Reach was my home, *our* home. Mages from all the continents would come and train in the Temple of Gallico. But it was less about what spells they could cast or what they could create, it was more about what they could become. What kind of positive impact could magic bring to the nations of Elessia? That was what we were taught and believed. But it all changed the moment Caulder and the Living Death came to Arcadia. They blamed us, Arcadians that is. Emperor Valyris banished our kind once we had expelled Caulder. I was there when our dignity was stripped from us, when we cast into lines and beaten! My best friend was killed before me… And what good has it done? Mages who had helped to shape this world were exiled or enslaved and since this, war has ravaged Elessia. Mercians and Alterrans at each other's throats. Arcadians and Galbraithians creeping inevitably towards another war. We need to put an end to the bloodshed, yet I fear if Caulder has returned more blood will flow."

"What can I do?" Emrys asked. "I am the Primal, what can I do to stop this from happening?"

Hal met his eyes and took a few moments to consider his response. "The only thing we can do," he said. "You must defeat Caulder, Emrys. There is no other way. Show to the world that magic can be used for good. That is can be used to create life not death. But you will not have to carry this burden alone. With luck, the Circle will listen to reason and help you develop your abilities."

"Will you take me there?" Emrys looked on in hope.

"I will," Hal smiled rising to his feet. "We are not far from Emrakul. I will bring you to the Circle, but from there it is up to you to be the Primal. Save the world from the Living Death, Emrys, or I fear no one else will."

Emrys smiled briefly and took Hal's outstretched arm in agreement. He felt optimistic for the future despite the fear that raced his heart whenever he thought of Caulder. As he stood there alongside his sister, Rheinar and the newest member of their group Hal, he reflected on the months that had fleetingly passed him by. There had been ups and downs across Galbraith, Daal, and Carpathia but he was happy in the knowledge that he was so close to his final destination. From the beginning the journey had been fraught with peril. In Galbraith he had witnessed civil unrest and hoped Rheinar's message had reached his father. Crossing the Sea of Tears had been a voyage of bafflement, shame and wonder. He could not help but feel guilty about the sailors whom the pirates had slaughtered and wished to turn back the clock and act differently. Leviathan had given him the courage to stand to his abilities even if now he did know what those abilities were. Daal was not a place Emrys would remember with fond memories. From his capture by the slavers to the fighting pits of Kelpis Magna, the Great Market City had shown nothing but cruelty to the young Prince. He felt sorrow when he thought on the departure of Velstadt and wished for nothing more than to be navigating the seas aboard the Crimson

Tempest. Grief struck him as he thought on Jakob and he promised he would attempt to find some manner of peace in completing his journey. Aurora troubled him still, and her final words to him echoed in his mind '*Mark my words Primal You have not heard the last from me.*' Deep down Emrys knew he would have to face her again, but he promised himself he would not falter, nor show the same mercy twice if it came to that. Then there was Hal. The strange mage was a curious fellow who hid truths that Emrys had to get to the bottom of. he knew that if he were to get to the root of those answers, they would lie in Emrakul. He had felt love and loss yet knew his true place in the world was yet to be discovered. He was the Primal in name only, his journey had just begun.